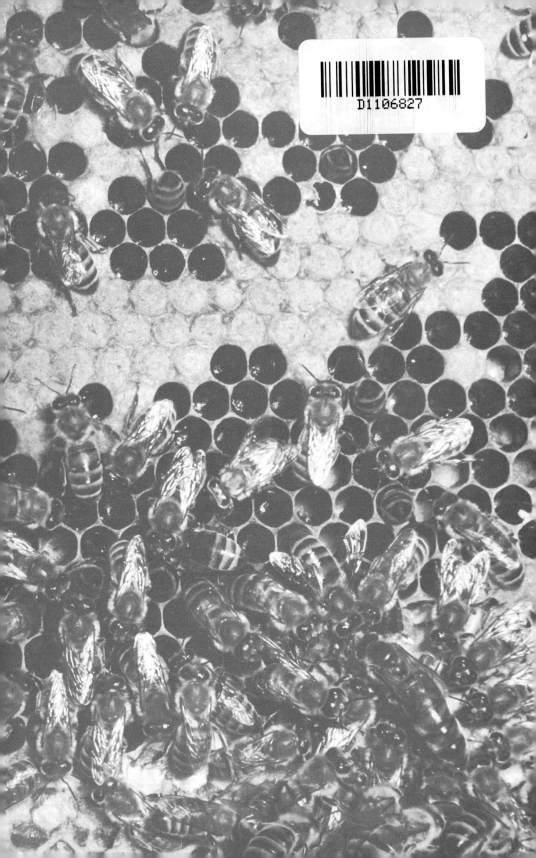

The Hive
and the Honey Bee

THE THREE EUROPEAN RACES OF BEES

DARK BEE
Apis mellifera mellifera

ITALIAN BEE
Apis mellifera ligustica

CARNIOLAN BEE
Apis mellifera carnica

ARTIST—Gezeichnet von M. Winmer, Vienna

The Hive
and the Honey Bee

A new book on beekeeping which succeeds the book
"Langstroth on the Hive and the Honeybee"

EDITED BY ROY A. GROUT

With the Collaboration of
A Staff of Specialists

Robert Banker, Dr. C. G. Butler, G. H. Cale, Sr., Dr. G. H. Cale, Jr.,
Dr. Eva Crane, H. C. Dadant, M. G. Dadant, Dr. J. E. Eckert, Dr. C. L.
Farrar, Dr. T. A. Gochnauer, Roy A. Grout, Dr. M. H. Haydak, C. E.
Killion, Dr. H. B. Lovell, Dr. F. Ruttner, Dr. R. E. Snodgrass, and
Dr. J. W. White, Jr.

REVISED EDITION

DADANT & SONS · HAMILTON, ILLINOIS
Publishers of the American Bee Journal

PRINTED IN THE U.S.A. BY STANDARD PRINTING COMPANY
HANNIBAL, MISSOURI

"I have determined, in writing this book, to give facts, however wonderful, just as they are; confident that in due time they will be universally received; and hoping that the many wonders of the economy of the honey-bee will not only excite a wider interest in its culture, but lead those who observe them to adore the wisdom of Him who gave them such admirable instincts."

L. L. Langstroth

FOREWORD

LANGSTROTH *on the Hive and the Honey-Bee, a Beekeeper's Manual* was the title of the original book by the Reverend L. L. Langstroth in 1853. This practical treatise made available to the world his fundamental discovery of the bee space and his invention of the top-opening, movable-frame hive which made modern beekeeping possible. More than a century has passed since Langstroth's discovery but our system of beekeeping still is based on his hive and methods.

Langstroth's book was well received: a second edition appeared in 1857, a third edition just 2 years later in 1859, and his last revision in 1875. Not wishing to attempt another edition alone, because of ill health, he began to correspond with Charles Dadant and his son, Camille Pierre Dadant, in 1881. This correspondence was to be interrupted often by Langstroth's nervous trouble until it became necessary for the Dadants to revise and publish the book. Langstroth entrusted the rewriting of the book to them in 1885.

The Dadant revision bore the title *Langstroth on the Hive and the Honey Bee, revised, enlarged, and completed by Chas. Dadant and Son.* It was published in 1889. A second edition appeared in 1893, a third in 1896, and the fourth in 1899. Charles Dadant translated it into French in 1891; a Russian edition appeared in 1892. It was later published in Italian, Spanish, and Polish.

Charles Dadant died in 1902, and the four succeeding revisions were the work of C. P. Dadant, retaining the title *Langstroth on the Hive and the Honey Bee.* His first revision was published in 1907 and was called the 20th Century edition. Consequently, succeeding revisions were called the 21st edition (1922), the 22d edition (1923), and the 23rd edition (1927). C. P. Dadant passed away in 1938.

James C. Dadant, a grandson, undertook the task of a new revision about the time of World War II. It was his proposal that a completely new book should be written by a group of authors, each dealing with the subject with which he was most familiar. But the war intervened and James was called to service, so the task evolved to the present editor. The new book was given the title *The Hive and the Honey Bee.*

The first edition was published in 1946 and a somewhat revised one appeared in 1949. This is the third edition and most extensive revision.

Previous authors who have passed away include A. Z. Abushady, Dr. O. W. Park, Frank C. Pellett, and Dr. Arnold P. Sturtevant. These noted writers are mentioned here in memoriam. Other contributors who for various reasons are not participating in this revision are James I. Hambleton, Dr. Vern G. Milum, and R. B. Willson. Their previous chapters are appreciated.

[*vii*]

Special mention is made here of the death of one of the present authors of this revision—Dr. Robert E. Snodgrass, a world authority on the anatomy and physiology of insects. His contribution to this and previous editions is deeply appreciated.

In this revised edition of *The Hive and the Honey Bee,* new authors have been selected, the chapters have been rearranged for classroom use, and an attempt has been made to bring to readers a worldwide picture of beekeeping.

The colored frontispiece of the three European races of bees is produced by permission of Ehrenwirth Verlag, Munich, Germany, publishers of the book *Biene und Bienenzucht* by Dr. A. Büdel and E. Herold (1960) in which it appeared. The drawing of the three European races of bees was made by Gezeichnet von M. Wimmer, of the Zoological Institute of Vienna, Austria. It is believed that this fine art reproduction adds materially to this revision of *The Hive and the Honey Bee* by making this illustration available to the English speaking world.

Dadant & Sons, Inc. is publishing this edition of *The Hive and the Honey Bee* as a special feature in the observance of its Centennial Year. Charles Dadant emigrated to America in 1863 with his son, Camille Pierre, and, together, they dedicated their lives to beekeeping throughout the world. The present organization, which represents the third and fourth generations, is privileged to celebrate its Centennial—a century of progress in beekeeping—with the publishing of this book.

ACKNOWLEDGMENT

D ADANT & SONS, INC., publishers of the *American Bee Journal,* especially desire to express their thanks and appreciation to the co-authors of this revision and for illustrations furnished by them. Fully recognizing that these persons have contributed generously of their time and knowledge, due acknowledgment is given here to:

Robert Banker	Clayton L. Farrar
Colin G. Butler	Thomas A. Gochnauer
Gladstone H. Cale, Sr.	Roy A. Grout
Gladstone H. Cale, Jr.	Mykola H. Haydak
Eva Crane	Carl E. Killion
Henry C. Dadant	Harvey B. Lovell
Maurice G. Dadant	Friedrich Ruttner
John E. Eckert	Robert E. Snodgrass

Jonathan W. White, Jr.

Appreciation and acknowledgment likewise is given to the Rothamsted Experimental Station for permission to publish the manuscript of Dr. C. G. Butler; to the University of California for permission to publish the manuscript of Dr. J. E. Eckert; to the Central Experimental Farms, Canada, for permission to publish the manuscript of Dr. T. A. Gochnauer; to the University of Minnesota for permission to publish the manuscript of Dr. M. H. Haydak; to the U.S. Department of Agriculture for permission to publish the manuscripts of Dr. C. L. Farrar and the late Dr. R. E. Snodgrass; to the University of Louisville for permission to publish the manuscripts of Dr. H. B. Lovell; to the Bee Research Association for permission to publish the manuscript of Dr. Eva Crane; and to the Federal Institute of Beekeeping, Austria, for permission to publish the manuscript of Dr. F. Ruttner.

Various portions of previous editions of this book have been freely incorporated with or without individual citation. For the use of this material, due acknowledgment is gladly given by the authors.

The editor also desires to express his appreciation to G. H. Cale, Sr., editor of the *American Bee Journal,* and to Dr. G. H. Cale, Jr. for advice and counsel; to Minnie S. King for critical reading and help with manuscripts; and to Joyce Tetrick and Adelaide Larson for assistance in the production of the book.

TABLE OF CONTENTS

[*xi*]

The Hive
and the Honey Bee

CHAPTER I

THE WORLD'S BEEKEEPING—PAST AND PRESENT

by EVA CRANE*

THE PRESENT BOOK is the direct successor to one written by Lorenzo Lorraine Langstroth, published in 1853 under the title *Langstroth on the Hive and the Honey-bee*. Langstroth's book made known to the world his fundamental discovery of the bee space in 1851, and laid the foundation of the whole of our modern beekeeping. In this introductory chapter the story of beekeeping is told briefly, as it leads to and from the climax in 1851, and a short account is given of the position of beekeeping in the world today, which stems largely from Langstroth's work and the book he wrote.

BEEKEEPING UP TO 1500

Honey bees now live in all parts of the world except the extreme polar regions, but this was not always so. Until the 16th century they were confined to the Old World, where they had evolved and were widely distributed long before man appeared on the earth. Primitive man learned to get honey by robbing the bees' nests in hollow trees or rock crevices; a painting made in a rock shelter in the mountains of eastern Spain in Mesolithic times, probably about 7000 B.C., survives to show us how this was done (Fig. 1). Bee hunting is still carried out in various parts of the world, and honey can still be a lifesaving food for primitive peoples in times of famine.

Beekeeping proper started when man learned to safeguard the future of the colonies of bees he found in hollow tree trunks or elsewhere, by a certain amount of care and supervision. Gradually, separate hives came to be used as substitutes for the natural dwellings of bees; for convenience and safety they were collected together in an apiary. Hive construction depended on what local materials were at hand, and on the local skills of the various communities. It is almost certain that the beehive had no single origin: it was an inevitable development in any region populated by honey bees, as soon as man advanced from hunting and collecting food to producing it, and thus started a settled existence.

In the great forests of Europe, the earliest hive probably was a log from a fallen tree in which wild honey bees had nested. The log

---

*Eva Crane, Ph.D. Director of the Bee Research Association. Editor of *Bee World, Apicultural Abstracts,* and *Journal of Apicultural Research.* World authority on bees and beekeeping.

FIGURE 1. Rock painting depicting honey gathering. Discovered in the Cuevas de la Araña near Bicorp in Valencia, Spain. *(Courtesy of E. Hernández-Pacheco, Museo nacional de ciencias naturales, Madrid)*

would be separated by chipping away the rest of the tree with axe and adz, a technique used throughout the Stone Age. Cork and other types of bark were also made into hives and, later, planks cut from tree trunks (Fig. 2).

The earliest centers of culture were in the Middle East, in hot, dry open country which was not forested. The first hives there were probably pots in which swarms happened to settle. Pottery vessels were made during most of the Neolithic period, from perhaps 5000 B.C. onwards, and water pots are still used as hives in some Mediterranean lands (Fig. 3). In ancient Egypt and adjoining regions, pipe hives were used—long tubes lying horizontally and piled together, made of clay and other materials.

In agricultural communities, techniques were developed for making containers of basket work as well as pottery, and these baskets were also used to house bees. Baskets have changed little through the ages, and baskets of coiled straw are made today in the same way as before 5000 B.C. The bone awl (Fig. 4), effectively the same as that of a

FIGURE 2. Log hives in North Carolina in 1958. The trunks containing bee colonies have been cut from the black gum *(Nyssa sylvatica). (Photo by W. A. Stephen)*

FIGURE 3. Apiary of clay pots, common in Israel and Lebanon. The bottom of the pots can be detached for taking honey. *(Photo by Brother Adam)*

FIGURE 4. Left, coiled straw skep and, right (larger scale) bone awl used to make it. Yorkshire, England, 1953. The skep is flat-topped for use with a cap. *(Courtesy of Museum of English Rural Life, University of Reading)*

FIGURE 5. Apiary of wicker hives in Belgium, 1960. *(Photo by Eva Crane)*

Mesolithic basket maker, was in fact used for making skeps for bees within the last decade in a Yorkshire dale in England. Woven baskets came later, and were made of various materials such as pliable hazel twigs; examples made between 3000 and 2000 B.C. have been found in Egypt. Wickerwork hives still linger on in a few parts of Europe (Fig. 5).

All these primitive hives fulfilled certain necessary functions: they protected the bees and their combs from wind, rain, and extremes of heat or cold; their flight entrances were small enough for the bees to guard; and there was some other opening through which the beekeeper could get at the honey and wax which constituted his harvest. Wood, bark, and clay were themselves weatherproof; straw and wicker hives were generally protected with an additional cover, and wicker hives were often plastered with mud and cow dung.

Primitive hives were usually small, because the beekeeper wanted to encourage swarms to populate his empty hives. Primitive beekeeping consisted of little more than providing the hives, and killing the bees (for instance by plunging the hive into boiling water) to get the honey and wax. In ancient Egypt, smoke was used to drive bees from their hive, and by ancient Roman times bees were fed. At some time in the Middle Ages, beekeepers devised a form of protection to wear when handling their hives (Fig. 6).

FIGURE 6. One of the earliest pictures of bee dress, from Sebastian Münster's *Cosmographia*, 1545. *(Courtesy of Bee Research Association)*

Until the 16th century—a significant one for the honey bee—the beekeeper's calendar remained virtually unchanged; in early summer he caught and hived the swarms which issued; in late summer he killed the bees in most of his hives, cut out the combs and strained the honey from the wax; in the fall, if necessary, he provided food in the remaining hives, which he overwintered. Burning sulfur was commonly used for killing the bees.

Little was understood as to what went on inside the hive, for the events there could not be seen. It was not realized that the large "king" bee was in fact a female, the mother of the other bees in the hive, nor were the sexes of the workers and drones understood, let alone the facts of mating between queen and drone. It was not known that the bees themselves secreted the wax with which they built comb, nor that their visits to flowers had anything to do with the formation of seeds and fruits.

BEEKEEPING—1500 TO 1851

Three separate streams of events, each of great significance in the history of bees and beekeeping, were set in motion in the 16th century, and led on to Langstroth's discovery in 1851. First, scientific and technical developments enabled beekeepers to understand the fundamental facts of the life cycle and biology of their bees; second, and coupled with the first, there were developments in beekeeping methods which gave beekeepers slightly more control over their bees, as well as greater opportunities for observing the bees inside the hive; and third, the honey bees themselves spread over two new continents, from one of which was to come the greatest single advance in the science and craft of beekeeping.

Discovery of the Fundamental Facts about Bees. The first description of the queen bee as a female, which laid eggs, was published in Spain in 1586, by Luis Méndez de Torres. Then in England Charles Butler showed, in his *Feminine Monarchie* (1609), that the drones were male bees, and Richard Remnant, in his *Discourse or Historie of Bees* (1637), that the worker bees were females; Remnant had observed that they possessed "a neat place for the receipt of generation." Meanwhile in 1625, in Italy, Prince Cesi had published the first drawings of bees made under a microscope.

The fact that bees could raise a queen from eggs or very young larvae was published in Germany in 1568 by Nickel Jacob, but the primary facts about the mating of the queen with the drone were not available until 1771, when Anton Janscha in Slovenia published an account of the event. A correct description of the production of beeswax by bees was published by H. C. Hornbostel in Germany in 1744.

The fact that the pollen which the bees collect is the "male seed" of the flower, which fertilizes the ovum, was discovered in England in 1750 by Arthur Dobbs; he also observed that bees gathered pollen from only one kind of flower on each flight, and he suggested that disastrous cross-fertilization would result if this were not so. The part played by bees in fertilizing flowers was established clearly by C. K. Sprengel in 1793, a year after the publication of the observations of Francois Huber, the blind Swiss beekeeper, which properly laid the foundations of modern bee science.

Developments in Beekeeping Technique. Between 1500 and 1851 there were many attempts to devise ways of taking the honey from hives without killing the bees. For instance, several colonies were united together in a single hive for overwintering, instead of killing all but one colony. The uniting was done by "driving" the bees; their own hive was inverted, and an empty hive placed on it with the two open ends in contact but held apart at an angle; the sides of the inverted hive were "drummed," causing the bees to leave it by running up into the empty hive. Several other colonies were driven into the same hive, where the queens would fight it out until only one remained. The process of driving had been known in the Middle Ages, but had not then been favored.

Alternatively, where fairly large hives were used, like those made of logs or cork, the lower third of all the combs might be cut out with a specially shaped knife; the remainder constituted a permanent brood nest, and each year the "honey comb" was built afresh by the bees and cut out by the beekeeper. With the small straw skeps this was not possible, and various types of extension were added *at the top,* over a hole left in the top of the skep. The extension might be a smaller skep (a cap) or a glass jar (a bell). The bees stored honey but they did not breed there: it was a true honey super. Alternatively an "eke" was placed *under* the skep; this was a straw cylinder a few inches high which formed an extension of the skep downwards. All these extensions could be removed complete with honey combs without disturbing the brood nest.

Hives made of wooden boards were also used. Initially these were simple boxes, but various elaborations were devised later, and "collateral hives" had boxes *at the side* for honey storage.

Throughout these centuries the minds of beekeepers in the most progressive areas were constantly occupied with the problem of getting more control over the bees and their activities, and of learning what was going on inside the hive. It is difficult for us now, with the problem solved and therefore no longer a problem, to enter into the minds of these experimenting beekeepers, who struggled so long and so unsuccessfully to find a way of getting *combs they could easily remove from the hive.* Observation windows in the hive walls were easy enough to make, but did not show much of what was going on inside. There is a tantalizing entry in Samuel Pepys's Diary (1665): "After dinner

FIGURE 7. Bees in a reproduction of Huber's leaf hive. *(Photo by Eva Crane)*

to Mr. Evelyn's; he being abroad, we walked in his garden, and a lovely noble ground he hath indeed. And among other rarities, a hive of bees, so as being hived in glass, you may see the bees making their honey and combs mighty pleasantly."

Réaumur tells us that the Italian astronomer Maraldi found single-comb observation hives in the garden of the French Royal Observatory in Paris in 1687. Huber's leaf hive (Fig. 7) came over a century later; it consisted of a number of frames hinged together at one side like the leaves of a book, and the bees built combs in the frames. It was invaluable for his observations, but was an observation hive only and quite unsuited to practical beekeeping.

Between 1650 and 1850 many hives with top bars and frames were invented, but after these two centuries of effort there was still failure on the fundamental point: *whatever bars or frames were used, the bees attached their comb to the walls of the hive as well, and the combs could, therefore, only be removed from the hive by cutting them out.* Only two of the many inventions need be referred to here. About 1806 a Ukrainian beekeeper Peter Prokopovich produced the first movable-comb hive to be used on a commercial scale (and he kept up to 10,000 colonies). This hive had three vertical compartments, the top one having wooden frames with notched bee passages in the end bars; the frames were removed from the back of the hive, but as the bees attached the frames to the hive walls with comb or propolis, this was not at all easy. The second invention was so fundamental, and made so early, that it might well have altered the whole history of beekeeping if it had been more widely known and understood.

Woven basket hives were in early use in Greece, and at some stage—we shall probably never know when—some beekeepers started using them *with the open end uppermost*. The open end was covered with wood which, by the 17th century at any rate, was cut into "bars" about 1½ inches wide. Each bar was made slightly convex on its under side, and the bees attached their combs along the ridges so formed, i.e. one along the under side of each bar. What distinguished this hive from all the other "bar hives" was the fact that it was wider at the top than at the bottom and, presumably because of this slope of the hive walls, *the bees did not attach their combs to them* (Fig. 8). News of these hives reached England in 1682, when Sir George Wheler described them in his book *A Journey into Greece*. He reported that in spring the number of occupied hives was doubled by removing half the combs from each hive and placing them in an empty one. The Greek beekeepers had in fact produced a workable movable-comb hive. Aristotle's account of the life of the bee makes it seem possible that he used one of these hives when writing his *Natural History*.

Wheler's report had a considerable influence on hive development in England and elsewhere, but the crucial step—which would have given the desired movable-comb wooden hive—was never taken. It seems to

FIGURE 8. Apiary of movable-comb wicker hives in Greece. The beekeeper is holding one comb by the lugs of the top bar. *(Courtesy of Pan D. Georgantas)*

the author that if one of the many bar hives had been wider at the top than the bottom, the bees would have made their own bee space between the combs and the hive wall, and modern beekeeping might have started 150 years earlier than it did.

The Spread of Honey Bees over the World. We must now leave this story of beekeepers' unsuccessful attempts to invent the hive they needed, to follow the adventures of the bees themselves during the same 2½ centuries. The honey bee belonged to the Old World—to Europe, Africa, and Asia. Prior to 1500 there were no honey bees in the New World—in the Americas, Australia, and New Zealand. But, like the dog, the honey bee had accompanied man on most of his major migrations, and the early settlers in each part of the New World took hives of bees with them. Records of the establishment of honey bees in America are scanty enough, but we know that they were taken from Portugal to Brazil around 1530, and it seems likely that there were other importations into South, Central, and North America in the same century. The first records of importations into North America are, however, over a hundred years later, from 1638 onwards. The first honey bees were landed in Australia at Sydney in 1822, and W. C. Cotton took the first consignment to New Zealand (from England) in 1842. Honey bees were not introduced to the west coast of North America until the 1850s, when they were landed in California; from there they were taken to Oregon, and thence to British Columbia. It is thus little more than a hundred years since honey bees—members of the genus *Apis*—have lived in all five continents.

BEEKEEPING—1851 AND AFTER

By 1851 the honey bee had completed its colonization of almost the whole world, the major unconquered territory—Siberia—not being occupied until the land itself was settled during the present century. The more progressive beekeepers knew enough about their bees to do great things with them, but this was prevented because, in spite of all their efforts, they still had no suitable hive.

The step which changed this was made in 1851 by Lorenzo Lorraine Langstroth (Fig. 9), an American born in Philadelphia, and living there at the time. Langstroth had shown a rather unusual interest in insects as a child, and this was revived when, as a young pastor in Andover, Massachusetts, he visited a friend who kept bees, and saw a glass globe filled with honey in the comb. Before he returned home he bought two colonies of bees in box hives. He soon also acquired a Huber leaf hive and obtained various books on bees, including Huber's *Letters* and Edward Bevan's *The Honey-bee* (1838). He used the bar hive with a shallow super described by Bevan, and improved it by deepening the grooves on which the bars rested, *leaving about ⅜ inch between the cover and the bars* (this is the origin of our present top bee space).

FIGURE 9. Lorenzo Lorraine Langstroth, the father of modern beekeeping.

He found that this facilitated the removal of the cover board on which the glasses rested. The key development, which cuts the history of beekeeping into two halves, was made in the fall of 1851, and we have Langstroth's own words to describe it: "Pondering, as I had so often done before, how I could get rid of the disagreeable necessity of cutting the attachments of the combs from the walls of the hives, and rejecting, for obvious reasons the plan of uprights, close fitting (or nearly so) to these walls, the almost self-evident idea of using the same bee space as in the shallow chambers came into my mind, and in a moment the suspended movable frames, kept at a suitable distance from each other and the case containing them, came into being. Seeing by intuition, as it were, the end from the beginning, I could scarcely refrain from shouting out my 'Eureka!' in the open streets."

Langstroth's intuition was justified: the bees did in fact "respect" the bee space left between the hive and the frames in which the combs were built; they did not build comb across the space, and the frames were, therefore, truly movable.

The movable-frame hive itself was in common use in the United States by 1861. It was introduced into England in 1862, and the writings of Charles Dadant in the French and Italian journals, starting in 1869, brought about its introduction into Europe; it soon spread to other countries, each of which used variants, built on the same basic principle.

With this discovery modern beekeeping began, and development in the next half-century was in the nature of an explosion compared with the slow and halting progress of the centuries before. The use of movable frames led directly to the invention of beeswax foundation by Johannes Mehring in Germany in 1857; this saved beeswax, and ensured that the bees built regular worker comb in the frames. Langstroth was thinking only of the brood chamber when he devised his frames; he used glasses above the crown board for the honey. But it was soon realized that if the honey chamber or super was furnished with similar frames, these could easily be removed when filled with honey. If means could then be found to extract the honey without destroying the comb, the comb in its frame could then be used again. This led to the invention of the centrifugal honey extractor in Austria in 1865 by Major F. Hruschka and possibly in France a few years earlier. The perfection of the queen excluder by Abbé Collin of France in 1865 enabled the beekeeper to keep the queen, and hence the brood, out of the honey chamber. By using the bee escape, produced in 1891 by E. C. Porter in the United States, he could get the honey chamber free from bees before he removed the frames of honey.

The pattern of modern beekeeping was thus established in the half-century between 1850 and 1900. Equipment invented in that period, or based on principles discovered then, has since undergone important developments, which are dealt with in other sections of this book. We now know vastly more about *the honey bee* than Langstroth did, but his discovery in 1851 remains the basic principle of *the hive,* and thus of our beekeeping today.

OTHER BEES OF ECONOMIC IMPORTANCE TO MAN

The honey bees in the whole of the New World, and in Europe whence they came, are various races of the European honey bee *Apis mellifera*—Italian, Caucasian, Carniolan, etc. Those in Africa north of the Sahara are other races of the same species. In most of Africa south of the Sahara the honey bees are a subspecies *adansonii* of *Apis mellifera:* the darker bees around the African coast may well have originated from colonies of European bees landed by Portuguese and earlier settlers (for additional information on races of bees, see Chapter II).

In Asia the situation is different. The genus *Apis,* which probably evolved in southwest Asia, has three representative species widely distributed in southern Asia today. One is very similar to *Apis mellifera* but slightly smaller; this is the native hive bee of Asia, known in India as *Apis indica,** and kept there in hives similar to those for *Apis*

---

*The name *Apis cerana* is now preferred by many authorities and is synonymous with *Apis indica.*

mellifera but smaller, and with smaller combs containing smaller cells. There are several races of *Apis cerana,* some of which extend north up the eastern part of Asia as far as the east coast of the U.S.S.R. and Japan. In most areas the European honey bee surpasses the native honey bee in honey yield, and in certain other characteristics desirable in hive bees. For this reason beekeepers in China, Japan, and elsewhere are replacing their native hive bee by the European bee. In India and other tropical countries of Asia this has not been successful, because the European bees fall prey to the many enemies which they encounter there.

There are two other species of the genus *Apis* in southern Asia, which are entirely tropical. Both build only a single comb, and both nest in the open, not in a dark cavity like the European bee. Neither species can be kept in a hive, although honey can be obtained from nests of wild bees. The "giant bee" or "rock bee" *(Apis dorsata)* gets its names from its large size and its habit of nesting on rock faces. The "little bee" *(Apis florea)* is the most primitive of the honey bees, and its comb yields only a few ounces of honey.

Another group of tropical social bees also produces honey—the Meliponidae or stingless bees. Different species of these are native to tropical Asia, Africa, Australia, and America, and in Africa and America they are kept in hives for their honey. Some of the indigenous peoples of Central America, such as the Maya in Yucatán, have a very old and rich tradition of beekeeping, and bees and honey have a part in their folklore and legends similar to that in European countries. It should be made clear, however, that although these bees are "stingless," they have other means of defending themselves which are equally unpleasant to their enemies, including man.

It is only within this century, when agricultural practices have become intensive and mechanized, that attention has been directed towards keeping bees for pollination, in contrast to the production of honey and wax. And whereas the honey bee is unsurpassed as a pollinator because of the large numbers which can easily be brought to a crop, certain other bees are individually far better pollinators of certain plants. In many countries bumble bees are valued for pollinating crops whose florets have a long corolla, such as red clover, and much work has been done recently on devising a hive for these bees, and ways of getting them to occupy the hive, so that they can be taken to crops for pollination.

In parts of the Northwest of the United States there is a native soil-nesting alkali bee *(Nomia melanderi)* which is a most efficient pollinator of alfalfa. By making the soil conditions suitable for nesting, and by importing prepupae from neighboring sites, these bees can be housed on the edges of alfalfa plots, and left there to multiply and to do their useful work. *Megachile* is another important wild pollinator.

THE PATTERN OF BEEKEEPING TODAY

We have seen that beekeeping is now spread over all the habitable parts of the world. It is practiced over a greater area of the earth's surface than perhaps any other single branch of agriculture, and on it the success of some of the other branches of agriculture depend.

The patterns of beekeeping in the Old and New Worlds tend to be different. In general the New World gives the richer honey harvest, but the Old World is more densely populated with honey bees, as it is with people. In general the New World provides more useful inventions for handling bees and their products, whereas the Old World still contributes more fundamental discoveries about bees.

Broad distinctions can be drawn between the equipment used for beekeeping in the Old and New Worlds, although here again, as with every generalization, notable exceptions exist. Tradition plays an important part in European beekeeping, and it often seems to act as a brake on practical developments, whereas in some of the newer countries beekeeping techniques have forged ahead unimpeded. Beekeeping equipment used in the New World tends to be simple, uniform, and mechanized as far as possible because labor is expensive; Langstroth or Dadant hives are mainly used. In Europe the hives differ from country to country, and a wide variety of "standard" hives may be used even within one country. These hives may take frames, and hence foundation, of different shapes and sizes, and also cover boards and queen excluders. Many of the hives are complicated, and in ways which decrease rather than increase honey production. In one of the socialist countries of eastern Europe a state beekeeper is expected to look after 100 hives; in England a commercial beekeeper will manage 200 to 250, and in Australia 300 or more; the most mechanized beekeepers of all, in California, can run 1000 hives each.

In the New World bees are generally kept as a means of livelihood; average honey yields in most individual countries vary from 40 to 80 pounds per hive, and average yields in the best beekeeping districts may be 200, 300, or even 400 pounds. In the Old World the proportion of hobby and sideline beekeepers is much higher, each owning 5, 10, or up to 50 hives, and getting a harvest of 10 to 40 pounds per hive.

In good areas beekeeping can be done (although not with maximum efficiency) without knowing a great deal about the bees themselves, and the beekeepers are not necessarily very interested in them—nor in beekeepers' organizations. At the opposite end of the scale, the strongest beekeepers' organizations are in the European countries with the greatest density of hives, each of which gives a poor return—Austria, Czechoslovakia, Germany, the Netherlands, and Switzerland. All these countries have more than 12 colonies per square mile, and their honey yields are among the lowest in Europe.

Europe (excluding the U.S.S.R.) has about 12½ million hives of bees, an average of 6 per square mile, a hive density three times as great as in any other continent. The average honey yield per hive is about 20 pounds a year; although this is higher than in Africa (where most of the hives are primitive ones), or Asia (where the indigenous bee gives a low yield), it is less than half that in the New World as a whole.

In spite of the great density of bees, more honey is consumed than can be produced, and western Europe is the world's great honey-importing region; eastern European countries in the socialist bloc normally import only those goods which are considered essential, and honey is not included in this category. Europeans are in general familiar with honey because it is part of their heritage from past centuries, when beekeeping belonged to the pattern of life of every rural community, and the towns were small enough to keep in touch with the country around them.

In 1955 around 50,000 tons* of honey were imported into Europe from the New World, 30,000 tons going to West Germany. By 1960 the figures had increased with West Germany importing 38,000 tons. The honey production of Europe (excluding the U.S.S.R.) is probably about 110,000 tons a year.

Just as tradition helps to maintain honey consumption, and also interest in bees among the general public, so it plays a material part in sustaining centers of learning where research on bees is carried out, and where many of the advances in our knowledge of bees and their habits are made.

U.S.S.R. This is such an immense country, occupying large territories in both Europe and Asia, that it is best dealt with separately. More than half the colonies of bees there perished in World War II, but the number is now nearly up to the prewar figure of 10 million. The honey production is about 100,000 tons a year (about 22 pounds per colony), and virtually none is imported or exported. Many of the remarks about European equipment and methods apply also to the U.S.S.R.

Certain factors are common to most countries of the socialist bloc. The larger owner-beekeeper is replaced by the beekeeping section of the state farm, owned and run by the state, or by the collective farm, run on a co-operative basis under state directives. In the U.S.S.R. two-thirds of the hives are on these farms; a collective farm has 80 on the average, and state farms specializing in beekeeping may have up to 6,000, certain combines running 25,000 to 30,000.

In socialist countries many activities, which elsewhere are left to the initiative of individuals or private enterprises, are directed from

---

*Metric tons are used (1000 kg. or 2204.6 lbs.). The British ton is 2240 pounds avoirdupois (1016.06 kg.); the U.S.A. ton is 2000 pounds (907.20 kg.).

a central authority. One result is the absence of conflict between what elsewhere may be rival interests, such as crop spraying and beekeeping. The value of bees as pollinators is accepted as a fact, and beekeeper and fruit and seed grower must work together in the matter: the beekeeper provides bees for pollination as part of his duty, and there is no question of his receiving a fee from the grower for this work.

Other honey-producing countries import the beeswax they require, and restrict beeswax production in order to get more honey from the hive, beeswax production then being about 2 per cent of honey production. But the socialist countries aim to be self-supporting, and methods of managing bees are designed to obtain a surplus of both wax and honey from each apiary.

Asia. Statistics are difficult to establish for many countries of Asia. Excluding the U.S.S.R., there are possibly about 4 million hives in Asia, many being primitive types without movable frames. A considerable part of the honey produced in the tropical South is collected from wild nests of *Apis dorsata.* The average honey yield from hives may be up to 15 pounds, and the total production 30,000 tons. This will probably be increased, especially with the continued replacement of unproductive native bees with European stock. The People's Republic of China has already taken vigorous action in this direction, and is also developing beekeeping greatly in some areas: figures quoted for one province show an increase from 8,000 to 195,000 colonies of European bees between 1949 and 1959. The general picture of Asian beekeeping may well be changed if the developments in China continue, and especially if more productive bees can be found which will fluorish in India and other tropical parts of the continent.

Africa. Beekeeping on the north coast of Africa is not dissimilar from that in other Mediterranean countries, but south of the Sahara desert the pattern is quite different, and tropical Africa plays a unique part in beekeeping, as the source of most of the world's beeswax. Africa has some 8 million hives of bees in all. Over three-quarters of them are primitive hives in tropical countries, notably Tanganyika and Angola, which are managed primarily for the wax extracted from the combs cut out of them. Honey is a sideline which may not even be worth carrying by hand (or on the head) the long distance through the bush to a town where it might be sold. Some of the factors which have brought about this state of affairs are as follows: first, the evolution of a native subspecies of the honey bee, *Apis mellifera adansonii,* which is prolific, building sizable colonies which swarm freely in the conditions under which they live; second, vast areas of woodland which provide forage and nesting places for wild colonies, and shade for hives hung in trees; third, the presence of tribes with a tradition of beekeeping, and to whom the production and sale of beeswax is an accepted form of livelihood. The total beeswax production of Africa is about 3,500 tons, which represents most of the beeswax offered on the world's markets. The total amount of honey collected from hives in Africa is about 45,000 tons.

Farther south, beekeeping is carried out by settlers from Europe using modern hives. In the extreme south of Africa the climate is again more Mediterranean; this area is noteworthy for the occurrence of the Cape bee *(Apis mellifera capensis),* characterized by the ability of its workers to lay fertile eggs from which queens and workers are reared, although these have no father (parthenogenesis).

America. Plants native to the New World evolved in the absence of honey bees, but some of these plants provide the richest forage available anywhere. Some of the present forage is derived from Old World species, but this was not so when bees were first established there, nor does all the harvest now come from introduced plants. But it is certainly true that the continents of the New World—North and South America, and Australasia—give far higher harvests from bees than the Old World, and this is an impressive demonstration of the adaptability of the honey bee.

North America has about 5½ million hives, with an average production of 46 pounds in the U.S. and 88 pounds in Canada. Over the whole country, there are nearly two hives per square mile in the U.S., and less than one for every 10 square miles in Canada—one-quarter and one-eightieth, respectively, of the average density in Europe. Beekeeping is in general a full-time or part-time profession, with holdings up to several thousand hives. In areas in the East where the climate is more like that of Europe, the honey yields are lower, the holdings are very much smaller, and—as in Europe—there tends to be a greater interest in the bees themselves.

There are 1½ million colonies in Central America, with an average hive density of nearly two to the square mile. But it is still under-populated with honey bees, and large areas of nectar-producing land are unexploited by beekeepers. The performance of the firm Miel Carlota in Mexico, which now controls about 50,000 hives between Acapulco and Veracruz, shows what can be done. About 20,000 tons of honey are produced a year, and almost all of it is exported.

The tropical part of South America is the home of many species of the stingless bees mentioned previously in this chapter; some of these species are kept for honey, but European bees thrive there, and experiments are proceeding with *Apis mellifera adansonii* from Africa. Elsewhere in South America honey bees flourish, and the average yield per hive of 40 pounds could almost certainly be increased. The total annual production is about 26,000 tons, from 1½ million hives, and nearly all of it is exported. The colony density is about one to every 4½ square miles, and—as in Central America—many areas are under-exploited.

Australasia. There are about 200,000 colonies in New Zealand, yielding about 6,000 tons of honey, of which three-quarters or more is exported to Europe. There are about 2 hives to the square mile, giving an average of 65 pounds of honey. The eucalypts, which dominate Australian beekeeping, are not native to New Zealand, and beekeeping there is not dissimilar from that in parts of America. Australia gives some of the highest honey yields in the world; the average for the whole country is 80 pounds, slightly lower than for Canada, but in Western Australia the average is over 200 pounds. Most of the honey comes from different species of eucalypt, and is obtained by extensive migratory beekeeping to stands of different species, which flower only once every 2, 3 or more years. As the indigenous forest is cleared in successive areas, the honey yield declines, even where the forest trees are replaced by nectar-bearing agricultural crops; it then becomes comparable with that in other good beekeeping areas of the world.

Australia produces about 15,000 tons of honey a year, 11,000 tons of which are exported to Europe; over the whole country there is only about one colony per 7 square miles.

SUMMARY

Beekeeping thus follows a varied and interesting pattern in different parts of the world. It is a pattern which has changed through the centuries with man's colonization of new regions, and which now changes every decade with changing agricultural practices, for these affect the forage which gives the bees—and the beekeepers—their harvest. As new areas are brought into cultivation, new crops grown, and new agricultural methods used, the pattern of beekeeping inevitably changes. New bee forage may be provided by new crops, but the promotion of a clean agriculture by killing weeds before they flower, and the rapid harvesting of fodder crops, both reduce the bees' forage. In some areas the control of insects which damage agricultural crops has destroyed many wild bees and other beneficial insects, whose nesting places may also be endangered by the reduction of waste land. This has left the so-called domesticated honey bee as the only pollinator available in large enough numbers, and has brought a new form of return to the beekeeper in colony hiring fees.

The present world production of honey is nearly 500,000 tons, the work of 40 to 45 million colonies of bees in the hands of perhaps 5 million beekeepers. The estimated human population of the world is about 3,000 million, and the number of individual honey bees will be about 500 times as great as this.

With all the changes noted here, two factors in beekeeping are, so far, beyond the power of man to change materially: the climate which determines what bee forage will flourish, and the habits of the bees themselves. Perhaps the challenge presented by these factors helps to mold beekeepers into the class of people that they are.

CHAPTER II

RACES OF BEES
by F. Ruttner*

Throughout the world, the honey bee of today is a domestic animal. Wild colonies are a rare and temporary phenomenon at least in the temperate zone. Nevertheless, the honey bee is much older than man and its present forms developed without human interference. This is a basic difference between honey bees and other domestic animals, all of which were changed intensively by man's breeding interference.

Today one can find the honey bee wherever climatic circumstances make its existence possible. Its adaptability is quite astonishing; its habitat extends from the equator to beyond the Arctic Circle. However, it is necessary to notice the differences between the honey bees of their original homeland and those of new territories invaded by them only after settlement by the white man. Honey bees first came to these new territories (America, Australia, and East Asia) about 100 to 400 years ago. They do not differ much in their appearance from honey bees of the country from which they were imported (Alpatov[4]). However, there is an important difference in their variation. The bees of the new territories represent in their variation only a part of the natural variation of the bees in the original countries. This is because all of the millions of colonies in the New World today descended from a relatively small number of queens brought across the sea in those days.

In its original homeland, that is in Europe, Africa, and the Near East, the honey bee remained under the effect of natural selection for a long time. Man's influence in the early days on its habitat was small and probably of local significance only, such as establishing colonies on some islands and in semiarid regions (steppes). In the different regions, under the influence of selection by climate, flora, and enemies, adjusted types developed in the same manner as did other wild animals and plants. These types generally are known as *natural* or *geographic* races or subspecies. "Race" therefore has not the same meaning in bee breeding as in the breeding of other animals. "Race" in the breeding of dogs, cattle, or chickens means a result of long planned breeding. The *geographic* races of bees are the results of natural selection in their homeland: they became adjusted to their original environment but not always to the economic requirements of beekeepers. Therefore, they are not the result but the raw material for breeding.

*Friedrich Ruttner, Ph.D. Federal Institute for Beekeeping, Lunz am See, Austria. Authority on races of bees and bee breeding.

ORIGIN OF THE WESTERN HONEY BEES

There has been much discussion about the origin of the honey bee, *Apis mellifera* L. We may accept as an established fact that the three other species of the *Apis* genus live in Southeast Asia. Two of them, the little honey bee, *Apis florea,* and the giant honey bee, *Apis dorsata,* show primitive features in certain ways. They live on a single honeycomb under the open sky and the communication among the workers is not as perfect as with *Apis mellifera* (Lindauer[24]); in addition their number of chromosomes is only half that of our honey bees (Deodikar[16]). The third species, *Apis cerana,** more closely resembles *Apis mellifera.* Its body is quite similar; it makes its nest in hollows on several combs; and its communication in principle is the same as that of *Apis mellifera* (Lindauer[24]). Its mode of life made possible its living in colder climates; it spread from the tropics across China as far as Siberia. Crossbreeding of *Apis mellifera* and *Apis cerana* seems to be possible only in exceptional cases, if ever; they are surely two separate species, although very much alike.

Transition forms between *Apis mellifera* and *Apis cerana* have been found in Northwest India, according to Deodikar. He assumes, therefore, that *Apis mellifera* developed from the more primitive *Apis cerana* in the Himalayan region. Since the variety of forms of *Apis mellifera* is unusually large in the regions between the eastern Mediterranean and the Caucasus, one may look for its center of origin somewhere in the Near East.

DISTINCTIVE CHARACTERISTICS OF RACES OF BEES

Before discussing the important races of bees and their individualities, we should mention a few characteristics which are used today to distinguish among the races. More details are discussed by Ruttner.[28] Mentioned here are a few characteristics which change under the influence of environment only to a very small extent, and therefore will be retained entirely under different environments.

Size. Differences in size between races may be observed with the naked eye. By measuring certain individual parts of the body (width of thorax and abdominal segments, length of tongue, legs and wings) smaller differences in size can be objectively determined also. In Europe, the northern Dark bee is larger than the southern races (Carniolans, Italians, and Cyprians). The African races all seem to be smaller. Differences in size of body also affect the size of natural cells (Alber[2]); smaller races build smaller cells.

It seems to be a general rule, at least in Europe, that smaller bees have longer legs, wings, and tongues in proportion to the size of their bodies (Fig. 1) (Alpatov[5]).

---

* *Apis cerana* is synonymous with *Apis indica* used elsewhere in this book.

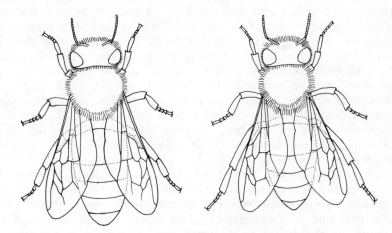

FIGURE 1. Differences between bees with large bodies and relatively short appendages (*A. m. mellifera*, left) and bees with small bodies and relatively long legs, wings, and tongues (*A. m. ligustica* and *A. m. carnica*, right). Schematic.

FIGURE 2. Color markings on the abdomens of worker bees, showing bright "spots" (center) or "bands" (right).

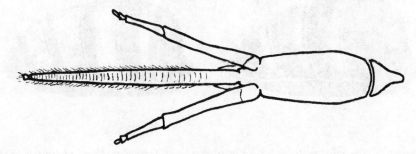

FIGURE 3. The tongue (proboscis) of a worker bee as it is measured to determine its length.

Color. The first dorsal segment of the abdomen varies in color
between light yellow and entirely dark (Fig. 2); the scutellum also
can be of yellow color. One can determine a typical average color
pattern for each race of bees. But it should be emphasized that variability of color in the same race is much greater in the original homeland
than most beekeepers believe. The value of color as a distinctive character must not be overestimated. Not all the bees with yellow or
brown markings are hybrids. Inasmuch as these less reliable markings
are noticeable without any difficulty, practical judging used to be done
almost exclusively on the basis of color. On the other hand, quick
results in selection, based on color, can be obtained for the same
reasons (e.g. Ligustica in the U.S.).

Length of Tongue. There is a 1.7 mm. difference between the
tongues of the two extremes in races (Fig. 3), the Egyptian and the
Caucasian bee; that is, about 25 per cent of the entire length. This
is the only one of the discussed characteristics which have a direct
influence on the honey crop. Races with long tongues are able to
work red clover (Caucasian, Carniolan, and Italian); races with
short tongues are unable to do this. Selection based on tongue length
is entirely possible (Goetze,[20] Henriksen and Hammer[21]).

Hair Coverage. Some races have wide, dense tomenta ("grey" Carniolan and Caucasian), others have only narrow and dispersed bands
(dark bees), or nearly none at all (Tell bees). The overhairs on the
abdomen are long (0.5 mm.) in the case of dark bees, short (about
0.3 mm.) in most other races (Fig. 4).

The colors of the hairs on the drones show great differences; black
in Caucasians, dark brown to black in the Dark bees of northern
Europe, grey to greyish brown in the Carniolan, and yellow in Italians
(Goetze[19]).

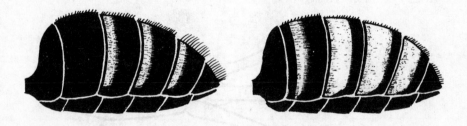

FIGURE 4. The hairs on the abdomens of worker bees: Tomentum (band of hairs in the
middle of three abdominal tergites of workers) and "overhairs" shown in profile. Left
Mellifera, right Carnica.

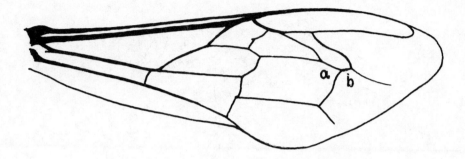

FIGURE 5. Venation of a worker fore wing. Ratio a:b = cubital index.

Veins of the Wings. In the taxonomy of the honey bee, the veins (blood vessels) of the wings play a big role. The shape of certain cells, their size and proportion, as well as their angles, show numerous characteristic differences. The so-called cubital-index (Goetze[18]) is most frequently used. This is the proportion between line *b* and line *a* in Figure 5.

Besides some of the above characteristics, others are used to distinguish among the races. These include the number of hooks on the wings, width of the metatarsus, the shape and size of the wax glands, and the shape of the chitinous plates of the male sexual organs (penis valves).

RACES OF BEES OF THE WORLD

Generally one can divide the races of *Apis mellifera* into three groups:

1. European races
2. Oriental races
3. African races

One can determine certain relationships between these three groups, e.g. between the European Dark bee and the North African Tell bee, and between Caucasians, Anatolian bees, and Carniolans.

Figure 6 shows the geographic distribution of the most important races. It is not complete inasmuch as some territories are not explored enough and exact judgment is not possible at the present time. This is true, for instance, of the bees of Iran and Anatolia, which probably will play a specific role in future breeding of bees.

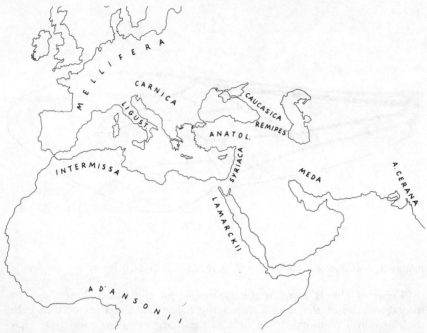

FIGURE 6. Geographical distribution of the most important races of *Apis mellifera* in the Old World.

The four races which have acquired significance in modern bee culture will be discussed in detail in this chapter. Other races will be mentioned only briefly. They either are not yet tested completely or have failed to meet the requirements of modern beekeeping.

The Cyprian bee, *A. mellifera cypria,* (like the Italian but smaller and its yellow color more reddish or carrot colored) was appreciated in the past (Alley[3]). But it soon disappeared because neither the pure race nor the crosses with other races proved to be successful, not to speak of the aggressive behavior of the race (Br. Adam[10]). The same is true of its close relative, the Syrian bee, *A. m. syriaca.* Because of its inferior performance, this bee, since 1948, has been replaced systematically by Italian bees imported from the U.S.A. (Blum[7]).

The African races have played almost no role outside of their homeland so far. A review of the taxonomy of this group recently has been published by Smith.[30] Only Kerr[22] imported some queens of *A. m. adansonii* from tropical Africa to the likewise tropical Brazil. Large modern apiaries in North Africa are operated with imported European queens or with their hybrids.

In South Africa, *A. m. capensis* has a special biological feature; the worker of this race has a large spermatheca, but it was never found to be filled with sperm (Anderson[6]). In queenless colonies, the workers soon start laying eggs which, in a high percentage, develop without fertilization into females. Thus from these fertile eggs queens may be raised. According to Mackensen,[26] the same phenomenon occurs with other races, but only in a very low frequency.

A final judgment of these or other lesser known races would be premature. Some may prove successful in certain crossbreeding combinations. The natural variations of the honey bee are great and this provides an invaluable supply of building stones for bee breeding of the future (Br. Adam[9]).

The Four Races of Well-Known Economic Value

It is much easier to describe the appearance of a race than its nature and economic value. It is possible to study the body characteristics of a dozen samples from different geographical regions in a quiet laboratory. But to determine the economic value, one must observe at least the same number of colonies for a number of years, and the evaluation still may not be perfectly uniform. This is because the features of significance for the existence and economic value very often show greater variability than, for example, do the biologically unimportant veins of the wings. It is easy to recognize the causes of this variability.

Let us take the inclination to swarm for instance. It can be a big advantage for a colony in a good year and it may lead to the destruction of the colony in a bad year. The selection works, therefore, sometimes in one direction, sometimes in the opposite direction, and maintains a certain automatic variability even within a single strain. The beekeepers are interested in many characteristic features but only a part of these is common to the *entire* race and even here one can expect limited differences. Besides, the evaluation of the same bees might be very different in dissimilar environments and unlike circumstances.

In the case of the three European races,* we can overcome these difficulties. They have been tested and compared so many times that a valid, correct evaluation is possible.

If by chance, the "Italian bee" is to be discussed, we have to bear in mind that this means an *average type,* and that some strains of this race, for example, a selected one, may show a different behavior. We wish to describe these "typical" features in as objective a manner as

---

*The three European races are shown on the frontispiece of this book. This is a marvelous color reproduction of Mellifera, Ligustica, and Carnica. American readers may have preferred the inclusion of Caucasica since it is more familiar to them than Mellifera. Dr. Ruttner points out that Caucasica differs only slightly from Carnica in color tint—Caucasica being lead-gray and Carnica brownish-gray. The reproduction was made possible through the courtesy of Ehrenwirth Verlag, Munich, Germany, publishers of the book "Biene und Bienenzucht."

possible, and we do not want to enter them simply under the usual headings of "advantages" and "disadvantages." Valuation in these terms based on fixed circumstances could only be very subjective.

Poor wintering ability, a serious disadvantage in colder regions, has no significance whatsoever in a warm climate; excellent gentleness, generally much appreciated with good reason, may cause the extermination of the colony in some territories because of inadequate self-defense. Each beekeeper should classify for himself the characteristics of the bees as favorable or unfavorable for his own requirements. There is no "absolute best bee" for any circumstances. For these reasons we shall not pay too much attention to the usual comparisons of the honey-production capabilities of the races. These are valid only under fixed conditions. The often contradictory results of these comparisons support this statement (Abushady[1]). Tests carried out with a number of strains of the same race over a long period are more convincing; large scale comparisons have led to replacing one race by another (Dark bees by Italians in the U.S.A., Syrian bees by Italians in Palestine, and Dark bees by Carniolans in Germany).

The use of the correct scientific names in abbreviated forms instead of the popular names of the races is common in Europe today. So one speaks of Mellifera, Ligustica,* Carnica, and Caucasia (Fig. 7).

DARK BEES (*Apis mellifera mellifera* L.)

Original homeland: All of Europe north and west of the Alps, Central Russia. The bees of the Iberian peninsula are very close to the Dark bee (Br. Adam[11]). Since the 17th century, Dark bees were brought across the ocean to North and South America, and across the Ural to Siberia. But in the last decades, the development of modern beekeeping was not favorable to them and they lost ground almost everywhere. As a pure race they have at present local significance in some parts of Spain, France, Poland, and Russia; a few beekeepers breed some selected strains of them in Switzerland (strain Nigra), in the Austrian Alps, Germany, and Scandinavia. Elsewhere they were crossed with Carnica, Ligustica, or Caucasica, or they became displaced entirely.

Appearance: Big bees with short tongues (5.7 to 6.4 mm.), broad abdomen, color of the chitin very dark and uniform, partly with small yellow spots on the 2d and 3d terga but no yellow bands. Long overhairs, tomenta narrow and dispersed. Hairs on the thorax of drones dark brown, sometimes black. Cubital index small (1.3 to 2.1).

Behavior: Generally nervous in the open, they run from the comb readily. Frequently, but not always aggressive. Somewhat slow development in spring to medium-size colonies. Strong colonies late in summer and during winter (flat development curve, Ruttner[29]). Weak disposition to swarming. (The once famous "heather bee" (Dutch bee) was a special strain of this race, a result of long crossbreeding and

---

*Ligustica is the name for the Italian race of bees.

Mellifera

Ligustica

Carnica

Caucasica

FIGURE 7. The four races of well-known economic value. The individual bees are approximately three times life size. (*Photos courtesy of F. Ruttner except the one of Ligustica which is by G. P. Piana, Bologna, Italy*)

selection for inclination to swarm.) Good wintering under severe climates. The industrious behavior of this race has been praised many times (Br. Adam[9]) but in the clover flow, the Dark bee is much inferior to the long-tongued races. Susceptible to brood diseases and wax moths.

The Dark bee developed under the mild western European climate influenced by the ocean. For this reason, its brood production is not great; the springtime development is tardy. With the advancement of modern agriculture, the honey production of the Dark bee became inferior to other races, particularly in spring. Thus modern beekeeping, with a few exceptions, does not prefer the Dark bee. According to Brother Adam[11] and Lunder,[25] it is superior to any other race in the heather flow in England and Norway. There is always enough honey in its brood combs and danger of starvation is very small. In poor territories, other races often consume all their honey, but the thrifty Dark bee, with economic work, always produces some surplus.

It is a question whether the Dark bee, after careful selection in particular territories, would play any role in the future. If crossed with other races, its hybrid offspring shows unusual vitality and performance, but at the same time its strong tendency to sting remains a significantly bad habit.

ITALIAN BEES (*Apis mellifera ligustica* Spin.)

Dzierzon brought the first "yellow bees" from Venice to Germany in 1853. On the ground of his enthusiastic reports, the first Italian queens came to the U.S.A. very soon after (1859). Here as well as in other countries, the Italian bee became the commercial bee. "It is a question whether beekeeping without the Italian bee would have been able to make the great progress of the last 100 years" (Br. Adam[11]). In Italy in the vicinity of Bologna, as well as in the U.S.A., productive breeding enterprises came into existence from which the queens of this race were sent all over the world.

Original homeland: Italy exclusive of Sicily.

Appearance: Somewhat smaller than the *mellifera* with slender abdomen and relatively long tongues (6.3 to 6.6 mm.). Color of the chitin of the abdomen brightened on the sterna as well as on the first two to four terga (yellow bands on their front segments). In the original homeland, the extension and shades of yellow show great variation; there are colonies with wide, light bands and others with smaller markings of brown shades (Goetze,[19] Br. Adam[10]). Light-colored bees often have a yellow scutellum, similar to the Cyprian bee. Very light forms of Ligustica, with only a small black spot on the tip of the abdomen, are known as "golden bees" (Aurea). Also the hairs of Ligustica have yellowish color; this is particularly distinct on the drones.

The overhairs are short, the tomenta are wide and dense. Cubital index varies from medium to high (2.0 to 2.7).

Behavior: Calmness on the combs variable, mostly good. Generally gentle. Extraordinarily strong disposition to breeding; the colonies start to breed early in spring and maintain a large brood area regardless of flows until late fall. Exceptionally strong colonies occur in this manner which show good performance, especially in midsummer. In spite of the strong disposition for brood rearing, the inclination to swarm is very small, saving much work during the main season. Overwintering with strong colonies and with high consumption of food. In northern latitudes, the overwintering causes difficulties; there is a loss of worker bees due to early brood rearing, thus colony development in spring will be slow and tardy. In case of a poor honeyflow in summer, a shortage of food occurs easily because the consumption is high. The long tongue of the Italian makes the utilization of red clover feasible. The good building instinct of this race has been praised many times; it covers the honey with brilliant white cappings and no other bee produces such beautiful comb honey as the Italian.

The Ligustica is the child of the Mediterranean climate: short, mild, humid winters, dry summers with long honeyflows. The Italian bee has proved excellent in similar climates for many decades, but for longer winters and tardy springs with many relapses it has no defense. It always has been difficult for southern races to settle down in the North. In Europe this can be readily seen; many unsuccessful attempts were made with Italians north of the Alps. For more than 100 years they have been imported again and again, but they have never been able to establish themselves in good fashion.

On the other hand, we have to emphasize the good performance of Ligustica when the flows are good. In addition to colony strength, the particular shrewdness of this race contributes greatly to its performance, although it also may lead to robbing, an extremely undesirable trait known in apiaries long ago (Abushady,[1] Kleine[23]). If among different races, robbing arises, the Italians always begin it, and it makes no difference whether they are from Italy or from the U.S.A. If you open a new colony during a poor honeyflow, the first yellow explorers will appear there quite soon.

The sense of orientation has some role only in apiaries where many colonies live close to each other in a beehouse as is common in central Europe. The sense of orientation of the Italians proves to be very weak there, the bees often flying to the wrong hives.

According to Alpatov[4] Italian bees in the U.S.A. show the same characteristics as the Italians in their homeland. The increase in yellow color is the only difference; it is the result of a preference for uniform light-colored bees. Similar to this color preference, a certain selection occurred in the U.S.A. regarding the rate of brood development, calmness on the combs, and the disposition to certain flows. Thus speaking of an "American bee," meaning "American strains of *Apis mellifera ligustica*," is entirely justified.

CARNIOLANS (*Apis mellifera carnica* Pollmann)

Original homeland: Southern part of the Austrian Alps and the North Balkan (Yugoslavia)—Carnica in a broader sense: Macedonia with the entire Danube Valley (Hungary, Rumania, and Bulgaria). The bees of these areas do not differ from the Carnica of the Alps; certainly they belong to the same systematic unit. The eastern borderline of their area is not clearly discernible; obviously the Carnicalike southern Russian "steppe bee" (*A. mellifera acervorum* Alp.) forms a gradual transition to the Dark bee.

Particularly in the last decades, the extension of Carnica has increased greatly. One can distinguish two steps in the economic utilization of these bees: 1. Before World War I they were shipped by thousands in primitive wooden boxes without frames (Carinthian farm hives). They increased by simple natural swarming, but the results with these bees, selected according to their inclination to swarming, were very disappointing. Some of them still exist in Carinthia and Slovenia, but their honey-producing ability is entirely inadequate. 2. Since about 1930 a well-planned breeding program has taken place in Austria; certain strains have been selected with regard to productive performance and inclination to swarming. These strains are known as Carnica.

Appearance: Generally quite similar to Ligustica. Slender with long tongues (6.4 to 6.8 mm.). Hairs short and dense ("grey bee"). Chitin overwhelmingly dark, on the 2d and 3d terga of the abdomen often brown spots, sometimes a leather-brown band. Color of hairs of the drones grey to greyish brown. Cubital index very high (2.0 to 5.0).

Behavior: The Carnica is the quietest and most gentle race according to Brother Adam.[9] One may leave the combs outside of the hive for a long time and not a single bee of a good strain will move away. Their rhythm of brood production is very steep. They overwinter with small colonies and with small food consumption. Brood rearing starts with the first income of pollen and fast development occurs thereafter. During summer, the Carnica maintain a large brood nest only if the pollen supply is adequate; the brood rearing will be limited in case of a poor pollen flow. In fall the population of the colony declines rapidly. It would be quite impossible for the Carnica to overwinter with strong colonies like Ligustica. However, overwintering is very good even under unfavorable climatic conditions. There is a strong disposition to swarm accompanying the fast development of the colonies and their great vitality, but this disposition can be influenced by selection.

Very good sense of orientation, no inclination to robbing. Their use of propolis is very small. Brother Adam[11] found the building instinct of the Carnica too weak; we cannot agree with this statement. Good utilization of the red clover. Diseases of the brood are almost unknown in the homeland of the Carnica. This is a particular feature because very often painstaking carefulness is not practiced there in the apiaries. No explanation of this curious fact so far has been given.

The Carnica developed in a part of Europe where the climate is influenced by strong continental air movements that result in long severe winters and hot summers following a short spring. Corresponding to these circumstances, the characteristic features of this bee are vitality and a fast, energetic reaction to any changes in the environment. It is the "spring flow bee par excellence" because of its good development in spring (Br. Adam[11]). In Central Europe with mostly early flows and long, often severe, winters, this race is the most popular among bee-keepers. Crossbreeding with other races produces very high brood production and lively colonies.

CAUCASIANS (*Apis mellifera caucasica* Gorb.)

Original homeland: The high valleys of the Central Caucasus (Gruzinian and Mingrelian bees).

Appearance: Shape and size of the body and hairs very much like those of Carnica. Color of the chitin dark, but frequently of brown spots on the first bands of the abdomen. The hairs of the workers of Carnica are more grey-brown; for Caucasica they are less grey. The hairs on the thorax of drones are black. Very long tongues (up to 7.2 mm.). Cubital index medium. Other differences only can be determined by biometric methods.

Extensive biometric tests proved the existence of many local forms in the Caucasus area (Alpatov[5]). Numerous transition forms led to the more yellow colored *A. mellifera remipes* of Transcaucasian lowlands. Also the Caucasian bees have no uniform color in their original homeland, and the "pure grey bee" is rather an ideal of breeders than a reality in nature.

Behavior: We have less data for the evaluation of the Caucasica than in the case of the three races just discussed. Most of the strains existing today in the West were imported from the U.S.S.R. between the two world wars. They are probably crossed with other dark races, especially with the quite similar Carnica. Our experience has been limited to a few queens which were acquired from Prof. Glushkov, of Moscow, in 1957. The most extensive experiments have originated in Russia.

Gentleness and calmness on the combs are the characteristics commonly emphasized for Caucasians. Ardent brood production, raising strong colonies; however, they do not reach full strength before midsummer. Their disposition to swarm is weak. Very great users of propolis; in fall the entrance will be closed by a curtain of propolis with the exception of a small hole. Overwintering in northern regions is not very good because of their susceptibility to nosema (Taranov[32]). In Russia their honey production is definitely better than that of the Dark bee, but their performance on red clover is not up to expectations based on the length of their tongues. Cappings of the honey are flat (dark). Inclined to drifting and robbing.

This bee certainly will share an important role in bee breeding; some of its qualities are valuable. Although it closely resembles Carnica, it has distinct characteristics of its own.

A Few Local Forms from Transition Areas. A few, which have recently been discussed, should be mentioned. The **Macedonian bee** (*A. mellifera cecropia* Kicsw.) from southern Yugoslavia and northern Greece was described by Georgandas.[17] This bee as well as the **Carpathian bee** of Rumania, after closer testing, proved to belong to the Carnica race. They have not shown any better performance than the other Carnica under Central European conditions.

The **Anatolian bee** has been tested for a number of years by Brother Adam.[12] This name refers, however, only to its origin and not to a distinct race. According to Bodenheimer[8] and Brother Adam, several different sub-races occur in Anatolia; an acceptable classification has not yet been established.

The Utilization of the Natural Differences among Bees

A successful bee economy needs, in addition to good flows and ambitious beekeepers, first of all a capable bee. Vigor and ability to develop the colony, gentleness and quietness on the combs, and the capability of gathering large amounts of stores are the qualities primarily required of the bee. The environment may make further claims as winter hardiness, resistance to specific diseases, response of brood rearing to seasonal variations, and orientation. One cannot expect from natural selection, the development of a race perfectly fulfilling the requirements of the modern beekeeper. But the comparison of the typical characteristics of the different races shows that one race approaches the ideal more closely than another one. Sometimes a natural race can simply be replaced by another one in order to increase production. As has already been mentioned, this has been done many times. Certainly, careful consideration should be given to the climatic conditions of the original homeland in the case of transplantation of a race. Bees from a mild climate can hardly adjust themselves to a rugged environment.

Further increase of production can be achieved by selection within a race. To a certain extent, the results of this method have proved to be satisfactory, if the breeder was able to avoid too intensive inbreeding. Inbreeding generally decreases the fertility and vigor of the colony, in extreme cases so far that the colony becomes incapable of living alone (Mackensen[27]).

In other fields of animal breeding, synthetic races originated mostly by crossbreeding different geographical races, or even strains, and by long selection and inbreeding a new stable combination developed. In bee breeding this way has not been used frequently so far, because of difficulties in controlled matings, although great possibilities exist in this field (Br. Adam[9]).

In the cultivation of plants, one uses the heterosis effect (hybrid vigor) to a great extent today. Hybrid corn is the best known example of what can be achieved in this manner. Only a few kinds of animals are adaptable to this method; the honey bee is one of them because of the great number of its offspring. Hybrid vigor, with the performance of the first hybrid crossing better than that of the better parent, can be achieved in the bee in two different ways.

1. *Hybrids or double hybrids from inbred lines.* The classical methods used in corn production show very promising results in bee breeding also (Cale,[14] Cale and Gowen[15]). In egg laying, as well as in honey production, the hybrids surpassed the control strains. The increase in production amounted to 34 per cent.

2. *Crossbreeding between two geographical races.* Hybrid vigor also occurs in many cases when two geographical races are crossed without previous inbreeding. Since there are mostly large genetical differences between the races, the results are greater than that of any other method but are not always repeatable.

Cross	Increase in honey production
Carnica x Mellifera	31 per cent compared to the better parent (selected Carnica) (Ruttner[28])
Carnica x Caucasica	50 to 100 per cent compared to selected Carnica (Ruttner unpubl.)
Caucasica x Mellifera	15 to 41 per cent compared to the average of the strains (Taranov[32])
Caucasica x South Russian	61 to 65 per cent compared to the South Russian control strain (Solodkova and Guba[31])
Anatolian x Buckfast bee	128 to 151 per cent compared to the general average of the bee yard (Br. Adam[13])

The combining ability within a geographical race shows some differences as well as many other characteristics. In crossbreeding not all the strains of two races create the same beneficial heterosis effect. The specific combining ability has to be tested in every single case. Another difficulty in crossbreeding lies in the development of unfavorable characteristics in many cases. The extraordinary vigorous and hardy hybrids (Mellifera x Carnica) are very aggressive; the crossbreeds Caucasica x Carnica are the best in regard to production, development, and behavior, but in cold winters are very susceptible to nosema. In spite of all this, it is evident that well-planned crossbreeding will play an extraordinary role in beekeeping of the future.

REFERENCES CITED

1. Abushady, A. Z. 1949. **In** Grout, Roy A. The hive and the honey bee. Hamilton, Ill. pp. 11-20.

2. Alber, M. 1956. XVI Intern. Beekeeping Congr. Vienna. Apic. Abstr. 241/56.

3. Alley, H. 1883. The new method of queen rearing. Wenham, Mass.

4. Alpatov, W. W. 1929. Quart. Rev. Biol. 4:1-58.

5. ----------------- 1948. The strains of the honey bee and their contribution in agriculture. Moscow. (In Russian)

6. Anderson, R. H. 1961. XVIII Intern. Beekeeping Congr. Madrid.

7. Blum, Robert. 1951. Am. Bee J. 91(9):378-379.

8. Bodenheimer, F. S. 1941. Studies on the honey bee and beekeeping in Turkey. Ankara.

9. Brother Adam. 1951. Bee World 32:49-52,57-62.

10. ----------------- 1954. Bee World 35:193-203,233-244.

11. ----------------- 1957. Sudwestdeutscher Imber 9:14-23.

12. ----------------- 1958. XVII Intern. Beekeeping Congr. Rome. Apic. Abstr. 388/58.

13. ----------------- 1961. Bee World 42:252-255.

14. Cale, G. H., Jr. 1957. Am. Bee J. 97:48.

15. Cale, G. H., Jr., and J. W. Gowen. 1956. Genetics 41:292-303. Apic. Abstr. 245/56.

16. Deodikar, G. B., C. V. Thakar, and Pushipa N. Shaw. 1959. Proc. Indian Acad. Sci. 49:194-206.

17. Georgandas, P. 1957. Am. Bee J. 97:314.

18. Goetze, G. 1930. Arch. Bienenkunde 11:185-236.

19. ----------------- 1940. Die Beste Biene. Liedloff, Loth & Michaelis, Leipzig.

20. ----------------- 1956. Ins. sociaux 3:335-346.

21. Henriksen, C., and O. Hammer. 1957. Nord. Bitidskr. 9:11-19. Apic. Abstr. 323/57.

22. Kerr, W. E. 1957. Brazil Apic. 3:211-213. Apic. Abstr. 184/589.

23. Kleine, G. 1960. Am. Bee J. 100:177.

24. Lindauer, M. 1957. Bee World 38:3-14,34-39.

25. Lunder, R. 1953. Nord. Bitidskr. 5:71-83. Apic. Abstr. 49/55.

26. Mackensen, O. 1943. J. Econ. Entomol. 36(3):465-467.

27. ----------------- 1956. XVI Intern. Beekeeping Congr. Vienna. Apic. Abstr. 247/56.

28. Ruttner, F. 1957. Deutsche Bienenwirtschaft 8:81-87.

29. ----------------- 1960. Biene und Bienenzucht. Ehrenwirth, Munich. p. 5-22.

30. Smith, F. G. 1961. Bee World 42:255-260.

31. Solodkova, N., and F. Guba. 1960. Pchelovodstvo 6:28-31.

32. Taranov, G. F. 1956. XVI Intern. Beekeeping Congr. Vienna. Apic. Abstr. 240/56.

CHAPTER III

THE HONEY-BEE COLONY — LIFE HISTORY

by C. G. BUTLER*

IN THE HONEY BEE, as in other social animals, the colony, rather than the individuals of which it is composed, is the unit whose efficiency determines the fate of the species. Although it is convenient to consider the various parts of the colony, such as the queen, workers, and drones, separately for some purposes, it is the relationships between these parts which are so important and which together make colony life possible, and beekeeping practicable.

Ancestry of Bees

Unfortunately we know very little about the ancestry of bees, as their fossil records are extremely scarce. Nevertheless, there is good reason to suppose that sometime in the distant past, perhaps as long as eighty million years ago, the first bees developed from some wasplike ancestor, forsaking a carnivorous diet for a vegetarian one.

Although nectar and other sugary substances form a necessary but small part of the diet of many kinds of wasps, they have remained essentially carnivorous in habit, feeding mainly on insects and related creatures. There is, however, a small and interesting group of rare solitary (nonsocial) wasps, the Masarinae, only found in warm countries, which eat pollen and nectar and supply their larvae with a pastelike mixture of these materials, just like solitary bees.

In adopting a vegetarian habit in place of a carnivorous one, the bees have gradually developed a number of specialized structures that greatly aid them in collecting and handling pollen and nectar. Their bodies have become very hairy so that pollen tends to stick to them when they touch the stamens of flowers, and rows of hairs and bristles have been developed as brushes and combs with which the pollen on the body may be collected together. It is carried home either in pollen-carrying devices beneath their abdomens (as in the case of many solitary bees), or in pollen baskets on their hind legs (as in bumble bees and honey bees). Their tongues have in many cases become longer, sometimes even as long as their bodies, helping them to get to deep-seated

---

*Colin G. Butler, M.A., Ph.D. Head of the Bee Department, Rothamsted Experimental Station, Harpenden, Hertfordshire, England. Studies in bee physiology and behavior. Author of about 80 scientific papers and several books on bees and other insects.

nectaries which many other nectar-seeking insects cannot reach with their short tongues. Their crops have become enlarged as "honey stomachs" for carrying large loads of nectar, and in some species wax-producing glands and other special organs have been developed. These adaptations culminate in the western honey bee *(Apis mellifera)*, making it one of the most successful insects in the world today.

CLASSIFICATION

In 1758, the great Swedish naturalist Linnaeus published the tenth edition of the *Systema Naturae* in which the so-called binomial system of classification, which is universally used today, was applied to animals for the first time. In this system each animal is given two names and our western, or European, honey bee was called *Apis mellifera*. The first, or generic, name *(Apis)* refers the honey bee to a group of closely related bees which have a number of characteristics in common; the second, or specific, name *(mellifera)*, by further defining the western honey bee, distinguishes it from all other members of the genus *Apis*.

The honey bees (i.e. all the species, or members, of the genus *Apis*) belong in their turn to a larger group of related insects, the family Apidae, which includes the bumble or humble bees, the carpenter bees, and the so-called stingless bees. This family of bees is grouped with a number of other families of bees to form the superfamily Apoidea, whose members all share a number of characteristics, such as possessing plumose (feathery) body hairs and the habit of feeding on nectar and pollen. This superfamily contains, then, a number of truly social bees—the honey bees, bumble bees, and the so-called stingless bees—a few social and subsocial bees belonging to the family Halictidae, and a great many solitary bees which, as their name implies, are not social in their behavior and do not live in colonies. Examples of this last group are the familiar leaf-cutting mason and carpenter bees.

The superfamily Apoidea is joined by a number of others, including the superfamilies Formicoidea (ants) and Vespoidea (true wasps) to form the suborder Apocrita which, with another suborder, Symphyta (wood wasps, sawflies, and their allies), make up the great order Hymenoptera, with about 100,000 species. This, with some 28 other orders, constitutes the class Insecta of the phylum of the animal kingdom known as the Arthropoda (insects, crustaceans, spiders, mites, millipedes, centipedes, and others). It is clear, therefore, that this system of classification recognizes that lobsters, crayfish, centipedes, spiders, mites, ticks, insects, and all other members of the phylum Arthropoda, are more closely related to each other than to the animals of any other phylum. It recognizes that *Apis mellifera* is more closely related to a fly or a grasshopper than to a lobster, and yet is more akin to a bumble bee and still more so to other species of honey bees (i.e. species of the genus *Apis*).

It is almost certain that the ancestral home of the honey bees was in South Asia, and of the four species of honey bees living today three are indigenous to South India, Ceylon, and other parts of South Asia. These are the giant honey bee *(A. dorsata),* the little honey bee *(A. florea)* and the eastern, or Indian, honey bee *(A. indica).** Each of these species lives wild in these countries and it should be emphasized that those colonies of *A. indica,* or for that matter of *A. mellifera,* living in hives in apiaries are just as wild and undomesticated as their sister colonies living in hollow trees in jungles, fields, and forests.

EVOLUTION OF SOCIAL LIFE IN BEES

The great majority of the hundreds of species of bees in the world live solitary, unsocial lives like flies, grasshoppers, and most other insects, their only important contact with other members of their species being that between males and females during courtship and mating. Only in 8 of the 30 or so orders of insects recognized by taxonomists is any form of organized communal life found; and only in 2 of these 8 orders, the Isoptera (termites or white ants) and the Hymenoptera (which includes the ants, bees, and wasps), has it developed to the stage in which two female castes, queen and worker, are present.

The social life of ants, bees, and wasps developed independently of that of the termites, and similarities of social structure between their communities afford an excellent example of convergent evolution.

Of the six families of bees (Apoidea) only two, the Halictidae and Apidae, contain fully social species in which a worker caste has evolved. It is among the bees of these two families that indications of the probable path taken by bees in the evolution of social life are found. Fossil history does not help much. All that has been deduced from it is that social insects may have existed twenty-three million years ago, as bees found embalmed in Baltic amber of the Oligocene period, although not belonging to modern genera, belonged to groups which now contain some social members.

The probability that social life developed in bees and wasps later than in ants and termites is suggested by two facts. First, there are today many species of bees and wasps still living solitary or subsocial lives whereas no termites or ants do so; and second, the caste system of even the most highly social bees and wasps is much less advanced than that of termites or ants.

Many kinds of insects are gregarious and respond to various environmental stimuli by coming together, at least temporarily, to form large groups. For example, monarch butterflies hibernate together in enormous numbers on trees, similarly thousands of ladybird beetles sometimes hibernate together, web-spinning caterpillars of certain moths share a communal web, locusts form dense swarms, and hundreds of

---

**Apis indica* is synonymous with *Apis cerana* used in Chapter II, "Races of Bees."

female solitary bees will build their nests side by side in burrows in a bank or path. But, these insects do not really cooperate with one another, and there is little evidence to suggest that the cooperation between individuals found in a community of social insects developed from such gregarious behavior. Social behavior seems to have been brought about by lengthening of the life of the female parent (sometimes, as in termites, of that of the male parent as well) sufficiently for her to live for a time with her own offspring in a common nest and to cooperate with them in some degree. All truly social insect communities are, in fact, families.

Most kinds of bees live entirely solitary lives. After mating, each female builds her own nest without help from her mate or any other individual. Each nest consists of a few cells, often only 6 to 8, built in a burrow in the ground or in rotten wood, the hollow stem of a plant, a crevice in a wall, an empty snail shell, or other sheltered place according to her species. As soon as she has built the first cell of her nest, she collects pollen and nectar, mixes them together to form a paste and places a pellet of it in the bottom of the cell. She now lays one egg on the paste, which supplies all the food required by the grub when it hatches, and seals the cell before starting to build another one. She continues building, provisioning, and laying eggs in cells in this way until she dies without ever seeing her offspring.

An early stage in the evolution of social life is shown by a few species of small bees belonging to the genus *Halictus,* the females of which live long enough to see their eggs hatch and to provide the larvae that come from them with food (pollen mixed with nectar) when they require it, instead of providing it all at once. This type of feeding is known as progressive provisioning in contrast to the mass provisioning practiced by most bees. The honey bees all practice progressive provisioning.

The next stage is a great advance towards a truly social life and is found in several other species of *Halictus*. Each female founds a nest entirely on her own in early spring and, although she mass provisions its cells, she continues to live not only while her larvae are developing but for several months after they have become adults. These adults are all females which are slightly smaller than their mother and continue to live with her. They all help to build further cells and to collect food and provision them. They do not mate but act as workers, their mother, the queen, laying all the eggs. Later, in summer, males and larger females (queens) are reared and, after mating, these young females hibernate, separately or in small groups, until the following spring when each tries to found a nest on her own. The old queen, workers, and males die in the autumn. So each nest is founded by a single overwintered queen and lasts for less than a year.

Another step in the evolution of social life is seen in the bumble bees. Each nest is founded in spring or early summer by a single overwintered queen which mated during the previous autumn. At first the queen has to do everything, including nest building, foraging, egg laying and, in most species, progressive feeding of the larvae. But, the first of her offspring to appear are all imperfect females, incapable of mating, indeed, workers, which take over many of the jobs, including foraging, that their mother, the queen, has hitherto carried out. Later in the season, when food is plentiful and the colony prosperous, queens are reared and mating occurs, usually between queens and males belonging to different colonies. The old colonies then die out and only the young impregnated queens are left to hibernate and found new colonies the following spring. In the bumble bees, then, we find a well-marked differentiation between the queen and worker castes, but the queens can, and do for a time, carry out all the duties that are later performed exclusively by their worker daughters, and their colonies are only annual affairs in the temperate regions of the world in which they abound.

In the misnamed "stingless" bees (Meliponinae), many species of which are found in South America, and some of which are even kept for honey production, caste differentiation is well marked, the queens have lost all trace of pollen-collecting apparatus, and the colonies are perennial. Colony reproductive swarming occurs from time to time as in honey-bee colonies. Indeed, the social organization shown by colonies of these bees is very similar to that of honey-bee colonies, except that the larvae are fed by mass provisioning of their cells rather than by progressive provisioning. They occupy, in fact, a social position between that of the bumble bees and honey bees.

The highest degree of social development in bees is found in colonies of the eastern and western honey bees *(Apis indica* and *A. mellifera)*. In their colonies there is a well-marked caste system, the queens differing in many respects from the workers. Whereas ancestral queen honey bees were, no doubt, like queen bumble bees and queen wasps today, able to carry out all the different tasks necessary to found their colonies, such as nest building, foraging for food, and feeding the larvae, modern queens have lost the ability to found their own colonies or even collect food for themselves, but have become extremely efficient egg-laying machines.

The queen of a honey-bee colony normally produces all the eggs from which the other members of her colony develop, and serves in various ways as the focal point of her colony, greatly helping in maintaining its cohesion. The worker honey bee, on the other hand, is an imperfect female in the sense that she is unable to mate and lacks a sperm-storage reservoir (spermatheca), and has almost rudimentary ovaries which only develop under certain relatively rare conditions, such as the sudden death of the colony's queen. She retains, however, many of the structures that once must have been possessed by queens, which enable her to carry out all those necessary tasks of which the queen is nowadays incapable. For example, worker honey bees have retained their pollen-collecting apparatus and their long tongues which enable them to reach the moderately deep-seated nectaries of some kinds of flowers. Their hypopharyngeal glands, which have been lost by queens, have become very large and produce the bulk of the food that is fed to larvae and to adult queens and perhaps to drones. Their mandibular glands, which produce the 10-hydroxydecenoic acid found in brood food,[16] have remained small compared with those of queens which have become relatively huge and produce, among other things, the important substance, 9-oxodecenoic acid,[14,15] which helps to control the behavior of the workers. They possess wax-producing glands, as well as scent-producing (Nassanoff) glands, which queen honey bees have lost altogether. In other words, the two female castes of the honey bee, queen and worker, are complementary to one another. The workers do most of the work necessary for the well-being of their colony, the queen's efforts being concentrated on the rest.

Colony Life

Unlike a bumble-bee colony, the life of a honey-bee colony is perennial, but the lives of its individual workers are short, only 4 or 5 weeks in summer, and a little more than as many months in winter. The life of the queen has, however, become prolonged to several years.

Just as there is a marked division of labor between the queen of a colony and her workers (Fig. 1), there is also a well-defined division of duties among the workers themselves, although every worker is, at one time or another, normally able to carry out all worker duties. For additional information on the division of labor in a honey-bee colony, see Chapter IV, "Activities of Honey Bees."

Here, then, in the honey-bee colony, we find a highly organized social community which has succeeded in becoming perennial because of its efficiency, particularly in controlling the temperature of its nest and in collecting large quantities of food during favorable conditions and storing them until needed during unfavorable ones. These characteristics are most marked in the western honey bee which has also succeeded in establishing itself throughout a large part of the world, extending from the tropics to the subartic.

FOOD STORAGE

The only food materials stored by honey bees are honey and pollen. The former is prepared by worker bees from nectar collected from the nectaries of flowers and from the extra-floral nectaries of certain kinds of plants, such as field bean *(Vicia faba)* and peach *(Amygdalus sp.)*, mixed occasionally with honeydew — a sugary liquid derived from plant sap and excreted by aphids and other plant bugs. Conversion of nectar into honey involves partial or complete inversion of any

FIGURE 1. Left, drone; center, queen; and right, worker. Enlarged slightly. *(Photo by O. W. Park)*

sucrose it contains into equal parts of two simple sugars, glucose and fructose, and reduction of its water content, by evaporation, from an average value of 60 to 65 per cent to 17 to 25 per cent. Inversion of sucrose by the enzyme *invertase,* which is produced in the hypopharyngeal salivary glands of worker bees and added to the nectar in their honey stomachs, begins in the honey stomach of the returning forager, is continued when the nectar is taken over by the house bees, and completed in the cells of the honeycomb in which it is eventually stored. These storage cells are sealed by the workers with wax cappings when their contents are "ripe" — i.e. have had their water content reduced to at least 25 per cent. Evaporation of excess water from nectar is encouraged by the house bees which expose drops of it to the hive atmosphere.

Honey is stored in both drone and worker cells, but, under natural conditions, in wild colonies in hollow trees for instance, it is said to be stored primarily in combs consisting almost entirely of drone cells. On the other hand, pollen is almost always stored in worker cells. Such cells are never completely filled with pollen, and are only sealed when the bees have covered the pollen with a layer of honey. Pollen stored in this way is said to retain its nutritive value for a year or more, and to be especially valuable to the bees in late winter and early spring when brood rearing for the year has started and fresh supplies are scarce or not yet available.

The same cell in a comb may be used at different times for food storage and for brood rearing. As a rule, however, the cells at or near the bottom of the center of the mass of combs, which together form the nest, are used primarily, though not exclusively, for brood rearing throughout the active season (Fig. 2). This part of the nest is often called the "brood nest," and is roughly spherical in shape and usually

FIGURE 2. A comb containing sealed worker brood—often found in the center of the brood nest. *(Photo by Laidlaw and Eckert)*

includes elliptical areas of cells containing brood in each of several adjacent combs. The comb in the center of the brood nest normally contains the most brood, those on either side of it slightly less, and so on until the lateral limits of the brood nest are reached.

There is usually a band of cells, 1 or 2 inches wide, containing stores of pollen, above and at the sides of the cells containing brood (brood area) in each comb (Fig. 3). The area of cells in which honey is stored lies immediately outside the band of pollen-storage cells and often extends to the edges of the comb. These honey-storage cells, irrespective of whether they are basically drone or worker cells, are frequently deepened by the bees, thus considerably increasing their volume. Both pollen- and honey-storage cells are usually most abundant at the top corners, or shoulders, of a comb.

This natural tendency of honey bees to store honey above the cells containing brood and pollen has been exploited by beekeepers to obtain combs containing nothing but honey. By dividing the nest into several parts horizontally, that is by using several combs in separate hive chambers (bodies or supers) one above the other and separated from each other by a bee space, which the worker bees keep free of comb, modern beekeepers find that their best bees tend to store honey in the combs of the chamber or chambers above the brood nest. By adding a queen excluder — i.e. a perforated metal or wire screen through which worker bees, but neither drones nor queens, can pass — immediately above the chamber of combs to which he decides that the brood nest shall be confined, the beekeeper makes certain that no eggs are laid, and therefore no brood is reared, in combs in the honey chambers or "supers."

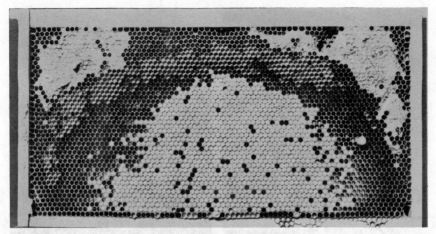

FIGURE 3. A comb containing sealed worker brood, a band of pollen cells, and honey stored above. *(Photo by W. W. Clarke, Jr.)*

THE NESTS OF HONEY BEES

The nests of honey bees consist of one or more vertical combs containing cells that are hexagonal in cross section and of two, or in the case of at least one species, *Apis florea,* three different sizes. The long axes of these cells are slightly inclined to the horizontal so that the cell mouths are higher than the cell bases. In addition, pendant acorn-shaped queen cells, attached to the side, bottom, or face of the comb, are present when queens are being reared. Drone and worker larvae are reared in the comb cells, which in such cases are often called "brood cells," and pollen and honey are also stored in them.

When new, the combs consist entirely of wax secreted by glands on the underside of the workers' abdomens. Later, the brood cells, in which several generations of larvae have been reared, come to contain a variable number of cocoons and also larval excrement, and the wax of the whole comb gets adulterated with pollen, cocoon fragments, and other materials, becoming darkened in the process. The darker a comb the older it is likely to be.

Two species of honey bees, the giant honey bee *(Apis dorsata)* and the little honey bee *(Apis florea),* build single-comb nests in daylight. Those of *A. dorsata* can be found attached to the undersides of high horizontal branches of trees (Fig. 4), or of overhanging rocks, to the arches of bridges, or even beneath the eaves of buildings. A single-comb nest of this species may be as much as 6 feet long and 3 feet wide, and the large cells in which drones and workers are reared are not only similar in shape but also in size. An adult worker of this species is about the same size as a queen of the Italian race of the western

FIGURE 4. Left, a single comb of the giant honey bee *(Apis dorsata)* about 18 inches long. Right, a colony of the little honey bee *(Apis florea)* on a single comb about the size of your hand.

honey bee. The nest of the little honey bee is very much smaller, often no larger than a man's hand, and attached to the underside of a twig of a bush or a small tree (Fig. 4). The comb contains tiny cells of three sizes, the smallest being those in which the workers (Fig. 5) are reared (about ten worker cells per linear inch), the next size larger are those in which drones are reared, and the largest of all being a group at the top of the comb in which honey and pollen are stored. These storage cells are, relative to the worker and drone cells, very deep and make the comb bulge out on either side at the top, thus forming a small platform on which successful foragers dance when recruiting other workers to exploit the sources of food they have found.[32]

The other two species of honey bees, the eastern honey bee *(Apis indica)* and the western honey bee *(Apis mellifera)*, usually build their nests in darkness in hollow trees, holes in walls, or similar cavities. The nest of each consists of a number of parallel, vertical combs, each of those of the western honey bee being separated from its neighbors by about a half inch. The combs of the eastern honey bee are slightly closer together. The combs conform in outline to the shape of the cavity in which the nest is built, unless the cavity is so large that there is no need for them to do so, and are usually roughly elliptical in shape, each being attached to the roof of the cavity by its upper edge.

Because the eastern and western honey bees habitually build their multicomb nests in dark cavities, they will readily settle down in wooden hives and other containers and are, indeed, the hive bees of the world. The giant and little honey bees with their single-comb,

FIGURE 5. Comparison of the size of the little honey bee *(Apis florea)* and the western honey bee *(Apis mellifera)*. Enlarged about 2X. *Florea*, at top; *Mellifera*, at bottom.

open-air nests, will not live satisfactorily in hives of any kind and, therefore, are of relatively little use to man apart from being robbed of their honey and wax by "bee hunters."

The eastern honey bee has just under seven worker cells per linear inch of its comb, compared with just under five in the case of the western honey bee. The former is somewhat more primitive in its behavior than the western honey bee and is better adapted to a hot climate and to avoiding such predators as the oriental hornet. It is about a third smaller in size than the western honey bee which is better adapted to withstand long cold periods successfully than its eastern sister (Fig. 6).

Under natural conditions, the vertical combs of the nest of the western honey bee run more or less parallel to one another throughout their lengths. Although they often appear to be spaced irregularly, the distance between worker brood combs is about 1⅜ inches, measured from the center (midrib) of one comb to that of the other. Drone combs are spaced about ⅛ inch farther apart. The distance between combs containing honey often increases to 1⅝ inches, sometimes even more.

About 1850, the Reverend Lorenzo Lorraine Langstroth improved the bar-frame hive he was using by arranging to have a space of ⅜ inch between the cover board and the wooden top bars of the frames containing the combs. He found that this space made it much easier to remove the cover because the bees no longer glued it firmly to the top bars of the frames with propolis, a sticky exudation of certain plants, such as poplars, which is collected by the western honey bee but not the eastern honey bee or the other species.

Langstroth greatly disliked having to cut or break away the bits of comb and propolis, with which the bees attached the frames to the walls of their hives, before he could remove them for inspection. In October 1851, he discovered that he could prevent the bees attaching them in this way by leaving a space 5/16 to ⅜ inch between the end bars of the frames and the sides of the hive. This space, which in modern practice is usually made about ¼ inch wide, is now known as the "bee space." When the space between the sides of the frames and the hive walls is made less than 5/16 inch, the bees plug it up with propolis and wax; similarly, when it is made more than ⅜ inch, they either fill it with these materials or build bits of brace comb in it.

Langstroth's discovery of the bee space led to the development of the hive as we know it today with frames which, because they have bee spaces all around them, can be removed without difficulty, and thus present methods of beekeeping were made possible.

The Queen

A queen honey bee is readily distinguished from both workers and drones. She is considerably larger than a worker and longer than a drone, though not nearly as broad. Her wings are much shorter in proportion to her body length than are those of either drone or worker, but are in fact longer than those of a worker. Because of her long tapering abdomen she appears rather more wasplike than drones or workers. Her curved sting, which she appears to use only against rival queens, is, unlike that of a worker, only slightly barbed. Her movements

FIGURE 6. Comparison of the size of the eastern honey bee (*Apis indica* syn. *cerana*) and the western honey bee (*Apis mellifera*). Enlarged about 2X. Each picture shows the queen surrounded by her attendants. *Indica,* at top; *mellifera* at bottom.

usually appear slow and deliberate, though, when necessary, she can move quite fast.

A mated, laying queen will, when undisturbed, usually be found on or near the combs containing the youngest brood in the hive, and she is generally surrounded by a "court" of young workers who face her, examine her with their antennae, lick her, feed her, and remove her excrement (Fig. 7).

For centuries, naturalists have made observations on honey bees, but the queen's sex remained undetermined until the beginning of the seventeenth century. Aristotle (*History of Animals,* Book 9, p. 128. Cresswell Translation, London. 1907) and other early naturalists, believed that the queen ruled over the workers, who were her subjects, and, therefore, called her the "king" bee. Nevertheless, he seems to have felt uncertain of her sex because when writing of queens, he said: "By some they are called mother bees, as if they were the parents of the rest; and they argue that unless the ruler is present, drones are only produced and no bees (workers). Others affirm that they have sexual intercourse and that the drones are males and the bees (workers) females."

In 1609, the Reverend Charles Butler published his famous book, *The Feminine Monarchie,* in which he announced that the "king" bee was a female and should, therefore, be called the "queen;" that the workers were also females and the drones males. However, he made the mistake of believing that the drones mate with the workers who then lay the eggs from which both drones and workers come.

In 1737, Jan Swammerdam (*Biblia Naturae,* Leyden) announced the discovery, by dissection, of the sexes of drone, queen, and worker, and, in 1745, John Thorley, in his *Melissologia, or the Female Monarchy* (London), correctly stated that the queen lays the eggs, but went on to suggest that the drones, which he believed to be males, fertilize them, after they have been laid. A few years later, Anton Janscha, Imperial and Royal Beekeeper to the Empress Maria Theresa, described how young virgin queens mate outside their hives and eventually become the mothers of colonies, thus preceding some of the discoveries of the great Swiss naturalist, Francois Huber, by 25 years.[19]

Today it is, of course, recognized that the queen produces all the eggs necessary for her colony, having mated in the open air, while on the wing, with several drones in succession and thus acquired a lifetime supply of spermatozoa. The workers are capable of laying a few eggs, but incapable of mating, and normally remain inhibited from egg laying so long as a queen is present. Eggs produced by "laying workers" are unfertilized and almost all give rise to drones that are usually undersized, having been reared in worker cells and grossly undernourished.

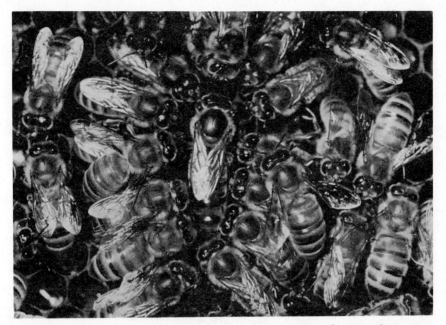

FIGURE 7. A queen and her "court" of young workers which take care of her every need night and day. *(Photo by Wolfgang Wittekindt)*

In temperate climates, the brood-rearing season starts on a small scale early in January, gradually increases until, by about May, it reaches its height. When circumstances allow, it continues at this level until near the end of July when it starts to fall off gradually and it stops altogether for a few weeks, usually in November or December. Different races of honey bees vary greatly in this respect. At the height of the brood-rearing season, a prolific queen of some races will lay between 1,500 and 2,000 eggs a day for a short period.

Although a worker bee can live on her own for a week or 2 in a cage in the laboratory, no worker will willingly do so; she will take the first opportunity to join other bees. Stray bees are attracted to groups of workers by scent, vibration, sight, and temperature.[20] The workers composing such a group, or cluster, tend to remain together even when they have no queen, brood, or even combs, and a division of labor between them is apparent, only a few bees foraging for the rest who remain in the cluster.[23] However, even though a queen is not necessary either to cause bees to cluster or to keep them together once they have clustered (except in the case of a recently clustered swarm), the presence of one is most important in maintaining colony cohesion and organization quite apart from her essential function as mother of future members of the colony.

It has been shown that a scent produced by the queen, probably mainly in her mandibular glands, is very attractive to workers,[12,39] and that another scent (inhibitory scent), found on many parts of her body, and particularly in her mandibular glands, acts synergically with another substance (9-oxodecenoic acid), also produced in her mandibular glands, to inhibit queen rearing by the workers of her colony and also to prevent development of their ovaries — i.e. the production of laying workers.[13] This inhibitory scent has not yet been identified, but the queen substance has been shown to be a fatty acid (9-oxodec-*trans*-2-enoic acid) that is closely related to the 10-hydroxydecenoic acid found in larval food and produced in the mandibular glands of worker bees.[14]

Queen substance* spreads all over a queen's body, probably when she grooms herself, and is licked off by some of the young bees forming her "court," which share it in regurgitated food with other bees, which share it with still others, and so on.[8] Provided the workers of a colony obtain enough queen substance and inhibitory scent, which is very weak and only appears to supplement and enhance the pronounced inhibitory effect of 9-oxodecenoic acid,[13] they remain inhibited from queen rearing. When, however, a colony loses its queen suddenly by accident, thus losing its source of these inhibitory materials, the workers soon begin to rear a new queen for themselves, often within 5 or 6 hours.

They modify one or more worker cells containing young female larvae to form emergency queen cells (Fig. 8). All being well, one of the queens produced in this way will become the new queen of the colony and the others will be destroyed either by workers, or by the oldest queen, the one that normally becomes the new head of the colony. During the period when the new queen is being reared, the absence of inhibitory queen substances allows the workers' ovaries to develop slightly and, if something goes wrong and the bees fail to rear a new queen, the ovaries of many of the younger ones continue to develop until they become functional laying workers.[9]

It is, of course, unusual for a colony to lose its queen suddenly and be compelled to rear another by this emergency procedure; queens are normally replaced during one or another of the processes known respectively as queen supersedure and swarming. The former differs from the latter in that the queen is replaced without the colony dividing and swarming.

Queens that have been superseded by their colonies, and are living alongside their daughter queens which have replaced them, have been found to produce under a quarter the amount of inhibitory material of a normally mated laying queen and, as might be expected, to be able

---

*Queen substance is now known to be complex and to contain at least 9-oxodec-*trans*-2-enoic acid and an "inhibitory scent." (Butler, C. G., and Patricia N. Paton. 1962. Proc. Roy. Entomol. Soc. London (A) 37:114)

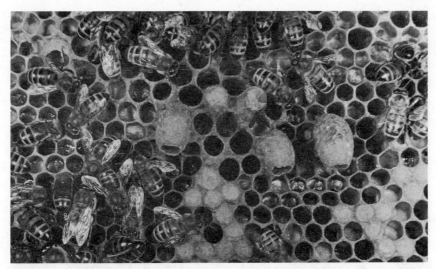

FIGURE 8. A group of emergency queen cells. Each has been built by the worker bees from an ordinary worker cell.

to keep small, but not large, numbers of bees from queen rearing. Similarly, queens taken from swarms emitted by uncrowded colonies produce about the same quantities of inhibitory material as superseded queens and are usually, if not always, superseded soon after their swarms have settled down in their new homes. It seems likely, therefore, that queen rearing, both in connection with queen supersedure and with noninduced swarming (i.e. swarming by uncrowded as opposed to overcrowded colonies) is caused by shortage of inhibitory queen substances.[11]

Queens reared in preparation for supersedure and swarming do not usually come from emergency queen cells, although it must be emphasized that some of them sometimes do; normally they are reared in queen cells especially constructed by the workers for this purpose and not modified from worker cells (Fig. 9). The queen usually lays eggs in these cells but there is evidence suggesting that workers can, and sometimes do, transfer fertilized eggs from worker cells to queen cells.[10]

At the time when a queen lays an egg in a queen cell, only the foundation of the cell exists and in this condition it is often called a "queen-cell cup." Such cups appear spasmodically, but fairly regularly, in colonies throughout the summer but by no means always do eggs appear in them; often nothing comes of them and they are eventually destroyed by the workers. The appearance of queen-cell cups in a colony should not be taken to indicate that it is likely to swarm or to supersede its queen at any time during the season, because it has

FIGURE 9. Usually queen cells of this kind are swarm cells. They are always constructed on the edges and bottom of combs. *(Photo by O. W. Park)*

not been possible to show that such a tendency exists.[48] Furthermore, although there does seem to be a tendency for a colony that is preparing to swarm to possess more occupied queen cells than a colony of the same size and strain that is preparing to supersede its queen, it is unsafe to assume that the presence of only a few occupied queen cells, say three or four, indicates the likelihood of supersedure rather than swarming.

It has also been found that the presence of occupied queen cells does not mean that the colony is going to rear even one new queen to maturity. Time and again, when left to themselves, colonies will destroy the queens they have started to rear, or even those they have actually reared. Some colonies begin to rear queens, but never complete the process, again and again for weeks or even months.[49] We do not yet understand the significance of such behavior, but it is clear that at least half the colonies that start to rear queens fail to complete the process.[47]

QUEEN REARING

Colonies of honey bees rear queens in connection with three distinct processes: 1. Replacement of a queen that has been lost suddenly by accident, 2. supersedure of a queen that is still heading the colony, and 3. colony reproduction or swarming. In each case queen rearing begins when the workers become short of inhibitory substances.[6]

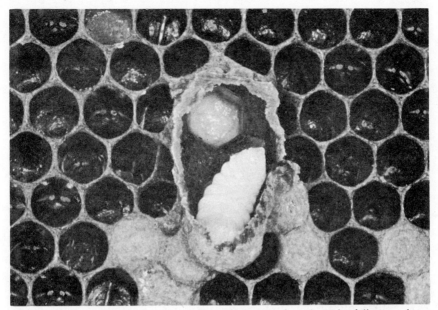

FIGURE 10. An emergency queen cell *(supersedure)* opened to show the full-grown larva and origin of cell from a worker cell. Enlarged about 2.5X.

In the first of these processes, a number of queens are reared in emergency queen cells prepared from normal worker cells, each containing a young female larva or, occasionally, an egg. We do not yet know why the worker bees select any particular larva in preference to others to rear as a queen. Because of their origin, the cavities of emergency queen cells always extend back to the midrib of the comb, unlike the queen-cell cups that are mainly used for queen rearing in connection with supersedure and swarming, the thick, bulbous bases of which are usually attached to the faces or edges of combs by short pedicels of wax, so that they project from the comb face and hang with their mouths downwards.

Early in their construction, emergency queen cells are flooded with food, produced in the hypopharyngeal and mandibular glands of the workers. The larvae in them float out of the worker cells in which they were hatched (Fig. 10), which now form only the innermost parts of the queen cells, and into the bodies of the new queen cells.

The larvae selected for rearing as emergency queens are usually less than 2 days old, but can be as much as 3 days old. If, as sometimes happens when few, if any, younger larvae are available, the workers try to rear queens from older larvae; only very imperfect individuals with at least some worker characteristics are produced. So it appears that a larva must be less than 3 days old if a "perfect" queen is to be produced. It should be realized, however, that one can obtain a continuous series of female bees ranging from the "perfect" worker at one extreme, through a long series of intercastes showing progressively fewer workerlike and more queenlike characteristics, to the "perfect" queen at the other.

If the larva the workers select for rearing as a queen is, let us say, 2 days old, the young virgin queen should emerge from her cell 11 days later. If the weather is suitable she can be expected to have mated and be starting to lay about 10 days afterwards. So it is seldom less than 3 weeks from the time that a colony loses its queen until it has a new one that is laying.

Queens produced from larvae that have been reared in worker cells for not more than 2 days do not appear to differ greatly from those reared from eggs laid by queens in queen cells. Most queens reared in connection both with supersedure and with swarming develop from eggs laid by the colony's queen in special queen cells built initially for this sole purpose, which are used only once and are destroyed soon afterwards.

Queen cells vary considerably in appearance. They are usually about an inch long, taper slightly in diameter from base to tip, have thick externally sculptured walls, and always hang with their mouths downwards.

The number of queen cells a colony builds varies a great deal, depending mainly on the race and strain of bee and the size of the colony. It has been reported that bees of the Italian and Caucasian races tend to produce fewer queen cells than some strains of other races, such as the Carniolans. When rearing queens preparatory to swarming, colonies of the Cyprian, Syrian, and Egyptian races are said sometimes to produce a hundred or more queen cells each.[40]

It seems generally true that a given colony will build fewer queen cells when it is preparing to supersede its queen than it will when preparing to swarm. Often only two or three queen cells are built when superseding.

The queen cells of a colony are not all begun at the same time, nor, in cases of emergency queen rearing, are the larvae chosen necessarily all of the same age. Nor for some unexplained reason, is the first queen that emerges always allowed to survive and to mate and head the colony; she is often killed when a later queen emerges.[49]

CASTE DETERMINATION

Both queen and worker honey bees are females and develop from fertilized eggs and, because of this, beekeepers are able to rear large numbers of queens by transferring (grafting) young female larvae from worker cells into artificial queen cells and giving them to queenless colonies to rear. It, therefore, is clear that differentiation between the queen and worker castes in the honey bee cannot be due to any genetical difference but must be due to something else, such as differential feeding. Indeed, as long ago as 1888, von Planta[41] pointed out that whereas larvae in queen cells appear to be fed throughout their development on glandular secretions, those in worker cells appear to have a lot of honey added to their food from about the 3d day of larval life onwards. This glandular food contains a lot of protein derived from the hypopharyngeal glands of the worker bees and a fatty acid, 10-hydroxydecenoic acid, produced in their mandibular glands. Unfortunately, however, analyses of larval food by various workers have given variable results.

This led Haydak[24] to conclude that the composition of larval food varies more or less fortuitously and that such variations cannot explain caste determination. He, therefore, supposed that differentiation between queen and worker is not due to a change in the composition of the food, but rather to the amount of essential nutrients consumed by queen and worker larvae, respectively. He cited the conclusions of several other workers in support of his theory, and pointed out that from the time of hatching until about the 3d day of life all female larvae in strong colonies are given as much, if not more, food than they can eat, but that, whereas queen larvae continue to be fed in this lavish manner, worker larvae are only fed at intervals after these first 3 days and are apparently undernourished. The result is that queen and worker larvae grow at about the same rate for the 1st day or 2, thereafter the queen larvae, always surrounded by abundant food, continue to grow quickly while growth of the underfed workers slows down. He pointed out that, even after her cell has been sealed, a queen larva continues to feed on the food in her cell, whereas the worker larva, having little or no food in its cell when it is sealed, is unable to do so and actually loses weight.

Haydak supposed that, as a direct consequence of such underfeeding, sexual development of worker larvae is retarded and checked, and that the endocrine function of the ovaries is interfered with to such an extent that the hormone, or hormones, secreted are insufficient to cause the larva to develop into a queen. Something of this sort has been shown to occur in bumble bees.[21]

Haydak[24] set out to test his hypothesis that workers are essentially undernourished queens by removing larvae from queen cells that had either just been sealed or were about to be sealed, so that they could not get any more food. Most of these larvae died as advanced pupae; seven of these pupae had worker rather than queen characteristics; several others showed characteristics intermediate between those of queen and worker. Of nine that emerged as adults, eight appeared to be normal queens, while the ninth resembled a worker, having a typical worker's head and mandibles, and a straight sting.

The average initial weight of larvae that developed into queens was 14 per cent greater than that of larvae which became workerlike individuals. Because the weight of a larva may be taken as a reasonable index of its age, it is safe to assume that those larvae that developed into queens, despite their starvation treatment, were the older ones whose sex organs were probably already well developed when they were taken from their cells; whereas those that produced workerlike individuals were not only smaller but also younger and had less well-developed sexual organs, so that in their case there was greater opportunity for undernourishment to have an effect.

These results strongly suggest that continuous liberal feeding of queen larvae plays an important part in their development. But that this is not the only factor involved is shown by the work of von Rhein[43] and others who have failed to obtain queens by continuously supplying female larvae with an abundance of food taken from queen cells. These results led to the suggestion that worker bees add an unstable differentiating substance to the food of queen larvae, and that this substance is lost quickly when the food is stored.

Weaver[53,54] has recently carried out feeding experiments similar to those of von Rhein and obtained queens when he fed female larvae, taken from worker cells, on food freshly collected from queen cells containing larvae about the same age as the experimental ones. But when he fed other female larvae, kept under the same conditions, with similar food that had been stored for some time, he only obtained workers. These results appear at first sight to confirm von Rhein's hypothesis of the existence of a fugitive differentiating substance.

Jay[30] has pointed out that it is quite possible that this is not the correct interpretation of these results and that possibly the stored food becomes less palatable, perhaps because it loses some water or because of sedimentation of some of its denser particles, and in consequence insufficient is eaten to allow full development and the production of queens. Clearly more work is necessary before we shall know the answer to this interesting problem. Whatever the mechanism of differentiation, queen and worker honey bees differ profoundly not only in their anatomy but also in their behavior.

THE VIRGIN QUEEN*

When the queen larva is fully grown, the worker bees seal her cell with a wax capping. Having completed her feeding, the larva spins a cocoon inside her cell with numerous strands of silk from her thoracic glands, comes to rest head downwards, and turns into a pupa and eventually into an adult. When ready to emerge, she bites through the silk of the cocoon and the cell's wax capping with her mandibles, until

---

*The reader also is referred to "Activities of the Queen" in Chapter IV for descriptions of the behavior of virgin queens.

FIGURE 11. A queen cell just vacated. Note the hinged lid still attached.

FIGURE 12. A queen emerging from her cell. *(Photo from "Honey Bee" Encyclopaedia Britannica Films Inc.)*

she has cut almost all the way round and is able to push back the lid thus formed (Fig. 11) and crawls out of her cell (Fig. 12), the remains of which are soon removed by the workers.

When a colony is preparing to swarm, however, the worker bees frequently prevent the young queens from emerging from their cells for some hours or even days, feeding them from time to time through the slots the queens have chewed in their efforts to escape from their cells.[27] Later, after the first swarm has left headed by the old mated queen, or sometimes by a young virgin that has been allowed to emerge from her cell, the workers allow a virgin to emerge and leave the hive with a second swarm. With some strains of bees, under certain conditions, this may be repeated several times until at last the bees allow a virgin to emerge, destroy her rivals, mate, and become the new queen of their colony.

Normally, when a colony is not preparing to swarm, the first virgin to reach maturity is allowed to emerge from her cell as soon as she is ready. On emerging she soon helps herself to honey from a storage cell and, indeed, continues very largely to feed herself during the next 3 or 4 days. At first the worker bees appear to take very little notice of her, though they can sometimes be seen, in an observation hive, forming a small "court" around her and both feeding and examining her with their antennae, and licking her.

A few hours after she has emerged the young queen starts to search for and destroy actual or potential rivals — other adult queens and queen pupae in their cells. In a case of supersedure, however, the young queen often takes no notice of her mother, the old queen, and the two frequently live together in the same hive for some time without fighting. When, however, one virgin queen meets another, they fight until one of them is killed. Sooner or later, the virgin queen also attacks any occupied queen cells she finds, particularly the sealed ones.

Huber[27] gives the following description of such behavior: "Hardly had ten minutes elapsed after the young queen emerged from her cell, when she began to look for sealed queen cells. She rushed furiously upon the first that she met, and by dint of hard work made a small opening in the end. We saw her drawing with her mandibles, the silk of the cocoon, which covered the inside. But probably, she did not succeed according to her wishes, for she left the lower end of the cell and went to work on the upper end where she finally made a larger opening. As soon as this was sufficiently large, she turned about to push her abdomen into it. She made several motions in different directions till she succeeded in striking her rival with the deadly sting. She then left the cell; and the bees which had remained so far perfectly passive began to enlarge the gap which she made, and drew out the corpse of a queen just out of her nymphal shell. During this time, the victorious queen rushed to another queen cell and again made a large opening, but she did not introduce her abdomen into it, this second cell containing only a royal pupa not yet formed. There is some probability that at this stage of development, the nymphs of queens inspire less anger to their rivals; but they do not escape their doom; for whenever a queen cell has been prematurely opened, the bees throw out its occupant whether worm, nymph, or queen. Therefore, as soon as the victorious queen had left this second cell, the workers enlarged the opening and drew out the nymph it contained. The young queen rushed to a third cell, but she was unable to open it. She worked languidly and seemed tired from her first efforts."

Although Huber described what often happens, it is untrue that workers always destroy a queen cell in which a queen has torn a hole. Nor it is true that queens always attack queen cells as soon as they find them. I have seen a virgin queen resting on top of a sealed queen cell for over an hour without attempting to attack it or, indeed, appearing to show any interest in it. Later, however, this same queen attempted to tear open the tips of several sealed queen cells in succession, but failed to do so. Presently she attacked three of them, one after the other, near their bases and succeeded in tearing large holes in them. She did not, however, attempt to sting their occupants, all of which were pupae, one being in an advanced stage of development. Instead of removing the occupants of these cells and tearing them down, the workers repaired the damage the queen had done to them; only after the queen had torn holes in them several times did the workers finally destroy them with their contents. Similarly, in an experiment with 25 queenless colonies in which a number of queen cells, sealed and unsealed, had holes cut in various parts of them with scissors, the workers repaired the damage in almost all cases.

Sometimes workers will destroy the occupants of queen cells without the assistance of a virgin, but she usually seems to attack some of the cells at least, and the workers then destroy these as well as others she has not attacked. Virgin queens very seldom attack unsealed queen cells; these are destroyed by the workers. The bodies of the helpless victims are sometimes dragged from their cells in one piece, especially when nearly mature; but when immature, they are usually removed piecemeal, the workers piercing their soft bodies and sucking the juices from them before removing the harder parts bit by bit.

In Huber's account of the virgin queen attacking queen cells, quoted earlier, it will be noted that she only stung the newly adult queen in her cell; she did not attempt to sting queen larvae or pupae. Other observers have reported the same thing and it seems to be generally true that queens will only sting and kill other adults.

Sometimes when a colony possesses a number of young adult virgin queens, either free on the combs or imprisoned in their cells by the workers, a queen will be heard to make a shrill piping sound "ze-e-e-ep, ze-e-ep, ze-ep, zeep." Often two or more queens will pipe one after the other and it has, of course, been suggested that the first queen to pipe is challenging her rivals who answer in defiance, even though some of them may still be in their cells and helpless. Virgin queens, in or out of cells, respond by piping to artificial piping sounds from 20 to 1,280 cycles per second, whether pulsed or continuous (Hansson, A. 1945. Opuscula Entomologica, Suppl. 6). However, they respond more to sounds from 600 to 2,000 c/s than to those of other frequencies, and to sounds transmitted through the substrata than through the air (Wenner, A. M. 1962. Science 138:446).

When piping, a queen squats down somewhat and her folded wings vibrate rapidly. Snodgrass[51] suggests that piping may be produced by vibration of small plates at the wing bases. Even a queen whose wings have been clipped off can still pipe. Recently it has been shown by Simpson[50] that the queen presses her thorax against a comb, or whatever she happens to be standing upon, when piping, and that it acts as a sounding board which radiates the sounds. If a queen pipes when standing on cotton-wool, or other material which absorbs vibrations, she only produces faint sounds. This is, of course, an argument against the suggestion of Woods[55] that piping is caused by forcible expulsion of air through the spiracles. In any case, the rhythm of the spiracular movements is not the same as that of the piping sounds.

Those workers that happen to be near a queen when she pipes "freeze," stopping whatever they are doing for a few seconds and remaining still. Such behavior can also be induced by a vibrating tuning fork applied to the glass of an observation hive or even by loud singing by a human being.

A newly emerged virgin queen is sometimes almost as large as a mated laying queen, but her size gradually decreases until, after a few days, she is often only slightly larger than a worker. This makes it difficult for a beekeeper to find her, especially as she is easily frightened and quickly hides amongst the workers.

MATING

Although Aristotle[3] thought it possible that queens mate, most of the earlier writers did not believe that bees do so. For example, in 1679, Rusden[46] wrote: "And if the bees do breed without copulation (as almost all writers do agree because it was never yet seen by any man) — it can be no otherwise but by the wind, as Aesop's Babylonian mares (in the fable) conceived by the horses that were in Egypt the same time." Swammerdam[52] believed that the queen is impregnated by the peculiar and unpleasant odor that is produced by drones when they are confined in a small space. Reamur,[42] in 1744, thought mating to occur within the hive, while Huish,[28] in 1815, believed that the eggs are fertilized by the drones after being deposited in the cells.

Janscha,[29] in 1771, was probably the first person to find that queens mate with drones away from the hive and, about 25 years later, Huber,[27] unaware of Janscha's observations, made experiments showing that mating does not take place in the hive and that a young queen never lays fertilized eggs (i.e. eggs from which workers and queens develop) until about 2 days after flying from the hive and, often (he thought always) returning with part of the drone's copulatory apparatus protruding from her vagina.

Half a century later the Reverend Millette published what appears to be the first eyewitness account of the mating of a queen honey bee. This observation, together with another made by Carey and Otis in the following year, was published in an article by Langstroth[31] in the first volume of the *American Bee Journal,* in 1861. Various other eyewitness accounts have appeared from time to time, mainly in bee journals.

A virgin queen sometimes makes a few exploratory flights from her hive when 3 to 5 days old, before making her nuptial flight or flights. Both prenuptial and nuptial flights usually occur during the warmest part of the day when the drones are flying freely. Occasionally a queen will return mated within a few minutes, but usually she is away between 10 and 30 minutes, on rare occasions even longer.

As already stated, a queen usually begins to lay within 2 or 3 days after mating and, once she has started to lay it is believed that she never mates again and, indeed, probably never leaves her hive except possibly with a swarm.

The age at which a queen mates depends considerably upon the weather, and possibly on the race of bee, but it appears that few matings occur before the 6th or after the 10th day. Oertel[37] studied the mating and laying of 60 queens at Baton Rouge, Louisiana, and found that queens' exploratory flights lasted between 2 and 30 minutes, and mating flights between 5 and 20 minutes. Virgin queens seldom flew more than three times. All flights took place in the afternoon, most between 2 and 4 o'clock. Over 50 per cent of all matings took place on the 8th and 9th days, the numbers being equal on these 2 days. The youngest queen seen at the hive entrance for the first time was 3 days old, and the oldest 11 days old; most appeared on the 7th day. The great majority of queens started to lay 3 days after mating, but the range extended from 1 to 8 days.

Roberts,[45] also working at Baton Rouge, found that the average duration of a mating flight in April was 19 minutes and decreased to 12 minutes in June. The longer mating flights earlier in the year could have been due to relative scarcity of drones.

Eyewitness accounts of matings, which almost certainly take place in the air, are rare. However, reports mention a comet-shaped swarm of swiftly flying drones weaving hither and thither, presumably chasing a virgin queen which was supposed to be at its apex. Observers have reported hearing a sharp crack at the time that they believed that copulation occurred and that the queen broke away from the drone which fell dead or dying to the ground. For additional information on queen mating, see "Activities of Queens" in Chapter IV.

During the very short time of copulation, the drone's semen is forced into the vagina and paired oviducts of the queen. It is prevented from running out of her vagina by a mucous plug which the drone ejaculates immediately after his semen. The spermatozoa, possibly stimulated by some attractant, pass up the spermathecal duct and so into the spermatheca (sperm reservoir) of the queen. Here they are packed tightly together and remain quiescent until required.

A queen receives sufficient spermatozoa, before she starts to lay, to fertilize all the eggs she lays in worker and queen cells during the rest of her life.

EGG LAYING

Soon after a queen has mated the workers seem to pay much greater attention to her than they have done hitherto and, as she moves over the combs, she forms the center of a "court" whose membership is continually changing (Fig. 7). The young bees forming this court feed the queen, examine her body with their antennae, and also lick it, so obtaining queen substances.[7] They also remove her excrement and any eggs she drops.

When laying, a queen moves around a comb in an apparently purposeful manner, putting her head into each cell as she comes to it, presumably to examine it. If she finds it empty and otherwise suitable she withdraws her head and, curving her body downwards, inserts her abdomen into the cell and, in a few seconds, lays an egg and withdraws.

The queen moves in a random manner over the comb, searching for empty cells that the workers have cleaned out after their last occupants and have prepared to receive eggs (Fig. 13). She frequently crosses and recrosses her path and spends quite a lot of time examining cells in which she has already laid eggs.

During the winter and early spring, a queen lays first in the cells near the middle of the relatively compact winter cluster. Later, as the cluster expands in volume encompassing more and more combs, the brood area also expands as further cells become suitable for the queen to lay in.

By the time a queen is 2 or 3 years old, sometimes much less, her rate of egg laying tends to diminish and she may even lay unfertilized, mainly drone-producing, eggs in worker cells as the supply of spermatozoa in her spermatheca becomes exhausted (Fig. 14). Such drone-laying queens usually disappear fairly quickly. If they have not been superseded earlier, queens usually die of old age when 3 or 4 years old, though a few have been reported to live as long as 5, 6, or even 7 years.

PARTHENOGENESIS

It used to be thought that the eggs of insects and other animals could not develop until they had been fertilized. However, although this is true in most species, it is known to be untrue in others, including the honey bee. This type of reproduction without intervention by a male is called *parthenogenesis*.

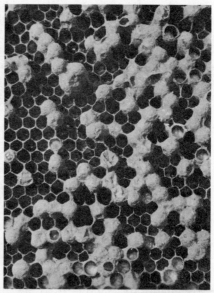

FIGURE 13. A good queen deposits her eggs methodically, one egg to a cell. (*Photo by O. W. Park*)

FIGURE 14. Scattered cells of drone brood is a sure sign of a failing queen or even the presence of laying workers.

Parthenogenetic development in general is not restricted to one sex. In aphids and certain crustaceans, both sexes can be produced in this way; in some grasshoppers and moths, females only are produced; while in most Hymenoptera, including the honey bee, unfertilized eggs usually give rise to males only, but occasionally to females. Fertilized eggs have never been known to produce males.

In 1845, Dzierzon propounded his famous theory about honey bees. He supposed that in honey bees, males (drones) are produced from unfertilized eggs, while females (queens and workers) only come from fertilized ones.[18]

A queen is able to lay either fertilized or unfertilized eggs "at pleasure," as Dzierzon put it, for, with rare exceptions, she always lays fertilized eggs in worker and queen cells and unfertilized eggs in drone cells. So, in the honey bee, an egg that receives a spermatozoon develops into a female which, as we have seen, can become a queen or a worker depending upon the way it is fed by the nurse bees. The drone or male bee develops from an egg that has not received a spermatozoon.

The mechanism that enables a queen to lay fertilized or unfertilized eggs "at pleasure" consists essentially of the spermatheca, in which the live spermatozoa she received when she mated are stored until required to fertilize an egg, and the so-called sperm pump. The spermatheca is a small, globular sac connected with the vagina by a small duct which serves first as entrance and later as exit for the spermatozoa. Part of this spermathecal duct forms a pump for discharging the spermatozoa. By means of this apparatus a queen is able either to withhold or discharge spermatozoa into her vagina where they meet an egg as it passes on its way to the exterior. One or more spermatozoa enter the egg through the micropyle, a small opening near one end (also see Chapter V, "The Anatomy of the Honey Bee"). Unfortunately, we do not know yet what stimuli a queen receives from a cell, when she is about to lay in it, which determines whether she will lay a fertilized or unfertilized egg; nor is it understood how a queen's vagina can become free of spermatozoa so quickly that she is able to lay an unfertilized egg in a drone cell a few seconds after laying a fertilized one in a worker cell. Errors in this connection appear to be very rare indeed.

Dzierzon's theory has required a limited amount of modification during the last 50 years, as further information has been obtained showing that in some cases unfertilized honey-bee eggs do give rise to females. The first evidence of this kind was probably that published, in 1872, by an Englishman, John Hewitt,[25] who discovered that "Punic workers have the power to raise both queens and drones from themselves." As an example of their ability to produce queens in this way, he gives the following instance: "In one case, a number of Punic workers entered a stock of queenless Carniolans and reared a queen from the eggs they laid." His experiments, with colonies of queenless workers of various races, led him to conclude that "the instinct seems perfect in Punic bees, only partly so in Syrians, and quite absent in our native bees."

In 1912, Onions[38] reported finding parthenogenetic workers and queens, as well as drones, in the Cape bee of South Africa *(Apis melli-fera capensis)* and, in 1943, Mackensen[33] reported the trait in three American-bred strains of European bees.

It should be remembered that Dzierzon was familiar with European races only and that there is now evidence that, although bees of these races do occasionally succeed in rearing females from unfertilized eggs, they do so much less frequently than the Cape bee. Indeed it is reported that queenless colonies of the Cape bee have been known to survive in this condition for months, parthenogenetic eggs laid by the workers providing all the new workers necessary.[2]

The Drones

Drones are much larger and stouter than either queens or workers, although their bodies are not quite as long as those of queens (Fig. 15). The drone, being a male, naturally has no sting (the modified ovipositor of female honey bees) with which to defend himself. The drone has a short tongue, which he uses to take food from workers and from honey-storage cells in the hive; he does not collect food from flowers. He has neither pollen baskets nor wax-secreting or scent-producing glands. So far as is known the drone does no work in the hive, his only function in life being to seek a nubile queen outside the hive and forfeit his life mating with her.

Normal colonies begin to rear drones in late spring or early summer. The number reared by a colony seems to depend upon its size, race, and the condition of its combs. When old combs become damaged, the workers often repair them by building drone cells in which the queen seems only too ready to lay. Some colonies contain thousands of drones at the height of the season, but a few hundred is more usual.

As each queen mates with only a small number of drones, such large numbers appear wasteful but, as mating takes place in the open air, large numbers are perhaps necessary to ensure that a nubile queen soon mates and returns to the relative safety of her colony.

Towards the end of summer, when fresh nectar becomes scarce, the workers of colonies headed by mated queens prevent the drones from feeding on the honey stores and eventually drag them half starved and chilled, or even dead, from the hive. When food is scarce in summer, the workers sometimes pull the drone larvae from their cells and throw them out of the hive.

FIGURE 15. A side view of a drone—the male bee of the colony. Enlarged about 3X. *(Photo from "Honey Bee" Encyclopaedia Britannica Films Inc.)*

Although drones are almost always destroyed by normal colonies when nectar becomes scarce, the workers of queenless colonies, or those containing virgin queens, will continue to tolerate and even feed them under these conditions, so that the mating of any virgin queen they rear will still be possible, although probably rather unlikely. It seems, however, that queens are quite as likely, if not more likely, to mate with drones from other colonies as they are with those from their own.

Drones are sometimes reared from unfertilized eggs laid in worker cells either by drone-laying queens or by laying workers. Such drones are very small, presumably because of underfeeding in the cramped quarters in which they have been reared. They are, however, perfectly capable of producing viable spermatozoa and presumably of impregnating queens.

The Workers

The workers are the smallest members of a colony and form the bulk of its population (Fig. 16). During winter and early spring the overwintered workers of the colony die off so that it decreases in size. In late spring it begins to grow again as the number of new workers produced exceeds the number of old ones dying. At the height of the season a strong colony will contain fifty to sixty thousand workers.

The workers are undeveloped females whose ovaries are small and, generally speaking, do not produce eggs except when their colony becomes queenless. They possess, however, all the organs, such as pollen baskets, wax glands, and scent glands, necessary for carrying out the many duties essential to the well being of their colonies, such as foraging and nest building.

FIGURE 16. A side view of a worker bee in motion. Enlarged about 3X. (*Photo by O. W. Park*)

DEVELOPMENTAL STAGES*

An egg when deposited by a queen is fastened, with a mucilaginous secretion, by its smaller end to the base of its cell and stands out more or less at right angles to the midrib of the comb. After 3 days it hatches, the larva being pearly white and soon becoming surrounded by the food given to it by the workers. It remains curled up on one side — either right or left — in the base of its cell until it is fully grown and the cell is sealed by the workers (Fig. 17). Then it stretches out and spins its cocoon, within which it turns into a pupa from which the adult insect eventually emerges (Fig. 18). During its development the larval honey bee sheds its skin five times.

Nelson[36] has described the development of the honey-bee embryo within its egg, and Bertholf[4] and DuPraw[17] have given detailed accounts of its subsequent development. The worker larva spins its cocoon towards the end of the 9th day after its egg was laid, and on the 10th day stretches out on its back with its head towards the mouth of its cell and becomes quiescent. This marks the beginning of the pre-pupal stage. Vital changes are already in progress so that the individual is no longer a true larva although it still looks like one; nor is it yet a true pupa, although this stage is commonly included as part of the pupal stage when not dealt with separately.

The larva passes gradually and without moulting into this intermediate stage towards the end of which the legs and parts of the head of the developing pupa can be distinguished underneath the old larval skin. About the end of the 11th day from the laying of the egg, the insect becomes slightly more active for a few hours and sheds its fifth and last larval skin, thereby revealing a motionless, uniformly white pupa. At this stage, the head, thorax, and abdomen are clearly

---

*For a more detailed description of the development of the honey bee from egg to adult, see "Development" in Chapter V, "The Anatomy of the Honey Bee."

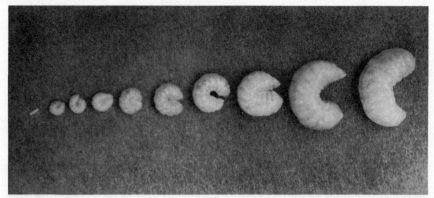

FIGURE 17. Successive stages of development from egg to mature larva. Enlarged slightly.

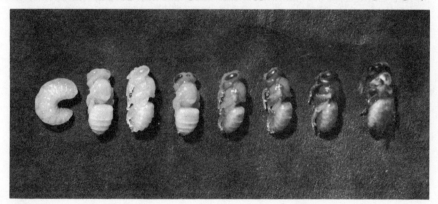

FIGURE 18. From mature larva to adult bee. About natural size. *(Photos courtesy U.S.D.A.)*

distinguishable, and the compound eyes and various appendages are also obvious.

Changes during metamorphosis do not occur abruptly but proceed gradually, so that the wormlike body of the larva is reconstructed into a distinct head, thorax, and abdomen, with adult appendages, at an imperceptible rate. Pigmentation appears first in the compound eyes which, on the 13th day, change to pink, then to red, purple, and finally to brown by the time of emergence when the pupal skin is shed and the active adult insect gnaws its way out of its cell.

The developmental stages of queen, worker, and drone are similar, but occupy different lengths of time, as the following table shows:

	Queen	Worker	Drone
		—— Day ——	
Egg hatches	3d	3d	3d
Cell is capped	8th	8th	10th
Adult emerges	16th	21st	24th

LIFE SPAN

The length of life of the individual worker honey bee varies tremendously at different times of year. Experiments with marked bees have shown that in a normal queenright colony in March the average expectation of life on emergence is about 35 days, but in June it has become reduced to an average of about 28 days, about 9 of which are spent foraging (Free and Spencer-Booth[22]). On the other hand many of the workers that are reared during September and October live throughout the winter. There is a record of such individuals living for 304 days (Anderson[1]).

Such differences in the average length of life of worker bees in summer and winter are due to much more than differences in wear and tear at these seasons, and are associated with profound physiological changes. For example, Maurizio[34] found, in experiments with caged bees, that the average expectation of life of a "winter" bee was 36 days whereas that of a "summer" bee was only 24 days, but that when pollen was added to the food of "summer" bees their expectation of life was increased, which was not the case when pollen was added to the food of "winter" bees. Further work by Maurizio[35] has shown that in a normal, queenright colony in summer the hypopharyngeal glands and, to a much lesser extent, the fat bodies of the young workers develop because of the protein they obtain from the pollen they eat. However, on account of their brood-rearing activities, the protein stored in their hypopharyngeal glands and fat bodies soon becomes exhausted and they become short-lived "summer" bees. In the fall, however, when little brood rearing is going on, the protein reserves in the hypopharyngeal glands and fat bodies of the workers increase to the maximum extent possible, provided there is plenty of pollen to eat, and they become long-lived "winter" bees. This can in fact occur at any time of year; queenlessness, or even a short interruption of egg laying at swarming time, causes the production of long-lived bees similar to "winter" bees but differing from them in one important respect, namely that their ovaries develop. This does not happen with true "winter" bees in normal queenright colonies, probably because the queens of such colonies continue to inhibit ovary development in the workers by producing adequate quantities of 9-oxodecenoic acid and inhibitory scent, which queens in uncrowded colonies that are preparing to swarm do not.

It is clear, therefore, that the length of a worker bee's life is determined to a great extent by pollen consumption and brood rearing, and that the amount of work that a bee does as a forager is of relatively little importance in this connection. It is, however, true, as might be expected, that foraging is a more hazardous occupation than work in the hive, as Ribbands[44] found that the expectation of life of bees that began to forage at an early age was significantly less (30.1 ± 1.2 days) than that of bees who started to forage later in life (37.1 ± 0.6 days), although the length of foraging life of an early forager was generally greater than that of a bee that started foraging when older.

The maximum life span of the drone honey bee in summer is 59 days, according to Howell and Usinger,[26] but there is some evidence that drones can survive for long periods in winter in queenless colonies.

There are records of queen honey bees living for over 8 years (Betts[5]), but 3 years is probably nearer the average length of life of a queen in a colony that is not disturbed in any way.

CONCLUSION

It is, I think, becoming clearer every day as research progresses that the apparently complicated behavior of a honey-bee community with its thousands of individual members is brought about by the fundamentally simple responses of each of them to a series of stimuli. There is good reason to suppose that research workers are on the threshold of many further interesting discoveries about the life history and behavior of the honey bee.

REFERENCES CITED

1. Anderson, J. 1931. Bee World 12:25.

2. Anderson, R. A. 1961. Personal communication.

3. Aristotle. 1907. History of animals. Transl. by Creswell.

4. Bertholf, L. M. 1925. J. Econ. Entomol. 18:380.

5. Betts, A. D. 1946. Bee World 27:26.

6. Butler, C. G. 1954. The world of the honeybee. Collins, London.

7. _____ 1954. Trans. Roy. Entomol. Soc. London 105:11.

8. _____ 1956. Proc. Roy. Entomol. Soc. London A. 31:12.

9. _____ 1957. Experientia 13:256.

10. _____ 1957. Insectes Sociaux 4:211.

11. _____ 1960. Proc. Roy. Entomol. Soc. London A. 35:129.

12. _____ 1960. Experientia 16:424.

13. _____ 1961. J. Insect Physiol. 7:258.

14. Butler, C. G., R. K. Callow, and N. C. Johnston. 1961. Proc. Roy. Soc. B. 155:417.

15. Butler, C. G., and J. Simpson. 1958. Proc. Roy. Entomol. Soc. London A. 33:120.

16. Callow, R. K., N. C. Johnston, and J. Simpson. 1959. Experientia 15:421.

17. DuPraw, E. J. 1960. Gl. Bee Cult. 88:104.

18. Dzierzon, J. 1845. Eichstädt Bienenztg. 1:113.

19. Fraser, H. M. 1951. Anton Janscha and the "Abhandlung von Schwärmen der Bienen." Apis Club, Royston, England.

20. Free, J. B., and C. G. Butler. 1955. Behavior 7:304.

21. _____ 1959. Bumblebees. Collins, London.

22. Free, J. B., and Y. Spencer-Booth. 1959. Proc. Roy. Entomol. Soc. London A. **34**:141.

23. Glynne-Jones, G. D. 1947. Personal communication.

24. Haydak, M. H. 1943. J. Econ. Entomol. **36**:778.

25. Hewitt, J. 1892. J. Hort. London **25**:134.

26. Howell, D. E. and R. L. Usinger. 1933. Ann. Entomol. Soc. Amer. **26**:239.

27. Huber, F. 1814. Nouvelles observations sur les abeilles, 1 and 2. Transl. 1926. Dadant, C. P., Hamilton, Ill.

28. Huish, R. 1815. A treatise on the nature, economy and practical management of bees. London.

29. Janscha, A. 1771. Abhandlung von Schwärmen der Bienen. Kurzbock, Vienna.

30. Jay, S. C. 1961. Personal communication.

31. Langstroth, L. L. 1861. Am. Bee J. **1**:65.

32. Lindauer, M. 1961. Communication among social insects. Harvard Univ. Press, Cambridge, Mass.

33. Mackensen, O. 1943. J. Econ. Entomol. **36**:465.

34. Maurizio, A. 1946. Beih. Schweiz. Bienenztg. **2**:1.

35. ----------------- 1950. Bee World. **31**:9.

36. Nelson, J. A. 1915. The embryology of the honeybee. Princeton Univ. Press, Princeton, N. J.

37. Oertel, E. 1940. Gl. Bee Cult. **68**:292.

38. Onions, G. W. 1912. Agr. J. Union S. Africa **3**:720.

39. Pain, J., and M. Barbier. 1960. C. R. Acad. Sci. Paris **250**:1126.

40. Park, O. W. 1949. In Grout, Roy A., The hive and the honey bee. Dadant & Sons, Inc., Hamilton, Ill.

41. Planta, A. von. 1888. Hoppe-Seyl. Z. **12**:234.

42. Reamur, R. A. 1740. Memoires pour servir a l'histoire des insectes. **5**:207.

43. Rhein, W. von. 1933. Arch. Entw. Mech. Org. **129**:601.

44. Ribbands, C. R. 1950. J. Exptl. Biol. **27**:302.

45. Roberts, W. C. 1944. Gl. Bee Cult. **72**:255.

46. Rusden, M. 1679. A further discovery of bees. London.

47. Simpson, J. 1957. Proc. Roy. Entomol. Soc. London A. **32**:185; J. Agr. Sci. **49**:287.

48. ----------------- 1959. Insectes Sociaux **6**:85.

49. ----------------- 1959. Personal communication.

50. ----------------- 1960. Personal communication.

51. Snodgrass, R. E. 1925. Anatomy and physiology of the honeybee. McGraw-Hill, New York.

52. Swammerdam, J. 1737. Biblia naturae. Leyden.

53. Weaver, N. 1956. Science **121**:509.

54. ----------------- 1957. Ann. Entomol. Soc. Am. **50**:283.

55. Woods, E. F. 1950. Brit. Bee J. **78**:766.

CHAPTER IV

ACTIVITIES OF HONEY BEES

by M. H. HAYDAK*

THROUGH THE CENTURIES man has tried to solve the mysteries of the hive. The cohesion of the colony — the marvelous coordination of the work in the hive — has led many observers to compare a colony of bees to human society. Consequently, the interpretation of the life of bees quite often reflected the social points of view prevalent among the human populations at any particular time.

Only now are we beginning to lift the veil of mystery from the life of bees. Although considerable work has been done in this respect, still the road ahead is long and will require a great deal of toil to reach the goal of the right interpretation of all phases of the life of "man's best friend" — the honey bee.

Division of Labor

The fact that worker bees perform various types of labor in the hive was already suspected in antiquity. In one of the books which appeared in Aristotle's time,[111] there is a statement: "So far as the work is concerned, in bees certain tasks are assigned: one group collects from flowers, the other brings water, still others polish and arrange combs, some prepare wax, and others honey, still others bee bread. Then some build combs, while others bring water to the cells and mix it with honey, others fly out for work." It was quite often believed that this work was directed and supervised by the queen or "the king" as she was called at that time.

Of course, there is a division of labor in the hive according to the castes of bees: the queen lays eggs, the worker bees do all the work in the colony, and the drones serve for fertilization of the virgin queen. We are interested, however, in the division of labor among worker bees in the hive.

Our present knowledge of this division of labor springs from observations made at the beginning of the 20th century. However, Langstroth,[119] in his famous book on *The Hive and the Honey Bee,* informs us that "Dzierzon states as a fact that worker bees attend more exclusively to the domestic concerns of the colony in the early period of life, assuming the discharge of the more active outdoor duties only during the later periods of their existence." Langstroth cites the experi-

---

*Mykola H. Haydak. Ph.D. Associate professor, Department of Entomology, Fisheries, and Wild Life, University of Minnesota. Studies on bee behavior and nutrition, caste determination, growth and aging in bees, pollen substitutes, food value of honey, vitamin content of bee foods, problems of management, swarming, and wintering.

ments of a German beekeeper, Dönhoff, who, by introducing an Italian queen into a colony of black bees, found that the first Italian bees which brought pollen and nectar into the hive were 17 to 19 days old. When Dönhoff gave a building frame with a starter to this colony, he observed that the young Italian bees were the ones which started building the comb.

"These repeated observations," writes Dönhoff, "forced me to conclude that during the first 2 weeks of the worker bee's life, the impulse for gathering honey and pollen does not exist, or at least is not developed, and that development of this impulse proceeds slowly and gradually. Nearly 3 weeks pass before the gathering impulse is sufficiently developed to impel her to fly abroad and seek for honey and pollen among the flowers." Dönhoff observed that the young bees covered brood combs and he suspected that "the brood is chiefly attended and nursed by the young bees."

Well-known students of the life of the bee, such as Gerstung, Brünnich, Zander, and Buttel-Reepen — all commented on the division of labor in the hive. But Rösch[206] was the first who undertook a thorough study of the question of division of labor in the honey-bee colony. For that purpose he constructed a special, large observation hive. Newly emerged bees were individually marked so that the life of each could be followed throughout the whole cycle. According to Rösch's observations, the activities of worker bees in the so-called normal colony can be roughly divided into three periods: 1. Taking care of the brood, 2. hive work, and 3. field work.

During the first 3 days after emergence, worker bees clean the cells from which young bees emerged. After this, they begin their nursing activities by feeding older larvae. When 6 days old, they begin to feed younger larvae and continue this activity until 11 to 13 days old. This period is characterized by a full development of their brood-food (hypopharyngeal) glands. Toward the end of this period an orientation flight takes place, which is repeated several times later. When about 13 days old the bees begin their hive work, in which they clean the hive, take out dead bees and debris, pack pollen, ripen the nectar, build combs, and apply propolis which they take from the propolis-gatherers. The last 2 days of this period, when they are 18 to 20 days old, they do guard duty. When 20 to 21 days old the bees become field workers, bringing nectar, pollen, water, and propolis into the hive. The total life span of an emerged bee under field conditions averages from 30 to 35 days. While such a sequence of duties was apparent in the hive, there was considerable variation in the age of bees starting any particular activity in and out of the hive.

Several investigators[8,75,91,165,191,248] have demonstrated that various necessary tasks can be performed normally in colonies consisting of either very young or very old bees. In his later experiments, Rösch[208] obtained similar results. He also proved that old bees can produce wax again.

In summing up, Haydak[75] concluded that these observations indicate that "the bees instinctively feel the kind of work which must be performed in the hive at any given moment, and do it regardless of age, when necessary. In a so-called 'normal colony' the principle of natural economy of work shows at what age certain work is most expedient, and, therefore, perhaps the bees can be divided into work groups according to age. But when the normal course of life in the colony is interrupted then the various tasks are performed by younger or older bees as occasion demands. Thus it appears that specific tasks are not necessarily performed by bees of any specific age."

About 10 years later, Milojevic[159] reported experiments in which bees kept in small nuclei in the laboratory were forced to rear brood until they were 72 to 75 days old. Seventy per cent of these bees had fully active brood-food glands. These experiments demonstrated that the state of development and capacity of functions of the organs are influenced by the social role of the individual, which apparently depends upon specific social factors.

Free[48] also came to the conclusion that, for the redevelopment of hypopharyngeal glands of foragers, the presence of larvae is necessary and that a protein diet alone is insufficient.

No further experimental work on the division of labor in the hive was done until 1952 when workers from the Rothamsted Experimental Station published a series of interrelated papers on food transmission, origin of odors, and division of labor in honey-bee colonies. Ribbands,[202] in his experiments on the division of labor in the honey-bee community, used two colonies of normal size to which he added marked bees of a known age. There was a considerable variation in the age at which individual bees started their foraging activities. Ribbands concluded that age is a factor but not the controlling factor in allocating worker duties.

In a series of experiments, Nixon and Ribbands[168] showed that there is a very quick and efficient food transmission in a colony of bees. In a colony of 24,500 bees, 62 per cent of the foragers and 16 to 21 per cent of all bees in the hive were radioactive within 4 hours, after six bees which had been fed 20 cubic millimeters of sugar solution containing radioactive phosphorus were returned to the hive. Seventy-six per cent of the foragers and from 43 to 60 per cent of all bees were radioactive within 27 hours.

Because only a very small quantity of the sugar solution was used, the authors consider that the widespread transmission of food cannot be related to storage requirements: "Such dissemination must have a more important function in that the efficient organization of the community life depends on it; food supply determines what proportion of the colony will be required for each task, and the ages of the individuals help to decide which of them will respond to these requiremnts."

All these experiments on the division of labor in the honey-bee colony were performed by following the activities of bees of a certain age as a group. Lindauer,[138] instead of marking the whole group of bees of the same age and then observing them, marked a single bee on emergence and introduced her to an observation hive. Each bee was kept under constant observation for the whole of her life.

To show the relative amount of time spent by a bee on each task, Lindauer presented the "time record" of bee No. 107. The bee was idle, sitting somewhere in the hive, doing nothing at all for 68 hours and 53 minutes. She patrolled for 56 hours, 10 minutes. The word "patrolling" signifies "that the bee moved about the hive without being compelled to do so. The word is meant to imply that she was obviously interested in all that was going on in the hive; she was constantly poking her head into cells, inspecting some hurriedly and others more thoroughly; sometimes the patrolling would be interrupted by a spell of 'casual work' or even come to an end if she found an empty work place. If she found no opportunity for work, she would at last come to rest — sometimes only after a very considerable period of patrolling — in some quiet corner." She cleaned cells for 11 hours and 44 minutes. In rearing younger larvae (that had just hatched to 3 days old) she spent 1 hour, 50 minutes; and in rearing older larvae (3 to 6 days old) she spent 2 hours, 8 minutes. She took part in building activities for 6 hours and 24 minutes and in capping cells for 12 hours, 27 minutes. She acted as a guard for only 34 minutes and spent 1 hour, 15 minutes in play flight. Her work as a forager took 9 hours and 59 minutes. Strange as it seems, she spent 71 per cent of her time in idling and patrolling. Of course, an idling bee fulfills an important function in regulating temperature and providing a reserve force. However, it is done indirectly. With the exception of foraging, bee No. 107 always performed several tasks during the same period. Thus the age limit of hive bees carrying out different work, as was found through actual observation in glass-walled cells, was:

    Cell cleaning—bees of ages 1 to 25 days
    Feeding larvae: Hatched to 1 day old—bees of ages 7 to 25 days
                  1 to 2 days old—bees of ages 2 to 24 days
                  2 to 3 days old—bees of ages 1 to 30 days
                  3 to 4 days old—bees of ages 1 to 28 days
                  5 to $5\frac{1}{2}$ days old—bees of ages 2 to 26 days
    Building activity, including capping—bees of ages 1 to 32 days

Lindauer found that nurse bees can feed brood and build combs. Calculations from actual observations showed that one bee is able to rear two to three larvae. The nurse bee is not attached to any particular brood area; only eight brood cells were attended twice by the same bee; only one cell with larvae was supplied three times by the same bee and another cell four times.

Most bees skip guard duty. Those which guarded did this work for only 1 day, few did it for longer. But one bee carried her guard duties throughout her whole life. Also some water carriers do this work throughout their lives. There is no sequence in feeding larvae — the same bee feeds larvae of various ages. This was supported recently by Free.[46] The rhythm of house duty runs evenly, without any rest periods related to the time of day or night.

The life histories of these individually marked and individually observed bees showed clearly "that age does exert a strong influence on the division of labor for the individual bee, but that the determining factor seems to be the need of the colony as a whole. It follows from this that each bee must be 'in picture' about the colony situation at all times."

The transition to field duties is made much easier by the guidance of older foragers. Out of 390 newly emerged and numbered bees only 17 started their field duties before their 20th day. Of 159 young field bees, 150 began their field duties by following the directions given by an older foraging bee (through the dance). Only 9 flew out without being alerted by the dance — these can be called "scout bees."

The choice of nectar or pollen as the first load is determined by the needs of the colony, and if not by that, then at least by the quantity of forage available.

Lindauer came to the conclusion that "the main outlines of the picture that Rösch gave us about the division of labor in the colony have been confirmed. However, in spite of the sequence of duties carried out by each bee and conditioned by her age, the program of work is kept very fluid, and many deviations are possible for each bee by which she can adapt her activity to the needs of the colony as a whole." In extreme cases this adaptability "degenerates" into specialization of one type of activity.

About the same time as Lindauer did his work in Europe, Sakagami[214] in Japan also studied the division of labor in a small bee colony using the same principle as Lindauer did, namely, following the work of an individually marked bee throughout the whole of her life. Sakagami found that there are great differences between individual bees. Some of the bees conduct all their activities with an outstanding eagerness, others proceed at a snail's pace. The longevity of bees in Sakagami's colony was 30 to 37 days.

Sakagami also observed that during field duties some bees performed certain activities in the hive. He even observed that pollen collectors packed their own pollen loads into the cell. However, such activities are much less frequent than in other periods of a bee's life. In general,

Sakagami's observations concur in many points with those of Rösch. However, there is great variability within each period, especially in the "afterbrood rearing" period, which is often shortened and even completely abandoned.

Istomina-Tsvetkova[98] observed numbered bees individually in a glass-walled hive during a daily period of 8 hours. She found that all the tasks are performed by the bees in various sequences and without any special order. There was a difference in the behavior of the individual bees. Apparently there is no grouping of bees according to age.

Bees continue work started by other bees but never finish the work they start themselves. For example, one bee started sealing a brood cell and continued working on it for 26 minutes and 36 seconds, did one-third of the job and then left. Two other bees finished the sealing. However, Smith[228] observed that one bee alone capped four cells completely, spending 15 to 20 minutes in capping one cell.

On the basis of her observations, Istomina-Tsvetkova considers that the life of any colony is composed of the work of separate bees, and that this work is coordinated and directed by the needs of the colony as a whole. One or another activity is done under the influence of a certain stimulus. If there is more need for a certain type of activity, a greater number of corresponding stimuli are present in the hive and a larger number of bees respond to them.

Sakagami[215] also studied the division of labor in a small colony of bees of approximately the same age. He noticed that the same bees performed several different tasks, one after another in the same day. The field work was quite often combined with other work, particularly nursing activity. Thus it was proved again that the same bees quite often carry out various kinds of activities during the same day. The age at which individual bees began various activities varied greatly. However, in the first days of adult life, the bees tend to perform hive duties because they correspond more to their age; at that time their glandular systems and their bodies are developing. Then the bees may assume other activities as they grow older. Hoffmann,[94] reporting work of Geschke, also found that in small colonies the division of labor is about the same as in normal colonies.

From this review of experiments done by various investigators on the division of labor in the honey bee it appears that, in a normal colony consisting of bees of all ages, there is a certain general sequence of work which the bees perform. However, this division of labor is very flexible, constantly changing according to the conditions inside and outside the hive, adjusting itself to the physiological and probably genetic setup of the individuals comprising the colony. In general, young bees, however, tend to do the work inside the hive; older bees are more inclined to the field duties. The most interesting and surprising finding is that there are enormous differences between the individual bees of the same colony and that the over-all character of the colony depends on the ratio of the "good," "eager" workers and those whose working pace is rather sluggish and inefficient.

The bees apparently "know" what work is needed to be done at any particular place or time and do it. The question of what makes the bees realize this need of the colony, so as to make it run as a well-adjusted organism, is still unknown. Whether it is "the necessity" (Wiltse, Haydak) or a "special factor" (Milojevic) or "the food transmission" (Ribbands and coworkers) or some "stimuli" (Istomina-Tsvetkova) we do not know. Certainly it looks as if every bee is "in the picture" about the colony situation at all times.

Butler[25] expressed the opinion that the so-called "liaison bees" are instrumental in the smooth running of the colony. "Three groups of bees," writes Butler, "can be recognized in every colony, two of which are readily distinguishable from one another, the older, well-established foragers, and the younger household bees. The third group, which consists mainly of younger bees which combine some work on household duties in the hive with some foraging in the field, acts, I believe, as a liaison between the two groups already mentioned."

Butler's theory, however, does not seem to explain fully the division of labor in a colony consisting of bees of the same age, be they very young or very old. It is apparent that more work is required to answer fully this question of the division of labor in the hive. We have already made a great deal of progress toward this goal and it seems to be easier now to approach the solution of this extremely interesting question.[85]

Language of Bees—Communication and Orientation

In examining a colony of bees, beekeepers of the past encountered certain phenomena which seemed to them to be without meaning. It is noted in one of the old European books that, in 1823, a prominent beekeeper showed his friends dancing bees and "everybody enjoyed watching the bee ballet." They did not know that earlier, in 1788, Father Spitzner had described these dances as a method by means of which bees communicate to the inmates of the hive the volume of honeyflow and the place of the source of nectar. Spitzner's observation had fallen into oblivion until more than a century later when Frisch[52] published his famous observations, *The Language of the Bees.*

Frisch described two types of dancing — the round dance and the wag-tail dance (Fig. 1). In the round dance, the bee "with quick short steps runs around in narrow circles on the comb, often changing her direction so that she rushes once to the right, then to the left and again describes one or two circles in either direction." She may continue to "waltz" for several seconds or even as long as a minute; then she may stop and begin the dance at a different place on the comb. Finally

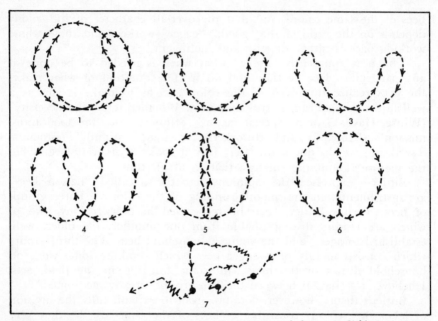

FIGURE 1. Diagram of the dances of honey bees. 1. Round dance. 2. Sickle or crescent dance. 3-5. Transitions between the round dance and the wag-tail dance. 6. Wag-tail dance. 7. Pull dance (Rucktanz of Hein).

she rushes toward the entrance and flies out again. The dance excites the bees; they follow "the performer," place their antennae on the dancing bee, and leave the hive in search of the source of nectar.

In the wag-tail dance the bee, before depositing the load, begins to dance on the comb making a narrow half-circle to one side, then executes a sharp turn and runs in a straight line to the starting point, then describes a half-circle in the opposite direction so that she completes a full circle. Then the bee again runs in a straight line to the starting point. However, while running in a straight line, the bee performs wiggling motions with all her body — hence the name "wag-tail dance." The inmates of the hive are excited by the dance and by the odor of flowers visited by the bee, and then fly out looking for the source.

Because the round dance was performed by the bees collecting sugar solution near the hive, Frisch considered it to be a "nectar dance" while the "wag-tail" dance, performed mostly by the pollen gatherers, became known as the "pollen dance."

However, the same year Park[177] reported "bees in this country may be out of date, for they still adhere to the old-time 'wag' and 'tail' dance regardless of whether they carry nectar, pollen, or water." Others observed the same phenomenon.

Later Frisch[53,54] published a series of papers in which he modified the interpretation of the meaning of the dances on the basis of his further experiments. When a bee returns from a source of food which is up to 100 yards from the hive, she dances the round dance. The bees following the dancer perceive the kind of source from the floral fragrance clinging to the hairy body of the forager and from the sips of nectar which they receive from the dancer. They fly out looking for the source in all directions at distances up to 100 yards from the hive. In case the distance of the source is more than 100 yards, the returning bee performs the "wag-tail" dance. In the latter case the dance gives more detailed information about the source of food.

The location of the find is indicated in the hive by the direction of the straight portion of the wag-tail dance in relation to the line of gravity, which represents an imaginary line between the hive and the sun (Fig. 2). If the source of food is in line with the sun, the bee "wag-tails" straight upward; if away from the sun, straight downward.

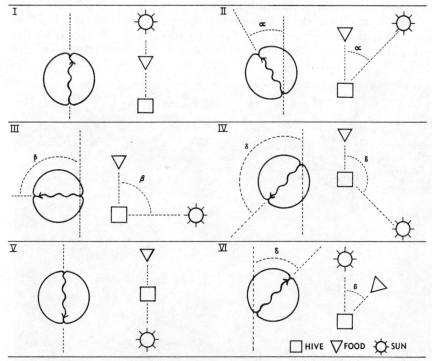

FIGURE 2. Diagram of the directional guidance of the wag-tail dance. The location of the food source does not change. When the sun is in line with the food source, the bees dance upward in the line of gravity (I), or downward (V) indicating that the source of food is away from the sun. When the source of food is to the left of the sun, the bees dance at an angle counterclockwise to the line of gravity (II, III, IV). When the source of food is to the right of the sun, the bees dance to the right of the line of gravity (VI).

Other positions are shown by the bee running at an angle from the vertical line. This angle corresponds to that by which the source of supply lies to the right or left of the sun, as the case may be. The bees which are aroused by the dancer on the comb recognize the angle of the dance relative to gravity and when flying to the source of food they remember this angle and relate it to the position of the sun. The bees hold quite precisely to the direction indicated by the dancer (Fig. 3). In experiments, the great majority (88 per cent) of bees did not deviate more than 15 degrees from the correct location.[56]

The distance to the source of food is indicated in a rather exact manner by the number of straight runs per 15 seconds in the wag-tail dance. At 100 yards there were 9 to 10 such runs within 15 seconds; at 600 yards, 7 runs; at 1 km. (0.6 mi.), 4; and at 6 km. (3.7 mi.), only 2 runs. The time spent on the straight wag-tail run is best correlated with distance.[61] The bees receive information about the value of the find by the duration and liveliness of the dance and also by the samplings of nectar from the dancer.

There are some deviations in the dance due to individual differences, but these deviations are slight. In older bees the tempo of the dance is somewhat slower. Head wind has the same effect on the dance as increased distance — it slows the dance.[222] In this way the

FIGURE 3. A worker bee performing the wag-tail dance indicates that the source of food is 25° to the left of the line from the hive to the sun. Interested bees are following her through the dance. *(Photo by Wolfgang Wittekindt)*

bees indicate the distance according to the energy and time spent in flight toward the source.[58,90]

If the comb is placed horizontally, the bee dances in the direction of the source. Dances on a horizontal surface are disoriented if the comb is placed in an enclosed room or in the dark, but they become correctly oriented when a piece of blue sky becomes visible to the dancing bees.[55] The light from the blue sky is partially polarized and its plane of vibration depends on the sun's position. Frisch[57] proved that a bee is able to analyze the polarization of the light of the sky. The light from clouds is not polarized.

According to Lindauer,[139] a beginner bee does not get ready for her first foraging flight immediately after her first dance-following. It can take hours (if dancing is lethargic it can take even days) before the bee is alerted and flies off. The reason for the delay in the stimulation of these fledgling bees is that there is "always a considerable delay before they are able to follow a dancer without interruption. To begin with they appear quite clumsy, and are easily pushed aside by the other dance followers, with the result that they keep losing contact with the dancer. The instant when the dancer comes to the end of her straight run and turns sharply to return to its starting point seems to be particularly difficult. Experienced bees can follow the dancer at this time without any interruption, but again and again our beginners would remain a moment too long in the same spot, and in the next instant found themselves facing the dancer only to be pushed aside by the next 'waggle' of the dancer or by another dance follower."

While an old forager is alerted only by a dancer of her own foraging group, the beginner follows every dancer that comes her way — be it nectar or pollen dancer. The question arises — how well do these beginners understand the message brought by the dancing bees? Observations showed that "of the 150 marked bees which departed after following the dancers, 91 brought home nectar or pollen, and 79 of these returned with the same kind of load as the dancers that they followed; moreover, 42 of them also indicated by their own dances that the direction and the approximate distance of their first source were the same as those given by the dancers." In a colony consisting of young bees, the foragers know how to dance correctly even if they have never come into contact with a dancer.

Tschumi,[237] working with Italian bees, observed that when the source of food was more than 10 but less than 100 yards from the hive the bees performed the "sickle" or "crescent" dance (Fig. 1-2) — running variously to form a bent figure 8. They indicate the direction of the source by an imaginary line which runs from the middle of the crescent curvature through the middle distance between the ends of the crescent. At a distance of 14 yards the bee introduces a wag-tail movement at the corners of the crescent. As the distance to the source increases, the number of these movements also increases. Simultaneously, the opposite ends of the crescent come closer together (Fig. 1-3 to 5), so that at a distance of about 100 yards the crescent dance is transformed into the typical wag-tail dance. Thus the crescent dance occupies an inter-mediate position betwen the round and the wag-tail dances.

Boch[17] and Lindauer[145] extended these investigations to other races. Carniolan bees do not have the sickle dance and they have the fastest dancing tempo, in which they are followed by Black German and Punic bees, then Italian and Caucasian. The slowest is the Egyptian bee. The distance at which various races start the sickle dance and then the wag-tail dance is, in descending order, German, Punic, Caucasian, Italian, and Egyptian which starts the crescent dance at a distance of about 4 yards and the wag-tail dance at about 12 yards. When the bees from one of these races are introduced into a colony of a different race, they interpret the dances in their own measurements and fly accordingly, closer or farther from the source of food depending on their "code." This signifies that each geographical race has its own "dialect."

Hein[89] observed that Dutch bees at a very short distance (2 yards) perform the "pull dance" (Rücktanz) (Fig. 1-7) which at about 8 yards changes to the sickle dance and then gradually to the wag-tail dance at a distance of 50 yards. Frisch[54] ascertained that when bees come from the field with a load of nectar or pollen they bring the odor of the flowers on their hairy bodies and absorbed in nectar. The latter source of odor is most significant; in experiments, when collectors were induced to alight on flowers of one kind but to drink sugar solution scented with the odor of flowers of another kind, about twice as many recruited bees visited the flowers having the odor of sugar solution as they did those on which the bees alighted while drinking the sugar solution. At greater distances, bees are directed almost exclusively by the odor of the nectar. Scout bees do not dance until they have paid several visits to the food source; they dance only when they have assured themselves that this is a rich and abundant source. The sweeter the nectar, the livelier and more persistent is the dance. The scent gland also plays an important role; the bees expose it sometimes when partaking the sugar solution. When the scent glands of the scout bees were covered with shellac, the number of newcomers to the place was only one-tenth of the controls.

Bees can perceive the sun even when the sky is completely covered with clouds. This ability is due to the extreme sensitivity of a bee's eye to ultraviolet light, which penetrates through the clouds directly in front of the sun.[59]

Various odors have a negative or positive influence on the dance. Even a slight denaturation of sugar solution with an unpleasant odor leads to suppression of the dance. At such a time bees may perform the "trembling dance" (Zittertanz).[136] On the other hand, an addition of essential oils increases the liveliness of the dance, although too strong an odor causes a suppression of the dance.[107]

Lindauer[136] noticed that on sunny days there is a period of relative quiet between 1:00 and 3:00 p.m.; dancing at that time is markedly restricted. In the region of the equator when the sun is at zenith, the bees stop dancing and collecting flights cease at that time. If the bees are retained at the feeding place and allowed to return at noon, their dances are disoriented and remain so as long as the sun is closer than 2.5° from the zenith.[144] New and his coworkers[167] calculated that when the distance of the sun from the zenith was less than 5°, the frequency of the arrival of recruited bees was about half that at larger zenith distances. However, some recruited bees were still arriving even when the zenith distance was less than 1°. The observers concluded that either the perception of the relative position of the sun by some bees is extraordinarily acute, or that some method of communication is involved which is independent of the position of the sun.

For their orientation, bees use landmarks as well as the position of the sun and polarized light.[62] In the presence of closely located continuous landmarks (forests, shore line, highway) they pay more attention to the latter than to the position of the sun. If bees have to fly around an obstacle (big rocks, high mountains) to the source of food, they will indicate by their dance the direction toward the feeding place in the straight line which they have never flown. "That they should be able," writes Frisch,[58] "(without protractors, slide rule, and drawing board) to work out so exactly the direct line between the hive and the feding place from the detour they have made is surely one of their most amazing achievements." There is, however, no doubt that the language of the bees is on a higher level than the means of communication among birds and mammals, with the exception of man.[63,114]

Lindauer[140] found that the searching bees, looking for an abode for their swarm, danced even during the night and into the morning. What is astonishing is that those bees correctly referred to the position of the sun at the time of dancing, thus showing that they were able to "calculate" the position of the sun during any time of night without ever seeing it. Experiments of Kalmus[104] and Lindauer[146] showed that bees' orientation on the sun is inborn, but their calculation of the path of the sun must be learned. It took 42 days for the bees from the southern hemisphere to learn to compensate correctly for the northern "reverse" movement of the sun.[146]

Bees give direction in one horizontal plane only and do not show how high or low is the source in relation to the position of the hive.[60]

Since bees relate their dances in the hive to the line of gravity, it is felt that they must have a sense of gravity. Lindauer and Nedel[147] demonstrated that bees recognize the pull of gravity because they have two sets of organs of gravity — the neck organs, in the place of the articulation of the head and thorax, and the petiole organs, between the thorax and the abdomen. The latter can replace the former in emergencies. Normally the petiole organs merely confirm the information supplied by the neck organ and supplement it.

The character of mobilizing dances is conditioned by the state of the colony as a whole. In a colony exposed to robbing, marked bees in the course of 5 hours brought in sugar solution 26 times, danced irregular dances 11 times and regular dances 9 times. Next day, in a quiet state (no robbing), in the same amount of time the same bees brought in sugar solution 98 times and performed regular dances 84 times.[238]

Even the form of the container in which the sugar solution is offered plays a role in the duration and liveliness of the dance. Containers which corresponded to natural forms of flowers evoked a longer and livelier dance.[106]

The influx of new foragers on feeding places farther from the hive is smaller than on those near the hive because, with the same strength of sugar solution, fewer bees coming from farther places are dancing (11 per cent of those coming from distances of 2,100 yards danced) than those coming from the nearer ones (68 per cent coming from distances of 100 yards danced). When the concentration of the sugar solution on the farther place was increased, more bees began to dance.[16] So the dance is the result of a certain level of excitement of the nervous system of the bee. Lowering the level of excitement leads to suppression of the dance while an increase in the level of excitement encourages the dance.[148]

Bees will dance even when they have to walk to the feeding place, but they start the wag-tail dance considerably sooner than under normal circumstances. At a distance of 1 to 3 yards, they perform the round dance; at 3 to 4 yards, transitory dances; and over 4 yards more bees perform the regular wag-tail dance.[14] Readiness to dance and the intensity of the dance are clearly increased when temperatures in the hive remain between 28 and 36° C. (82.4 and 96.8° F.). In colonies where combs contained only a small amount of honey, more foragers were induced to perform the dance and it lasted longer than where bees were on full combs. Environmental condition of the hive can also directly affect the dance readiness of its foragers.[249]

Frisch[58] was amazingly correct when he said, "What these animals can tell each other about feeding places they have discovered and how, in doing this, they deal with abnormally different situations is beyond anything we should have expected of insects. And their brains are not bigger than a grain of millet. Nothing could more clearly illustrate the marvelous structure of the nerve cells. It would be presumptuous to say that we can understand it."

The communicative dances described above can be normally observed during the active season when bees discover rich sources of nectar or pollen. But there are some other dances which we can notice at any time during the year when appropriate conditions exist.

"Rocking" or "Washboard" Movements. Many beekeepers have observed in their apiaries, especially in the evening, bees performing a mass dance on the front wall of the hive. The bees stand firmly on the second and the third pair of legs, facing the entrance. Their heads are bent down and the front legs also are bent. The bees perform "rocking" or "washboard" movements swinging their bodies forward and backward. At the same time, with short and quick movements of the bent tarsi of the front legs, they scrape the surface of the hive, and their mandibles, with a rapid shearing movement, slide over the surface as if scrubbing it. The tips of the antennae touch the surface, moving constantly as if checking on the work. After a while one can observe some material accumulated on the lower edge of the mandibles. Periodically the bees clean their mandibles as well as the tarsi of the front legs. Occasionally they move and continue their "dance" at another place. Careful investigations have shown that these rocking movements serve as a mechanical cleaning process by which the bees scrape and polish the surfaces of the hive. Usually this "scrubbing" dance, both inside and outside of the hive, is performed by young bees, probably as a part of their duties in taking care of the hive. Such a dance by individual bees has been observed inside of a glass hive even during winter, but it was always of short duration.[2]

"Alarm" Dances. Schneider[220] observed that, when bees brought into the hive a sugar solution contaminated with dinitrocresol, a few minutes after their arrival the bees became excited and many field and hive bees started to perform an "alarm" dance. The bees ran in spirals or irregular zig-zags and vigorously shook their abdomens sidewise. The flight activity of the bees stopped completely and neighboring bees began to pay attention to the dancers. As the poison spread many more bees began to dance. The highest mortality occurred 1 to 2 hours later. In another 2 to 3 hours the colony returned to normal and flight began again.

Leppik[126] described a phenomenon which he called "bee struggle." The bees which took nerve poison with the sugar solution were allowed to enter the hive by the guards. But shortly afterwards, in extreme excitement, the bees started killing each other. Severe fighting started between the poisoned and nonpoisoned bees; the struggle continued until all bees which contained poison were killed. Schick,[219] however, claims that the dances described by Schneider are nothing else than the "Zittertänze" observed by Frisch.[52] These dances can be aroused by different substances and are the result of various disturbances which may happen to bees. Schick's conclusions were confirmed by Istomina-Tsvetkova[99] who observed the "alarm" dances of Schneider performed by ordinary nectar gatherers.

Haydak[73,82] described the following dances: 1. "Cleaning" dance, 2. "joy" dance, and 3. "massage" dance.

"Cleaning" Dance. Occasionally a bee feels the need of being cleaned. In such cases it performs a special dance, consisting of a rapid stamping of the legs and a rhythmic swinging of the body to the sides. At the same time the bee rapidly raises and lowers the body and tries to clean around the bases of the wings with the middle pair of legs. Such a "shaking" dance may be observed any time during the year, even during winter. Usually the bee which is closest to the dancer touches the latter with its antennae and begins to clean the dancer. With the mandibles widely spread the "cleaner" touches the thorax of the dancer just under the base of the wings. As soon as the dancer feels the touch of the cleaner it stops dancing, slowly spreads out the wings of one side, bends the abdomen and curves the body to the side and somewhat upward as if accommodating the cleaner. The latter works energetically; its antennae are held close to the mandibles. With shear-like motions of the mandibles it cleans around the base of the wings. From time to time it stops, standing on the last two pairs of legs, the front pair being held in the air, and works with the mandibles as if chewing something that it found while cleaning, holding the antennae close to the tips of the mandibles. Then the cleaner continues her work "clipping" with the mandibles over the scutum from the rear to the front, sometimes over the head, and in the grooves of the thorax; sometimes she climbs on the dancer, crawls to the other side and cleans under the opposite pair of wings and then quits.

If the dancer is satisfied with the work she cleans her tongue, antennae, and the body in general and goes about her duties. In case she is not satisfied, the bee continues to dance, and either the same cleaner or another bee starts the process of cleaning all over again.

There are also "general cleaners;" sometimes as many as 10 of them at one time present on a single comb. Without invitation they clean various bees in succession. Beecken[10] also described the activity of general cleaners. Milum[161,163] who refers to this dance as "grooming" reports that such a groomer barbered 26 bees in 25 minutes. Even the drones may be groomed if they happen to be in the way. Milum observed that this is the activity of bees in their hive age.

"Joy" Dance. A bee places its front legs on some part of the body of another bee and then makes five or six shaking movements up and down with the abdomen, with a simultaneous slight swinging forward and backward. Then it crawls farther and performs such a dance

touching another bee, then another, and so on. Usually a number of such dancers can be observed during a quiet warm afternoon or evening after a good honeyflow in colonies where everything is normal. Sometimes one can see such a dance on a sealed queen cell. When a virgin queen had just emerged from a cell in a queenless colony, a large number of bees started performing such a dance. Because he observed this dance performed only when hive conditions were optimum, Haydak named it "joy" dance, "good-time" dance, or "dance of contentment."

Milum[162] observed this dance performed by bees of predominantly field age or at least old enough to perform field duties. The youngest bee was 9 days and the oldest 151 days. He called this dance "dorso-ventral-abdominal vibrations—DVAV," or "spirit tap" dance. It was exhibited on many occasions, at all hours of the day and night, at all seasons, with or without flight in progress, even in queenless colonies and in those at the point of starvation. DVAV can be intermixed with wag-tail or crescent dances; they can be performed on the queen or the queen cells, before swarming, or on virgins before they fly out. There is no response of bees when shaken except that they keep still. Allen[5,6] found that the age of the participating bees varied widely but most were older bees.

"Massage" Dance. This dance begins when one of the bees on the comb bends its head in a peculiar way. One or more neighboring bees become excited and immediately begin to investigate her, using their antennae and front legs. They climb over and under her, pull the joints of the hind and middle legs, but mostly touch her sides from below with their antennae, mandibles, and front legs, cleaning their antennae periodically. The bee which aroused so much attention has the mandibles wide open and the upper part of the tongue protruded as with the nurse bees, but the protruded part is entirely dry. The bee turns her head toward the "examining" bee as soon as the latter approaches the front part of her body. Then she unfolds the entire tongue, extends the second pair of legs as if sitting on the third pair and constantly cleans the tongue with her front legs, stroking it from above downward.

Sometimes the tongue becomes completely distorted, the tongue appendages spreading in various directions so that an impression is obtained that the bee has cramps of the tongue. At the same time the bees that started "the massage" frantically continue their treatment, sometimes pulling the "sick" bee by the mandibles or tongue, sometimes licking the latter. Several minutes later everything quiets down and the "sick" bee begins normally to clean its antennae, eyes, hind legs, wings, and tongue, and then quietly crawls away. Such a phenomenon has been observed usually in the fall or during the winter but the same treatment was observed in early spring, being given to chilled bees when they were placed on the entrance of their hives.

Activities of Hive Bees

Comb Building. In summer a worker spends one half of her life as a hive bee and the other half as a fielder. Of the many kinds of work carried on within the hive, comb building and brood rearing may be considered major activities. They fulfill fundamental biological needs— shelter and reproduction, respectively.

Beeswax, the material used by honey bees in the construction of their combs, is a product of their own bodies. It is secreted by certain glands possessed by workers only. Wax glands are at the height of their development and productivity in bees 12 to 18 days old. The wax appears in the form of small, irregularly oval flakes, or scales (Fig. 4), which project from between the overlapped portions of the last four abdominal segments visible on the underside of the bee. Two scales are produced on each of these segments, one on either side of the midventral line, making eight in all. Wax can be secreted only at relatively high temperatures, stated by different authors at from 92° to 97° F., and after the consumption of relatively large amounts of honey or nectar. Thus, indirectly, beeswax is derived from flowers, but is not gathered directly from them as was believed by the ancients.

Various attempts have been made to determine the amount of honey consumed in producing 1 pound of wax. Studies by Whitcomb[247] using four queenright colonies, approximately equal in population, showed that in building comb from foundation the least productive colony used 8.80 pounds of honey per pound of wax produced; the most productive used only 6.66 pounds; and the average for the group was 8.40 pounds of honey.

Experiments described by Taranov[233] proved that besides nectar, protein food—pollen or bee bread—is of great importance in wax pro-

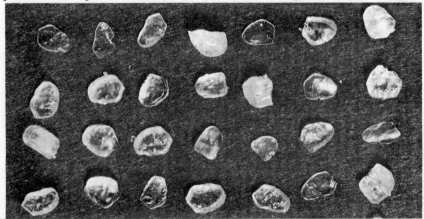

FIGURE 4. Tiny scales of beeswax as produced by bees. *(Photo by John F. Brook)*

duction. When young bees were fed sugar solution only, they lost up to 20 per cent of their body protein in 15 days of intensive wax production. In experiments with 14 equalized colonies forced to build combs, a direct relationship was found between the quantity of wax obtained from a colony and the amount of pollen brought into the hive. Experiments by Freudenstein[51] support these findings.

Workers actively engaged in secreting wax gorge themselves with honey and hang in festoons at or near the site of building operations. Here they hang very quietly while their organs of digestion and secretion transform the content of their honey sacs into energy and beeswax, and after about 24 hours they begin to build comb. For additional information, see "Comb Building" in Chapter VIII.

The following description of how bees manipulate wax scales and build comb is based largely upon the excellent studies of Casteel.[31] Wax scales, unless lost by accident, always are removed from their "pockets" and manipulated by the bee that secretes them, although scales that have been dropped sometimes are recovered and used by others. Wax scales are removed from their pockets (Fig. 5) by means of the spines on one or the other of the hind tarsi (Fig. 8). While the scale is thus held, the hind leg bearing it is flexed toward the mouth, where the scale may be grasped conveniently by the forelegs or by the mandibles (Figs. 6, 7). Bees do not follow any definite sequence in the order in which they remove scales from the several pockets.

Usually the forelegs assist in transferring the scale to the mandibles, and they also manipulate the scale during the thorough mastication given it by the mandibles before it is affixed to the comb. Secretion of mandibular glands is used in masticating the scales and building combs.[173] When first deposited by the producing bee, masticated wax is spongy and flaky but later it is reworked and thereby becomes smoother and more compact. The whole process of removing, masticating, and affixing one scale to the comb requires about 4 minutes.

In building combs, bees often appear to work in opposition to one another.[139] One bee sticks a little ball of wax on and molds it carefully, then a moment later another bee gnaws it off and sticks it on a fraction of an inch farther away. This is particularly noticeable when cells are being capped. If the stacked building wax is not quite sufficient for the job, the bee will gnaw some from the stack of the neighboring cells, which probably also need cappings. All this is due to the fact that hundreds of bees contribute to the construction of a cell, and an individual worker may be relieved after as little as half a minute's work. This has been confirmed by the work of Meyer and Ulrich.[157]

Gontarski[70] ascertained that when building combs bees can adjust themselves in the direction of gravity. Queen cells are also built under the influence of gravity. He stated that bees can perceive a slight de-

FIGURE 5. Ventral view of a worker bee in the act of removing a wax scale. The two middle legs and the right hind leg are used for support, while the left hind leg removes the scale. (*After Casteel*)

FIGURE 6. Ventral view showing the position of the wax scale just before it is grasped by the forelegs and the mandibles. The scale is still adhering to the spines of the pollen combs. (*After Casteel*)

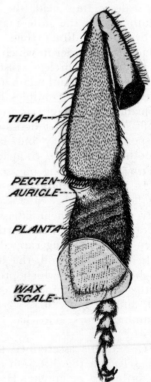

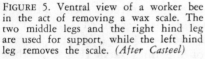 FIGURE 7. Side view of worker bee in the same position as that shown in Figure 6. (*After Casteel*)

FIGURE 8. Inner surface of the left hind leg of a worker bee, showing the position of a wax scale immediately after it has been removed from the wax pocket. The scale has been pierced by seven of the spines of the pollen combs of the first tarsal segment or planta. (*After Casteel*)

TIBIA---

PECTEN---
AURICLE---

PLANTA---

WAX
SCALE---

flection of their bodies from the vertical plane and can compensate for it. This has a great biological significance. Recent discovery of the organs of gravity by Lindauer and Nedel[147] supports the assumption of Gontarski. Darchen[35] demonstrated that the chains which bees form in their building cluster play an important part in regulating parallelism of the combs. They can exert torsion strong enough to twist a rectangularly attached sheet of comb foundation to the position parallel to the two adjacent combs.

Nursing. Young bees normally take up the work of nursing at the age of about 3 days. The nursing activities of the individual begin to slow down along with the decline of the functioning of their brood-nursing glands, which begins somewhat before the 13th day. Although workers beyond this age are still capable of performing nursing duties to a limited extent, most of them turn to other duties at about this time. The following description of the activities of nurse bees is based upon the observations of Lineburg[166] and Lindauer.[139]

Nurse bees begin to make visits to the cell as soon as the egg is laid and continue them at frequent intervals throughout the duration of the egg and larval stages. Some of these visits are very short—at most about 2 to 3 seconds—but in others the larvae and the brood present would be examined most conscientiously with the antennae, the bee leaving the cell only after 10 or even 20 seconds. Each actual feeding was preceded by such an examination. The time taken for one feeding (including inspection) is variable. Usually it is from $\frac{1}{2}$ to 2 minutes, in exceptional cases even 3 minutes.

During its first 2 days out of the egg, the nurse bees keep the tiny larva supplied with far more food than it can consume, so that it appears to float in the milky-white food. During the 3d day somewhat less food is provided in advance of needs, so that by the end of that day all excess has been consumed, and thenceforth a larva in a worker cell receives food only at intervals. The two types of feeding are distinguished as mass feeding and progressive feeding, respectively.

Lineburg's studies show that, during the 8-day period from the laying of the egg until the full-grown larva is sealed within its cell, nurses visit the individual an average of about 1,300 times daily—more than 10,000 visits in all. On the last day before the cell is capped, they visit it nearly 3,000 times, spending a total of approximately $4\frac{3}{4}$ hours within the cell. Lindauer calculated the working time for rearing one larva from the time the egg is laid to the capping of the cell, and also the number of bees taking part in the work: 2,785 bees spent 10 hours, 16 minutes, and 8 seconds in caring for the cell and the larva during this period.

Food Transmission. In a colony of bees, food is passed from one worker to another and also from worker to queen and drones (Fig. 9). Observations on individual bees showed that reciprocal feeding con-

FIGURE 9. At left, food is being passed from one worker to another; at right, food is being given to a drone by a worker. Food transmission is important to the life and cohesion of the colony. (*Photos by Wolfgang Wittekindt*)

tinues throughout the life of bees, except that up to 2 days of age the bee is more fed than feeding. Most feedings last 1 to 5 seconds, some 6 to 20 seconds, and only a few are 20 seconds or more.[97] The transfer of food between two bees starts when one of them is either begging or offering food to the other. Both types of behavior are directed more toward the head than to any other part of the bee's body.[43] The antennal contact is important. During feeding, the antennae of both bees are in constant motion, continuously striking each other. This apparently helps the bees to orient themselves to each other and, possibly, to communicate with each other. The scent of the bee's head is also important.[39] Individual bees show a great variation in their behavior. Both begging and offering are innate reactions and improve in precision with age.

Food transmission is important for the cohesion of a colony. It may serve as a form of communication, by informing about the availability of food and water supply, and also it serves as a medium for transmission of queen substance and possibly other substances important for the life and cohesion of the colony.

Guard Duty. The hive entrance is a portal through which both friends and enemies can enter the hive. Butler and Free,[28] whose work will be reviewed presently, observed that during the honeyflow, if the colony is not disturbed, very few guards if any are present at the entrance, and any strange forager loaded with nectar or pollen may enter without difficulty or any examination. But when the colony is greatly disturbed (vigorously thumped) then many strange foragers entering the hive are liable to be intercepted and examined, though they can still enter the hive without difficulty. When very little nectar is available, the colony is constantly alert, guard bees are persistently present at the entrance, and they examine all bees coming to their hive; would-be robbers are intercepted and quite often stung to death.

In an alerted colony the guards assume a very typical attitude (Fig. 10). They stand on four legs, having their forelegs lifted from the ground, with their antennae held forward and their mandibles closed. When there is greater excitement, they open their mandibles and spread the wings as if ready to attack. Each of the guards patrols her particular area of the alighting board, examining all bees entering the hive. Such examination lasts from 1 to 3 seconds only. The guard approaches a suspect very closely, actually touching her body with the antennae before she can be certain of her identity. Apparently the guard recognizes the examined bee by the smell.[105]

Butler and Free noticed that when a bee inadvertently drifted into a strange colony and was approached by a guard, she either continued on her way, taking no notice of the guard which had attempted to examine her, or she stopped and submitted to a detailed examination or mauling (massaging). Young bees without pollen loads, that had only recently started flying, were much more ready to submit to examination and massaging than were the older strange foragers carrying loads of nectar or pollen. The older bees usually assumed a dominant attitude toward the guards and did not hesitate to enter the hive

FIGURE 10. A worker bee guarding the entrance to the hive. (*Photo by Wolfgang Wittekindt*)

without stopping, even if the guards sometimes ran after them trying to examine them. If the bee submits to examination she behaves quite similarly to a bee being "massaged" (see "Massage" Dance in this Chapter). However, in this case she offers a drop of fluid (presumably regurgitated from the honey stomach) to the "massaging" guards. This offer is usually ignored.

Robbing. Robber bees can be recognized by their peculiar flying to-and-fro in front of the hive entrance. This behavior of robber bees is an innate response. Free[38] considers that this type of flight occurs only when there is a congestion of bees at the hive entrance. Strange foragers did not assume the robber flight, entered the strange hive without hesitation and took honey from combs in the presence of the bees belonging to this colony, but kept away from the entrance by a screen. Free concluded that guard bees quickly recognize robbers by their flight behavior and use the sense of smell just for closer identification.

That movements are sufficient to alert the guards was evident from the experiments of Butler and Free[28] who proved that moving a dead-bee lure in front of the entrance was enough to alert the experimental colonies, so that the guards afterwards remained at the entrances for an average of 28.5 minutes. Recently Free[47] supported these conclusions by demonstrating that the stinging response is released and guard bees sting even cotton balls rapidly moving in front of the hive entrances. But Ribbands[203,205] is of the opinion that the important factor in the recognition of robber bees is the strange body odor and that the characteristic flight of robbers is the consequence of their recognition and not its cause. Lecomte[124] in trying to clarify the question and to reconcile the diversity of the viewpoints of Free and Ribbands, suggested that there exist two types of recognition: 1. recognition of an intruder as a stranger, and 2. her recognition as being undesirable. In the first instance the guards use the sense of smell; in the second, the would-be intruders are recognized by their behavior. Under natural conditions a robber bee is identified as undesirable by her shifting flight and as a stranger because of her foreign odor. While an accidental intruder becomes submissive and could be mauled and even carried out of the hive, a robber bee, if she had alighted near the hive entrance and was approached by the guard, would always attempt to fly away; if not seized by the guard, she would resume a swaying flight. When a guard succeeds in seizing the robber, the latter always tries to break away. If a guard bee succeeded in getting a firm hold of a robber, she would immediately attempt to sting her. In this case a fight ensues and either of the adversaries may be killed.

Fanning. In warm weather, bees reduce the temperature within the hive by fanning at the entrance (Fig. 11). During the honeyflow season, air currents thus set up within the hive hasten the elimination of

FIGURE 11. Bees fanning at the entrance to pull air currents through the hive—cools the hive and helps to dehydrate the nectar and transform it into honey. *(Photo by Wolfgang Wittekindt)*

excess moisture from unripe honey in the open cells. Fanning bees may be observed at their work any day in summer, but especially during late afternoon and early evening on a day when there has been a heavy harvest of nectar.

The number of fanners varies with the need for forced ventilation, ranging from just a few individuals, when the need is not great, to several hundred bees in extreme cases. Occupying the alighting board, usually for about half the width of the hive but often less, fanners, with their heads toward the rear of the hive, stand just far enough apart so as not to interfere with each other's movements. By operating their wings vigorously, they set up outgoing air currents through their half of the entrance. As the need for ventilation increases, such operations may extend along the bottom board almost to the rear of the hive. In case of extreme conditions, two batteries of fanners may operate simultaneously, the second group establishing itself on the other side of the bottom board but mostly within the hive, and facing in the opposite direction so that their fanning increases the rate of flow of air passing into the hive. This speeds the circulation of air, which enters at one side of the entrance and goes out at the other. In extremely hot weather, if the bees are unable to ventilate the hive sufficiently to keep the temperature at a comfortable level, they cluster outside on the front and sides of the hive as if in an attempt to escape the unbearable heat within.

In this "ventilation fanning," the bees have their abdomens curved. But when the incoming bees are prevented from alighting at the entrance for some time by an obstacle in front of the hive, and then allowed to alight, a different type of fanning could be observed. The bees have their abdomens up, the last tergite of the abdomen bent down and the scent gland exposed (Fig. 12). This is the "orientation fanning" usually performed by bees that had been lost and again have found the entrance to their hive. They fan to mark the hive entrance for other bees that also might be lost.

Orientation Flights and Drifting. Short flights in front of the hive and in its vicinity enable bees to become intimately familiar with the appearance of their home and its surroundings. First flights taken by bees about a week old, are short and are confined to the immediate vicinity of the hive, but on successive occasions they are increased in duration and scope. Since numerous young bees of a given colony commonly take their first flights together, this activity frequently assumes the appearance of a social occasion to which the term "play flight" often is applied. Such flights are especially noticeable in spring on a warm, sunny noon following several days of inclement weather. All of a sudden there is a great activity in the air in front of some hive entrance. At first glance one might suspect that a robbing escapade is underway, but closer scrutiny reveals no fighting. Moreover, the bees taking to the air do not fly away, as with booty, but join the dancing, swaying throng that hovers before the hive. One need not remain long in doubt, however, for so-called play flights are of short duration, seldom lasting more than 5 minutes or thereabouts. They end as abruptly as they start and activity at the front of the hive immediately resumes its normal appearance. At one time or another, during the pleasantest part of such a day in spring or summer, similar flights by young bees may be observed in front of practically every hive in the apiary.

When young bees make their first orientation flight some of them may drift to other colonies, especially during a strong wind. Rausch-meyer[198] studied drifting of bees in German bee houses and found that, when there are no orientation marks, bees drift in extraordinary large numbers—up to 50 per cent. If there are enough orientation marks, only single bees drift. Painting hives with different colors, particularly close to the entrance, is helpful. But when the same colors are repeated, bees drift to hives having the same colors even at great distances. Young bees, especially during the first 4 days of their orientation flights, drifted very often, even when the front walls of the hives had been painted with different colors. The youngest bees which drifted were 5 days of age. The majority of bees (80 per cent) drifted at the age of 6 to 11 days, and only 16 per cent drifted at the age of 12 to 37 days. This is in agreement with King's[108] observations that drifting was most prevalent among bees 5 to 10 days of age. Corkins,[33] under Wyoming conditions, observed no appreciable drifting between

FIGURE 12. A fanning worker bee with the scent gland exposed toward the tip of its abdomen. (*An outstanding photograph by Wolfgang Wittekindt*)

colonies (average 2.2 per cent). Borchert[20] in Germany observed between 3.4 to 7.8 per cent drifting.

According to Free,[41] drifting occurs during the 1st and, to a lesser extent, the 2d week of life, and mostly during the play flights before the bees become foragers. Free noted that bees which emerged in August and September drifted less. Drifting is especially noticeable when bees have been confined for long periods or when colonies were moved to a new site. The amount of drifting varies considerably depending on the arrangement of hives (straight rows facilitate it). When hives were arranged in repetitive patterns, bees were drifting to hives occupying similar positions. Facing hives in different directions considerably reduced drifting. Individual bees were more likely to drift from a weak to a strong colony, or from a queenright to a queenless colony,[50] than vice versa. Drones drift two to five times as frequently as workers.

Working Habits of Field Bees

Activities involving flight sometimes begin as early as the 3d or 4th day, but normally few foraging trips are made under the age of about 3 weeks. It is uncertain what field duties are first performed by a young forager. Probably this depends on the circumstances existing in the hive at any given time. Observations of Bonnier[19] and Park[186] showed that marked fielders engaged in carrying water, nectar, or pollen continued their respective kinds of work for days together. But Ribbands[201] observed that bees were frequently seen to change their attachment from a pollen crop to a nectar crop, but never vice versa. The period of attachment to any particular crop varied considerably from a few days to 20 to 21 days. It was observed[186] that bees working on flowers or on sugar-solution feeders,[72] which supply food during a certain portion of the day only, remained idle in the hive during the remaining portion of the day when the food was not present. Such time memory of bees has a great biological significance with flowers which yield pollen or nectar only at a certain period of the day.[112]

Fidelity to Plant Species. Centuries ago, Aristotle noted that on any one trip a honey bee confines her visits to the flower of a single species. In general, bees are true to the species of flowers they began to work on as long as food is available. But mixed loads of pollen can be found among those brought by the bees to their hives. Betts[11] found 3 per cent mixed loads, and 15 per cent of loads contained a few foreign grains. Maurizio,[152] in 3 years of examination, ascertained an average of 0.9 to 3 per cent of mixed loads (0.1 to 11 per cent per individual sample). In Schwan and Martinovs'[221] observations, the number of mixed pollen loads containing more than one kind of pollen was equal to only 0.1 per cent, while Tushmalova[241] established that 12.6 per cent of bees visited several plants differing in odor and structure of flower on the same trip. She also cited Gubin who found that 23.8 per cent of bees visited different kinds of flowers on the same trip. Probably different environmental conditions and the individual variability among bees played a role in the differences reported. Ribbands[201] considers that in suitable circumstances a bee can become attached to and forage from two very different crops at one time. Mixed loads are brought in by the bees throughout the season and are not more frequent at the time of scanty forage than in time of the main pollen foraging.[152]

Area of Work. It is generally agreed that an individual bee works in a restricted area of the field or she may be attached to a particular group of trees, or even a single tree or bush.[36,186,190] From observations on bees working on smaller plants, Butler[24] concluded that a bee working on a group of plants (her fixation area) almost always alights on one particular plant when arriving from the hive, and comes back to it when ready to take off for home. But Ribbands[201] and Singh[225] claim that bees do not start or finish their trip on any fixed point; flowers on which they make their first and last visit are scattered throughout the foraging areas. Ribbands[201] also disagrees with Butler that foraging bees have their rigid fixation areas (4 to 5 yards) on which they work. On the basis of his observations, Ribbands concluded that foraging behavior is not fixed but is adaptable. He considers "that the basic and cardinal feature of foraging behavior is the continuous exercise of choice and the comparison of the present with the memory of the past, and that it is the resultant of these factors whether the bee will remain attached to any particular crop and area." Weaver[245] supports this view.

The size of the foraging area may be quite variable, the chief factors probably being the number of flowers available, their nectar and pollen content, and the amount of competition provided by other foragers or other insects.[201] Ribbands observed that when a crop becomes unsuitable and is deserted in favor of another, the bee continues to return, although less and less often, to inspect the original source, provided it had been better than the new one. A characteristic behavior of bees on a failing crop is that they become more restless, so that instead of visiting flowers quite close to each other, they jump from one position of their usual foraging area to another and even beyond it.

Speed of Work. This depends on the type of plant—from about 5 flowers in hairy vetch,[245] to 42 flowers in sweet clover[227] per minute. The rate at which bees visit flowers depends on the amount of nectar and pollen present, and this varies with the type of flower, the stage of development, climatic conditions, and the number of foreign insects present.[44] Rymashevsky[213] found that for visitation of 5 flowers, the bees spent (average time in seconds): apple—34, apricot—36, strawberry—38, cherry—40.7, raspberry—58, and black currants—67. For collection of nectar a bee spends about twice as much time as for the collection of pollen. Park[186] also found that trips for pollen collection were considerably shorter in time than those for nectar collection.

Field activity of bees depends on temperature. Bodenheimer[18] found that below 8° C. (46.4° F.) there was none; at 9 to 16° C. (48.2 to 60.8° F.), average activity; from 16 to 32° C. (60.8 to 89.6° F.), optimal; at 33° C. (91.4° F.) there was a reduction in activity; and at 34 to 39° C. (93.2 to 102.2° F.) there was a considerable increase in activity—mainly bringing water to the hive.

Learning Ability. Reinhardt,[200] working with alfalfa, and Weaver [244,245] with hairy vetch, found that bees, which had never worked the flowers, had to learn by experience some method of collecting nectar or pollen. Young bees usually begin as "nectar trippers" inserting the tongue into the open corolla. The sexual column is thus released and traps the proboscis of the working bee. She sometimes has difficulty freeing herself from such a situation. Sooner or later the bees learn to insert their tongues between the petals of the standard and the keel at the base of the corolla tube, thus becoming "side or base workers." Their efficiency markedly improves. The time which is required for a bee to become a "side worker" depends on the individual adaptability of the bee in question. Tucker's[239] observations support these findings.

The work of pollen gatherers is more difficult because normally they have to trip the blossom in order to get pollen. Gaining in experience, such bees become more efficient in their work, avoiding the trap quite successfully. Reinhardt[200] concluded: "The change in habitual approach of bees to flowers, success in avoiding the trap, followed by pattern improvement and changes in working speed, lead to the conclusion that honey bees learn to work alfalfa flowers." The same can be said about bees working on hairy vetch. What is most astonishing is that, according to Weaver,[245] "the bees differ so widely from one another in their methods and approach to foraging that the individuality of the bees is the most obvious and striking phenomenon." There are efficient and inefficient workers.

Weaver also observed that when the amount of nectar in the flowers began to decrease, competition starts: "Often a bee was observed to collide with a near-by forager in a purposeful manner, or to fly threateningly toward another bee without actually touching her. Sometimes there is a prolonged struggle. This aggressive behavior of foraging bees is probably an aid in keeping a foraging area free of too much competition from other bees."

Some blossoms and crops are more attractive to bees than others, which is possibly associated with the quantity and quality of food available. Bees preferred, in descending order: sweet clover, alsike, alfalfa, and red clover.[64,93] Marked variations in the sugar composition and the proportion of various sugars, both within and between the crops, were encountered, which possibly may have some relation to the different attitudes of bees to these plants. Bees also prefer pollen from certain species of flowers; other pollens are brought to the hive to a lesser degree.[101,135]

Distribution of Foragers. Eckert[36] observed that bees may fly up to 8 miles for the source of food, and that they have a tendency to fly in only one or two major lines of flight, neglecting similar forage plants in other directions. Levin,[132] working with colonies deprived of old field bees, found that young bees undertaking foraging duties for the first time dispersed similarly to the more experienced foragers from undisturbed colonies. Most of the young bees were recovered within 300 yards. At the end of the 1st day most of them were still working close to the hive, but some were found as far away as 450 yards. Most of them remained foraging at this range. According to Levchenko[128] young bees, as they grew older, only gradually became acquainted with wider and wider areas around the hive. None of the 5-day-old bees released at a distance of 100 yards from the hive returned to the parent hive, while 80 per cent of 10-day-old bees returned home from this distance, but none returned from 200 yards. However, 80 per cent of 35-day-old bees returned from a distance of 500 yards. When a large area of honey plants was nearby, most of the bees were working at a distance of 200 to 500 yards. When colonies were moved to a new location, their acquaintance with the new area was also gradual, as was the case with the young bees.[127] Foragers also worked close to their hives when their colonies were placed in the center of an alfalfa field. When additional colonies were located nearby, their foragers became dispersed in the same way as in the case of the first group, although they showed a tendency to orient farther afield.[133]

Dispersion of bees over a field from two neighboring apiaries depends more on the attractiveness of the bloom than on competition from another apiary.[134] Lee[125] placed two groups of hives in an apple orchard 800 feet apart. He observed that the bees were not distributed at random in the area between the apiaries but more bees from each apiary worked in the proximity of their respective apiaries, their number diminishing as the distance increased from the apiaries.[225]

Speed of Flight. According to Park,[176] the speed of flight for loaded bees varied only a little, from 13 to 16 miles per hour, while the average was approximately 15 miles per hour. The speed of empty bees varied from 6.8 to 18 miles per hour, while the average was 12.5, or 2.5 miles per hour less than that for the homeward-bound bees. This suggests the possibility that a bee on her outward journey may not in all cases make a so-called "beeline" for the source of supply, but may sometimes do scouting on the way. It is significant that, when flying at right angles to the wind, the outgoing bee flew at the rate of 13.3 and the incoming bee 14.6 miles per hour, because each approaches rather closely the general average of its respective class. Furthermore, in spite of the heavier load, the homeward journey usually was accomplished in less time than the outward one. The only case in which the outgoing bee made better time than the incoming one was when flying directly against the wind.

The least speed was shown when flying with the wind, on both outward and homeward trips; the greatest speed in each case was attained when flying directly against the wind. It appeared that, when going with the wind, the bee showed a tendency to slacken her own efforts; whereas, when traveling against the wind, she increased them in an attempt to overcome the wind's retarding influence. The bees did not long continue to work in a wind blowing much over 15 miles per hour. A maximum of approximately 25.5 miles per hour was recorded for both outgoing and incoming bees.

ACTIVITIES IN GATHERING AND STORING POLLEN

The well-being of the honey-bee colony during the brood-rearing season is as dependent on pollen as it is upon honey. Pollen is practically the sole source of proteins, fatty substances, minerals, and vitamins for the production of larval food and for the development of the bodies of newly emerged bees.[77,153] The latter cannot rear

FIGURE 13. The lady is emptying the tray of a pollen trap onto a pile of pollen which contains 27 pounds of dried bee-gathered pollen. This represents about one-third of the requirements of a strong colony during a year, and demonstrates, better than words can describe, the tremendous amount of work which bees do in maintaining the colony and in pollination of crops. *(U.S.D.A. Photo)*

brood if they do not have pollen available.[79] Older bees can rear brood without consuming pollen[78,80] but they do this at the expense of their own bodies and the amount of brood produced is rather small. It is known that a prosperous colony will bring in about 75 pounds of pollen during the season (Fig. 13).

The following description of the manipulation of pollen from the time it is taken from the flower by a bee until it is stored within a cell in the comb is a summary of a comprehensive description presented by Casteel.[30] Describing bees collecting from sweet corn, which yields pollen in abundance, Casteel states that the bee alights on a tassel and crawls along the spike, clinging to the pendent anthers. The tongue and mandibles are used in licking and biting the anthers with the result that pollen grains stick to the mouthparts and become thoroughly moistened. Also, a considerable amount of pollen is dislodged from the anthers, and adheres to the hairy legs and body. The branched hairs of the bee are suited to retaining the pollen which is dry and powdery.

After the bee has crawled over a few flowers, she begins to brush the pollen from her head, body, and forward appendages and to transfer it to the posterior pair of legs (Fig. 14, left). This may be accomplished while she is resting on the flower, but more often while she hovers in the air before seeking additional pollen. The wet pollen is removed from the mouthparts by the forelegs. The dry pollen clinging to the hairs of the head region also is removed by the forelegs, and added to the pollen moistened by the mouth.

The second pair of legs collects free pollen from the thorax, more particularly from the ventral region, and receives the pollen collected by the first pair of legs. In taking pollen from the foreleg, the middle leg of the same side is extended forward and is either grasped by the

FIGURE 14. A flying bee (at left) showing the manner in which the forelegs and the middle legs manipulate the pollen. The forelegs are removing the pollen from the mouthparts and face. The middle leg of the right side is transferring the pollen upon its brush to the pollen combs of the left hind planta (basitarsus). A small amount of pollen already has been placed in the baskets.

A bee on the wing (center) showing the position of the middle legs when they touch and pat down the pollen masses. A very slight amount of pollen reaches the corbiculae through this movement.

A bee on the wing (at right) showing the manner in which the hind legs are held during the basket-loading process. Pollen is being scraped by the pecten spines of the right leg from the pollen combs of the left hind planta (basitarsus). (*Drawings after Casteel*)

flexed foreleg, or rubbed over it as the foreleg is bent downward and backward. Much sticky pollen is now assembled on the inner faces of the broad tarsal segments of the second pair of legs.

Pollen is transferred to the pollen baskets in at least two ways. A relatively small amount may reach the pollen baskets directly, as the middle legs sometimes are used to pat down the pollen accumulated there (Fig. 14, center). But by far the larger amount is first transferred onto the pollen combs on the inner surfaces of the hind legs. One of the middle legs and then the other alternately is grasped between the first tarsal segments of the hind legs and then drawn forward and upward, thus combing the pollen from the middle legs. The pollen now held in the combs of the hind basitarsus is next transferred to the pollen baskets on the outer surfaces of the hind tibiae.

With the two hind legs drawn up beneath the abdomen, the pollen combs of one leg are scraped by the pecten spines of the opposite one as the legs are moved up and down in a sort of pumping action (Fig. 14, right). Thus the pollen removed from one basitarsus is caught on the outside of the pecten comb of the opposite leg, the two combs scraping alternately. The planta is gently bent backward bringing its auricular surface into contact with the outer side of the pecten comb. By this action, the pollen mass is pushed along the slightly sloping lower end of the tibia, and thence out onto the surface of the pollen basket at its lower end (Fig. 15). Each new addition of pollen is pushed against the last and, simultaneously, the masses of pollen on both legs grow upward, a very small amount being added at each stroke.

Finally, each leg is loaded with a mass of pollen, held in place by the long recurved hairs of the elevated margins of the tibiae. If the loads are very large, these hairs are pushed outward and become partly embedded in the pollen, allowing the mass to project beyond the margins of the tibiae.

The bee accomplishes these brushing and combing actions so rapidly that the observer probably will fail to see some of the steps in the process without repeated observations.

When the bee has fully loaded her baskets she hurries to the hive. Some walk leisurely over the combs, while others appear to be greatly agitated, performing the characteristic "dance" which announces to the other fielders the existence of a source of pollen. Many pollen-bearing bees eagerly solicit food from other workers or take it from the cells.

Presently the pollen bearer will be seen to put her head into cell after cell as if looking for a suitable place to leave her load. For no apparent reason a certain cell will be selected which often is situated in the area immediately surrounding the brood, above and to the sides. The bee grasps one edge of the cell with her forelegs and arches her abdomen so that its posterior end rests on the opposite side of the cell. The hind legs are thrust into the cell and hang freely within it.

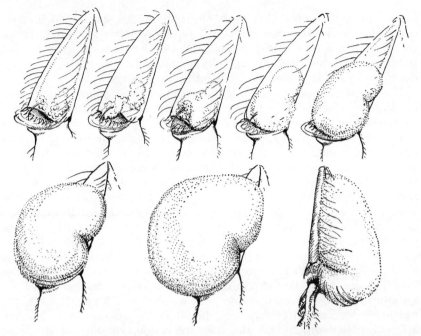

FIGURE 15. Progressive packing of the pollen load. A single hair pointing downwards on the floor of the corbicula is gradually pushed into a horizontal position, acting as a pin through the middle of the load. (*Drawing by Dorothy Hodges*)

The middle leg of each side is raised and its basitarsus is brought into contact with the upper end of the tibia of the hind leg. The middle leg now is pushed betwen the pollen mass and the corbicular surface so that the mass is pried outward and downward and falls into the cell. The hind legs now execute cleansing movements to remove any remaining bits of pollen.

After ridding herself of the two pellets, the bee usually leaves the cell without paying further attention to its contents. Parker[187] gave a good description of what happens next. "Shortly afterward another bee, usually a house or younger bee, comes to the cell and examines it and its contents. On finding the loose pellets, it begins working them to the base of the cell by a pushing motion of the head and with the closed mandibles, while the antennae are in contact with or near the pellets. When the pellets reach the base of the cell, where pollen may already be packed, they are broken up and incorporated into the mass, and the whole is smoothed off with the mandibles and tongue of the bee. During this process the bee often moistens the pellets with its tongue. The resultant mass takes on a more moist appearance and becomes darker." Casteel[30] shows that honey, nectar, or saliva is added to the mass of stored pollen, and that the sugar content of the latter is higher than that of pollen from the same plant species taken from corbiculae, indicating that the added liquid is nectar or honey. Pollen stored in this way is called "beebread." Velich[243] showed that in such tightly packed pollen lactic acid fermentation starts. Lactic acid produced by bacteria preserves beebread from spoilage.

Field trips of pollen gatherers are considerably shorter than those of nectar gatherers.[18,175,201] The number of flowers visited by pollen gatherers, the time spent in making a load, the number of trips per day, and the weight of pollen loads is variable, depending on the species and condition of the flowers, temperature, wind velocity, relative humidity, and possibly other factors. According to Vansell,[242] to make a load of pollen, a bee visited 84 flowers of pear trees, and 100 flowers of dandelion. Ribbands[201] gives only 8 to 32 flowers for dandelion. To make a full load of pollen a bee may spend 6 to 10 minutes[175] or as much as 187 minutes.[225] The number of trips per day may be 6 to 8[175] and up to 47,[201] the average probably being about 10 trips per day.[225] Using pollen traps, Hirschfelder[92] calculated that, during good gathering weather, between 50 to 54 thousand bees brought pollen into the hive daily. The weight of the pollen loads ranged from 12 mg. for elm to 29 mg. for hard maple fresh weight,[175] or 8.4 to 21.4 mg. dry weight.[152] Marked differences were found in the amount and the character of pollen brought to the hive by various colonies of the same apiary.[42,149,152,229] When visiting flowers in which both pollen and nectar are available, a considerable number of foragers take both. Of the total of more than 13,000 bees observed, 25 per cent were gathering pollen only, 58 per cent nectar only, while 17 per cent were collecting both on the same trip.[187] Rashad[197] observed that in the spring pollen was collected at temperatures as low as 46 to 52° F.; above 95° F. pollen collection was reduced. At wind velocity above 11 miles per hour the activity of pollen gatherers slackened, and ceased at 21 miles per hour. High relative humidity decreased pollen collection.

In spite of intensive grooming, pollen grains in large quantities still are found on the bodies of pollen collectors: from 10,000 to 25,000 pollen grains per bee[150] and even up to 250,000 to 3,000,000 grains.[226] The quantity of pollen carried on the body of the honey bee is larger than that of any other hairy insect.[150]

ACTIVITIES IN GATHERING, STORING, AND RIPENING NECTAR

Nectar is a sweet liquid secreted by plant nectaries usually located within the flowers, but in some species they are situated elsewhere. Nectar is the reward offered to bees and other insects in return for their indispensable services in cross-pollination. It is composed almost entirely of sugar and water, but the proportion of these ingredients varies widely.[13,45]

Sight and smell enable bees to locate sources of pollen and nectar. Technique employed in visiting flowers depends upon whether the forager seeks pollen only, nectar only, or both, and differs also with the type and size of flower. A fielder collecting nectar only, when in flight, carries her hind legs well apart, hanging at ease beside the abdomen. If the size of the flower permits, as in the apple blossom, the bee alights within the flower (Fig. 16). But if small, as in hard maple or sweet clover, she alights upon any convenient part of the plant that will support her weight. Upon alighting, the proboscis is brought forward from its inactive position beneath the "chin" and is inserted into that part of the flower where nectar accumulates. Typically this is at the bottom of the corolla, as in the florets of clover.

Bees are probably guided to nectaries by the difference in the odor of the nectaries and of the rest of the flower.[9] Observations on field bees at work suggest that a bee cannot tell whether there is nectar in a given blossom without inserting her proboscis. By this means, however, she very quickly determines its presence or absence. Ribbands[204] suggested that foragers may avoid flowers visited shortly before by other bees, recognizing the odor of a previous visitor still lingering on the flower. When nectar is found, the bee remains to suck until all nectar within reach of her proboscis has been taken up. In case none is found, the proboscis is withdrawn immediately and she passes on to another flower or floret without delay.

FIGURE 16. A worker bee sipping nectar from an apple blossom. Note the pollen in the basket on the hind leg clearly demonstrating that bees often collect both pollen and nectar on one trip. (*"Honey Bee," Encyclopaedia Britannica Films, Inc.*)

Owing to the difficulty of following a bee throughout the entire course of a trip, exact data on the number of visits to get a load are lacking, but calculations based upon incomplete data suggest that several hundred visits may be necessary to obtain a load of nectar from small flowers such as those of sweet clover.[201] To get a load of nectar, a bee visited 1,110 to 1,446 flowers of *Limnanthes*. Any species from which a load may be gathered in less than 100 visits should be a highly desirable honey plant; from it large loads could be secured in a relatively short time, thus permitting numerous trips per day for each fielder. Other things being equal, size of nectar load depends upon the abundance or scarcity of nectar, so the size of loads brought into the hive is a fair index of the intensity of the honeyflow.

The fielder loaded with nectar hustles through the entrance and into the hive. Once she has reached a place among fellow workers on the comb, her conduct depends largely upon conditions she has just encountered in the field. If the nectar flow is weak she walks about until she meets a house bee to which she gives part of her load. Occasionally she gives her entire load to a single house bee, but more often she distributes it among three or more. If the nectar source is bountiful, the loaded nectar gatherer usually performs the dance already referred to as a means of communication. At irregular intervals the dancer pauses long enough to pass out a taste of her booty to one or another of the near-by workers. But soon she meets a house bee to which she gives a considerable portion of her load. As they approach each other, the field bee opens her mandibles wide apart and forces a drop of nectar out over the upper surface of the proximal portion of her proboscis, the distal portion being folded back under the "chin." Assuming that the house bee approached is not already loaded to capacity, she stretches out her proboscis to full length and sips the proffered nectar from between the mandibles of the fielder (Fig. 17, A). While the nectar is being transferred in this manner, the antennae of both bees are in continual motion, and those of one bee are constantly striking those of the other. At the same time, the house bee may be seen to stroke the "cheeks" of the field bee with her forefeet as if eagerly coaxing for more.

Upon disposing of her load, a nectar gatherer sometimes leaves for the field immediately, but usually she pauses long enough to secure a small amount of food. In any case her departure is immediately preceded by certain characteristic maneuvers. She first gives her proboscis a swipe between her forefeet, then rubs her eyes, and often cleans her antennae. Then, with a quick look around, she takes her bearings, and forthwith starts for the field. Once aware of the significance of these preliminary maneuvers, one need never doubt the intention of a forager that so behaves. The entire process of disposing of her load often is accomplished in less time than it takes to describe it.[186]

Storing and Ripening. In the manufacture of honey from nectar, two distinct processes are involved: One brings about a chemical change in the sugar and the other results in a physical change whereby surplus water is eliminated. The sugar content of nectars is variable with various amounts of sucrose present in almost all nectars. Due to the action of the enzyme invertase, sucrose, a compound sugar of the nectar, is changed in the hive into two simple sugars, glucose and fructose. According to Park,[179] when the house bee has received her portion of the field bee's load, she meanders about the hive in search of a place where she will not be crowded. Here she usually takes up the characteristic position shown at B in Figure 17, having the long axis of her body in a perpendicular position with head uppermost. She at once begins to go through a series of operations which are illustrated diagrammatically at right in Figure 17.

Starting with the mouthparts at rest, as shown in the first diagram, the mandibles are opened wide and the whole proboscis is moved somewhat forward and downward. At the same time the distal portion of the proboscis is swung outward a little and a small droplet of nectar appears in the preoral cavity, as shown in the second diagram. The whole proboscis is then raised and retracted almost to the position of rest, but is depressed again, and is again raised as before, and so on. With each succeeding depression, the distal portion of the proboscis swings outward a little farther than before, but it makes only the beginning of a return to its position of rest.

Accompanying the second depression of the proboscis an increased amount of nectar appears in the preoral cavity, some of which begins to flow out over the upper surface of the proboscis. As the proboscis is raised and retracted the second time, the beginning of a drop of nectar usually may be seen in the angle formed by its two major portions, as shown in the third diagram. This droplet increases in size each time the proboscis is alternately depressed and raised until a maximum droplet is produced, as illustrated in the fifth diagram. The bee then draws the entire drop inside her body. As the nectar begins to be drawn in, the drop assumes a concave surface at its lower end, as shown at "a" in the sixth diagram. The distal portion of the proboscis is extended as at "b" until the drop has disappeared, when it is again folded back to the position of rest indicated at "c."

A house bee commonly spends from 5 to 10 seconds in carrying out the series of activities illustrated at right in Figure 17. This procedure is repeated with only brief pauses for about 20 minutes, although both of these intervals are subject to considerable variation. Upon the completion of this part of the ripening process, the bee searches out a cell in which to deposit the drop she has been concentrating. Into this cell she crawls, ventral side uppermost, as shown in Figure 17, C. This position is characteristic of a bee depositing unripe honey. If the

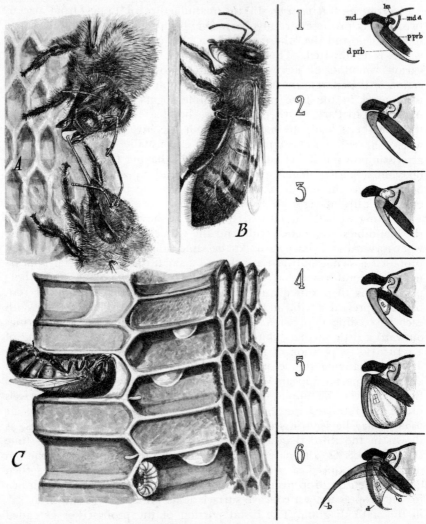

FIGURE 17. At left, drawing depicting three steps in the transfer of nectar from the field bee to the house bee, until the honey is stored in a cell. A. Nectar being transferred from a loaded nectar carrier (upper) to a house bee (lower). B. House bee ripening nectar. C. House bee depositing nectar or unripe honey. At right, diagrammatic sketches of the mouthparts of a bee engaged in transforming nectar into honey. See text for description of process. (*Drawing by A. R. Janson under the direction of O. W. Park*)

cell is empty, she enters until her mandibles touch the upper rear angle of the cell. The nectar is forced out over the dorsal surface of the folded proboscis, between the mandibles, which are held well apart. Then, using the mouthparts as a brush, and turning her head from side to side, she "paints" the unripe honey across the upper wall of the cell so that it runs down and occupies the rear portion of the cell. But if the cell already contains honey, she dips her mandibles into it and adds her drop directly without the "painting" process.

When nectar is coming in rapidly, and particularly if it is very thin, the house bees do not always stop to put it through the ripening process, but deposit it almost at once. Instead of depositing the entire load in a single cell, the house bee often distributes it by attaching a small drop to the roof of each of several cells as shown in three cells in Figure 17, C. The hanging drop exposes a maximum surface for evaporation.

Sometimes droplets thus "hung up to dry" may be seen in super combs, but usually they are to be found in greater abundance in cells within the brood nest, where the air is especially warm and doubtless dry. And they are fully as apt to be found in cells that contain eggs or young larvae (Fig. 17, C) as in empty ones. Later these droplets are collected and it is assumed that they are then put through the process of ripening by manipulation. Whether the nectar, or perhaps it should be called unripe honey, ordinarily is put through this phase of the ripening process repeatedly before it becomes fully ripened is a moot question, but it seems probable that some of it may be worked over several times. The procedure described above results in the rapid evaporation of water from the freshly gathered nectar.

The other important phase of the honey-ripening process, the inversion of sugar, may be expedited by this process also. Although it was found that the inversion process begins while the nectar is being gathered and carried to the hive, it is just possible that more invertase may be added by the house bee while thus manipulating the nectar prior to depositing it in the comb.

Since the change from nectar to honey takes place gradually over a period of many hours, Park[186] suggested that the term nectar be restricted to the sugary liquid secreted by nectaries up to the time this product is deposited in the comb, after which it may be referred to as unripe honey until its concentration approximates that of ripe honey.

Park[185] reported that nectar containing 45 per cent sugar when brought into the hive was found to contain approximately 60 per cent sugar when first deposited in the comb as unripe honey. Since in no case did it remain in the comb to exceed 30 minutes, direct evaporation after deposition in the cells would be wholly inadequate to account for any considerable part of the observed increase. It is believed, therefore, that this 15 per cent advance in concentration is attributable to the activities of house bees in manipulating the nectar by means of their mouthparts prior to depositing it in the comb.

Experiments to determine the rate of increase in concentration of nectar and of sugar solutions placed within the hive, but screened from the bees, were reported by Park.[181,182] Using nectars and sugar solutions of various initial concentrations, it was shown that the rate of advance in concentration was about twice as great in cells filled only one-fourth full as in those filled three-fourths full. When circumstances permit, bees make excellent use of this fact by spreading out the newly deposited unripe honey, placing only a small amount in each cell, later to be gathered up and stored compactly before being sealed.

From cells filled one-fourth full, evaporation takes place at a rate sufficient to advance a sugar solution to the concentration of ripe honey within 3 days if the initial concentration is not less than 20 per cent, and within 2 days if the initial concentration is not less than 30 per cent. In cells filled three-fourths full, the 60-per cent solution reached the concentration of ripe honey after $2\frac{3}{4}$ days, the 40-per cent solution after $3\frac{1}{4}$ days, while the 30- and 20-per cent solutions required $4\frac{1}{2}$ and 5 days, respectively.

Observations show that when adequate comb space is available, few cells are more than half-filled with unripe honey at the close of a day of heavy flow, and many contain less. If such combs are shaken, unripe honey flies out freely. Examination first thing the next morning reveals important changes. The widely scattered cells that contained small amounts the preceding evening now are empty, while comb areas that were not quite full are now completely filled, and cells in adjacent areas are fuller than they were. Scarcely a drop can be shaken from any comb. Surely no one can doubt the wisdom of providing an abundance of comb space to facilitate the ripening process. It is an important consideration in the maintenance of colony morale. While adequate comb space for evaporation may be provided readily enough in extracted honey production, its provision in comb honey production is a real problem because drawn combs cannot be used and also because crowded conditions usually are considered essential. This is one of the reasons why colony morale is so difficult to maintain under conditions of comb honey production.

For centuries there was the idea that honey bees eliminate from nectar a considerable part of its surplus water while in flight. This so-called excretion theory was based upon two observed and well-substantiated facts: That bees carrying thin sirup or nectar often expel droplets of clear liquid while in flight; and that honey newly deposited in the cells is more concentrated than the nectar from which it was produced.

Direct answers to these and related questions were obtained by Park[184] who compared the sugar concentration of the honey-stomach content of the bee entering the hive with that of nectar or sirup taken directly from the same source from which the bee obtained her load.

By means of these researches it was learned that the honey bee changes the concentration of nectar or sirup only very slightly while en route to the hive, and that the change is a decrease instead of an increase as had been assumed heretofore. The average decrease for Iowa nectars commonly gathered by the honey bee was about 1 per cent. For most practical purposes, it may be considered that the honey bee does not appreciably change the concentration of nectar while gathering a load and carrying it into the hive. Inasmuch as the results of this investigation have shown that no increase in sugar concentration occurs while the bee is en route to the hive with her load, it is certain that the expelled droplets bear no significant relation to the elimination of surplus water from nectar.

It is obvious that the rate at which water can be eliminated from fresh nectar and unripe honey is greatly influenced by a number of factors, other than those which have been discussed. These factors may be classified with respect to the beehive as external and internal, weather and honeyflow conditions, colony strength, amount and concentration of nectar brought in per unit of time, extent of available storage cells, temperature, humidity, movement of air within the hive, and, last but not least, ventilation.

The rate at which evaporation takes place in the beehive varies directly with the temperature and inversely with the humidity, other things being equal. Movement of air strictly within the hive speeds up evaporation in proportion to the rate of movement, but at an ever decreasing rate as the air approaches its point of saturation for moisture. It is for this reason that there is need for an almost continuous exchange of air between the interior of the hive and the outside atmosphere, so that drier air from the outside may replace the moisture-laden air within. Whenever humidity is higher outside than inside, the action is reversed, and honey in uncapped cells, in particular, absorbs moisture due to the hygroscopic properties of the sugars of honey.

Jessup[102] found that the relative humidity within the hive varied from a low of 20 to a high of 80 per cent; the lowest average recorded for one day was 30 per cent and the highest 65 per cent. In the brood nest the relative humidity is fairly constant, varying between 35 and 45 per cent.[21] In connection with his studies on humidity within the hive, Jessup[103] measured the rate at which bees by their fanning are able to ventilate the hive. The work was conducted during a good honeyflow and, as the mean temperature for the period was 81° F., ventilation was essential to cool the hive and carry off the large amounts of water vapor from the abundant supply of fresh nectar.

The rate of air travel varied from 189 to 312 feet per minute with a mean of 256 feet for a 24-hour period. The calculated loss of water during the 24-hour period was 5.7 pounds, or 50 per cent of the gross gain in weight. More than two-thirds of this loss occurred during the daytime. From calculations based on weighings of the hive with and without bees, it was found that there were nearly 15 pounds of bees in the colony. Only about 10 pounds of bees were in the hive at 2:15 when the colony was shaken from its combs. The other 5 pounds returned later from the fields with their loads. From this it was assumed that for each bee that worked in the field, two were needed at the hive to look after the brood and for storing and ripening of honey, besides numerous other home duties. The results of Jessup's investigation emphasize the need for providing ample ventilation, especially during hot weather.

Reinhardt[199] provided varying degrees of ventilation in four normal colonies, as nearly alike otherwise as possible. In each of these he determined the daily rate of change in the concentration of unripe honey which had been freshly stored by the bees in clean empty combs during the course of a single afternoon. These combs were enclosed in individual screen cages to prevent the bees from removing the unripe honey or depositing more, and each was placed between combs of ripening honey in a super of one of the colonies. Extra ventilation showed little, if any, effect on the rate of ripening during excessively hot and dry weather with only a moderate to light honeyflow. Special ventilation was most effective when temperatures averaged around 80° F., when atmospheric humidity was relatively high, and when nectar was being brought in at a good rate. These experiments show that there really is a honey-ripening problem and a need for adequate ventilation.

Park[183] determined that on sweet clover a nectar gatherer spends on an average from 27 to 45 minutes per trip depending on the nectar flow. The most frequent interval spent in the hive between field trips was 4 minutes. Ribbands,[201] however, observed bees working for 106 to 150 minutes to get a load of nectar from *Limnanthes* blossoms. Apparently the duration of a trip depends on the species of flowers visited. The highest number of trips per day by nectar carriers was 24, the average being between 7 and 13, depending on the condition of the honeyflow. This is in quite close agreement with the average of 10 trips per day given by Heberle[88] and Lundie.[151] Thus we can assume that 10 trips per day probably is as reliable a general average as can be derived from the data at hand.

Large loads of nectar were found to weigh on the average about 70 milligrams or 85 per cent of the weight of the bee which, in the case of Italians, was found to be approximately 82 mg.[175,178] Average loads of nectar during a honeyflow weighed about 40 mg., but the net weight of nectar delivered to the house bee from each collecting trip probably does not exceed 30 mg., because the field bee retains some nectar as fuel to provide power for her next outgoing trip. While the amount retained varies widely, 10 milligrams appears to be a fair estimate. Thus a nectar gatherer making 10 trips in a day would bring in about 300 mg. of nectar. Lundie[151] gives 25.3 mg. as an average load of nectar. But Gontarski[68] observed that the load taken by the bees increased with the concentration of the sugar solution. At 20-per cent concentration the load was 56.2 mg., at 80-per cent concentration, about 80 mg. The load also increased as the temperature rose, up to a certain point. Consequently, the loads will vary considerably with the temperature and the quality of nectar secreted by the flowers visited by bees.

ACTIVITIES IN GATHERING AND STORING WATER

Water has various uses in the beehive, some of which are highly essential. Water is required by the nurse bees whenever it becomes necessary to thin down ripe honey in the elaboration of larval food. When fresh nectar is available, it usually can be used in the preparation of brood food without dilution. Hence, we find that the activity of water carriers is most noticeable in early spring before the honeyflow begins, and that it practically ceases when nectar is coming into the hive in abundance, unless the nectar is highly concentrated. The extent to which water is needed by adult bees has not been determined. Workers or queens caged on candy take water with avidity when it is offered to them and live longer than do those that lack water. This would indicate that adult bees also need water.[250]

According to Park,[177] when a water carrier brings her load of water into the hive and climbs on the comb, she begins vigorous dancing. Usually there were from one to four or five bees following each dancer, and at more or less frequent intervals the dancer paused long enough to pass out a sip of water to one of the near-by workers. At times, a water carrier will dance for a full minute before offering to give up her load. Again, a water carrier enters and performs a brief dance; then proceeds rapidly to dispose of her load. Sometimes she gives a small sip to each of a half-dozen bees in quick succession before resuming her dance, and then, after dancing awhile, transfers the balance of her load to one or two bees. It is not unusual to see two or three bees being supplied all at one time by a single water carrier. In some instances, the entire load is disposed of to two or three individuals, while a single load may be distributed among as many as 18 workers.

Having disposed of her load, she begins preparation for her next field trip by securing a small amount of food from one or more of the house bees; or, failing in that, she goes to a cell and takes a sip of honey. But, before making the final start, she almost invariably gives her tongue a swipe between her front feet, rubs her eyes, and often cleans her antennae. Then she sets off for the exit in great haste. These preparations and the quick start are so characteristic that an observer soon is able to tell whether a bee is starting for the field, or whether she is just going to another part of the hive.

As the dancer proceeds with her maneuvers, every now and then, one of the interested followers may be seen to leave for the field, until by the time the dancer has disposed of her load, a dozen or more may have departed for the field to search out the source of supply. Sometimes these bees obtain a little food from other bees or from cells of honey before leaving. Upon their return with loads of water they also perform the dance. Park was the first to observe water carriers dancing upon their arrival into the hive.

In hot and dry weather, water may be deposited in the hive. Parks[188] noted that water is deposited on the top bars in small cell-like enclosures generally made of old wax and propolis. It is also deposited in every indentation in the cappings of brood, so that the comb looks as if it had been sprinkled with water and the droplets had spread out in the cavities over the points where the hexagons meet. Lindauer[141] observed that tiny droplets of water are also placed in the cells, especially in those containing eggs and larvae. This water is employed for the cooling effect derived from its evaporation, and also to provide a certain degree of humidity necessary to keep the larvae from drying out.[137] Water so deposited apparently is intended only for immediate use in the regulation of temperature and humidity in the hive. To produce the cooling effect through evaporation, the bees, besides water spreading, unfold their proboscises.[141] While they do so, a drop of liquid is drawn into a film by the movement. This process greatly speeds up the evaporation. Lindauer showed that even in the case of nectar handling[179] such movements, besides helping to concentrate the nectar, are also connected with temperature regulation in the hive. Lindauer also demonstrated that only when the hive is overheated (over 35° C., 95° F.) are the water carriers engaged in active dancing. As soon as the overheating ceased, there was less dancing and gradually the visiting at the watering place decreased.

In most localities there nevertheless appears to be an actual need for some means whereby the bees can store a larger supply of water sufficient to last the colony from one flight day to the next during the early spring brood-rearing period. Park,[177] using a one-frame observation hive, found that on such occasions the water was stored in the honey stomachs of numerous bees of the colony. As the water was transferred, the abdomen of the water carrier decreased in size while that of the "reservoir-bee" became distended. The reservoir-bees were quite inactive and occupied places surrounding the brood area, rather than within it. When a good flight day was followed by a period of several days without access to more water, the abdomens of these reservoir-bees became greatly reduced in size. Then, on the first subsequent flight day, it became evident that they were being refilled.

On several occasions, an observation colony was fed water that had been colored with a harmless and tasteless dye, so that the water was easily distinguished through the semitransparent abdomen of any bee that obtained it. The feeder was so placed that it was possible to mark every bee that took a load of water. Rarely did an unmarked bee appear at the water pan, but those already marked made repeated trips for more water. By evening, several hundred unmarked bees in the hive showed the presence of large loads of colored water. Tests revealed that these "reservoirs" were filled almost entirely with water. The following morning it was found that about 1,300 bees, or half the colony, were acting as reservoirs. Of 31 bees tested, the majority contained honey somewhat diluted. Thus it was found that, in storing water to last from one flight day to another in spring, the bees did not keep the water by itself longer than a few hours, but combined it with honey. A small amount of this diluted honey sometimes was deposited in or near the brood area, but most of it was retained in the honey stomachs of numerous reservoir-bees. This behavior explains most of those puzzling instances in which the beekeeper, in the early spring, finds what appears to be new honey recently deposited in cells within or near the brood nest, when he knows well enough that nectar is not yet available.

Park concluded that under hot, dry conditions, bees deposit water in the hive to regulate temperature, and doubtless humidity; under normal conditions in temperate climates, they store water by combining it with honey in the honey stomachs of numerous reservoir-bees.

There is a clear relationship between the amount and the stage of brood in the hive and the need for water. This need is especially acute when foragers cannot fly because of cold, rainy weather. Lindauer, by computing the number of water carriers which visited watering places every day and also the number of larvae being fed, estimated that about 5 water carriers worked through the day in order to supply 100 larvae. In a hive without brood the bees do not bother much about regulating the temperature. They avoid the hot places and then when there are no cool corners left in the hive, they cluster in front of the entrance.

According to Lindauer[141] a water carrier bases her activity simply and solely on how quickly the load of water is taken from her by the house bees. When the delivery was completed within 2 minutes, water carrying was continued without interruption. If it took 2 to 3 minutes, the bee continued to bring water, but for a short time remained idle in the hive. If getting rid of the water took longer, intervals between the foraging trips increased and water carrying stopped entirely when the bee could not dispose of her load of water within about 10 minutes. The dancing of water carriers also was closely related to the delivery time. When it took less than 40 seconds for the bee to get rid of her load, there was nearly always a dance. With the increase in delivery time, dancing decreased and completely stopped when the delivery time took more than 2 minutes. Lindauer[142] considers that "the delivery time itself gives only a rough indication of whether or not the bees in the hive are anxious to have water. If there is a great scarcity, one can see the water carrier being met at the entrance by 2 or 3 bees; these eagerly take the water from her, while carrier and receiver caress each other in a lively way with their antennae. If the need for water is only moderate, there is at best a single bee at the entrance, and the water carrier may have to walk around on the comb, offering her load of water, until eventually it is taken from her, accompanied by only slight caressing with the antennae. If the need for water has been completely met, the carrier will go offering her load in vain; now and again a house bee will taste from her glossal groove, but she immediately draws in her tongue, cleans it, and runs away; thus it may be a good many minutes before the honey stomach is emptied. It may be that the water carrier adjusts her behavior not so much according to delivery time as according to the greedy or indifferent behavior of the house bees."

Lindauer explains the question of what stimulates the first water carrier to bring water to the hive in the following way. The honey-stomach content of the house bees and that of the foragers is about the same due to food transmission. When a shortage of water appears in the hive and there is no new nectar coming, the content of the honey stomach becomes well concentrated. Soliciting for water may start in the hive and this may induce the water carriers to start their activity.

The mean time per trip of water carriers varies considerably. A bee commonly spends a minute or more in taking up a load of water, and it takes 1 minute for the bee to fly a quarter of a mile. Of all field trips recorded by Park,[183] 67 per cent were completed in 3 minutes or less, and 92 per cent in 10 minutes or less. The time spent in the hive was 2 to 3 minutes, as a rule, and seldom did one remain as long as 5 minutes. One hundred or more trips are made in a day by a single water carrier, but the average is probably nearer half this number. The weight of water a bee can carry at one load has not been determined. According to Park[180] a maximum load of water would be in the neighborhood of 50 milligrams and an ordinary load about 25 mg. The average amount of water brought into the hive in a day by one bee making 50 trips and carrying 25 mg. at a load would total about 1/400 of a pound. Thus, about 400 water carriers would be required to bring in daily a pound (a pint) of water. Data secured by Park in May, following a 1-day period of confinement, showed that between 6:30 and 11:15 a.m. three colonies on scales carried water to the extent of 3, 4, and 8 ounces. At this rate, the amount would average 10 ounces for the whole day, with a maximum of a full pint for the strongest colony.

It would appear that the daily water requirement for an average colony during spring brood rearing probably ranges in the neighborhood of a third of a pint under average conditions. For strong colonies and especially under hot, droughty conditions, it must sometimes amount to well over a pint if not indeed several pints per day.

ACTIVITIES OF BEES GATHERING PROPOLIS

Propolis is a sticky substance which honey bees use for covering the walls of their hives, fastening the frames, reinforcing the comb, plugging holes, filling crevices, narrowing the entrances, or sealing down larger animals which they cannot carry out of the hive. Such sealing, in the latter case, prevents all putrefaction since by the action of propolis all microbes which could cause decay are killed.[108]

Bees gather propolis from the buds of various plants. They also use pitch from coniferous trees, and other sticky material. The word "propolis" was derived from the Greek words "pro"—before, and "polis"—city. It originated because beekeepers of ancient times noted that bees would frequently build a rampart for the defense of the entrance to their "cities"—hives. Therefore, this material became known as "propolis"—before the city.

Buttel-Reepen[29] considers that the habit of propolizing is a very old one. It originated at the time when honey bees in the wilderness were in a constant fight with intruders. As an example, Buttel-Reepen mentions *Apis florea,* the little bee of Southeast Asia. These bees, in order to protect their combs which they had built at the end of a branch, covered the limb with a very sticky propolis so that ants, their constant enemy, could not reach the combs. Apparently the propolizing instinct is an absolute necessity for bees living in the wilderness.

At the time of Aristotle, the ancients were already aware of the presence of propolis in the hives of honey bees. The famous Roman naturalist, Pliny, in his *Historia naturalis* writes extensively about propolis. The renowned French naturalist, Huber,[96] described in detail his investigations on the collection and use of propolis in the hive. His is a most interesting series of observations and worth reading by every person interested in the life of bees.

The description of the process of propolis gathering differs somewhat in reports of various observers.[3,76,154,156,207] In general, a propolis gatherer, after finding the source of propolis, bites immediately into it with her mandibles and tries, with the assistance of the first pair of legs, to tear a little piece off. She may knead the latter a little between her mandibles and then, with the help of one of the second legs, she quickly transfers the piece of propolis to the pollen basket on the same side. She may do this in a sitting position or in flight. Next the bee places a piece of propolis in the pollen basket on the other side. The clumps of propolis are patted frequently with the second leg to put them in their proper shape. Such alternate loading continues until both baskets are fully loaded. To make a load, the bee has to work from a quarter of an hour to an hour, depending on the weather. She may even interrupt loading to fly home for some food.

When such a bee enters the hive with her load of propolis, she immediately runs to the place where the propolis is needed and there remains quiet. Another worker bee approaches, bites at the propolis and pulls until she succeeds in tearing off a little piece. Then she runs directly to the place where the propolis is to be applied and presses it firmly into place. While applying propolis, the "cementing bee" may work some wax into it. The propolis carrier immediately makes the load smooth again by patting. She may be freed of her load in the course of an hour, or several hours, depending on the need for propolis in the hive.

The bees gathering propolis never deposit their own loads. When freed of their load, they immediately fly back for more. They start working about 10:00 a.m. and discontinue their work about 4:00 p.m. On a very hot day, they may start working sooner and continue working later.

According to Meyer,[156] two types of bees do propolizing in the hive, "cementing bees in the strict sense" and "casual workers." The former do propolizing only; the latter help in other ways besides working with propolis. The "cementing bees" also bring propolis into the hive. Although all propolis gatherers were observed doing cementing work, not all cementing bees were seen bringing propolis into the hive. Propolis gatherers remain faithful to their work, but there are very few of them in each colony. Bees of foraging age do this work.

Offered a chance, at the time of dearth of nectar, propolis gatherers can easily be turned into nectar foragers and back again into propolis gatherers. Meyer observed few propolis gatherers dancing the recruiting dance after bringing a load into the hive. Some of the hive bees followed the dancer but none of them were mobilized for the propolis-gathering activity.

Contrary to described observations, Küstenmacher[117] and Philipp[192] were of the opinion that there are different kinds of propolis. According to Philipp, there is the "true" propolis and the "extraneous" propolis, the latter brought from outside the hive. The "true" propolis is produced whenever bees eat pollen. The covers of the pollen grains contain some quantity of resinous material—balm. During the process of digestion, balm is loosened from the pollen grains, regurgitated and applied wherever needed, especially to cover the inside walls of the cells of the brood combs before each new brood is reared. The "extraneous" propolis is used to seal the cracks, fasten the frames, and for other purposes. Haydak[84] critically examined Philipp's theory and concluded that "unless further proof is supplied, this theory on the origin of propolis appears to be untenable."

ACTIVITIES CONNECTED WITH SWARMING

Swarming is the bees' way of reproduction by colonies. The ability to swarm makes it possible for bees to maintain their kind in the world. By swarming, bees increase the number of colonies already existing and replace those that perish from adverse living conditions. By fitting together all pieces of information that we now have available in the beekeeping literature, we can obtain a clearer picture of what goes on in the hive in connection with the phenomenon of swarming.

Early in the season the bees are found in a relatively compact cluster in the hive. As the season advances, the bees begin to occupy more and more space. At any given temperature there is a certain number of bees per unit area present on the brood combs. Because the young bees have a tendency to seek and to remain in the warmest place, the newly emerged bees remain on the comb and the older bees have to move out. Experiments of Taranov[231] with marked bees have shown that bees up to 3 days of age remain on the brood combs, while 4- to 10-day-old bees are displaced. However, these older bees do not move far, but remain on the combs adjacent to the brood area where they begin to clean cells.

When the queen comes to such a comb, she starts to lay immediately and the young displaced bees begin to feed her and the larvae that subsequently appear. Therefore, the egg-laying activity of the queen is governed by the displaced nurse bees since she can lay only as many eggs as there are cells prepared by the nurse bees.

According to Taranov and Ivanova,[234] in a normal colony the queen's retinue consists of 10 to 12 nurse bees surrounding the queen in a more or less closed circle, leaving some space between them and the queen. They constantly touch the queen, especially her abdomen, sometimes licking it. If the queen wanders to the part of the hive where there are no nurse bees, the old bees do not pay any attention to her. During intensive laying, the rest periods of the queen last 10 to 15 minutes, at which time she receives food from five to seven bees.

During the swarming season, before the queen cells are started, there is an increased activity in egg laying. In one case the queen deposited 62 eggs in 45 minutes, i.e. 1,968 eggs per day. The circle around the queen is formed in close proximity to the queen and the bees in the circle become excited. They constantly and persistently offer food to the queen, even pushing their heads under the head and thorax of the queen. Apparently the bees are attempting to force the queen to accept food but she refuses. Sometimes the queen, while resting, places her head inside a cell as if trying to escape from the surrounding bees. The latter, however, increase in number, and force the queen to start egg laying. At that period the queen covers large distances (in the course of 17 minutes—284 cm. (112 inches), i.e. 240 m. (787 feet) per day). During this search for empty cells the queen loses a large number of eggs (one lost 30 eggs during 45 minutes). The queen retinue increases to 22 or more bees which are constantly offering food to the queen. Those in front of the queen sometimes jump on top of her and perform the DVAV dance lasting 3 to 4 seconds. The queen examines all the queen cups and lays eggs in them.

After the eggs in the queen cups hatch, the nurse bees supply the larvae with an abundance of food. The number of bees feeding the queen diminishes and sometimes they even refuse to feed her. In spite of this, the queen may continue to lay a few eggs each day up to and including the day of swarming. Because of this decrease in feeding, the abdomen of the queen diminishes in size; consequently she becomes lighter. The decrease in egg laying results in a further increase of the number of jobless and displaced nurse bees. They fill all the available space in the hive, sometimes even hanging outside. Taranov calls them the "active swarm bees" because these are the bees that leave with the swarm.

According to Allen,[4] about a week before the swarm issues the queen may be pushed about and treated roughly. There appears to be no particular desire to force her in any definite direction, but the tendency seems to be to keep her moving. Sometimes workers even bite at her legs if she stops moving.

The queen shows more interest in the queen cells, laying eggs in them or inspecting those with larvae without showing any animosity toward them. However, sometimes she may try to destroy some of the unsealed queen cells with larvae in them. The bees do not interfere with these visits.

The old queen may start "piping." Apparently contact with queen cells has some connection with "piping" because on one occasion, about an hour before the swarm left, the old queen "piped" 25 times during 25 minutes; on 14 occasions she was on a queen cell, 6 times she was near one, and the remaining 5 times she was elsewhere on the comb.

Several days before swarming, an abnormal number of bees may be seen sitting quietly on the bottom of the combs. According to Lindauer,[143] at this time the searchers may begin to look for a new nesting place. The searchers start doing this mainly, if not exclusively, because of the overabundance of sealed brood, pollen, and honey in the mother hive, and because the hive bees refuse to take the loads of nectar from the field bees. Thus the unemployed field bees who know the locality become searchers for a new home. The searchers perform the wag-tail dance in the hive indicating the direction and the distance to the prospective new site. The nest searchers, contrary to the food gatherers, do not interrupt the dance but continue dancing for hours, or even days, changing the direction of their dance according to the change in the position of the sun.

Shortly before the swarm departs, the bees fill themselves with honey. This is important. Taranov[232] shook the bees and the queen from a colony prepared to swarm into a nucleus which was then placed on a new stand. Only when the bees had their honey stomachs full, did 37 to 51 per cent of them remain with the queen. If such shaking was done when the bees had their honey stomachs empty, almost all of them returned to the original hive, except for a few hundred which remained with the queen. Apparently it is only when the swarm bees have their stomachs full of honey that they forget their old location.

To incite 20,000 to 30,000 bees quickly to swarm, the searchers perform a special characteristic "whir dance."[143] Highly excited and nervous, they force their way among the bees in zigzag running steps, vibrating their abdomens and producing a perceptible whir with their wings. One or two bees start this "whir dance" but after a minute there are dozens; the number of whirring bees increases until the whole hive is in tumult. By this time the queen is undoubtedly pushed by one or two bees at a time.[4,234] Some queens appear to be trying to resist, even staggering while doing this. When the swarm is leaving, the queen may still be trying to run away from the bees which obviously attempt to force her out.

The number of bees going out with the swarm (Fig. 18) may be from about half to 90 per cent of the parent colony. According to the majority of observers,[23,155] the age of bees in a prime swarm is mostly from 4 to 23 days, although bees of all ages can be found in a swarm.

FIGURE 18. A populous swarm of bees settled on a limb of a tree. (*Photo by O. W. Park*)

Meyer[155] found that when a swarm settles it consists of two distinct parts: an outside shell about three bees thick, quite compact; and the inner, loose part, consisting of chains which are connected with the shell in many places. The shell gives protection to the swarm against outside influences and provides the swarm with necessary mechanical strength. In the shell there is a distinct entrance to the inside of the cluster.

There is a division of labor in the swarm cluster. The searchers are all over 21 days old; the bees in the shell are 18 to 21 days of age; and those inside the cluster are house bees, up to the age of 18 days. The bees in the shell are constantly changing places; during a 10-minute period two-thirds of the surface bees changed places with those of the inside portion of the shell.

According to Lindauer,[143] after the swarm is settled the searchers dance, doing "wag-tail" runs in various directions on the surface of the shell, because they usually come from different prospective nesting places. From all the available places, the searchers will select the best one. They prefer a wooden hive over a straw skep, a wind protected location over one not protected, and an abode far away rather than close, within certain limits. Also, roominess, exposure to sun's rays, and infestation with ants play roles in the selection of a prospective nesting place. The most important factor is protection from wind.

The better the nesting place, the more lively is the dance of the searchers. Inferior places evoke a less vigorous dance, and the bees dancing it observe the dances of the searchers from a better place, inspect the latter and, upon returning, announce this place to the bees in the cluster.

The searchers also make repeated visits to the future nesting place, to check up on the conditions. They may even stop "advertising" the place if the conditions turn unfavorable. When there are two equally good places, two strong groups are dancing. If the bees do not come to an "understanding," the cluster may divide and start flying, but after a short time the parts come together again and the searchers may try to "agree" again. If this becomes impossible, then the swarm builds its nest where it has settled.

When the searchers "agree" on the place, they start the "whir dance," boring their way within the cluster. One can hear a very loud humming inside the cluster, the bees start to clean themselves, and start running to and fro, creating a tumult. When the excited running reaches its highest point, 5 to 10 bees simultaneously fly out from the cluster, hundreds follow and in a few seconds the whole cluster disbands. It appears that the swarm is led by about 100 bees which fly quickly toward the new nesting place, while the bulk of the swarm proceeds at a slower pace. The "leading bees" return, fly at the border of the swarm, and then "shoot" quickly to the fore. The searchers perform the "whir dance" also on the new location after the swarm starts to occupy it. The significance of this dance is not yet known.

Several theories are advanced for explanation of the swarming behavior of bees.[224] Probably both the internal and the external factors confronting the colony, coupled with the hereditary and the physiological makeup of its members, play an important part in swarming preparations.[87]

ACTIVITIES OF QUEENLESS BEES

Honey bees are social insects and stray workers tend to join together to form a cluster, even in the absence of a queen. Lecomte[121] noted that when he placed worker bees in a darkened box, they always tended to aggregate. When 75 or more were present, they always formed a cluster; with 50 bees it was formed in only half of the cases. When a smaller number was present, bees segregated in small groups of 5 or 10 individuals. Lecomte[122] concluded that the sense of smell and the vibrations caused by the movements of bees are the stimuli for cluster formation. Free and Butler,[49] who studied this question further, concluded that the stimuli of scent, vibration, heat produced by the bees in the cluster, and sight can each induce individual bees to join the cluster, provided they are of sufficient magnitude. There is also a division of labor in such a small cluster, usually a few older bees starting foraging for the community.[27,159]

When a normal colony becomes queenless, bees start building queen cells. There is no difference in the division of labor between the queenright and the queenless colonies, but the latter are more aggressive and irritable and the number of guards is higher.[94] The ancients knew that when a colony loses its queen there is lack of order in the hive, and that "drones are reared in worker cells."[110] Now we know that this happens because of the appearance of laying workers in such colonies. According to Gontarski,[69] the first observations on laying workers were made in 1770 by von Riehm, and his observations were confirmed by Huber in 1788. Laying workers can also be found in normal queenright colonies, especially during the swarming season. Tuenin[240] and Perepelova[189] demonstrated that workers with developed ovaries (anatomical laying workers) were present in from 20 to 70 per cent of colonies which showed signs of swarming. Koptev[113] found that such workers are present during the whole season in normal colonies, especially in those having poor queens. Normal colonies at the end of the honeyflow had 7 to 45 per cent anatomical laying workers. When the colony becomes hopelessly queenless such workers begin to lay eggs.

In summarizing the data presented by various investigators[69,172] we can obtain the following picture of the activities of laying workers. As a real queen does, a laying worker inspects the cell by dipping the head and the thorax into it. Sometimes she even cleans the cell before laying. While laying, the worker gets her abdomen more or less deeply into the cell; sometimes also a part of the thorax is immersed into the cell. In most cases she has her back, sometimes her side, toward the lower wall of the cell. She was never observed depositing her eggs with the ventral side of her body downward. During her egg laying a circle of bees sometimes is formed around her, but the circle is considerably poorer and less stable than in the case of the queen. The bees in this entourage do not pay the same attention to the laying worker as they do to the queen. Other laying workers may be present in the circle. Such a worker lays only one egg to a cell. Other eggs in the same cell are laid by other workers. The time a laying worker spends in laying varies from 17 to 261 seconds, an average of 50 to 70 seconds. The behavior of the laying workers toward other bees is normal. But with the beginning of drone rearing, other workers show hostility toward them, the latter being mauled, pulled, and driven through the hive.[94,216] Usually the laying worker makes no resistance, shows submissive behavior, strops her tongue characteristically, and tries to escape from the aggressiveness when the mauling becomes too severe.

Sometimes the so-called "false queen" may be observed in a queenless colony.[217] She is a laying worker which is treated like a queen, and has a circle of bees around her even when resting. Such "false queens" are normal workers externally except for a slightly extended and polished abdomen. Their movements become markedly slow as in the true queen, and their life consists only of alternating between egg laying, resting, and moving. Bees may show an aggressive behavior toward the "false queen" as they do toward normal laying workers.

Sakagami[218] and Hoffmann[94] reported that in a colony with laying workers, division of labor resembles that of normal colonies. The division of labor between the laying workers and other workers in the colony could not be established. Laying workers behaved like normal worker bees; besides laying eggs they participated in all other tasks of the hive, eating pollen and honey, and flying out. Older bees in a queenless hive participated in both brood rearing and foraging activities.

The presence of brood in queenless colonies has an inhibitory effect on the development of ovaries in workers.[160] Building activity in a queenless hive is also impaired. Darchen[34] observed that 50 bees, 6 days old, built comb in the presence of a mated or a virgin queen; in the presence of a dead one, 200 bees could also build combs. But 10,000 queenless bees are necessary to assume the same task, while 5,000 bees in the presence of laying workers can build combs. That the absence of a queen has a depressing effect upon comb-building activity was also shown by Genrikh.[67] The drones are expelled from a laying-worker colony in the same way as in normal colonies.[94]

The queen has a great attraction for bees. Any group of queenless bees has a very strong urge to join any queenright colony of which its members become aware.[26] Queenless bees will sometimes even desert young brood to join a group of bees with a queen.[22] According to

Genrikh,[67] removal of the queen resulted in the disturbance of the hive and flight activities of bees in four experimental colonies as compared with the control colonies. The flight intensity diminished by 77 per cent, the number of bees coming in with loads of pollen by 73 per cent, the weight of pollen loads by 50 per cent, the filling of the honey stomach by 62 per cent, nectar income by 81 per cent, and rapidity of drawing out foundation by 73 per cent. The counts were made 3 days before queen removal and 3 days afterwards. The counts before removal of the queen were the same in both control and experimental colonies. The maximal diminution of activities was at the beginning of queen cell building; afterwards it gradually returned to normal.

Gontarski[69] observed that in laying-worker colonies bees stored honey and pollen below the brood and not above the brood as they do in normal colonies. When a queen was introduced, the method of storage became normal. According to Haydak,[86] in hopelessly queenless colonies the nurse bees do not recognize the sex of larvae, as they do in queenright colonies, and they feed the drone larvae as if they were female larvae. Apparently the queen has considerable influence on the orderly life processes in the colony.

ACTIVITIES OF BEES IN WINTER

Temperature exerts an important influence upon the activities of the honey bee. Rarely does a honey bee perform any useful work at temperatures below 50° or above 100° F. At temperatures closely approaching 100° or above, bees seldom go to the field but remain idle within the hive or cluster listlessly on the outside. A single inactive bee soon loses the ability to fly at 50° and at temperatures below 45° soon loses all power of motion. But the honey-bee colony possesses the ability to maintain and regulate its own temperature to a remarkable degree; in an active brood nest every bee acts as a thermostat. When the temperature in the brood area falls below 96° F., the heating process starts in the thoraces of bees to increase the temperature to the normal level. In winter cluster the temperature of the thoraces of bees oscillates between 68° F. and 96° F., independently of the outside temperature. Normally it stays around 84° F.

There is only a small area in the winter cluster where the bees maintain the temperature at 96° F. by keeping the temperature of their thoraces at this level. There is no rhythmicity in heating the cluster. Bees wander at irregular intervals in the cluster, drink honey, and after this the heating activity starts. A single bee having enough food can maintain considerably higher temperatures than her surroundings.[37] Bees are able to produce heat during long periods without any muscular movements.[120]

When the temperature immediately surrounding the bees falls to 57° F. or lower, they form a cluster.[193] The winter cluster when first formed is usually located in the lower part of the hive, often near the front. Throughout the course of the winter it moves upward and to the rear of the hive. By spring the cluster in a 2-story hive is found most often in the upper story. It has been noticed, however, that when the cluster was formed in the fall a part of it, consisting of 100 to 200 bees, always protruded over the end bars of the frames.[81] This "connective cluster" was found to be the seat of communication between the interspaces. The position of the "connective cluster" shifted with the movement of the main cluster. When the bees began to move toward the rear of the hive, the connective cluster on the end bars of the frames disappeared and simultaneously a new one was formed on the top bars of the frames.

At relatively warm temperatures the bees on the surface of the connective cluster are almost motionless excepting that they sometimes quickly move their wings. Their wings are somewhat extended so that they overlap each other forming a kind of cover as if preventing the escape of heat. At low temperatures the bees perform frequent and quick movements with their wings, as if shaking them; the lower the temperature the more often they move their wings. During the severe cold the bees on the surface of the cluster bury their heads and thoraces inside the cluster so that only the abdomens are visible, and at the same time they move their abdomens with screwlike motions. When at such times one listens at the entrance, using a special hearing device resembling a physician's stethoscope, one can hear screaky noises suggestive of a procession of carts with unoiled axles. As soon as it becomes warmer the bees spread out again. The temperature inside the hive may be quite low. On one occasion, when the outside temperature was $-14.5°$ F., a thermometer located 1 inch from the side of the cluster showed $17°$ F. The "connective cluster" also disappears during extremely cold weather, the bees contracting inside the interspaces.

The "communicative cluster" plays an important part in the life of bees in winter. Quite often one can see single bees marching from one interspace to another. There are openings toward the inside of the cluster and frequently, especially during the morning, a bee or two can be seen ventilating on the edges of such openings. The moisture from the air of the cluster condenses on the wall of the hive and sometimes is utilized by the bees for drinking. During the winter the bees scrub the bars with "rocking movements." Sometimes they clean each other. At this time they perform a "grooming dance."

There are losses of bees during the winter; bees may die from various causes[74]—those that left the cluster because of need of defecation (nosema, dysentery); bees which somehow remained behind on the combs when the cluster contracted; or those which left the cluster in search of water or for some other cause. These losses in some cases may be extremely heavy. For additional information, see Chapter XIII, "The Overwintering of Productive Colonies."

ACTIVITIES OF THE QUEEN*

Upon emergence from the queen cell, a virgin queen is very active and, if not prevented by the workers, will seek to destroy all other queen cells present in the hive. With her powerful jaws she makes an opening in the side wall of the cell and, inserting her abdomen into the opening, she stings her rival to death. The bees dispose of the carcass and destroy the queen cell. In swarming time the virgin is prevented from destroying the queen cells by the bees that cluster around them. The virgin from time to time stops her running and, clinging to the comb, produces a sharp, high note resembling "tee-tee-tee-tee." The bases of her wings tremble at that time.[83] If one listens carefully, and usually the bees are then extremely quiet, one can hear another type of voice resembling "quahk-quahk-quahk"—the answers of the virgins confined in the queen cells. Langstroth was probably right remarking that "the difference in their voices being, probably, due to the confinement of the latter (the virgins) in the cells." In this case the virgin which emerges first usually leaves the hive with the second swarm or "after-swarm." If another virgin emerges while the first one is still in the hive, then a fight ensues in which one of the queens is killed.

Hammann[71] observed the behavior of bees and virgins in 16 glass observation hives in which the bees reared emergency queens after the old queen was removed. The first few hours after emergence, the workers pay no attention to the virgin. From noon of the 1st day, she is licked and touched by the workers who also perform certain movements on or around her, such as "shaking" (DVAV), rocking movements (a bee stands on her two hind pairs of legs and, moving the whole body forward, pushes the virgin with her head and front legs, sometimes with her front legs only or with open mandibles). The workers may pull the virgin by her wings or legs, and cling to her or roll her over. The queen either takes this without resistance or she may start "piping" which immediately stops all attacks, or she runs away. In the latter case the bees chase her throughout the hive. From the 3d day on the virgin begins to open her posterior end while the bees touch her with their antennae, lick her, or stroke her with their forelegs. At this time the queen begins to retaliate the assaults by raising her body the same way the guard bees do, beating down on the assaulting bee with her thorax and forelegs, or by performing the same rocking movements as the workers. One can observe that the queen becomes more agile every day and her endurance increases.

---

*The reader also is referred to "The Virgin Queen" in Chapter III for descriptions of the behavior of queens.

The first flight occurs usually on the 5th or 6th day. The queen excitedly runs over the combs for 5 to 10 minutes, whirring her wings. During previous periods, the virgin stayed away from the light, but now she suddenly becomes phototactic and rushes toward the entrance. The bees pay no attention to her at first, but then the guards follow her and push her with their heads. In about 10 minutes the virgin returns from her orientation flight. After each flight, the attacks on her lessen but increase again before the virgin starts on her next flight. Such attacks are not stopped until the queen starts laying.

Ruttner,[209] however, states that during the first 5 days the virgin seems to have no relations with workers. This may be because Ruttner used small colonies consisting of a comb of emerging brood, a food comb with young bees adhering to it, and a building frame to which a ripe queen cell was attached.

There may be a difference in behavior toward the queen in various colonies of bees. Allen,[7] from her studies of the behavior of the queen and her attendants, concluded that "perhaps the most notable feature of the results was the variability exhibited by the individuals, which may indicate that the behavior of workers toward the queen is very plastic and closely related to the needs of the colony at the time."

Ruttner[209] observed that about 5 days after emergence the virgin makes convulsive movements with her abdomen and at the same time the abdominal orifice opens for several seconds, signifying that the virgin is sexually mature. In the midday hours of the day of mating the number of excited workers around the queen increases. Some of them run toward the entrance and one can often see a continuous line of bees between the virgin and the entrance. Finally a group of bees fanning, with their scent glands exposed, gathers in front of the entrance and normal flying and foraging almost ceases.

The virgin appears at the entrance accompanied, and often driven there, by several workers. If for some reason the queen is hesitant to fly, workers will prevent the queen's return into the hive and try to force her to flight. So the mating of the queen is not only an affair between the queen and the drone, but the whole colony participates in the event.

Ruttner[210] considers that the development of the desire to mate in the virgin is not innate but is induced by the workers through their aggressive behavior and specific feeding. Hammann[71] thinks that the attacks of bees on the virgin improve her physical efficiency and, consequently, speed her readiness to flight. By experiments Hammann proved that, when the virgin was assaulted very vigorously, she flew out for the first time much sooner; when she was not assaulted she did not fly at all. Colonies vigorously attacking their virgins always contained a high percentage of anatomical laying workers. There seems to be a relation between the aggressiveness of the workers toward the virgin and ovary development in the workers. There is no direct relation, however, since in one colony which did not receive any pollen (so that the ovaries of the workers could not develop) the bees were attacking the virgin just as strongly as in normal colonies.

There is a difference of opinion concerning the relative position of the queen and drone during the act of mating. Some earlier observers claimed that the queen and the drone "appeared to meet face to face."[15]

The majority of observers agree that one insect mounts the other.[12,118,246] Gary,[66] after observing many matings, gives the following description of this event: The drone lights on the back of the abdomen of the queen, grasping her with all six legs, his head extending over her thorax. The abdomen of the drone curls under and upwards. If the queen opens for him, the penis everts and ejaculation occurs very rapidly. If the queen fails to open, the drone may remain in this position for 3 to 4 minutes or until another drone knocks him off. As soon as ejaculation occurs, the drone releases his hold on the queen and topples over backwards, and 2 to 3 seconds later a distinct "pop" is heard as the two separate. If this explosion fails to occur, they may fall to the ground where they separate in upwards to 10 minutes. Drones are strong fliers and are capable of carrying the queen along with them in flight. In their mating efforts the drones are very aggressive. One drone will knock another from the queen's back, or even push him aside at the completion of his act. Gary has observed a queen mate 11 times, one right after the other.

Oertel[170] observing flights of 60 virgins found that the duration of nonmating flights ranged from 2 to 30 minutes, and that of mating flights from 5 to 30 minutes. Virgin queens frequently mated on the first flight. Thirty-two of 54 virgins mated in 8 to 9 days after emergence, 16 from 6 to 7 days, and the remainder in 10 to 13 days.

When the queen returns from a mating flight she is continuously followed by the excited workers which touch her and lick her mating sign,* or may pull it out with their mandibles. The queen makes convulsive contractions of her abdomen which could be observed in the interval of about 1 minute. After removal of the mating sign the vaginal orifice remains open. The queen may fly out on another mating flight scarcely 10 minutes after returning from the prior one. It is known that the virgin may mate several times during the same nuptial flight.[230,235,251] The queen may mate with 7 to 10 drones and at distances up to 10 miles from the apiary.[194,195]

Triasko[236] considers that, during the multiple matings, the mating and separation of the queen and drone occurs very quickly—time just sufficient for the eversion of the penis. At the separation there is no

---

*Remains of part of the penis of the drone and the coagulated mucus from his mucous gland.

tearing off of the penis or its parts—only the exfoliation of the chitinous plates from the wall of the bulb without injury to the latter. Quick mating and separation enables the queen to mate several times during a single mating flight. Before the second and subsequent matings, the mating sign is removed from the sting chamber of the queen by being glued to the base of the penis of the next drone. At these successive matings the sting chamber of the virgin remains open. Only at the last mating does the queen close the chamber, thus cutting off the bulb of the penis, and returns to the hive with a mating sign.[1]

After mating the oviducts are filled with sperm. By bending her abdomen the queen causes the valve fold partially to close the vaginal passage. The muscles of the oviducts begin to contract and the sperm is squeezed into the spermatheca, but only a part of it enters the spermatheca; the greater part is pushed out past the fold, into the vagina and out in the form of thin threads which the bees carry away from the hive.[209]

Mating flights take place only between 12 noon and 5:00 p.m., with the greatest frequency between 2:00 and 4:00 p.m. The better the weather and the greater the number of drones, the better is the chance for mating. Mating almost always takes place at temperatures higher than 20° C. (68° F.). Wind velocity of 12 to 17 m.p.h. greatly reduces the number of matings; at 17 to 23 m.p.h. no matings were observed. Queens mating during unfavorable weather received little sperm and were short-lived, usually superseded.[209] When there was bad weather or lack of drones, there could be 5-, 9-, 15- or even 24-day intervals between the first and the last mating flights.[1]

On the 2d to 4th day after mating the queen usually starts egg laying. However, she may commence laying as early as 14 hours after successful multiple mating. Before laying an egg the queen walks over the comb and places her head in the cell as if inspecting whether it is ready for oviposition. Then she withdraws her head, curves her body and quickly pushes the abdomen into the cell. In a few seconds she turns to the right or to the left and withdraws the abdomen out of the cell. The egg-laying process (the time between the instant the abdomen is pushed into the cell and the subsequent movement outward) takes approximately 9 to 12 seconds. After laying for a period of time the queen rests.

There are various estimates as to the number of eggs a queen can lay daily. Nolan[169] made a thorough investigation of the brood-rearing cycle of the honey bee. He took weekly photographs of every frame containing sealed brood and made counts from the negatives, obtaining an equivalent of 53 individual seasonal brood-rearing records. The highest daily average during any 12-day period was found to be 1,587 eggs. Most of the queens had a lower average than that. A good queen in a strong colony may lay up to and over 200,000 eggs a year. Chauvin[32] found that egg laying is independent of external factors; only lack of nutrition will stop egg laying. There is a spontaneous stoppage of egg laying in the fall which nutrition cannot change and this could be attributed to diapause.

It is accepted that a mated and laying queen never leaves the hive unless with the swarm. There are, however, several reliable observations of such queens actually flying out of the hive at other times than during swarming.[83]

After studying the activities of the bees in a colony, it would appear that the workers are actually masters of the hive. They can produce either workers or queens from fertilized eggs; they actively participate in the events of mating and of swarming, often pushing and forcing the queen out of the hive. Actually, some observers have been inclined to think that there are so-called "control bees" who govern the life in the colony. The queen, in the minds of beekeepers, became just an egg-laying machine that had very little to do with influencing the course of events in the colony.

However, when we consider the reaction of bees when their queen is lost, the attention paid to the queen in the brood nest, and the eagerness with which the bees try to obtain queen substance, we will realize that the queen is not only an egg-laying machine. She is a very important cog in the machinery which holds the colony together and, indirectly, through the queen substance, influences the most important life activities for the preservation of the continued existence of the colony—supersedure, swarming, and emergency queen-cell building.

ACTIVITIES OF DRONES

After biting his way out of the cell, the drone remains most of the time on the comb in the brood nest. According to Free,[40] the drones usually remain stationary on the comb, often in the company of other drones. These periods of rest are broken by periods of movement over the comb, usually lasting 2 minutes or less. Orösi-Pál[174] observed that the workers feed drones in much the same way as they do each other, or their queen. He also described an unusual behavior of a drone which, while being fed by a worker, was standing on four legs and kept tapping the feeding worker's head from right and left with his forelegs. Free[40] found that during the first days of their lives drones are fed by workers. Drones 1 day old or less are not fed as much as those 2 to 5 days old. This was probably because very young drones were unable to beg for food as effectively as the older ones, and were sometimes seen begging from the abdomen of a worker or even from another drone. As they grow older, the drones are fed by the workers less often, and finally they eat honey themselves and stay out of the brood area.

Workers between the age of 2 to 26 days were seen to feed drones, but younger workers, 4 to 6 days old, did so more frequently. Free considers that it is most probable that workers feed young drones with brood food. Orösi-Pál[174] proved that older drones, 7 to 8 days old, are fed honey and not the glandular secretion. Mindt[164] showed chromatographically that young drones are fed with the content of honey stomachs of the workers.

The dissimilarity in care received by the drones of different ages was strikingly demonstrated by Jaycox[100] when he placed cages with young drones, 6 to 7 days old, in a nursery colony beside the cages of older drones, 21 to 22 days old. The workers, which had been heavily clustered on the cages with the older drones, almost completely deserted them in favor of the younger ones. This neglect continued for about 3 days after which there was no difference.

The flight activities of drones were studied by several investigators[95,116,158,171] whose observations coincide quite closely, in spite of the fact that they were carried out in different parts of the world. The first flight of drones occurs when they are 4 to 14 days old, the majority of them coming out when they are 6 to 8 days of age. Before flying out, a drone elaborately cleans himself paying special attention to the antennae and the eyes. Upon his return the drone executes a complicated maneuver, flying from one side of the hive to the other. Sometimes such maneuvers carry him above, below, or to the side of the entrance and necessitate another attempt. The drones fly in abundance between 2:00 to 4:00 p.m., although single drones may fly out as early as 11:00 a.m. and return as late as 5:30 p.m. There are variations from colony to colony, from day to day, and from season to season. Probably clouds, shade from near-by trees, and possibly other factors influence the time when the peak of drone flight occurs.

The duration of the orientation flight is 6 to 15 minutes; that of searching or mating flights is 25 to 57 minutes. The latter are taken by drones over 12 days of age when they are sexually mature.[115] Drones do not eat much honey before short orientation flights; before searching or mating flights they feed themselves lavishly. The drones do not fly farther than about 2 miles from the apiary; few of them when released at $2\frac{1}{2}$ miles, returned to the hive.[130] Drones probably do not orient themselves by the position of the sun, but rather by landmarks. A drone's flying speed is 5.7 to 10.0 miles per hour. They make an average of three to four flights on sunny days, and one on cloudy days. A temperature of 60° F. is probably too low for the drone's flight. Flight takes place at approximately the maximum temperature and the minimum relative humidity of the day, when the sky is clear and the wind velocity is fairly low.

Levenets[129] found that during orientation flight 0.8 to 1.7 per cent of drones may drift to other colonies. More drones drift from weak to near-by strong colonies than vice versa. Drones which drift during their orientation flight remain with the colonies to which they drift for the rest of their lives. Prost[196] observed that thousands of drones fly above the hives in warm, sunny weather, signifying their presence with a loud hum. During mating flights, a dense swarm of drones, looking like a whirlwind or a tail of a comet, follows the queen. Some observers claim the presence of special "wedding markets" when the drones fly in abundance waiting for the queen. Ruttner[211] observed that drones are attracted first by quick movements and second by certain odors. At the first flight after a period of bad weather, the drones follow anything that moves in the air—worker bees, other insects, and even swallows. Cases were recorded[65,223] when a drone mated with a worker, the penis of the drone entering betwen the fourth and fifth tergites or the fifth and sixth sternites of the worker's abdomen. Ruttner explained the appearance of swarms of drones during mating flights, and the so-called "wedding markets" by the drones being attracted by the quickly moving pair of the queen and the pursuing drone. However, the question needs further investigation.[212]

Toward the end of the season the drones are driven out of the hives. First they are forced to the outside frames, then to the walls of the hive, finally to the bottom board, and then they are expelled. However, there are individual and racial differences.[131]

Drones do not dance, but on one occasion Orösi-Pál[174] observed a drone on the top bar of a frame performing a wag-tail dance, but without the "tail wagging." The loops were larger. After the dance the drone flew away. Drones live about 54 days.[95] Lecomte[123] presented a good review of the activities of drones.

LITERATURE CITED

1. Alber, M., R. Jordan, and H. Ruttner. 1955. Z. Bienenforsch 3:1-28.
2. Alfonsus, E. C. 1932. J. Econ. Entomol. 25:815-820.
3. _____. 1933. Gl. Bee Cult. 61:92-93.
4. Allen, M. D. 1956. Animal Behaviour 4:14-22.
5. _____. 1959. Animal Behaviour 7:66-69.
6. _____. 1959. Animal Behaviour 7:233-240.
7. _____. 1960. Animal Behaviour 8:201-208.
8. Armbruster, L. 1920. Arch. Bienenkunde 2:152-155.
9. Aufsess, A. V. 1960. Z. vergl. Physiol. 43:469-498.
10. Beecken, W. 1934. Arch. Bienenkunde 15:213-275.
11. Betts, A. D. 1935. Bee World 16:111-113.
12. _____. 1939. Bee World 20:20-24,33-36.
13. Beutler, R. 1953. Bee World 34:106-116,128-136,156-162.
14. Bisetsky, A. R. 1957. Z. vergl. Physiol. 40:264-288.
15. Bishop, G. H. 1920. J. Exptl. Zool. 31:225-286.
16. Boch, R. 1955. Z. vergl. Physiol. 38:136-167.
17. _____. 1957. Z. vergl. Physiol. 40:289-320.
18. Bodenheimer, F. S., and A. Ben-Nerya. 1937. Ann. Appl. Biol. 24:385-403.

19. Bonnier, G. 1906. C. R. Acad. Sci. **143**:941-946.
20. Borchert, A. 1928. Arch. Bienenkunde **9**:115-177.
21. Büdel, A., and E. Herold. 1960. "Biene und Bienenzucht." Ehrenwirth Verlag, Munich. 379 pp.
22. Butler, C. G. "Some observations relating to queen introduction." A lecture. The Central Assn. of Bee-Keepers.
23. ---------------- 1940. Bee World **21**:9-10.
24. ---------------- 1945. J. Exptl. Biol. **21**:5-12.
25. ---------------- 1954. "The world of the honeybee." The New Naturalist, Collins. 223 pp.
26. ---------------- 1954. Trans. Roy. Entomol. Soc. London **105**(Pt2):11-29.
27. ---------------- 1957. Proc. Roy. Soc. B. **147**:275-288.
28. Butler, C. G., and J. B. Free. 1952. Behaviour **4**(4):262-292.
29. Buttel-Reepen, H. 1915. "Leben und Wesen der Bienen." Friedrich Vieweg & Son. Verlag. Braunschweig. 300 pp.
30. Casteel, D. B. 1912. U.S.D.A. Bur. Entomol. Bull. No. 121.
31. ---------------- 1912. U.S. Bur. Entomol. Circ. **161**.
32. Chauvin, R. 1956. Insectes Sociaux **3**:499-504.
33. Corkins, C. L. 1933. Am. Bee J. **73**:208-209.
34. Darchen, R. 1957. Insectes Sociaux **4**:321-325.
35. ---------------- 1959. Ann. Abeille **2**:193-209.
36. Eckert, J. E. 1933. J. Agric. Res. **47**:257-285.
37. Esch, H. 1960. Z. vergl. Physiol. **43**:305-335.
38. Free, J. B. 1954. Behaviour **7**:233-240.
39. ---------------- 1956. Animal Behaviour **4**:94-101.
40. ---------------- 1957. Animal Behaviour **5**:7-11.
41. ---------------- 1958. J. Agric. Sci. **51**:294-306.
42. ---------------- 1959. J. Agric. Sci. **53**:1-9.
43. ---------------- 1959. Bee World **40**:193-201.
44. ---------------- 1960. J. Animal Ecol. **29**:385-395.
45. ---------------- 1960. Bee World **41**:141-151,169-186.
46. ---------------- 1960. Proc. Roy. Entomol. Soc. London. Ser. A. **35**:141-144.
47. ---------------- 1961. Animal Behaviour **9**:193-196.
48. ---------------- 1961. Proc. Roy. Soc. London (A). Pts. 1-3, April, pp. 5-8.
49. Free, J. B., and C. G. Butler. 1955. Behaviour **7**:304-316.
50. Free, J. B., and Y. Spenser Booth. 1961. J. Agric. Sci. **57**:153-158.
51. Freudenstein, H. 1961. Arch. Bienenkunde **38**:33-36.
52. Frisch, K. v. 1923. Zool. Jahrb. Abt. 3. **40**:1-186.
53. ---------------- 1946. Osterrichische Zool. Z. **1**:1-48.
54. ---------------- 1946. Experientia **2**(10):1-21.
55. ---------------- 1949. Experientia **4**:142-148.
56. ---------------- 1950. "Bees, their vision, chemical senses and language." Cornell Univ. Press. 119 pp.
57. ---------------- 1950. Experientia **6**:210-221.
58. ---------------- 1952. Bee World **33**:19-25,35-40.
59. ---------------- 1958. Am. Bee J. **98**:100-101.
60. Frisch, K. v., H. A. Heran, and M. Lindauer. 1953. Z. vergl. Physiol. **35**:219-245.
61. Frisch, K. v., and R. Jander. 1957. Z. vergl. Physiol. **40**:239-263.
62. Frisch, K. v., and M. Lindauer. 1954. Naturwiss. **41**:245-253.
63. ---------------- 1956. Ann. Rev. Entomol. **1**:45-48.
64. Furgala, B. 1959. Dissertation Abstr. **20**(4):1113-1114.
65. Fyg, W. 1960. Schweiz. Bienen-Ztg. **83**:395-398.
66. Gary, N. 1962. Personal communication.

67. Genrikh, V. G. 1957. Pchelovodstvo 34(5):8-12.
68. Gontarski, H. 1935. Arch. Bienenkunde 16:107-126.
69. _____. 1938. Deutsch. Imkerzführer 12(4):107-113.
70. _____. 1949. Z. vergl. Physiol. 31:652-670.
71. Hammann, E. 1957. Insectes Sociaux 4:91-106. Also Bee World 39:57-62. 1958.
72. Hammond, J. A. 1958. Bee World 39:179-180.
73. Haydak, M. H. 1929. Cesky Vcelar 63:229-231.
74. _____. 1929. Pasichnyk 5(9):262-267.
75. _____. 1930. Cesky Vcelar 64:166-168. Also Wis. Beekeeping 8(5):36-39. 1932.
76. _____. 1930. Cesky Vcelar 64:48-50.
77. _____. 1934. J. Agric. Res. 49:21-28.
78. _____. 1935. J. Econ. Entomol. 28:657-660.
79. _____. 1937. Ann. Entomol. Soc. Am. 30:258-262.
80. _____. 1937. J. Agric. Res. 54:791-796.
81. _____. 1944. Am. Bee J. 84:346.
82. _____. 1945. Am. Bee J. 85:316-317.
83. _____. 1949. Iowa State Apiarist Rept. pp. 68-94.
84. _____. 1953. Iowa State Apiarist Rept. pp. 74-87.
85. _____. 1954. Iowa State Apiarist Rept. pp. 108-121.
86. _____. 1958. Sci. 127:1113.
87. _____. 1959. Gl. Bee Cult. 88:265-269,307.
88. Heberle, J. A. 1914. Gl. Bee Cult. 42:904-905.
89. Hein, G. 1950. Experientia 6:142-144.
90. Heran, H. 1956. Z. vergl. Physiol. 38:168-218.
91. Himmer, A. 1930. Leipziger Bienen-Ztg. 45:39-43,64-67.
92. Hirschfelder, H. 1951. Z. Bienenforsch 1:67-77.
93. Hobbs, G. A., W. O. Nummini, and J. F. Virostek. 1961. Can. Entomol. 93:409-419.
94. Hoffmann, I. 1961. Z. Bienenforsch 5:267-279.
95. Howell, D. E., and R. L. Usinger. 1933. Ann. Entomol. Soc. Am. 26:239-246.
96. Huber, F. 1814. "New observations upon bees." Am. Bee J., Hamilton, Ill. 1926. 230 pp.
97. Istomina-Tsvetkova, K. P. 1953. Pchelovodstvo 30(1):25-29.
98. _____. 1953. Pchelovodstvo 30(9):15-23.
99. _____. 1957. Zool. Zhur. 36(9):1359-1370.
100. Jaycox, E. R. 1961. Ann. Entomol. Soc. Am. 54:519-523.
101. Jaxtheimer, R. 1949. Arch. Bienenkunde 26:1-16.
102. Jessup, J. G. 1924. "The humidity within the bee colony." Unpubl. Thesis. Library, Iowa State Univ., Ames, Iowa.
103. _____. 1925. Iowa State Apiarist Rept., pp. 35-36.
104. Kalmus, H. 1957. Bee World 38:29-33.
105. Kalmus, H., and C. R. Ribbands. 1952. Proc. Roy. Soc. B. 140:50-59.
106. Kappel, I. 1952. Z. vergl. Physiol. 34:539-546.
107. Kaschef, A. H. 1957. Z. vergl. Physiol. 39:562-576.
108. King, G. E. 1929. 29th Ann. Rept. Ill. State Beekeepers' Assn. pp. 64-67.
109. Kivalkina, V. P. 1959. Pchelovodstvo 36(10):50-52.
110. Kleck, G. 1926. Arch. Bienenkunde 7:41-81.
111. Kleck, G., and L. Armbruster. 1919. Arch. Bienenkunde 1:185-240.
112. Kleber, E. 1935. Z. vergl. Physiol. 22:221-262.
113. Koptev, V. S. 1957. Pchelovodstvo 34(6):31-32.
114. Kraeber, A. L. 1952. Sci. 115:483.

115. Kurennoi, N. M. 1953. Pchelovodstvo **30**(11):28-32.
116. _____ 1954. Pchelovodstvo **31**(12):24-28.
117. Küstenmacher, M. 1911. Ber. Deutsch. Pharmazeut. Gesellschaft **21**:65-92.
118. Laidlaw, H. H. 1944. J. Morphol. **74**:429-465.
119. Langstroth, L. L. 1859. "The hive and the honey bee." 3rd. Ed. A. O. Moore Co. 405 pp.
120. Lavie, P., and M. Roth. 1953. Physiol. Comparata et Oecol. **3**(1):57-62.
121. Lecomte, J. 1949. C. R. Acad. Sci. **229**:857-858.
122. _____ 1950. Z. vergl. Physiol. **32**:499-506.
123. _____ 1958. Ann. Abeille **1**:31-39.
124. _____ 1961. Ann. Abeille **4**:165-270.
125. Lee, W. R. 1961. J. Econ. Entomol. **54**:928-933.
126. Leppik, E. E. 1951. Am. Bee J. **91**:462.
127. Levchenko, I. A. 1959. Pchelovodstvo **36**(2):38-40.
128. _____ 1959. Pchelovodstvo **36**(7):37-38.
129. Levenets, I. P. 1951. Pchelovodstvo **28**(1):25-30.
130. _____ 1954. Pchelovodstvo **31**(8):36-38.
131. _____ 1956. Pchelovodstvo **33**(10):28-29.
132. Levin, M. D. 1959. J. Econ. Entomol. **52**:969-971.
133. _____ 1961. J. Econ. Entomol. **54**:431-434.
134. _____ 1961. J. Econ. Entomol. **54**:482-484.
135. Levin, M. D., and G. E. Bohart. 1955. Am. Bee J. **95**:392-393,402.
136. Lindauer, M. 1949. Z. vergl. Physiol. **31**:348-412.
137. _____ 1951. Naturwiss. **38**:308-309.
138. _____ 1952. Z. vergl. Physiol. **34**:299-345.
139. _____ 1953. Bee World **34**:63-73,85-90.
140. _____ 1954. Naturwiss. **41**:506-507.
141. _____ 1954. Z. vergl. Physiol. **36**:391-432.
142. _____ 1955. Bee World **36**:62-72,81-92.
143. _____ 1955. Z. vergl. Physiol. **36**:263-324. Also Nature **179**:63-73. 1957.
144. _____ 1957. Naturwiss. **44**:1-6.
145. _____ 1959. Naturwiss. Rundschau. Heftl. **1**:5-13.
146. _____ 1959. Z. vergl. Physiol. **42**:43-62.
147. Lindauer, M., and J. O. Nedel. 1959. Z. vergl. Physiol. **42**:334-364.
148. Lopatina, N. G. 1956. Pchelovodstvo **33**(12):19-24.
149. Louveaux, J. 1958-1959. Ann. Abeille **1**:113-188,197-221. **2**:13-111.
150. Lukoschus, F. 1957. Z. Bienenforsch **4**:1-19.
151. Lundie, A. E. 1925. U.S.D.A. Bull. **1328**. 37 pp.
152. Maurizio, A. 1953. Beihefte Schweiz. Bienen-Ztg. **2**:485-556.
153. _____ 1954. Landwirtschaft. Jahrb. Schweiz. **68**:115-182.
154. Meyer, W. 1954. Z. Bienenforsch **2**:185-200.
155. _____ 1956. Insectes Sociaux **3**:303-324.
156. _____ 1956. Bee World **37**:26-36.
157. Meyer, W. and W. Ulrich. 1952. Naturwiss. **39**:264.
158. Mikhailow, A. C. 1928. Opytnaia Paseka **3**:209-214.
159. Milojevic, B. D. 1939. Schweiz. Bienen-Ztg. **62**(12):689-695.
160. Milojevic, B. D., and U. Filipovic-Moskovljevic. 1958. XVII Internatl. Bee-keeping Congr., Rome. p. 82.
161. Milum, V. G. 1947. Ill. Acad. Sci. Trans. **40**:194-196.
162. _____ 1955. Am. Bee J. **95**:97-104.
163. _____ 1956. Proc. X Internatl. Congr. Entomol. **4**:1085-1088.
164. Mindt, B. 1962. Z. Bienenforsch. **6**:9-33.

165. Nelson, F. C. 1927. Amer. Bee J. 67:242-243.
166. Nelson, J. A., A. P. Sturtevant, and B. Lineburg. 1924. U.S.D.A. Bull. 1222.
167. New, D. A. T., F. R. Burrows, and A. F. Edgar. 1961. Nature 189:155-156.
168. Nixon, H. L., and C. R. Ribbands. 1952. Proc. Roy. Soc. B. 140:43-50.
169. Nolan, J. W. 1925. U.S.D.A. Bull. No. 1349. 56 pp.
170. Oertel, E. 1940. Gl. Bee Cult. 68:292-293,333.
171. _____. 1956. Ann. Entomol. Soc. Am. 49:497-500.
172. Örösi-Pál, Z. 1932. Zool. Anzeiger 98:259-267.
173. _____ 1957. Bee World 38:70-73.
174. _____ 1959. Bee World 40:141-146.
175. Park, O. W. 1922. Am. Bee J. 62:254-255.
176. _____ 1923. Am. Bee J. 63:71.
177. _____ 1923. Am. Bee J. 63:553.
178. _____ 1925. Iowa State Apiarist Rept. pp. 83-90.
179. _____ 1925. J. Econ. Entomol. 18:405-410.
180. _____ 1925. VII Internatl. Beekeeping Congr., Quebec. 1924. pp. 472-478.
181. _____ 1927. J. Econ. Entomol. 20:510-516.
182. _____ 1928. J. Econ. Entomol. 21:882-887.
183. _____ 1928. Iowa Agr. Expt. Sta. Res. Bull. 108.
184. _____ 1932. Iowa Agr. Expt. Sta. Res. Bull. 151. pp. 211-244.
185. _____ 1933. J. Econ. Entomol. 26:188-193.
186. _____ 1949. "Activities of honey bees" from "The hive and the honey bee" R. A. Grout. Am. Bee J., Hamilton, Ill. pp. 79-152.
187. Parker, R. L. 1926. Cornell Univ. Agr. Expt. Sta. Mem. 98. 55 pp.
188. Parks, H. B. 1929. Iowa State Apiarist Rept. pp. 53-56.
189. Perepelova, L. I. 1928. Opytnaia Paseka 3:214-217. Also Bee World 10:69-71. 1929.
190. _____ 1959. Pchelovodstvo 36(11):30-32.
191. Peterka, V. 1928. Cesky Vcelar 62:312-313.
192. Philipp, P. W. 1928. Biol. Zbl. 48:705-714.
193. Phillips, E. F., and G. Demuth. 1915. U.S.D.A. Farmers Bull. 695.
194. Peer, D. F. 1956. J. Econ. Entomol. 49:741-743.
195. _____ 1957. Can. Entomol. 89:108-110.
196. Prost, J. P. 1957. C. R. Acad. Sci. 245:2017-2110.
197. Rashad, S. E. D. 1957. Dissertation Abstr. 17(7):1435.
198. Rauschmeyer, F. 1928. Arch. Bienenkunde 9:249-322.
199. Reinhardt, J. F. 1939. J. Econ. Entomol. 32:654-660.
200. _____ 1952. Am. Naturalist 86:257-275.
201. Ribbands, C. R. 1949. J. Animal Ecol. 18:47-66.
202. _____ 1952. Proc. Roy. Soc. B. 140:32-43.
203. _____ 1954. Proc. Roy. Soc. B. 142:514-524.
204. _____ 1955. Proc. Roy. Soc. B. 143:367-379.
205. _____ 1955. Am. Bee J. 95:313,320.
206. Rösch, G. A. 1925. Z. vergl. Physiol. 2:571-631.
207. _____ 1927. Biol. Zbl. 47:113-121.
208. _____ 1930. Z. vergl. Physiol. 12:1-71.
209. Ruttner, F. 1956. Bee World 37:3-15,23-24.
210. _____ 1957. Z. vergl. Physiol. 39:577-600.
211. _____ 1959. Bienenvater 80:36-39,73-77,99-104.
212. _____ 1962. Bienenvater 83:45-47.
213. Rymashevsky, V. K. 1956. Pchelovodstvo 33(4):51-52.
214. Sakagami, S. F. 1953. Jap. J. Zool. 11(1):117-185.

215. _____ 1953. J. Fac. Sci. Hokkaido Univ. Ser. VI, Zool. 11:343-400.

216. _____ 1954. Insectes Sociaux 1:331-343.

217. _____ 1958. Behaviour 13:280-296.

218. _____ 1958. Z. Bienenforsch 4:1-8.

219. Schick, W. 1953. Z. vergl. Physiol. 35:105-128.

220. Schneider, F. 1949. Mitteil. Sweiz. Entomol. Gesellschaft 22:293-308.

221. Schwan, B., and A. Martinovs. 1954. Stat. Husdjurförsök. Meddelande No. 57. 35 pp.

222. Schweiger, E. M. 1958. Z. vergl. Physiol. 41:272-299.

223. Schulz-Langner, E. 1961. Z. Bienenforsch 5:227-229.

224. Simpson, J. 1958. Insectes Sociaux 5:77-95.

225. Singh, S. 1950. Cornell Univ. Agr. Expt. Sta. Mem. 288. 57 pp.

226. Skrebtsova, N. D. 1937. Pchelovodstvo 34(4):39-42.

227. Smith, M. V. 1959. Symposium "Food gathering behavior of Hymenoptera." 7th Ann. Meet. E.S.A. pp. 19-23.

228. _____ 1959. Bee World 40:153-154.

229. Synge, A. D. 1947. J. Animal Ecol. 16:122-138.

230. Taber, S., III. 1954. J. Econ. Entomol. 47:995-998.

231. Taranov, G. F. 1947. Pchelovodstvo 24(2):44-54.

232. _____ 1955. Pchelovodstvo 32(8):32-35.

233. _____ 1959. Bee World 40:113-121.

234. Taranov, G. F., and L. V. Ivanova. 1946. Pchelovodstvo 23(2/3):35-39.

235. Triasko, V. V. 1956. Pchelovodstvo 33(1):43-50.

236. _____ 1957. Pchelovodstvo 34(12):29-31.

237. Tschumi, P. 1950. Schweiz. Bienen-Ztg. 73:129-134.

238. Tsvetkova, K. P. 1956. Ber. XVI Bienenzucht Congr. Wein. p. 98.

239. Tucker, K. W. 1955. Proc. X Ann. Meet. N.C. Branch E.S.A. p. 51.

240. Tuenin, T. A. 1926. Bee World 8:90-91.

241. Tushmalova, N. A. 1958. Pchelovodstvo 35(1):25-29.

242. Vansell, G. H. 1942. U.S.D.A. Circ. 650. 32 pp.

243. Velich, A. 1926. Cesky Vcelar 60:132-134.

244. Weaver, N. 1956. Insectes Sociaux 3:537-549.

245. _____ 1957. Insectes Sociaux 4:43-57.

246. Weghtman, C. 1951. Brit. Bee J. 79:391-392.

247. Whitcomb, W., Jr. 1946. Gl. Bee Cult. 74:198-202,247.

248. Wiltse, J. 1882. Gl. Bee Cult. 10:596-597.

249. Wittekindt, W. 1961. Am. Bee J. 101:434-436.

250. Woodrow, A. W. 1941. U.S.D.A. Publ. E-529. 13 pp.

251. Woyke, J. 1956. Pchelovodstvo 33(8):32-36.

RECOMMENDED ADDITIONAL READING

Frisch, K. v. 1950. Bees, their vision, chemical senses and language. Great Seal Books, Div. Cornell Univ. Press, Ithaca, N.Y. 119 pp.

_____ 1954. The dancing bees. Methuen, London. 183 pp.

Lindauer, M. 1961. Communication among social bees. Harvard Univ. Press, Cambridge, Mass. 143 pp.

Ribbands, C. R. 1953. The behavior and social life of honeybees. Bee Res. Assn. Ltd., London. 352 pp.

CHAPTER V

THE ANATOMY OF THE HONEY BEE

by R. E. SNODGRASS*

THE ANATOMY of an animal is the assemblage of structural parts that enables the animal to do the things necessary for the maintenance of its individual existence, and for the perpetuation of its kind. As an individual the animal must obtain and distribute to its tissues both food and oxygen, eliminate waste matter, and correlate the activities of its various organs with one another, and its own activities with changing conditions of the environment. Hence the animal has a locomotor system, feeding and digesting organs together with a system of food distribution, a respiratory system, an excretory system, and a nervous system. To provide for the continuance of its species it has a reproductive system. In addition, nearly every animal has some specialty of its own—it may eat only a particular kind of food, it may inhabit a special kind of environment, it may adopt a particular method of locomotion, it may be individualistic or socialistic—and according to its habits or its way of life, it is equipped with special anatomical mechanisms.

To understand why an animal is made as it is, we study its structure and functions; to understand how it comes to be what it is, we must know something of its development. The honey bee, as every other complex animal, begins life as a single cell, the egg, or *ovum,* but the development of the embryo produces first the *larva.* The adult bee is then formed in an intermediate stage known as the *pupa.*

Development

In the narrowed inner end of each tubule in the queen's ovary (Fig. 22, B) are the primary female germ cells *(GCls)* or *oogonia.* Further down the tube these cells multiply and differentiate into larger cells, or *oocytes,* which become the eggs *(E),* and into smaller cells called *nurse cells,* or *trophocytes,* because they will be absorbed as nutriment by the growing egg cells. As new oocytes are formed, the egg tubes lengthen at their inner ends, and the older eggs, each accompanied by a mass of nurse cells, increase in size. An egg tubule thus becomes a succession of egg chambers *(EC)* alternating with nurse cell chambers *(NC).* The fullgrown eggs *(E)* in the lower ends of the tubes have absorbed practically all their nurse cells, and the walls of the containing chambers, or follicles, now secrete over each egg a shell, known as the *chorion.*

---

*Robert E. Snodgrass, Ph.D. Honorary Research Associate, Smithsonian Institute. Author of *Anatomy of the Honey Bee.* World authority on insect morphology.

In a similar manner the tubules of the male testes produce spermatozoa, but the spermatozoa remain as free, active, threadlike individuals.

The mature egg is discharged through the oviduct into the genital exit passage, or *vagina* (Fig. 22, A, *Vag*), with which is connected a small sac, the *spermatheca (Spt)*, containing the spermatozoa received from drones at the time of mating. A minute aperture, the *micropyle,* at the anterior end of the egg admits the sperm, but by some regulatory mechanism the queen discharges sperm on some eggs and witholds it from others. The eggs that become fertilized develop into female bees; those unfertilized become drones. By some stimulus the bee's egg develops whether fertilized or not.

The newly laid egg (Fig. 1, A) is elongate, rounded at the ends and slightly convex on what will be the under surface of the embryo. The interior consists of the egg cytoplasm and the nutritive material *(Y)* derived from the nurse cells in the ovary (called *yolk* because it is yellow in a bird's egg). The egg within the chorion is invested in a delicate *vitelline membrane (Vit)*. Just within the membrane is a peripheral

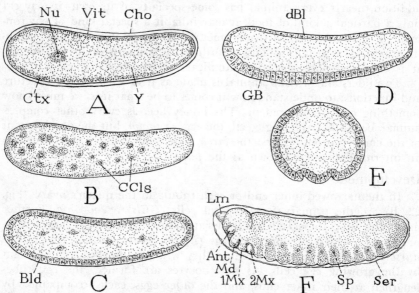

FIGURE 1. Development of the embryo in the egg (diagrammatic from Nelson. Embryology of the honeybee. 1915).

A, lengthwise section of egg in chorion. B, cleavage cells in the yolk, resulting from repeated division of the nucleus and daughter nuclei, migrating to the cortex. C, blastoderm formed by cleavage cells in the cortex. D, blastoderm differentiated into thick ventral germ band and thin dorsal blastoderm. E, cross section of egg, germ band grown dorsally, differentiated into lateral plates and ventral plate. F, the young embryo.

Ant, antenna; *Bld,* blastoderm; *CCls,* cleavage cells; *Cho,* chorion; *dBl,* dorsal blastoderm; *GB,* germ band; *Lm,* labrum; *Md,* mandible; *1Mx,* first maxilla; *2Mx,* second maxilla; *Nu,* nucleus; *Ser,* serosa; *Sp,* spiracle; *Vit,* vitelline membrane.

cortical layer of cytoplasm. The egg nucleus *(Nu)* is contained in a small cytoplasmic body near the anterior end of the egg.

Development begins with the division of the nucleus and the resulting nuclei. The *cleavage cells* (Fig. 1, B, *CCls*) thus formed migrate out into the cortical cytoplasm, where they form a layer of cells on the surface of the egg, which is the *blastoderm* (C, *Bld*). Soon the lower part of the blastoderm becomes thickened, forming what is known as the *germ band* (D, *GB*), while the dorsal blastoderm *(dBl)* by contrast becomes very thin. The germ band is the beginning of the embryo. Its edges grow upward on the sides and around the ends of the egg *(E)* as the thin dorsal blastoderm contracts and finally disappears, allowing the germ band to close over the back. The wall of the embryo is now complete, but as yet there are no internal organs.

While the germ band is growing upward on the sides of the egg (Fig. 1, E), it becomes differentiated into a pair of lateral plates and a median ventral plate. The ventral plate sinks into the egg and the lower ends of the lateral plates come together beneath it. The lateral plates thus become the body-wall epidermis of the insect, which secretes the external cuticle. The ventral plate becomes mesoderm, from which are derived the muscles, fat tissue, the heart, and the internal reproductive organs. The stomach, or *ventriculus* (Fig. 2, B, *Vent*), is formed of strands of endodermal cells proliferated from the two ends of the larva that come together and enclose the yolk, which will be the food of the growing embryo. At the mouth a tubular ingrowth of the ectoderm forms the *stomodeum (Stom)*, which opens into the anterior end of the stomach. Likewise an ingrowth from the anus forms the *proctodeum (Proc)*, which unites with the posterior end of the stomach. The insect alimentary canal always consists of these three parts.

The nervous system is of ectodermal origin, being formed from cells given off internally from the midventral line of the embryo. The nerve cells become aggregated first into paired segmental masses, or ganglia, connected crosswise by fiber commissures and lengthwise by connectives. The primary ganglia, however, unite to form a compound ganglion in each segment (Fig. 20), from which nerves grow outward to the muscles, glands, and other organs. Ganglia of the head form the brain. Nerves from the sense organs originate from cells of the epidermis and grow inward to the ganglia.

The tracheal respiratory system (Fig. 19) likewise is ectodermal, originating from tubular ingrowths along the sides of the body, the external openings of which are the spiracles.

Externally the young embryo (Fig. 1, F) becomes differentiated into a head region and a body. On the head, rudiments of the labrum *(Lm)*, antennae *(Ant)*, mandibles *(Md)*, and two pairs of maxillae *(1Mx, 2Mx)* are formed as small lobes. Wings and legs, however, are not apparent on the embryo or larva because their rudiments are sunken into shallow pockets of the epidermis beneath the cuticle. The full complement of 10 spiracles is present on each side of the embryo.

When the embryo is fully developed as a young larva, the latter hatches from the egg. During its life the larva goes through five stages of growth, or *instars,* moulting its cuticle after each instar. The bee larva (Fig. 2, A) is a very simple creature without external legs or wings as befits its life of inactivity in the comb cell. It has little to do except to eat the food the nurse bees give it. The larva has a small head and a body of 13 segments undifferentiated into thorax and abdomen. On the front of the head *(C)* are two small discs that mark the sites of the sunken antennae. The feeding organs include a pair of small mandibles *(Md)* and a pair of simple maxillae *(Mx)*. Between the maxillae is a median lobe on which the duct of the silk glands opens between raised lips, forming a spinneret *(Spn)*. The spinneret lobe is formed by a union of the hypopharynx *(Hphy)* with the end of the labium *(Lb)*, the latter being fully exposed on the under side of the head *(D)*. The silk glands of the honey-bee larva are the salivary glands of most other insects, the terminal duct of which opens between the bases of the ununited hypopharynx and labium.

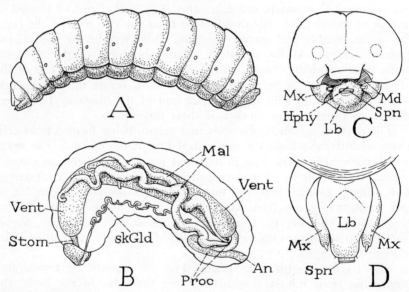

FIGURE 2. The larva.
A, a mature larva. B, same, alimentary canal, with Malpighian tubules, and silk glands of left side (from Nelson. Morphology of the honeybee larva. 1924). C, head, anterior. D, head, ventral.

An, anus; *Hphy,* hypopharynx; *Lb,* labium; *Mal,* Malpighian tubules; *Md,* mandible; *Mx,* maxilla; *Proc,* proctodeum; *skGld,* silk gland; *Spin,* spinneret; *Stom,* stomodeum; *Vent,* ventriculus.

Since the principal function of the bee larva is eating, it is provided with an enormous stomach, or ventriculus, a cylindrical sac (Fig. 2, B, *Vent*) almost as long as the body. A short intake tube, the stomodeum *(Stom)*, goes from the mouth to the stomach, and a looped intestine, or proctodeum *(Proc)*, connects the rear end of the stomach with the terminal anus *(An)*. Arising from the inner end of the proctodeum are four Malpighian tubules, two on each side *(Mal)*, which are the excretory organs of the insect. In a young bee larva the tubules are slender, but in the mature larva (B) they become greatly distended by the accumulation of secretion within them. In order to preserve cleanliness in the larval

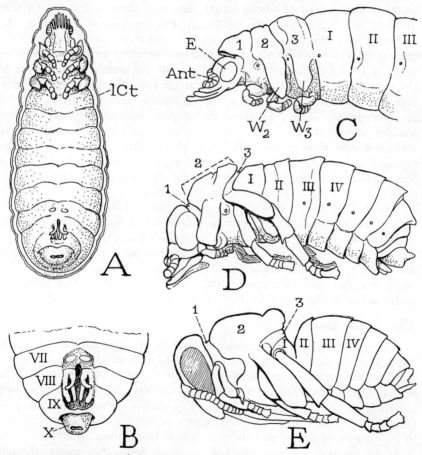

FIGURE 3. Development of the pupa.
A, the young pupa in unshed larval cuticle. B, same, end of abdomen, with rudiments of sting on under surface. C, same as A, lateral view, more enlarged. D, later stage of pupa, still in larval cuticle. E, the mature pupa.
Ant, antenna; *E*, compound eye; *1Ct*, larval cuticle; *W₂, W₃*, mesothoracic and metathoracic wings; *1, 2, 3*, thoracic segments; *I-X*, abdominal segments.

cell, both the Malpighian tubules and the stomach are shut off from the intestine until the larva is mature at the time the cell is capped. Then the tubules and the stomach open into the intestine and their contents are discharged from the anus into the inner end of the cell. Now the larva spins its cocoon and moults for the last time, but it does not shed the cuticle. The body wall has already taken on the form of the young pupa (Fig. 3, A), which is enveloped in the larval cuticle (ICt).

The antennae, legs, and wings of the pupa are now everted, compound eyes and the adult mouth parts are present (C). Otherwise, however, the young pupa still retains larval features. The three thoracic segments (1,2,3) are of about equal size, and there is no constriction between the thorax and the abdomen. On the posterior part of the abdomen of a female pupa (B) are the rudiments of the sting. At a later stage (D), still within the larval cuticle, the thorax has taken on more of the adult form by an expansion of the middle segment (2) at the expense of the first and third segments (1,3). There is as yet, however, no constriction separating the abdomen from the thorax. With the completion of development the mature pupa (E) distinctly resembles an adult bee. The thorax is now well separated from the abdomen, but it is to be noted that the constriction is between the primary first (I) and second (II) abdominal segments. The reduced first segment is intimately united with the thorax and becomes virtually a part of the thorax, known as the *propodeum*.

The fully formed pupa throws off the larval cuticle, and undergoes no further external change. Within it, however, the special larval tissues break down and go into dissolution as food for the growing adult tissues. Then when the adult is completed within the pupa it splits the pupal shell and emerges as an adult bee. The change-over from the larva to the adult is called the "metamorphosis" of the insect, but it is largely a replacement of the larva by the adult.

The Adult Bee

The adult honey bee is constructed on the general plan of an insect, but it leads a highly specialized kind of life and for this reason is provided with special mechanisms and gadgets that enable it to live in its particular way. Hence in studying the bee, while we must give attention to its fundamental insect organization, special interest pertains to the structures and modifications of organs that adapt the bee to its manner of living and differentiate it from other insects.

In its general structure the bee resembles any other insect, though its form (Fig. 4) is obscured by the dense coating of hairs with which the body is covered. The bee's coat is particularly fluffy because most of the hairs are featherlike, the shaft of each hair having many short side branches.

The *head* of the insect (Fig. 4, *H*) carries the eyes, the antennae, and the organs of feeding. It is joined to the next body division, the *thorax (Th)*, by a slender flexible neck. The thorax and the third section of the trunk, or *abdomen (Ab)*, are composed of a succession of rings called *segments*. In most insects the thorax consists of only three segments, but in the bee and related insects it includes four segments, which are the *prothorax (1)*, the *mesothorax (2)* the *metathorax (3)*, and the *propodeum (I)*. The propodeum of the bee is the first

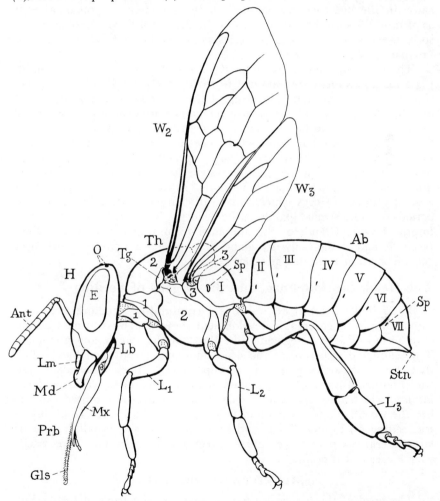

FIGURE 4. External structure of a worker bee as seen when the hairy covering is removed. *Ab*, abdomen; *Ant*, antenna; *E*, compound eye; *H*, head; *I*, propodeum; *II-VII*, abdominal segments; *L₁, L₂, L₃*, legs; *Md*, mandible; *Prb*, proboscis; *Sp*, spiracle; *Th*, thorax; *W₂, W₃*, wings; *1*, prothorax; *2*, mesothorax; *3*, metathorax.

abdominal segment of most other insects. The prothorax carries the first pair of legs *(L₁)*; the mesothorax and the metathorax, in addition to carrying each a pair of legs *(L₂,L₃)*, support also the two pairs of wings *(W₂,W₃)*. The thorax is clearly the locomotor center of the insect. A short stalk, the *peduncle,* attaches the thorax to the abdomen which contains the principal internal organs and bears the sting.

The feeding organs of the bee consist of the same parts as do those of a grasshopper or a cricket, but the parts are very different in form because in the bee they are adapted to the ingestion of pollen, as well as of liquid food to be obtained from the depths of flower corollas, while such insects as grasshoppers and crickets merely bite off, chew, and swallow particles of solid food.

The wings of the bee are adapted for swift flight and also for sustaining a load. The legs are modified in their structure for various uses besides that of locomotion. The sting of the bee represents the ovipositor of other female insects, sufficiently remodeled in structure to serve for piercing and for the injection of poison instead of eggs.

Most of the internal organs of the bee are much the same as in other insects, but the alimentary canal has a special adaptation for carrying nectar or honey. The respiratory system is greatly amplified. In the queen the ovaries are so highly developed as to be capable of producing a great number of eggs which can be discharged continually over long periods of time. Special glands of the head produce a rich food substance for the brood. Glands of the abdomen form wax for comb building. Near the end of the body is a gland that secretes a scent by which bees get information from one another.

The Head, the Antennae, and the Organs of Feeding

Though the head of an insect is a craniumlike structure with continuous walls, its embryonic development shows that it is formed by the close union of several segments like those of the thorax and abdomen. The segmental structure of the head, moreover, is attested by the fact that the head carries four pair of appendages. These appendages are the *antennae,* the *mandibles* or jaws of the insect, the *maxillae,* and the *labium,* which last represents a second pair of maxillae united. In the bee the maxillae and the labium together form the *proboscis,* an organ for feeding on liquids. The head bears also the eyes, usually a pair of large lateral *compound eyes* and, between the latter, usually three small simple eyes called *ocelli.*

STRUCTURE OF THE HEAD

The head of the honey bee is triangular as seen from in front (Fig. 5, *A*), flattened from before backward, somewhat concave on the posterior surface *(B),* and is set on the thorax by a narrow membranous neck. The lateral angles are capped by the compound eyes (A, *E*), and on the top of the head are three *ocelli (O)*. The antennae *(Ant)* arise close together near the center of the face. Below their bases a prominent arched groove *(es)* sets off a large area known as the *clypeus (Clp)*, from the lower margin of which is suspended a broad movable flap, the *labrum (Lm)*. Attached laterally to the lower part of the head behind the labrum are the two jawlike mandibles *(Md)*, and behind the mandibles, better seen from the back of the head (B) are suspended the two maxillae *(Mx)* and the median labium *(Lb)*. The long distal parts of the maxillae and labium, shown spread out at A of Fig. 6, either project downward or are folded back below and behind the head (Fig. 5, *E*); but in their functional position they are brought together to form a tubular proboscis (Fig. 4, *Prb*) for feeding on liquids.

On the back of the head, as seen when it is detached from the body (Fig. 5, *B*), is a central opening, the *neck foramen (For)*, by which the cavity of the head communicates with that of the body, and which gives passage for the oesophagus, nerves, blood vessel, air tubes, and salivary duct. Below the foramen the hard wall of the head is cut out in a large horseshoe-shaped notch with a membranous floor in which are implanted the long bases of the maxillae and labium. The depression of the notch, therefore, is designated the *proboscis fossa (PF)*.

Internally the walls of the head are braced by two large bars (Fig. 5, C, *Tnt*) that extend through the head cavity from the sides of the neck foramen to the grooves of the face at the sides of the clypeus *(Clp)*. The posterior ends of the bars are bridged by a slender cross-rod *(TB)*, which may be seen from behind just within the neck foramen (B). The bars and the connecting bridge constitute the *tentorium*.

THE ANTENNAE

The antennae are freely movable appendages with their bases set into small socketlike membranous areas of the head wall (Fig. 5, *A*). Each antenna is pivoted on a single articular point of the socket rim, and is provided with four muscles (D, *Mcls*) arising on the tentorial bar of the same side of the head. Each appendage, moreover, has an elbowlike joint between its basal stalk, or *scape (Scp)*, and the flexible distal part called the *flagellum (Fl)*. The scape of the drone antenna is shorter than that of the worker, but the flagellum is much longer and consists of 12 short rings, while there are only 11 in the worker and the queen. The antennae are important sensory organs. Each appendage is penetrated by a large double nerve from the brain. The flagellum is covered with small innervated hairs and other minute sensory structures of several kinds. It is difficult to determine the function of each variety of sense organ, but the antennae are responsive particularly to stimuli of touch and odor.

THE MANDIBLES

The mandibles (Fig. 5, A, *Md*) are suspended from the head at the sides of the mouth (F, *Mth*), which lies immediately behind the base of

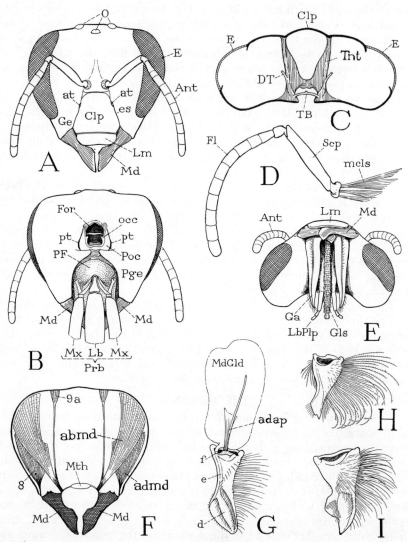

FIGURE 5. The head, antennae, and mandibles of a worker bee (except H and I).

A, facial view of head. B, rear view of head. C, horizontal section of head showing internal tentorium. D, antenna. E, under view of head and folded proboscis. F, transverse verticle section of head showing mandibles and their muscles. G, mandible and mandibular gland, mesal view. H, mandible of drone. I, mandible of queen.

Abmd, abductor muscle of mandible; *adap*, tendon of abductor muscle of mandible; *admd*, adductor muscle of mandible; *Ant*, antenna; *Clp*, clypeus; *d*, channel of mandible; *e*, groove of mandible; *E*, compound eye; *es*, suture defining clypeus; *f*, orifice of mandibular gland; *Fl*, flagellum; *For*, neck foramen of head; *Ga*, galea; *Gls*, tongue (glossa); *Lb*, labium; *LbPlp*, labial palpus; *Lm*, labrum; *Mcls*, muscles; *Md*, mandible; *MdGld*, mandibular gland; *Mth*, mouth; *Mx*, maxilla; *O*, ocelli; *PF*, proboscis fossa; *Prb*, proboscis; *pt*, posterior tentorial pit; *Scp*, scape; *TB*, tentorial bridge; *Tnt*, tentorium.

the labrum. Each jaw has an anterior and a posterior point of articulation on the head, and is provided with only two muscles (F, *abmd, admd*) which are attached on opposite sides of the axis of movement. The mandibles therefore swing sideways; but, because the anterior articulations are higher than the posterior, the points of the jaws turn inward and backward when the mandibles close.

The mandible of the worker bee (Fig. 5, G) is thick at the base, narrowed through the middle, and widened again distally in an expansion with a concave inner surface traversed by a median channel *(d)*. From the channel a groove *(e)* runs upward to an aperture *(f)* at the base of the mandible, which is the outlet of a large, saclike *mandibular gland (MdGld)* that lies in the head above the mandible. The gland secretes a clear liquid, the purpose of which is not definitely known, but the secretion is supposed to be used for softening wax. The mandibular glands are largest in the queen; in the drone they are reduced to small vesicles. The worker bee uses its mandibles for eating pollen, for working the wax in comb building, for holding the base of the outstretched proboscis, and for doing any of the chores about the hive that require a pair of grasping instruments. The mandibles of the queen (Fig. 5, *I*) are larger than those of the worker but they lack the special features of the worker mandibles and each has a broad inner lobe near the pointed apex. The drone mandibles *(H)*, on the other hand, are smaller than those of the worker, and each is sharply notched at the base of the apical point.

THE PROBOSCIS

The proboscis of the bee is not a permanently functional organ as it is in most other sucking insects; it is temporarily improvised by bringing together the free parts of the maxillae and the labium to form a tube for ingesting liquids—nectar, honey, or water. The maxillary and labial components of the proboscis are closely associated at their bases, which are suspended in the ample membrane of the fossa on the back of the head (Fig. 6, *A*). The base of the median labium includes a long, cylindrical distal part termed the *prementum (Prmt)*, and a small, triangular proximal plate, the *postmentum (Pmt)*. The prementum carries at its end the slender hairy *tongue (Gls)*; a pair of short lobes, the *paraglossae (Pgl)*, embracing the base of the tongue; and a pair of slender *labial palpi (LbPlp)*. Each palpus consists of two long basal segments and two short apical segments, and is individually movable by a muscle arising in the prementum. In each maxilla the principal basal plate (A, *St*) is the *stipes* (plural *stipites*), but the stipes is suspended by a slender rod *(Cd)*, the *cardo* (plural *cardines*), that articulates with a knob on the margin of the proboscis fossa. The distal ends of the two cardines are yoked to the postmentum of the labium by a V-shaped sclerite known as the *lorum (Lr)*. Each stipes carries a long, free, tapering, bladelike lobe, the *galea (Ga)*, and, arising lateral to it, a very small maxillary palpus *(MxPlp)*.

When the proboscis is not in use its basal parts are drawn up behind the head by swinging on the suspending cardines (Fig. 6, H), while at the same time the distal parts are folded back against the prementum and stipites. When the bee would imbibe liquid, the proboscis is protracted by swinging downward on the cardines, and its distal parts are extended. The broad maxillary galeae and the labial palpi are brought together around the tongue (Fig. 6, B, G) in such a manner as to form a tube (D), closed anteriorly by the overlapping galeae *(Ga)* and posteriorly by the palpi *(LbPlp)*, with the tongue *(Gls)* occupying an axial position and projecting beyond the enclosing parts (G). The two small end-segments of the palpi diverge at the end of the tube and probably have a sensory function. The tongue now begins a rapid back-and-forth movement, while its flexible tip is swung around with an agile lapping motion. Apparently by the action of the tongue the liquid food is drawn up into the canal of the proboscis (D, *fc*).

The long hairy tongue of the bee is an extension from the end of the labial prementum (Fig. 6, A, *Gls*). It has a closely cross-lined appearance owing to the presence in its wall of hard rings bearing the hairs, separated by narrow, smooth, membranous intervals. Because of this structure the tongue can be shortened and lengthened. On its base is a bonnet-shaped plate (Fig. 7, A) supported on a pair of arms *(b)* which are extensions of two straplike bars in the side walls of the prementum (D, *a*). The under or posterior side of the tongue is traversed by a deep groove (Fig. 6, A, *sc*) with thin membranous walls, through the middle of which runs a long rodlike thickening (D, *rd*) which is grooved on its free surface. At the tip of the tongue the rod ends in a small spoon-shaped lobe, the *flabellum* (A, G, *Fbl*), that has a smooth, rounded under-surface but is armed on the margin and the upper surface by minute branched spines. Basally the tongue rod curves backward to be firmly attached to the end of the posterior wall of the prementum (Fig. 7, A), and on this curved part are inserted two long muscles (20) arising in the prementum. It is the pull of these muscles on the basal curvature of the rod that shortens the tongue (B); extension is due apparently to the elasticity of the rod which straightens again when the muscles relax. Thus are produced the movements of protraction and retraction of the tongue from the end of the proboscis; but since the rod lies close to the posterior margin of the tongue its retraction gives the tongue also a slight backward curvature (B). The lapping motion of the tongue tip evidently is produced by the rod muscles acting separately in opposition to each other.

The food canal of the proboscis leads up into a channel on the base of the proboscis between the bases of the two maxillae and the labium, which appears as an open troughlike cavity when the proboscis is lowered from the head (Fig. 6, B, *FC*). At the upper end of this channel is the *mouth (Mth)* partly hidden behind a large soft lobe, the *epipharynx (Ephy)*, projecting from beneath the labrum *(Lm)*. The lower lip of the

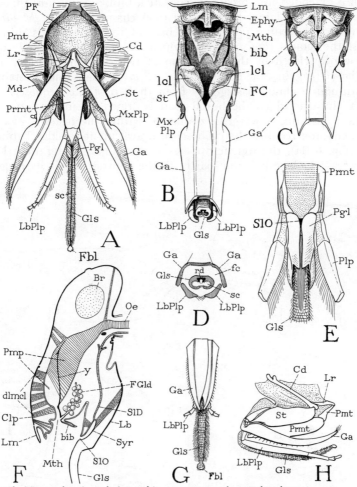

FIGURE 6. The proboscis and the sucking apparatus of a worker bee.

A, proboscis, seen from behind, with its parts artificially spread out. B, front view of base of proboscis pulled down from head, exposing mouth *(Mth)* and deep food channel *(FC)* leading up to mouth. C, same, food channel closed by base of proboscis brought up against the mouth. D, cross section through middle of proboscis. E, base of tongue, paraglossae, labial palpi, and distal end of labial prementum, anterior view. F, lengthwise verticle section of head showing sucking pump *(Pmp)*, salivary syringe *(Syr)*, and associated structures. G, distal part of proboscis with tongue protruded. H, side view of proboscis folded beneath head. *bib,* biblike fold from lower lip of mouth; *Br,* brain; *Cd,* cardo; *Clp,* clypeus; *dlmcl,* dilator muscles of sucking pump; *Ephy,* epipharynx; *Fbl,* flabellum; *fc,* food canal of proboscis; *FC,* food channel on base of proboscis; *FGld,* food gland; *Ga,* galea; *Gls,* tongue (glossa); *Lb,* labium; *LbPlp,* labial palpus; *lcl,* lacinial lobe of maxilla; *Lm,* labrum; *Lr,* lorum; *Md,* mandible; *Mth,* mouth; *MxPlp,* maxillary palpus; *Oe,* oesophagus; *PF,* proboscis fossa on back of head; *Pgl,* paraglossa; *Plp,* labial palpus; *Pmp,* sucking pump; *Pmt,* postmentum; *Prmt,* prementum; *rd,* rod of tongue; *sc,* salivary canal of tongue; *SlD,* salivary duct; *SlO,* orifice of salivary duct; *St,* stipes; *Syr,* salivary syringe.

mouth is extended in a broad, two-pointed, biblike fold *(bib)* that hangs down against the labial floor of the food channel (Fig. 8, A, *bib*). In the functional feeding position the base of the proboscis is drawn up against the mouth (Fig. 6, C), by which act the food channel (B, *FC*) is outwardly closed by the appression of two cushionlike lobes on the maxillae *(lcl)* against the epipharynx *(C, Ephy)*. There thus is established a continuously closed passageway from the tip of the proboscis to the mouth, through which the liquid food is drawn up to the latter. The sucking apparatus, however, is contained within the head.

When, after feeding, the proboscis is drawn up and folded behind the head (Fig. 6, H), the tongue appears to be much shorter than before. Its decrease in length is due partly to the contraction of its rings, but

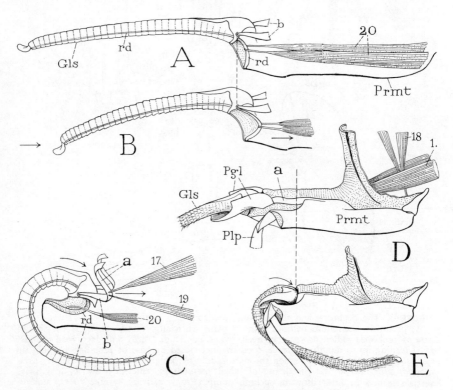

FIGURE 7. Mechanisms of the proboscis of a worker bee.

A, diagram of tongue extended from prementum, showing tongue rod and its muscles. B, tongue shortened by pull of muscles on base of tongue rod. C, tongue retracted and automatically curved backward by pull of muscles *(17, 19)* attached on supporting arms *(a)* of tongue base. D, base of labium, with tongue and paraglossae extended. E, same with tongue and paraglossae retracted and tongue curved back as at C.

a, supporting arms of tongue and paraglossae; *b,* pivotal supports of tongue; *Gls,* tongue; *Pgl,* paraglossae; *Plp,* labial palpus; *Prmt,* prementum; *rd,* flexible rod of tongue; *17, 19,* retractor muscles of tongue and paraglossae; *18,* adductor muscle of labium; *20,* muscles of tongue rod.

it may be noted (Fig. 7, E), by comparison with the extended position (D), that the bases of the tongue and paraglossae *(Pgl)* have been deeply retracted into the end of the prementum. The muscles that retract the proboscis are a pair of long labial muscles (D, *17*) arising on the top of the head and inserted on the distal ends of the premental bars (C, *a*) along with another pair of muscles *(19)* arising in the prementum. When these muscles contract they bend the premental bars sharply inward (C), and the bars bring with them the attached bases of the tongue and paraglossae. The tongue rod *(rd)*, however, is thus pulled so far out of the base of the tongue that its tension automatically curves the tongue backward beneath the prementum. Since there is no mechanism for extending the retracted parts, the reverse action probably results either from the elasticity of the flexed bars or from blood pressure caused by drawing the base of the proboscis close against the head. The flexing of the labial palpi and the maxillary galeae is produced by specific flexor muscles attached on the bases of these appendages.

THE SUCKING PUMP

The sucking apparatus of the bee is a large, muscle-walled sac lying in the head (Fig. 6, F, *Pmp*) extending from the mouth *(Mth)* to the neck foramen, where its narrowed upper end becomes continuous with the oesophagus *(Oe)*. Each lateral wall of the pump is traversed obliquely by a slender rod *(y)*, extending upward from a plate on the floor of the mouth (Fig. 8, B, *opl*). In other insects these rods and the oral plate pertain to a large tonguelike lobe known as the *hypopharynx* projecting between the mouth and the base of the labium. The true mouth lies between the upper ends of the rods and opens into the *pharynx,* which is the first part of the alimentary canal. The preoral food cavity before the hypopharynx is the *cibarium.* In the bee, therefore, the sucking pump is a combination of the preoral cibarium and the postoral pharynx. The hypopharynx of the bee is represented by the oral plate, the biblike fold (Fig. 6, F, *bib*) hanging from the latter, and the infolding ending at the opening of the salivary duct *(SlD)* into the so-called salivary syringe *(Syr)*.

The functional mouth of the bee *(Mth)* is simply the opening into the cibarium between the labrum and the hypopharynx. The cibarium is the operative part of the pump, five pairs of thick bundles of dilator muscle fibers *(dlmcl)* from the clypeus being attached on its anterior wall. Between these muscles (not shown on the figure) are strong compressor fibers running obliquely crosswise on the cibarial wall. Liquids are sucked up from the canal of the proboscis by the action of the dilator muscles; contraction of the compressor muscles then closes the mouth and drives the liquid into the muscular pharynx, from which it is driven into the narrow oesophagus. Inasmuch as regurgitation of nectar and honey is an important function of the bee's feeding apparatus, it is probable that the pump can serve for both ingestion and egestion.

THE SALIVARY SYSTEM

Between the root of the tongue and the distal end of the labial pre-mentum anteriorly is a deep depression (Fig. 6, E, *SlO*), mostly concealed by the overlapping paraglossae *(Pgl)*. At the bottom of this depression is an opening that leads into a small pocket of the prementum (F, *Syr*). By exposing the pocket, it is seen that its walls are provided with dilator and compressor muscles, and that into its inner end opens the common duct of the salivary glands *(SlD)*. This apparatus is a pump for the ejection of the saliva and may be termed the *salivary syringe*.

The saliva is secreted by two pair of glands discharging finally into one median duct. The glands of one pair lie in the back of the head, those of the other pair in the ventral part of the thorax. The *thoracic glands* (Fig. 8, C, *ThGld*) consist of masses of elongate or tubular saccules at the ends of branching ducts (E) that lead into a pair of reservoir sacs (C, *Res*). From the reservoirs two ducts go forward and unite just behind the head in the common median duct *(SlD)* that enters the neck foramen of the head and empties into the salivary syringe *(Syr)*. The *head glands* (C, *HGld*) are flat masses of small pear-shaped bodies (D) spread over the posterior head wall. Their ducts unite within the head with the common duct from the thoracic glands. The thoracic glands are developed from the silk glands of the larva, and correspond with the usual salivary glands of other insects; the head glands are developed in the pupa as outgrowths from the common salivary duct.

From the salivary syringe the saliva is ejected into the cavity on the labium at the root of the tongue, but it is here confined by the overlapping paraglossae (Fig. 6, E, *Pgl*), and within the latter is conveyed around the base of the tongue into the channellike groove on the posterior or undersurface of the tongue (A, D, *sc*). Through this channel probably it is conducted to the tip of the tongue where it flows out over the smooth undersurface of the flabellum (A, *Fbl*) to mix with the nectar or honey being drawn into the proboscis, or is used as a solvent if the bee is feeding on sugar.

THE BROOD-FOOD GLANDS

The glands of the worker bee that produce the food material called "royal jelly," which is fed to the queen, drones, and larvae, are two long strings of small saccules closely packed in many loops and coils in the sides of the head (Fig. 8, A, *FGld*). The axial ducts open separately by two small pores on the lateral angles of the oral plate on the floor of the mouth (B, *opl*). Since this plate belongs to the hypopharynx, the food glands are *hypopharyngeal* and not "pharyngeal" glands as they have long been called. The rodlike arms (*y*) of the oral plate give attachment to muscles from the head wall, and probably have some function in discharging the royal jelly from the mouth. The food evidently must run down the biblike flap that hangs from the edge of the oral plate

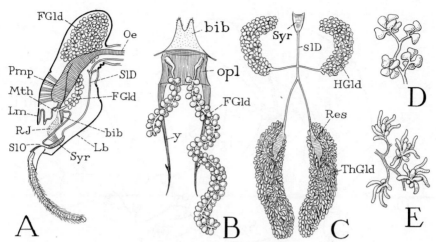

FIGURE 8. Glands of the head and thorax of a worker bee.

A, vertical section of head showing food gland *(FGld)* of right side. B, under surface of oral plate, showing openings of food glands. C, general view of the salivary system, including head glands *(HGld)*, thoracic glands *(ThGld)*, ducts, and salivary syringe *(Syr)*. D, detail of head gland. E, detail of thoracic gland.

bib, biblike fold from lower lip of mouth; *FGld*, food gland; *HGld*, head salivary gland; *Lb*, labium; *Lm*, labrum; *Mth*, mouth; *Oe*, oesophagus; *opl*, oral plate on floor of mouth; *Pmp*, sucking pump; *Res*, reservoir of thoracic gland; *RJ*, royal jelly; *SlD*, salivary duct; *SlO*, orifice of salivary duct; *Syr*, salivary syringe; *ThGld*, thoracic salivary gland; *y*, arm of oral plate.

(A, B, *bib*) and accumulate (A, *RJ*) in the food channel on the base of the proboscis. The open channel thus serves as a feeding trough for other adult bees, which obtain the royal jelly by thrusting the end of the proboscis over the base of the tongue of the feeder bee, the proboscis of the latter being turned back, the mandibles opened, and the labrum raised. When the nurse bees feed the larvae, however, the royal jelly is said to be discharged from between the partly opened mandibles.

The Thorax, The Legs, and The Wings

The thorax of an insect is the middle division of the trunk which carries the legs and the wings. Its cavity is largely occupied by the muscles of the locomotor appendages and the muscles that move the head and the abdomen, the other internal organs being mostly contained in the head and the abdomen (Fig. 17, A). The nerve centers of the thorax, however, are particularly large (Fig. 20) because they control the activities of the thoracic muscles.

STRUCTURE OF THE BEE'S THORAX

The thorax of the bee and related Hymenoptera, as already noted, consists of four body segments which, beginning with the first, are desig-

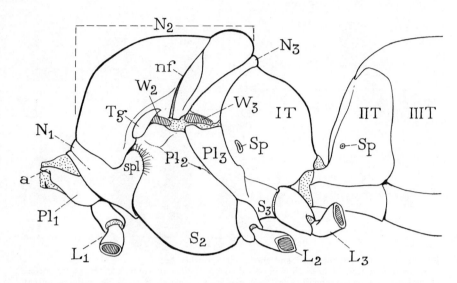

FIGURE 9. The thorax and base of the abdomen, left side, of a worker bee.
   a. pivotal point supporting head; *I T,* back plate of propodeum; *II T, III T,* back
plates (terga) of first and second abdominal segments; *L₁, L₂, L₃,* bases of legs; *N₁,* pronotum; *N₂* mesonotum; *N₃,* metanotum; *nf,* notal fissure; *Pl₁,* pleuron of prothorax; *Pl₂,*
pleuron of mesothorax; *Pl₃,* pleuron of metathorax; *S₂, S₃,* sternal areas of mesothorax and
metathorax; *Sp,* spiracle; *spl,* lobe of pronotum covering first spiracle; *Tg,* tegula; *W₂, W₃,*
bases of wings.

nated the *prothorax* (Fig. 4, *1*), the *mesothorax* (*2*), the *metathorax*
(*3*), and the *propodeum* (I), but the several segments are so closely united
that it is difficult to observe their limits. In studying a thoracic segment
we distinguish a back plate or *notum,* a ventral plate or *sternum,* and a
plate or group of plates on each side called the *pleuron.*
   The prothorax of the bee is merged with the neck to form a slender
support for the head, and carries the first pair of legs. Its back plate, the
pronotum (Fig. 9, N_1), is set like a collar on the front of the mesothorax,
and is expanded on each side in a flat lobe *(spl)* that covers the first pair
of breathing apertures. The pleural and sternal plates of the prothorax
support the first legs (L_1), and the head is pivoted on a pair of peglike
processes (*a*) projecting from the anterior ends of the pleura. The mesothorax is the largest part of the thorax. The mesonotum (N_2) lies above
the wing bases (W_2) forming the uppermost bulge of the thoracic wall
and sloping steeply downward to the pronotal collar. Below the wings
the pleural and sternal walls of the segment (Pl_2, S_2) are continuous from
one side to the other. The metathorax is a narrow band angularly bent
forward on the sides, closely wedged between the mesothorax and the
propodeum. The metanotum (N_3) widens somewhat toward the wing
bases (W_3); the pleural plates (Pl_3) are continuous with the sternum

(S_3) as in the mesothorax. The fourth thoracic segment, or propodeum, consists mostly of a large back plate *(IT)* firmly united with the meta-thorax. It has no pleural elements and its sternum is a weak ventral plate behind the third legs. Posteriorly the propodeum is abruptly nar-rowed to give attachment to the abdominal petiole. Further details of the thoracic structure will be described in connection with the wings and their mechanism.

THE LEGS OF THE BEE

The three pair of legs of an insect are seldom alike in size or shape, but each is divided into six principal parts or *segments,* movable on each other at flexible *joints* (Fig. 10, A). The basal leg segment is the *coxa (Cx)*; the second segment is the *trochanter (Tr)*; the third, usually a long segment, is the *femur (Fm)*; the fourth is the *tibia (Tb)*; the fifth is the *tarsus (Tar);* and the last is the *pretarsus (Ptar).* The tarsus, how-ever, is subdivided into several small parts or *tarsomeres.* The pretarsus is a very small segment but it carries a pair of lateral *claws* (E, *Cl*) and a median lobe termed the *arolium (Ar).*

The joints between the leg segments are mostly hinges with motion limited to one plane, no part of an insect's leg having anything like the freedom of movement at the joints of a vertebrate limb as the human arm. As a consequence the insect has little choice as to what it can do with its legs, and hence all individuals of a species do the same things in prac-tically the same way. The limitation of action at the joints is partly com-pensated by the number of segments that move in different directions.

Each leg of the bee is hinged to the body on an obliquely transverse axis and therefore swings as a whole only forward and backward. At the first leg joint, that between the coxa and the trochanter (Fig. 10, A), the part of the leg beyond the coxa turns up and down in a plane at right angles to the plane of movement of the entire leg on the body. The muscles of the trochanter hence raise and lower the leg at the coxo-trochanteral joint; but if the feet are against a support the contraction of the depressor muscles lifts the body on the legs. The trochanter has several small muscles arising in the coxa, but, to increase the lifting power, each trochanter is provided with a long muscle arising on an internal framework within the thorax (Fig. 10, C, *86).* The trochanter is joined to the femur by an oblique hinge in a vertical plane which thus does not interfere with the lifting power of the trochanteral muscles, though it gives only a slight backward bend to the femur. The articula-tion between the femur and the tibia is a typical knee joint, at which the tibia can be extended or flexed on the end of the femur by long extensor and flexor muscles arising in the femur.

The tarsus of the bee (Fig. 10, A, B, *Tar*) consists of five parts, or tarsomeres, of which the first is much longer and thicker than the others in all the legs, and is distinguished as the *basitarsus (Btar).* The large, flat basal subsegment of the hind tarsus (Fig. 11, C, *Btar)* is commonly called

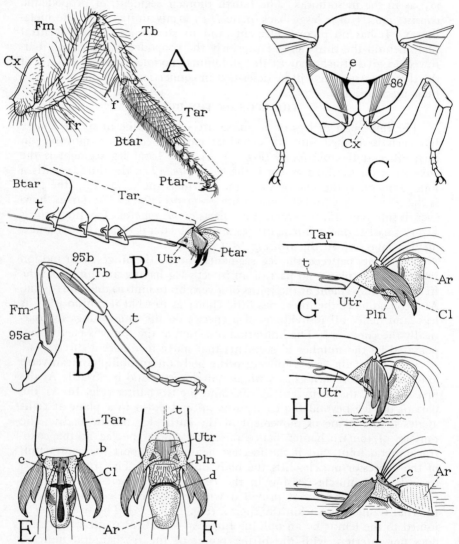

FIGURE 10. General structure of the legs of a worker bee.

A, middle leg of worker. B, tarsus and foot (pretarsus) more enlarged. C, cross section of mesothorax, with middle legs. D, outline of middle leg, showing muscles and tendon of pretarsus. E, pretarsus, upper surface. F, same, lower surface. G, diagram of foot (pretarsus) with claws extended. H, same, with claws grasping a rough surface. I, same, arolium spread out on a smooth surface on which claws fail to hold.

Ar, arolium; *b,* articular knob of claw; *Btar,* basitarsus; *c,* handle-like bar of arolium braced on end of tarsus; *Cl,* claw; *Cx,* coxa; *d,* elastic band in under wall of arolium; *e,* internal framework of thorax; *f,* spine of tibia; *Fm,* femur; *Pln,* planta; *Ptar,* pretarsus (foot); *t,* tendon of pretarsal muscles; *Tar,* tarsus; *Tb,* tibia; *Tr,* trochanter; *Utr,* unguitractor plate.

the "planta" by writers on the honey bee, but the word *planta* in Latin means "the sole of the foot," and the term is so used in general zoology. In insects the planta is properly a small ventral sclerite of the pretarsus (Fig. 10, F, *Pln*). The tibiotarsal joint differs from the other leg joints in that it allows more freedom of movement to the tarsus, which has three muscles attached on the basitarsus that give three separate movements. The large basitarsus is followed by three very small tarsomeres, and the fifth longer tarsomere carries at its extremity the pretarsus *(Ptar)*. Between the subsegments of the tarsus (B) there are no muscles, the tarsomeres being flexible on each other but having no power of individual movement. The entire tarsus, however, is traversed by the tendon (B, *t*) of the pretarsal muscles arising in the femur and the tibia (D, *95a, 95b*).

The pretarsus, which might be termed the "foot" of the insect, is a very important part of the leg since it bears the organs by which the insect clings to supporting surfaces. The pretarsal claws (Fig. 10, E, F, *Cl*) maintain a hold on rough surfaces; the arolium *(Ar)* adheres to smooth surfaces. The claws of the bee are double pointed and their deep bases are implanted vertically in the lateral walls of the pretarsus, but each claw is articulated to a small knob (E, *b*) on the end of the tarsus. The arolium projects from the end of the pretarsus between the claws. When not in use (G, H) it is turned upward and appears to be merely a soft, oval lobe, though closer inspection shows that it is deeply concave on its upper or anterior surface (E), that is, its sides are folded together upward. The basal lip of the aroliar cavity is braced against the end of the tarsus by a bottle-shaped sclerite *(c)* on the upper wall of the pretarsus bearing five or six long curved bristles. The arolium thus resembles a scoop with a long handle. Its convex outer wall contains a U-shaped elastic band (F, *d*).

In the lower wall of the pretarsus (Fig. 10, F) are two median plates; the stronger proximal one, which is partly concealed in a pocket at the end of the tarsus, is the *unguitractor plate (Utr);* and the distal one, covered with strong spines, is the *planta (Pln)*. The concealed proximal end of the unguitractor plate is connected with the end of a strong internal tendon *(t)* that runs through the entire tarsus (D) into the tibia where it divides into two branches; one branch gives attachment to a muscle in the tibia *(95b)*, and the other goes on into the femur and ends in a long muscle arising in the base of the femur *(95a)*. These muscles operate both the claws and the arolium by their pull on the tendon and the attached unguitractor plate.

The mechanism of the foot structure is illustrated diagrammatically at G, H, and I of Fig. 10. At G the claws are extended and the arolium *(Ar)* turned upward in the usual position. At H the unguitractor plate *(Utr)* has been retracted by its muscles into the end of the tarsus, and, as the plate is closely associated with the bases of the claws, the claws are flexed until irregularities of the surface of contact restrain their points.

In this way the bee is enabled to cling to rough surfaces. At I the bee is supposed to be resting on a smooth surface on which the claws have not been able to hold; the continued pull of the muscles, therefore, has turned the claws so far forward that they sprawl out helplessly with their points upward. But now the traction of the unguitractor plate is exerted on the planta and finally on the base of the arolium. The aroliar handle *(c)*, however, being braced against the tarsus, prevents a retraction of the arolium, but the tension and pressure on the base of the arolium, together with the pressure of the leg against the support, flatten the aroliar scoop to the form of a dustpan. The broad, soft undersurface of the spread-out arolium now adheres to the smooth surface which the claws failed to grasp. It has been said that the adhesive property of the arolium is due to a sticky liquid exuded from the spines of the planta. On release of the muscle pull on the unguitractor plate, the elastic band in the under wall of the arolium causes the latter to fold up again, and the claws, by the elasticity of their basal connections, are once more extended.

Though the legs are primarily organs of locomotion, various specialized parts of the legs of the honey bee serve for purposes other than that of walking or running. The brushes of stiff hairs on the inner surfaces of the long basal segments of the anterior tarsi (Fig. 11, I, g) are used for cleaning pollen or other particles from the head, the eyes, and the mouth parts. Similarly the bushy middle tarsi (Fig. 10, A) serve as brushes for cleaning the thorax. The long spines at the ends of the middle tibiae *(f)* are said to be used for loosening the pellets of pollen from the pollen baskets of the hind legs, and also for cleaning the wings and the spiracles. The wax scales are removed from the wax pockets of the abdomen by means of the legs, but there is some difference of opinion as to just how it is done. The special structures of chief interest on the legs, however, are the antenna cleaners on the forelegs of all castes, and the pollen-collecting and pollen-carrying apparatus on the hind legs of worker bees.

THE ANTENNA CLEANER

The structures used by the bee for cleaning its antennae are situated on the inner margins of the forelegs just beyond the tibiotarsal joints (Fig. 11, I, h). Each antenna cleaner consists of a deep semicircular notch on the basal part of the long basitarsus (A, *i*), and of a small clasplike lobe *(j)* that projects over the notch from the end of the tibia. The margin of the notch is fringed with a comblike row of small spines. The clasp is a flattened appendage, tapering to a point and provided with a small lobule *(k)* on its anterior surface; it is flexible at its base but has no muscles. As this gadget is used by the bee, the open tarsal notch is first placed against the antennal flagellum by appropriate movements of the leg; then by flexing the tarsus against the tibia (B), the flagellum is brought against the tibial clasp which resists the pressure because of a small stop-point *(l)* behind its base. The flagellum, thus held in the

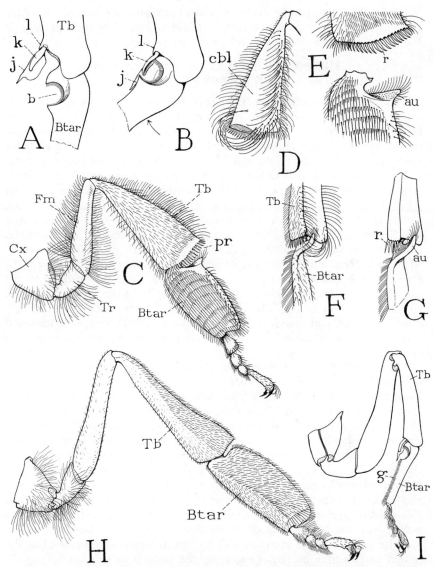

FIGURE 11. Special features of the legs of a worker bee (except H).

A, antenna cleaner of first leg, open. B, same, closed. C, hind leg of worker, inner surface, showing pollen collecting brush on basitarsus *(Btar)* and pollen press *(pr)*. D, pollen-basket (corbicula) on outer surface of hind tibia (C, *Tb*). E, end of hind tibia with pollen rake *(r)* and opposing end of basitarsus with auricle *(au)*. F, pollen press between tibia and basitarsus, dorsal view. G, same, better seen after removal of tibial hairs. H, hind leg of drone. I, first leg of worker, showing position of antenna cleaner.

au, auricle; *Btar,* basitarsus; *cbl,* pollen basket; *Cx,* coxa; *Fm,* femur; *g,* tarsal brush of first leg; *h,* antenna cleaner; *i,* notch of antenna cleaner; *j,* clasp of antenna cleaner; *k,* lobe of clasp; *l,* stop-point for clasp; *pr,* pollen press; *r,* pollen rake; *Tb,* tibia.

notch by the clasp, is now drawn upward between the comb of the notch and the scraping edge of the clasp. The antenna cleaner is present in the queen and the drone as well as in the worker.

THE POLLEN-COLLECTING APPARATUS AND THE POLLEN BASKETS

The hind legs differ from the other legs in their large size and the broad, flattened form of the tibia and basitarsus (Fig. 11, C), which latter parts differ also as between the worker (C), the queen, and the drone (H). It is only in the worker that there is any evident reason for the special shape of the hind legs. The smooth, somewhat concave, outer surface of the hind tibia of the worker is fringed with long, curved hairs (D), and the space thus enclosed is the so-called *pollen basket* or *corbicula (cbl)* in which pollen (also propolis) is carried to the hive. The pollen stored in the baskets is first collected from the body by the fore and middle legs and deposited on the large flat brushes on the inner surfaces of the broad basal segments of the hind tarsi, each of which is covered with about ten transverse rows of stiff spines projecting posteriorly (C, *Btar*). The appartus for transfer of the pollen from the brushes to the baskets are the deep notches in the upper margins of the legs between the tibiae and the tarsi *(pr)*. The tibial margin of each notch is armed with a *rake* of short, stiff spines (E, *r)*; the opposing tarsal margin is flattened transversely and extended laterally into a small triangular lip, or *auricle (au)*, fringed with hairs.

The transfer of the pollen from the collecting brushes to the baskets is accomplished as follows: When the basitarsal brushes are sufficiently loaded with pollen, the leg of one side is rubbed against the other in such a manner that the rake on the end of the tibia scrapes off a small mass of pollen from the tarsal brush of the opposite leg. The detached pollen grains fall on the flat surface of the auricle which is beveled upward and outward. Consequently, when now the tarsus is closed against the tibia (Fig. 11, F, G), the pollen on the auricle is forced upward and pressed outward against the outer surface of the tibia where, being wet and sticky, it adheres to the floor of the pollen basket. A repetition of this process, first on one side, then on the other, successively packs more pollen into the lower ends of the baskets, until finally both are filled.

The pollen baskets are used also for the transport of propolis, but the pollen presses play no part in loading the baskets in this case. Propolis is a resinous gum collected by bees with their mandibles from trees or other plants. The resin particles, it is said, are gathered up with the fore and middle legs and placed directly in the baskets of the hind legs.

THE WINGS OF THE BEE

The wings of an insect are flat, thin, two-layered extensions of the body wall, strengthened by tubular thickenings called *veins*. They arise from the sides of the mesothorax and the metathorax between the notal and pleural plates of these segments. In the honey bee the fore wings (Fig. 12, A) are much larger than the hind wings (B) and their venation is stronger, but the two wings of each side work together in flight. To insure unity of action the wings are provided with a coupling apparatus formed by a series of upturned hooks on the front margin of each hind wing (B, *h*), and a decurved fold on the rear margin of the fore wing (A, *f*). When the wings are extended preparatory to flight, the fore wings are drawn over the hind wings, and the hooks of the latter automatically catch in the marginal folds of the former (E).

Each wing is hinged by its narrowed base to the margin of the back plate of its segment, and is supported from below on the upper edge of the corresponding pleuron. The wings are thus free to move up and down; but progressive flight requires other movements, including a forward and backward motion of each wing, and a twisting or partial rotation of the wing on its long axis. These latter components of the flight movement depend on details of structure in the wing bases. All the wing movements, except such as may result from air pressure during flight,

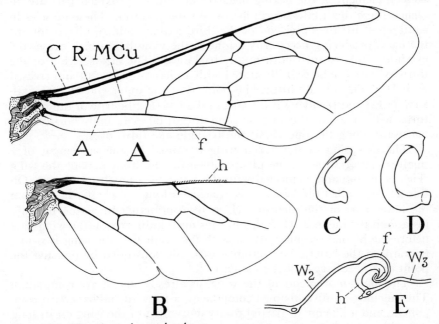

FIGURE 12. The wings of a worker bee.
A, right fore wing of worker. B, right hind wing. C, hind wing hook of worker. D, wing hook of drone. E, section of fore and hind wings showing interlocking by fold and hooks.

A, anal vein; *C,* costal vein; *f,* marginal fold of fore wing; *h,* marginal hooks of hind wing; *R,* radial vein; *MCu,* median and cubital veins united; *W₂,* fore wing; *W₃,* hind wing.

are produced by thoracic muscles; but most of the muscles involved are attached not on the wings themselves, but on movable parts of the thorax that indirectly affect the wings. Hence, for an understanding of the flight mechanism, we shall have to make a further study of the thoracic structure. Moreover, the wings when not in active use are folded horizontally backward over the abdomen. From this position of rest they can quickly be extended to the position of activity. In addition to the flight mechanism, therefore, we must distinguish a mechanism of *flexion* and *extension* for each wing individually. It will be logical to give attention first to the structures that produce these horizontal movements.

If the base of one of the wings, a fore wing for example (Fig. 13, A), is spread out flat it will be seen that it contains several small plates or *axillaries*. Two of the axillaries, the *first (1Ax)* and the *fourth (4Ax)*, are the hinge plates by which the wing articulates on the edge of the notum. Another, the *second axillary (2Ax)* lying behind the first, rests on the upper edge of the pleuron (B, Pl_2) and constitutes the pivotal plate of the wing base. A third long sclerite (A, *3Ax*) extends outward along the thickened margin of the basal wing membrane, and this axillary is the skeletal element of the flexing mechanism. On its proximal part are attached three small muscles (F) arising on the pleuron. These muscles in contraction lift the outer end of the third axillary and revolve it toward the back, producing necessarily a fold in the wing base which causes the extended wing to turn horizontally backward. The flexor action of the third axillary can be well illustrated with a piece of paper cut and creased as at D of Fig. 13. By lifting the point *d* at the outer end of the "axillary" *(3Ax)* and revolving it upward to the left *(E)*, the base of the "wing" turns with it along the line *bc;* and the distal part folds horizontally backward along the line *ab,* as the triangle *abc* turns over.

The extension of the flexed wing is caused by the movement of a small sclerite resting on the pleuron beneath the front part of the wing (Fig. 13, B, *Ba*) and connected with the latter by a tough membrane. On this sclerite, called the *basalare,* is attached a long muscle (G, I, *77)* from the lower part of the pleuron, which by contracting turns the basalare inward on the pleuron (H, *Ba),* and thus pulls indirectly on the wing base before the pivotal second axillary, with the result that the wing is swung forward on the latter. The action is easily demonstrated by pressing the point of a needle against the basalare.

The flight movements of the wing, as already stated, are compound. They include an up-and-down component, a forward-and-backward component, and a torsion, or partial rotary movement of the wing on its long axis. The up-and-down strokes are caused by vibrations of the back plate of the wing-bearing segment. Because the two wings of a segment are supported from below on the pleura, a depression of the back plate causes the wings, in the manner of a pump handle, to go up (Fig. 14, A), as can be demonstrated by pressing downward on the back of a bee. A

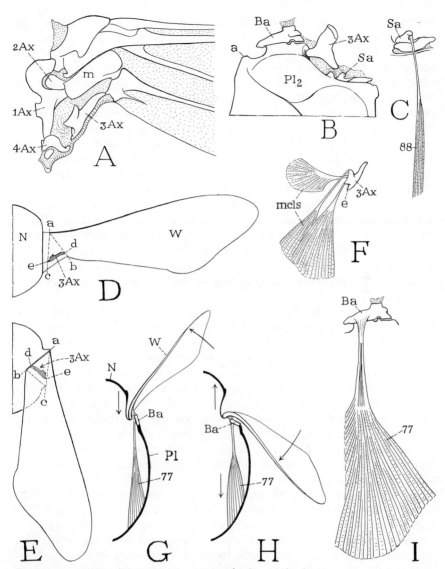

FIGURE 13. Details of the wing structure, and wing mechanisms.

A, base of fore wing, flattened, showing axillary sclerites and bases of veins. B, upper part of left mesopleuron supporting basalar sclerite *(Ba)*, second axillary *(2Ax)*, and subalar sclerite *(Sa)*. C, subalar sclerite and its muscle. D, diagram of extended wing and lines of folding in base. E, diagram of wing turned horizontally over back. F, third axillary (flexor sclerite) of fore wing and its muscles. G, diagram of raised wing with front margin elevated. H, same, wing lowered, front margin depressed by contraction of basalar muscle *(77)*. I, basalar sclerite of fore wing and its muscle.

a-b, b-c, lines of folding in wing base; *1Ax, 2Ax, 3Ax, 4Ax,* first, second, third, and fourth axillary; *Ba,* basalar sclerite; *d,* outer end of third axillary; *m,* median plate of wing base; *Mcls,* muscles; *N,* notum; *Pl,* pleuron; *Sa,* subalar sclerite; *W,* wing.

reverse movement of the back (B) depresses the wings. The major part of the wing mechanism produces the vibrations of the back plates.

If the thorax of a bee is cut open (Fig. 14, D, E) it will be seen that it is almost filled with great masses of muscle fibers. In each side of the mesothorax is a thick column of vertical fibers (*72*) attached dorsally on the notum, and another smaller muscle (E, *75*) is attached on the margin of the notum. These muscles are the depressors of the back and, therefore, the *elevator muscles of the wings* (A). Between the first pair are two flat bundles of fibers (D, E, *71*) running obliquely lengthwise from the median area of the mesonotum to a strong, internal U-shaped band, the *second phragma* (D, *2Ph*), extending from the mesonotum far back into the propodeum. These are the *depressor muscles of the wings* because their contraction compresses the mesonotum in a lengthwise direction, and hence elevates the back, causing the wings to turn downward (B). It will be recalled that the two wings on each side are hooked together during flight. The mesothorax has wing-elevator muscles of its own, but the downstroke of both pair of wings is produced by the mesothoracic muscles and depends on the coupling of the fore and hind wings with each other.

In most insects the back plates of the wing-bearing segments are sufficiently flexible to respond by vibratory movements to the alternating pull of the vertical and lengthwise muscles attached on them. The mesonotum of the bee, however, is a rigid and strongly convex plate. In order to perform its function in connection with the wings it is cut by a deep, crosswise groove (Fig. 14, D, F, *nf*) into a larger anterior plate, (F, *1N_2*) and a smaller posterior plate (*2N_2*). The middle part of the groove on the top of the back acts as a hinge between the two plates; the lateral parts open out into actual clefts (G, *nf*) having the edges united by infolded membranes. The front angles of the anterior notal plate are firmly braced on the pleura (as indicated by the arrow at *a*); the posterior notal plate is supported on the metanotum (*N_3*). Contraction of the vertical muscles (G, *72*), therefore, depresses the mesonotum at the hinge line *(d)* on the back and opens the lateral clefts *(nf)* between the two notal plates. Conversely, the contraction of the lengthwise muscles (F, *71*) restores the notum to its original shape by closing the lateral clefts. The opening and closing of the clefts, however, necessarily is accompanied, respectively, by a downward and upward movement of the adjoining tergal margins *(e, f)*, as is seen by comparing their positions in F and G relative to the line *g*. The action of the mesonotum may be exactly imitated by compressing half of a hollow rubber ball having a meridional cleft on each side (C). Each wing, being attached to the margin of the back just before and behind the notal cleft, is thus hinged at the points of greatest vertical movement in the notal margin, and it is this movement that causes the up-and-down wing strokes during flight.

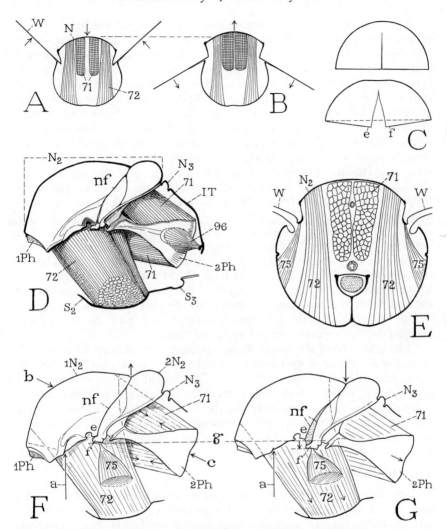

FIGURE 14. The mechanism of the up-and-down movement of the wings.

A, cross section of mesothorax with wings elevated. B, same, with wings depressed. C, diagrams of movements of mesonotum that depress and elevate the wings. D, thorax with left wall removed showing muscles. E, cross section of mesothorax through wing bases. F, diagram of position of back plates of mesothorax $(1N_2, 2N_2)$ when muscle 71 is contracted. G, same when muscles 72 and 75 contract, the notal fissure (nf) opened on the side, the marginal points e and f lowered. (Compare F and G with C).

a, point of support of mesonotum on pleuron; *b-c*, direction of contraction of muscle 71; *d*, hinge line on back between plates of mesonotum; *e, f*, points of greatest movement on margin of mesonotum as notal fissure (nf) opens and closes; *g*, horizontal line; *IT*, back plate of propodeum; *N, notum; N_2*, mesonotum, divided by notal fissure (nf) into anterior plate $(1N_2)$ and posterior plate $(2N_2)$; N_3 mentanotum; *nf*, notal fissure; *1Ph*, first phragma; *2Ph*, second phragma; S_2, mesosternum; S_3, metasternum; *W*, wing; 71, lengthwise muscles of mesothorax (depressors of wings); 72, 75, vertical muscles of mesothorax (elevators of wings).

A mere flapping of the wings cannot produce flight; the driving force results from a propellerlike twist given to each wing during the upstroke and the downstroke. As the wing descends it goes also somewhat forward and its anterior margin turns downward; during the upstroke the action is reversed. The tip of the vibrating wing, therefore, if the insect is held stationary, describes a figure 8. The mechanism that produces these components of the flight movement includes the basalar sclerite and its muscle (Fig. 13, B, I, *Ba*), already described as causing the extension of the flexed wing; and a similar musculated sclerite (C, *Sa*), designated the *subalare*, resting on the pleural margin beneath the posterior part of the wing base (B, *Sa*). The alternating pull of the basalar and subalar muscles on their respective sclerites not only turns the wings during flight forward and backward, but at the same time deflects their forward margins during the downstroke and reverses the movement during the upstroke. The action of the basalare is illustrated diagrammatically at G and H of Fig. 13. At G the wing is raised by the depression of the notum *(N)*, and its rear margin is turned downward by the pull of the subalare (not shown) on the rear part of its base. At H the wing is in the downstroke position caused by the elevation of the notum; but it is also turned forward, with its front margin deflected by the pull of the basalar muscle (77) on the basalar plate *(Ba)*, which latter in turn pulls downward and forward on the anterior part of the wing base.

The efficiency of the insect flying machine is most surprising, considering the simplicity of the flight mechanism. It is to be observed that the wings not only act as organs of propulsion, but also direct the course of flight as the insect has no other apparatus for steering. Many insects, moreover, can change abruptly the direction of flight without altering the position of the body, going forward, backward, or sideways with equal ease, while finally they can remain stationary, hovering at one point in the air. No airplane yet invented can perform in this manner.

The Abdomen

The abdomen contains the principal viscera of the insect (Fig. 17, A), such as the stomach, intestine, and reproductive organs, and bears externally the structures concerned with mating and egg laying. Its general outer form is simple as compared with that of the thorax or head (Fig. 4, *Ab*) and its component segments are nearly always distinct.

THE ABDOMEN OF THE BEE

The bee larva has ten abdominal segments; but in the adult bee and other related Hymenoptera the abdomen is reduced to nine segments by the transfer, during the pupal stage, of the first larval segment to the thorax. In order to keep the correspondence, or *homology*, of the segments in mind, it is customary to number the segments beginning with the transposed first segment, or propodeum, as segment *I*. The abdomen of the bee, however, is further shortened by a reduction and retraction of

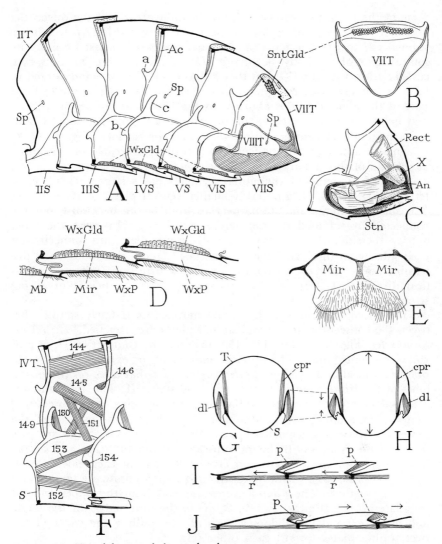

FIGURE 15. The abdomen of the worker bee.

A, internal view of right half of abdomen of worker. B, under side of back plate of abdominal segment *VII* showing scent gland. C, end of abdomen opened on left side, showing sting chamber. D, vertical lengthwise section of two consecutive sternal plates, showing wax glands and wax pockets (as seen also at A). E, outer surface of a sternal plate (segment *V*) with smooth "mirrors" *(Mir)* beneath wax glands. F, diagram of muscles in right half of a typical abdominal segment. G, H, diagrams illustrating mechanism of vertical compression and expansion of an abdominal segment. I, J, diagrams of mechanism of lengthwise contraction and protraction of abdominal segments.

An, anus; *cpr,* compressor muscle; *dl,* dilator muscle; *Mb,* intersegmental membrane; *Mir,* mirror; *p,* protractor muscle; *r,* retractor muscle; *Rect,* rectum; *s,* sternum; *SntGld,* scent gland; *Sp,* spiracle; *Stn,* sting; *T,* tergum; *WxGld,* wax gland; *WxP,* wax pocket; *X,* ninth abdominal segment, concealed in sting chamber.

some of the posterior segments. Thus in the worker and the queen the abdomen appears to have only six segments (Figs. 4, 15, A), which are segments *II* to *VII*, the tergal and sternal plates of the last forming the conical apex of the body. Segments *VIII, IX,* and *X* are not only concealed within segment *VII,* but they are so reduced in size and altered in form as scarcely to be recognized as segments. In the drone the exposed part of the abdomen ends above with the back plate of segment *VIII,* and below with the sternal plate of segment *IX* (Fig. 21, C). In both sexes the tenth segment is reduced to a small conical lobe (Fig. 15, C, *X*) bearing the anus *(An)*; in the female it is entirely concealed in a chamber at the end of the abdomen containing the sting *(Stn).*

Each of the exposed abdominal segments has a large back plate, or *tergum* (Fig. 15, A, G, *T*), and a smaller ventral plate, or *sternum (S).* The successive terga and sterna overlap from before backward, but are connected by infolded *intersegmental membranes.* Likewise the terga overlap the sides of the sterna (G), and the two plates are connected on each side by an infolded lateral membrane. Hence the abdomen is distensible and contractile in both a lengthwise direction (I, J) and a vertical direction (G, H), as may be observed when a bee is breathing strongly.

The mechanism of the abdominal movements is fairly simple. Between the consecutive tergal and sternal plates are stretched long *retractormuscles* (Fig. 15, F, 144, 145, 152, 153) that by contraction (I, *r*) pull the segments together. The opposite movement, or extension of the abdomen, is produced by short *protractor muscles* that arise on projecting lobes of the front margins of the terga and sterna (F, 146, 154), and are attached posteriorly on the overlapping rear margins of the preceding plates. These muscles by contraction (J, *p*) shorten the overlap of the plates and push the segments apart. The vertical movements are produced in the same way by lateral muscles between the terga and sterna. The *compressor muscles* are two crossed muscles in each side of each segment (F, 150, 151), which by contracting (G, *cpr*) draw the tergum and sternum together. The *dilator muscles* extend from the upper ends of long lateral sternal arms (F, 149; G, *dl*) to the lower edges of the terga, and hence expand the abdomen vertically by pulling the edges of the overlapping plates toward each other (H).

The abdomen is connected with the propodeum of the thorax by a short but narrow stalk, the *petiole,* and acquires thereby a high degree of mobility on the thorax. The principal muscles that move the abdomen as a whole are those of the transposed propodeum, which are the intersegmental muscles between the primary first and second abdominal segments.

The external features of chief interest in the bee's abdomen are the *wax glands* with their accompanying wax pockets, the *scent gland,* and the *sting.* In the drone there are two pair of small plates associated with the genital aperture, but they will be described in connection with the other parts of the reproductive system.

THE WAX GLANDS

The abdominal sterna have long posterior extensions that widely underlap in each case the sternum of the segment behind (Fig. 15, A). The anterior underlapped parts of sterna *IV, V, VI,* and *VII* in the worker each present two large, smooth, glistening oval areas separated by a narrow, darker median band (E); the exposed part beyond is densely clothed with hairs. The polished oval spaces are known as the *mirrors (Mir);* they are the areas of the sterna covered internally by the wax-secreting glands (A, D, *WxGld*). These glands are merely specialized parts of the body-wall epidermis, which, during the wax-forming period in the life of the worker, become greatly thickened and take on a glandular structure. The wax is discharged as a liquid through the mirrors and hardens to small flakes in the pockets (D, *WxP*) between the mirrors and the long underlapping parts of the preceding sterna. After the wax-forming period the glands degenerate and become a flat layer of cells.

THE SCENT GLAND

The scent-producing gland of the worker bee lies internally against the back of abdominal segment *VII* (Fig. 15, A, *SntGld*). Seen from the inner surface (B) the gland appears as a band of large cells extending crosswise near the anterior margin of the tergal plate. Outside the gland (A) is an elevation of the tergum with a smooth and slightly concave surface, suggestive of being an evaporating dish for the gland secretion; but the gland cells discharge their products by minute, individual ducts opening into the pocket at the base of the tergal plate.

THE STING

The sting of the bee is similar in its structure and mechanism to an egg-laying organ, known as the *ovipositor,* possessed by many other female insects, including most of the Hymenoptera. The ovipositor of some species is also a piercing organ capable of being inserted into the bodies of other insects, or of penetrating plant tissues, even hard wood; but in such cases its function is merely to form a hole in which the eggs may be deposited. The sting of the stinging Hymenoptera, therefore, is very evidently an ovipositor that has been remodeled in a few ways for the injection of poison instead of eggs.

The sting is ordinarily contained within a chamber at the end of the abdomen (Fig. 15, C) from which only its effective part, the familiar, tapering, sharp-pointed *shaft* is protruded. If the sting is removed from the body, or is examined in place within the abdomen, it is seen to include a large basal structure (Fig. 16, A) from which the shaft (*Shf*) is suspended by a pair of curved arms (only one arm visible on each side).

The sting base in turn is suspended in the membranous wall of the sting chamber (Fig. 15, C).

Though the shaft of the sting appears to be a solid structure, it is composed of three separable pieces, one above termed the *stylet* (Fig. 16, A, C, *Stl*) and two below known as the *lancets* (*Lct*). The stylet tapers to a point, but swells proximally into a long bulblike enlargement (A, *blb*) containing a deep cavity open below and continued as a shallow groove on the undersurface of the stylet (C). The lancets are long, slender, sharp-pointed rods lying side by side along the lower edges of the bulb and stylet. Grooves on their upper surfaces fit snugly over tracklike ridges of the bulb and stylet (C) so that, while held firmly in place, the lancets can slide freely back and forth. The lower edges of the lancets are in contact with each other; there is thus enclosed between the stylet and the lancets a channel (C, *pc*) leading from the bulb to the tip of the shaft.

This channel is the *poison canal* of the sting. The poison liquid is poured into the base of the bulb from a large *poison sac* (A, *PsnSc*), which is the reservoir of a long, slender poison gland (Fig. 22, C, *PsnGld*) that opens into its upper end. A second thick tubular gland associated with the sting (Fig. 16, A, *BGld*) opens externally below the base of the bulb. The terminal part of the stylet is armed with three pair of small lateral teeth; the lancets each have a series of nine or ten recurved barbs along the outer side near the end (Fig. 16, B).

The basal arms of the shaft are each composed of two closely appressed rods, one (Fig. 16, A, *2r*) narrowly attached to the base of the bulb and the other (*1r*) continuous with the lancet of the same side. The lancet arms slide on the bulb arms by ridge-and-groove connections continuous with those by which the lancets slide on the bulb and stylet.

The supporting basal structure of the sting is the motor apparatus of the stinging mechanism. On each side it presents three plates. The largest and uppermost plate is a four-sided sclerite known as the *quadrate plate* (Fig. 16, A, *Qd*); another is a small *triangular plate* (*Tri*) lying before the quadrate plate and connected anteriorly by its apex with the upper end of the basal arm of the lancet of the same side (*1r*); the third (*Ob*), because of its shape called the *oblong plate,* lies below the other two and is connected anteriorly with the corresponding basal arm of the bulb (*2r*). Posteriorly each oblong plate bears a long, soft, fingerlike lobe (*Sh*). The triangular plate articulates by its upper basal angle (*c*) with the anterior angle of the quadrate plate, and by its lower angle (*d*) with the upper edge of the oblong plate. The two quadrate plates are closely associated with two other plates partly overlapping them (D, *VIIIT*), which contain a pair of spiracles and hence are known as the *spiracular plates*. The spiracular plates belong to abdominal segment *VIII,* the quadrate plates to segment *IX*.

When the sting is not in action it is entirely retracted within the sting chamber of the abdomen (Fig. 15, C). In the retracted position (Fig.

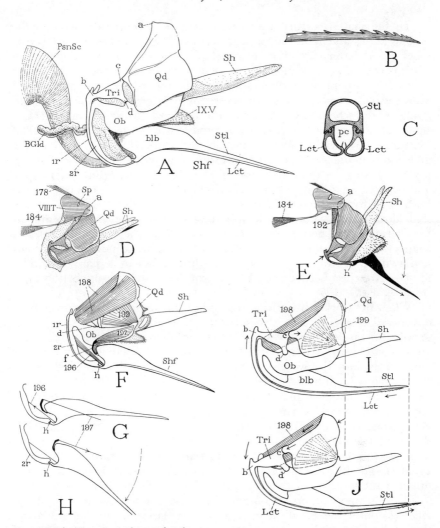

FIGURE 16. The sting of a worker bee.

A, entire stinging apparatus, left side. B, end of a lancet. C, cross section of shaft of sting. D, sting in position of repose, suspended from wall of sting chamber between spiracular plates *(VIII T)*. E, sting in position of protraction (arrows indicate the two essential movements). F, diagram of sting and its muscles. G, diagram of shaft of sting held in position of repose by muscle *196*. H, same, shaft turned down (as at E) by contraction of muscle *197*. I, J, mechanism of retraction (I) and protraction (J) of lancet.

a, attachment of quadrate plate with spiracular plate; *b*, apex of triangular plate continuous with lancet; *BGld*, "alkaline" gland of sting; *blb*, bulb of stylet; *c*, hinge of triangular plate on quadrate plate; *d*, hinge of triangular plate on oblong plate; *f*, forked rod (furcula) giving attachment to depressor muscles *(197)* of shaft; *h*, hinge of bulb with its basal arm *(2r); Lct*, lancet; *Ob*, oblong plate; *pc*, poison canal; *PsnSc*, poison sac (see Fig. 22C); *Qd*, quadrate plate; *1r*, basal arm (ramus) of lancet; *2r*, basal arm of bulb and stylet; *Sh*, sheath lobes; *Shf*, shaft of sting; *Sp*, spiracle; *Stl*, stylet; *Tri*, triangular plate; *VIII T*, spiracular plate associated with sting base.

16, D) the shaft is turned up so that its base is concealed between the oblong plates and its distal part ensheathed between the two projecting lobes of the latter (*Sh*). The protraction of the shaft from the abdomen (E) involves two simultaneous acts: first, a backward swing of the entire supporting apparatus; second, a downward swing of the shaft on its basal arms until it stands at right angles to the oblong plates. The backward swing of the whole structure gives the outward thrust to the extended shaft. This movement apparently is produced by a sharp upward tilt of sternum *VII* which lies immediately beneath the sting (Fig. 15, C). The deflection of the shaft is caused by the contraction of a pair of large muscles arising on the inner faces of the oblong plates (Fig. 16, F, 197), and inserted on a Y-shaped rod (*f*) attached by its stalk to the base of the bulb. The backward pull of these muscles on the bulb turns the entire shaft downward (H) on the flexible hinges (*h*) between the bulb and its basal arms (*2r*). The retraction of the sting into the chamber probably results from the restoration of sternum *VII* to its usual position; the shaft is drawn up again between the ensheathing lobes by a pair of slender muscles stretched between the base of the bulb and its supporting arms (Fig. 16, F, G, 196).

When the worker bee stings, the end of the abdomen is abruptly bent downward and with a sudden jab the tip of the out-thrust shaft is inserted into the flesh of the victim. Now another part of the sting mechanism comes into play by which the lancets are alternately forced deeper and deeper into the wound, holding each gain by the recurved points along their sides. The movements of the lancets depend on an interaction between the quadrate plates and the triangular plates of the motor apparatus. Two muscles arising on each quadrate plate (Fig. 16, F, 198, 199) are attached, one (198) on the anterior end of the oblong plate (*Ob*), the other (199) on the posterior end. The alternating pull of these two muscles vibrates the quadrate plate forward and backward (as shown at I and J). The forward movement of the quadrate plate (J) pushes on the upper basal angle (*c*) of the triangular plate (*Tri*); the latter revolves on its fulcral support (*d*) on the oblong plate, and the depression of its apical angle (*b*) pushes down on the basal arm of the lancet (*Lct*); and the lancet thus slides backward on the stylet and its tip protrudes from the end of the shaft. Conversely, as long as the lancet is free to move, the contraction of muscle *199* (I) pulls the quadrate plate backward, lifts the apical angle (*b*) of the triangular plate, and retracts the lancet.

If, however, the stinging bee has succeeded in inserting the point of the sting in an intended victim and the lancet first thrust out holds in the skin by means of its barbs, the force of the retractor muscle (I, *199*) is now expended on the oblong plate which revolves downward anteriorly on its articulation (*d*) with the triangular plate and drives the attached stylet into the wound made by the lancet. The lancet of the opposite side is then thrust out in the same way as the first and takes a still deeper hold in the flesh. Thus by repeated alternating thrusts of the lancets the point of the shaft sinks deeper and deeper, and the action of the sting apparatus continues even when the sting is separated from the body of the bee. Valves on the basal parts of the lancets drive the poison through the poison canal of the shaft and the liquid is expelled, not at the penetrating tip of the sting, but from a ventral cleft near the ends of the lancets.

The sting of the queen is longer than that of the worker and is more solidly attached within the sting chamber. Its shaft is strongly decurved beyond the bulb. The lancets have fewer and smaller barbs than those of the worker, but the poison glands are well developed and the poison sac is very large.

The Alimentary Canal

The food tract begins at the *mouth* in the lower wall of the head (Fig. 17, A, *Mth*). The mouth opens into the cavity of the *sucking pump* (*Pmp*) which stands vertically in the head. At its upper end the pump narrows to the slender, tubular *oesophagus* (*Oe*), which turns posteriorly through the neck and thorax, and in the anterior end of the abdomen enlarges into a thin-walled sac (*HS*). This sac corresponds with the *crop* of other insects, but it is commonly known to students of the bee as the *honey stomach* because it is used by the bee for carrying nectar or honey. Following the honey stomach is a short narrow part of the food canal called the *proventriculus* (*Pvent*). Next comes a long, thick, cylindrical sac (*Vent*) looped crosswise in the abdomen, usually in an S-shaped curve, which is the true stomach of the insect, or *ventriculus*. Following the stomach is the intestine, but the latter is distinctly divided into two parts: first, a narrow *anterior intestine* (*aInt*), which is looped or coiled in various ways according to the position of the stomach; and second, a large, pear-shaped *posterior intestine,* or *rectum* (*Rect*), opening by its tapering extremity through the *anus* (*An*) into the cavity that contains the sting (Fig. 15, C).

The structure of the sucking pump has already been described in connection with the feeding mechanism. The oesophagus is a tube with muscular walls, which passes the food along its length by successive waves of constrictions in the manner by which most animals swallow their food. The honey stomach, being the crop of the insect, serves the bee not only as a nectar-carrier but also as a storage place for food material. It is greatly distensible because its inner wall is thrown into numerous folds (Fig. 17, C, *HS*). The proventriculus is a regulatory apparatus that controls the entrance of food into the stomach. Its anterior end projects like a thick plug into the honey stomach (B, C) and contains an X-shaped opening between four thick, bristly, triangular, muscle-controlled lips (*B, SMth*). This structure constitutes a *stomach mouth;* by its action nectar or honey can be retained in the honey stomach while pollen is taken out and delivered to the ventriculus. The posterior end of the proventriculus extends in a long funnellike fold (C, *Vlv*) into the anterior end of the ventriculus (*Vent*), and probably acts as a valve to prevent regurgitation from the stomach.

The ventriculus is the part of the insect alimentary canal in which digestion and absorption of food material take place. Its inner wall (Fig. 17, D, *Epth*) is a thick cellular layer (epithelium) thrown into numerous crosswise folds that not only greatly increase the extent of the digestive

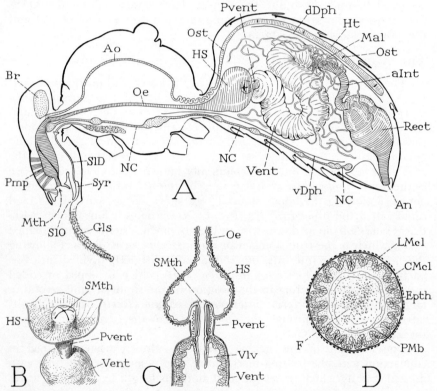

FIGURE 17. The alimentary canal and other internal organs of a worker bee.
A, lengthwise section of a worker bee, showing alimentary canal, dorsal blood vessel, diaphragms, brain, and ventral nerve cord. B, inner end of honey stomach cut open to show stomach mouth (*SMth*) at summit of proventriculus (*Pvent*). C, lengthwise section of honey stomach, proventriculus and anterior end of ventriculus. D, cross section of stomach (ventriculus).

An, anus; *aInt,* anterior intestine; *Br,* brain; *CMcl,* circular muscles; *dDph,* dorsal diaphragm; *Epth,* epithelium (cellular layer of stomach); *F,* food material; *Gls,* tongue; *HS,* honey stomach; *Ht,* heart; *LMcl,* longitudinal muscles; *Md,* mandible; *Mth,* mouth; *NC,* nerve cord; *Oe,* oesophagus; *Ost,* ostium; *Pmp,* sucking pump; *PMb,* peritrophic membrane; *Pvent,* proventriculus; *Rect,* rectum; *SlD,* salivary duct; *SlO,* salivary orifice; *SMth,* stomach mouth; *Syr,* salivary syringe; *vDph,* ventral diaphragm; *Vent,* ventriculus; *Vlv,* proventricular valve.

surface but also allow for expansion. Outside the cellular wall is first a layer of circular muscle fibers (*CMcl*), and surrounding the latter a sheath of lengthwise fibers (*LMcl*). Inside the stomach is a very thin, irregular *peritrophic membrane,* or several such membranes (*PMb*), forming a delicate cylindrical covering around the food mass (*F*). The cellular layer of the ventricular wall secrets the digestive juices and enzymes; the products of digestion go through the thin peritrophic membrane and are discharged through the stomach wall directly into the surrounding blood.

The intestinal tract usually is a relatively small part of the food canal. The narrow anterior intestine and the saclike rectum (Fig. 17, A, *aInt, Rect*) serve principally for the discharge of waste matter and for the absorption of water, but the rectum is also a storage chamber for the retention of feces until the latter can be evacuated outside the hive. In overwintering bees the rectum may become so greatly distended as to occupy a large part of the abdominal cavity before defecation occurs.

At the junction of the intestine with the ventriculus there open into the intestine a great number of long, threadlike tubes, probably a hundred or more of them. These tubes are known as the *Malpighian tubules* (Fig. 17, A, *Mal*); they are not digestive glands but excretory organs that remove waste products of metabolism from the blood, including both nitrogenous substances and salts. The tubules extend long distances in the body cavity, winding and twisting in numerous convolutions through the spaces about the other organs, where they are directly bathed by the blood. Their products discharged into the intestine are eliminated along with the waste food matter.

The Blood, Organs of Circulation, and Associated Tissues

The spaces in the body of an insect not occupied by the organs or other tissues are filled with a liquid which is the *blood,* or *haemolymph.* Floating in the blood are numerous blood cells, or *haemocytes,* of several kinds, but the blood cells do not serve for the transport of oxygen; they resemble the white blood cells of vertebrate animals. The blood liquid also carries but little oxygen; its principal known functions are the distribution of digested food material absorbed from the alimentary canal, the reception of waste products of metabolism which are removed by the excretory organs, and the transport of carbon dioxide to be eliminated through the respiratory organs and the skin. The blood is kept in circulation through the body by a pulsating tubular blood vessel and by vibratory membranes. The blood of the honey bee is of a pale amber color.

The single blood vessel is a long slender tube (Fig. 17, A, *Ao, Ht*) extending forward along the midline of the back in the abdomen from abdominal segment *VI* through the thorax and into the head, where it opens beneath the brain (*Br*). The abdominal part of the vessel is called the *heart* (*Ht*) and the thoracic part, the *aorta* (*Ao*). The sides of the heart are perforated by five pair of slits, the *ostia (Ost)*, in abdominal segments *II* to *VI,* inclusive, through which the blood enters the heart. The heart drives the blood forward by rhythmic pulsations of its muscular walls. The lips of the ostia project forward into the heart cavity (Fig. 18, C) and act as valves *(Vlv)* to prevent the escape or backward flow of the blood. The aorta has no ostia, is thrown into numerous small loops where it enters the thorax, and ends openly beneath the brain.

The heart is supported on a thin membrane, called the *dorsal diaphragm* (Fig. 18, A, *dDph*), stretched across the upper part of the abdominal cavity in segments *III* to *VII* (Fig. 17, A). The membrane contains five pair of fan-shaped bundles of fine muscle fibers attached laterally on the anterior margins of the tergal plates and spreading toward the heart where the fibers break up into numerous branching fibrils (Fig. 18, B, *Mcls*). The diaphragm shuts off above it a *pericardial cavity* containing the heart, but its lateral margins are free between the muscle attachments, thus leaving openings by which the blood can enter the pericardial cavity from the general body cavity. A rhythmic contraction of the diaphragm muscles causes the dorsal diaphragm to pulsate in a forward direction.

In the ventral part of the body above the nerve cord is a similar *ventral diaphragm* (Fig. 18, A, *vDph*), but this diaphragm extends from the metathorax into segment *VII* of the abdomen. It is more strongly muscular than the dorsal diaphragm and beats in a backward direction.

The blood discharged into the head from the aorta bathes the organs in the head and flows backward through the thorax and the abdomen by fairly well-defined channels, circulating also through the antennae, the wings, and the legs. The backward flow of the blood in the abdomen is

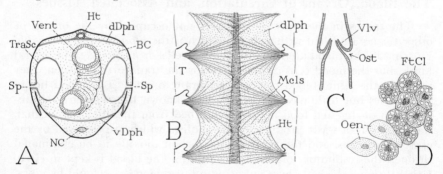

FIGURE 18. The body cavity, diaphragms, heart, fat cells, and oenocytes.

A, diagrammatic cross section of an abdominal segment. B, part of heart and dorsal diaphragm seen from below against the abdominal terga. C, lengthwise section of heart through a pair of ostia. D, group of fat cells and oenocytes.

BC, body cavity (filled with blood); *dDph,* dorsal diaphragm; *FtCl,* fat cells; *Ht,* heart; *Mcls,* muscles; *NC,* nerve cord; *Oen,* oenocytes; *Ost,* ostium; *Sp,* spiracle; *T,* tergum; *TraSc,* tracheal air sac; *vDph,* ventral diaphragm; *Vent,* ventriculus; *Vlv,* valvelike inner end of funnel-shaped ostial opening.

assisted by the pulsations of the ventral diaphragm; from the lower part of the abdomen it goes upward into the pericardial cavity where it is driven forward along the sides of the heart probably by the vibrations of the dorsal diaphragm, and finally again enters the heart through the ostia. Small pulsating membranes occur in the head between the antennal bases and in the upper part of the thorax, but the movements of these membranes appear to be produced by neighboring muscles.

Scattered all through the body cavity of the insect but especially in the abdomen are irregular masses of a soft, usually white tissue composed of large, loosely united cells (Fig. 18, D, *FtCl*). These cell masses are known collectively as the *fat body* because the cells contain enmeshed in their cytoplasm small droplets of oily fat. The fat tissue is particularly abundant in the larva; but the larval cells contain, besides large amounts of fat, also glycogen and, toward the end of the larval life, numerous minute protein granules. The fat body, in short, is a storage tissue for the conservation of elaborated food products not immediately needed by the individual. The larval fat cells thus carry over a large supply of food material into the pupal stage where it is thrown out into the blood by dissolution of the cells, and consumed by the pupal tissues developing into the adult organs. An underfed larva cannot properly transform into a mature bee.

Intermingled with the fat cells are other cells of larger size having a pale yellowish color, known as *oenocytes* (Fig. 18, D, *Oen*), and strands of special cells, called *nephrocytes,* lie along the sides of the heart, but nothing definite is known concerning the functions of these cells.

The Respiratory System

The chemical changes that go on constantly inside the body cells of living things require oxygen for consumption, and produce carbon dioxide which must be eliminated. All multicellular animals, therefore, are confronted with the problem of how to supply their tissues with oxygen and how to remove the carbon dioxide. Some have solved the problem in one way, others in other ways, but the anatomical means adopted, whatever its nature, constitutes a *respiratory system*.

Certain small, soft-bodied insects and some insect larvae have the very simple system of exchanging respiratory gases by diffusion directly through the skin. With most insects, however, the integument is too hard and dense for skin breathing and the majority of species, even very minute insects, have long, tubular, many-branched, thin-walled ingrowths of the integument that conduct air from outside the body to all the living tissues inside the body. These air tubes are called *tracheae;* collectively the tracheae constitute a *tracheal respiratory system*. The fine terminal branches of the tracheae go to practically all the cells of the body, the tissues thus receiving their oxygen direct without transport by the blood. The blood absorbs only what oxygen it needs for its own use.

The tracheal system of the bee is highly elaborate (Fig. 19), but a large part of it consists of air sacs (*TraSc*) which are thin-walled expansions of tracheae. The tracheal tubes open from the exterior by small breathing pores, the *spiracles* (*Sp*), situated along the sides of the body. Most insects have ten spiracles on each side, two on the thorax and eight on the abdomen. The adult honey bee, however, has three thoracic and seven abdominal spiracles because of the transfer of the first abdominal segment to the thorax. The first and largest spiracles of the bee (*1Sp*) lie between the prothorax and the mesothorax, but each is concealed beneath the lateral lobe of the pronotum (Fig. 9, *spl*), and is further protected by a dense fringe of long hairs on the covering lobe. Nevertheless, the first spiracle is entered by the parasitic mites, *Acarapis woodi,* that accumulate in the large tracheal trunk (Fig. 19, *Tra*) proceeding from this spiracle and cause a form of paralysis called acarine disease. The second spiracle (*2Sp*) is very small and lies between the upper angles of the pleural plates of the mesothorax and metathorax, but is normally concealed between these plates, and therefore is not seen in Figure 9 of the thorax. The third spiracle (*3Sp*) is fully exposed on the side of the propodeum (Fig. 9). The next six (*4Sp-9Sp*) are in the lower parts of the first six tergal plates of the abdomen (Fig. 15, A), but the tenth is not visible externally since it is in the so-called spiracular plate associated with the base of the sting (Figs. 15, A; 16, D, *VIII T*). All the spiracles, except the minute second spiracle, have an apparatus for closing the spiracular orifice to prevent the escape of inhaled air or to control air movement through the tracheae.

Respiration in the bee is effected partly by dorsoventral and lengthwise contractions and expansions of the abdomen, produced as already explained by opposing sets of abdominal muscles (Fig. 15, G-J). For the inhalation of air by respiratory movements, however, it is necessary that some part of the air passages inside the body should be able to expand. The tracheal tubes are more or less rigid by reason of spiral thickening in their walls that serve to keep them open, and hence do not respond much to increase and decrease of pressure around them. In the bee, therefore, as in most insects that breathe actively, parts of the tracheae are dilated into thin-walled *air sacs* that expand and collapse in the manner of lungs in response to the expansion and contraction of the rigid parts of the body wall. The honey bee is particularly well supplied with tracheal air sacs (Fig. 19, *TraSc*), two large sacs occupying much of the space in the sides of the abdomen while smaller ones are distributed all through the thorax, in the head, and even in the legs.

From the air sacs the tracheae continue as branching tubes that ramify to all the parts of the body, the appendages, and the internal organs. Finally the tracheae end in groups of minute tubes, called *tracheoles,* which terminate blindly against or within the tissue cells. The distal parts of the tracheoles are filled with a liquid that absorbs oxygen from the air delivered through the tracheae. The physiological activity of the cells causes the oxygen-saturated liquid in the tracheoles to be drawn through the tracheole walls and the cell walls into the protoplasm of the cells; when the cell activity (metabolism) decreases or returns to a minimum, the liquid again accumulates in the tracheoles and absorbs a fresh supply of oxygen. The carbon dioxide produced in the cells cannot be directed into the tracheoles; it is mostly discharged directly into the surrounding blood, from which it is carried off by diffusion through the tracheae or through the softer parts of the integument.

The metabolism of insects produces heat as in other animals, and the body temperature increases considerably during muscular activity, but the insect has no means of retaining the heat within its body; consequently it is given off almost immediately by radiation. Beekeepers well know that bees raise the temperature of the hive in winter by rapid

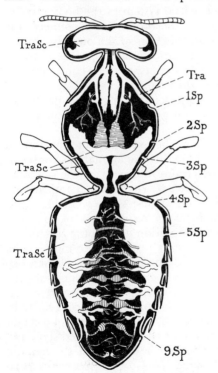 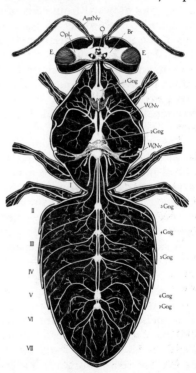

FIGURE 19. General view of the tracheal respiratory system of a worker bee, seen from above. *1Sp-9Sp*, spiracles; *Tra*, tracheal trunk from first spiracle; *TraSc*, tracheal sacs. Though not designated, the sixth, seventh, and eighth spiracles are the openings shown between the fifth and ninth spiracles.

FIGURE 20. The nervous system of a worker bee seen from above. *AntNv*, antennal nerve; *Br*, brain; *E*, compound eye; *1Gng-7Gng*, ganglia of ventral nerve cord; *I*, propodeum; *II-VII*, abdominal segments; *O*, ocellus; *Opl*, optic lobe of brain; *W₁Nv*, nerve to first wing; *W₂Nv*, nerve to second wing.

vibration of the wings, which involves sustained action of the huge masses of muscle fibers in the thorax.

The Sensory and Nervous System

A distinctive feature of animals is their ability to adjust their actions to conditions of the environment, particularly changing conditions. Animals are able to do this because they have cells or groups of cells close to the exterior of the body that are specifically sensitive to the common forms of energy in nature that are not destructive to them. These specialized cells and associated structures are known as *sense organs,* but the term does not necessarily imply conscious perception on the part of the animal.

From the receptive cells of the sense organs, *sensory nerves* extend inward to the central nervous system. Another set of fibers, called *motor nerves,* goes outward from cells in the central system to the body muscles and glands. A third set of intermediary *association fibers* connects the ends of the incoming sensory nerves with the roots of the outgoing motor nerves. In this way there is established a nerve circuit from the outlying sense organs through the central system to the muscles or glands, and the stimuli received from outside the body thus set up a nerve impulse that finally activates the motor system, or causes certain glands to produce a secretion. What the animal does in response to an external stimulus is called its *reaction.*

The nature of the reaction depends on the external stimulus and on the internal nerve pathways that are affected. If the animal has conscious control of its actions, volition may determine the path of the outgoing nerve impulse, otherwise the action is a *reflex;* co-ordinated reflexes are *instincts.* The sensory and nervous systems of insects are well developed and organized, and the honey bee is in many respects one of the most highly endowed in its powers of sensory reception and motor reaction.

Reaction to touch, or external pressure, is probably the most primitive of all the senses. In adult insects, as compared with soft-skinned larvae, the general body surface has relatively little sensitiveness to pressure because of the hardness of its outer covering. Hence, most of the sensory nerves of the skin end in cells at the bases of hairs. The hairs being delicately poised are easily moved by contact with objects or currents of air. Therefore, an innervated hair and its associated sense cell constitute an *organ of touch.* It is not known how many of the hairs of the bee are sensory organs, but innervated hairs occur on various parts of the body and appendages, and are particularly numerous on the antennae. Some insects respond to sound by the vibration of sensory hairs. We have no definite information on the hearing powers of bees, and the bee has no known auditory organs.

Some very small, thin-walled hairs of the bee, or hairlike structures reduced to small pegs, are supposed to be capable of being stimulated by minute particles of matter in air or liquids, and hence are regarded as *organs of smell or taste*. These organs are innervated each from a group of sense cells which sends a nerve strand into the hair or peg. Organs of this kind occur on the antennae and on parts near the mouth; some on the antennae are sunken into deep flask-shaped cavities. The most numerous organs on the antennae, however, appear on the surface as minute oval disks or plates. Each plate has a groove around the margin and covers a large group of sense cells. These structures are known as *plate organs;* they are supposed to be the principal organs of smell in the bee, though it is difficult to understand from their structure how they can be receptive to odor particles. Definite proof of their olfactory function has not been produced. Yet there is little doubt that the antennae are the principal seat of the olfactory sense of the bee. It has been estimated that there are 5 or 6 thousand plate organs on the antennal flagella in the worker, 2 or 3 thousand in the queen, and perhaps 30 thousand in the drone.

Still other organs, having the form of minute bells or inverted cups sunken into the body wall with a nerve ending inside, are distributed in groups on various parts of the body and appendages. These organs have been described as "olfactory pores," but recent experiments appear to show that they respond to strains, stresses, or bending of the integument, and thus give the insect "information" concerning its own actions.

Imaginative people like to speculate on the possibility of insects having some sense "totally unknown to us," but, considering that the senses are internal reactions on the part of the animal to external conditions of the environment, a supposed "unknown sense" must be based on something real in nature. An insect's reactions to sensory stimuli can be determined experimentally and its sense organs can be studied under the microscope, but inasmuch as its sense organs are so different from ours, and because various kinds of them occur on the same parts of the body or appendages, it is a difficult matter in the case of most of them to determine specifically what stimulus is effective on each kind of organ.

The best known of the insect sense organs are the eyes, because an insect eye is like any other eye in that its essential parts are an external *lens* for focusing light, and a sub-lying, light-sensitive *retina* connected by nerves with the brain. The bee, as we have observed, has three small simple eyes, or *ocelli,* on the top of the head (Fig. 5, A, *O*), and a pair of large *compound eyes (E)* on the sides of the head. A simple eye has one lens for the entire retina; a compound eye has many small lenses, and the retina is divided into parts corresponding with the lenses. It is supposed that the insect "sees" with a compound eye as many points of light as there are divisions of the eye, and thus gets a mosaic picture of the object or scene before it—and there may be several thousand separate light-receptive parts of the eye. However, it is impossible for us to know what the final effect on the insect's brain may be. It is certain that insects respond most quickly to movements of objects, but many insects, including the honey bees, perceive differences of color, shape, and position. Most insects "see" the higher colors of the spectrum visible to us (green, blue, violet), and even the ultraviolet which we do not see, but they are more or less insensitive to the lower red rays.

The ocelli have been supposed to be organs for close vision, but a current idea of their function is that they keep the insect continually in a state of stimulation to light, and thus make the compound eyes more quickly responsive. Many larval insects and other arthropods such as spiders have ocelli but no compound eyes.

The central nervous system of the bee (Fig. 20), as in insects generally, is fairly simple in its general structure. It consists of a *brain (Br)* in the head above the pharynx, and of a *ventral nerve cord* in the lower part of the body extending from the head to the posterior part of the abdomen. The brain is principally a sensory center, as it receives the nerves from the eyes and the antennae. The ventral nerve cord consists of a series of small, segmental nerve masses, or *ganglia,* united by paired intervening *connectives.* The first three ganglia of the ventral system are always condensed into a large composite ganglion, termed the *suboesophageal ganglion,* lying in the lower part of the head and supplying nerves to the feeding organs. The first body ganglion *(1Gng)* pertains to the prothorax. The second in the honey bee *(2Gng)* lies in the posterior part of the thorax, but it is composed of four primary ganglia belonging to the mesothorax, the metathorax, the propodeum, and the first abdominal segment, and supplies nerves to all these segments. In the abdomen are five ganglia. The first two *(3Gng, 4Gng)* are displaced forward so that each innervates the segment behind it; the third *(5Gng)* lies in its own segment *(V)* and gives its nerves to this segment; the fourth *(6Gng)* is in segment *VI* but innervates segments *VI* and *VII;* the fifth *(7Gng),* in segment *VII,* supplies nerves to segments *VIII, IX,* and *X.*

The brain and the ventral ganglia are masses of nerve cells and nerve fibers. The cells of the central system give rise to the fibers of the motor and the association nerves, but the fibrous parts of the ganglia include also the branching ends of the incoming sensory nerves from the peripheral sensory nerve cells. The organization of the brain or of a ventral ganglion depends mostly on the intricate tracts of intercommunication formed by the association fibers, which connect all parts of the central system. The brain of an insect owes its importance to the fact that it receives the sensory nerves from the eyes and the antennae, and transmits the nervous impulses from these sensory organs to the motor centers of the ventral nerve cord. The environmental stimuli received through the eyes and the antennal sense organs thus direct many of the insect's natural activities. If the head is removed from the insect it is deprived of these stimuli, as well as the ability to eat, but still retains the power of acting through its body motor centers. A decapitated insect is therefore able to walk or even to fly, and a bee without a head is even able to sting.

The Reproductive System

The reproductive organs of insects usually include external and internal structures, but in the honey bee the organs that subserve the reproductive function are almost entirely internal, the intromittent organ of the drone being a large sac within the abdomen that is everted only at the time of mating, and the instrument of the female used for egg laying by other insects being converted into a sting. Furthermore, the organs are fully developed only in the drone (Fig. 21, A) and the queen (Fig. 22, A). Female organs are present in the worker, but they are greatly reduced in size (Fig. 22, C), and only under certain conditions do they produce eggs. The mature reproductive cells of the male and the female, respectively, are the *spermatozoa* and the *eggs,* or *ova,* but they are developed from primary germ cells, set apart as such in the young embryo, that have little to distinguish them visibly from other cells of the body.

THE MALE REPRODUCTIVE ORGANS

The organs of the male that contain the primary reproductive cells, and in which the latter develop into spermatozoa are the *testes*. In the drone bee the testes are a pair of small flattened bodies (Fig. 21, A, *Tes*) lying in the sides of the abdomen. From each testis there proceeds posteriorly a duct, the *vas deferens* (plural *vasa deferentia*), at first coiled (*Vd*), but soon enlarging into a long slender sac, the *seminal vesicle* (*SV*). The narrowed posterior ends of the two vesicles enter the lower ends of a pair of huge *mucous glands* (*MuGlds*), lying side by side, and the two glands open together into a single long outlet tube, which is the *ejaculatory duct* (*Dej*). Finally, the ejaculatory duct opens into the anterior end of a large complex structure (*Pen*), termed the *penis* because by inversion at the time of mating it serves to discharge the spermatozoa.

Three consecutive parts may be noted in the structure of the inverted penis. The inner half is a large pear-shaped swelling, or *bulb* (*Blb*), which receives the ejaculatory duct at its anterior end, and has a pair of dark plates in its thick dorsal wall. The bulb passes into a narrowed, usually twisted neck, or *cervix* (*Cer*), having a series of dark crescent-shaped thickenings along its lower side, and a fringed lobe (*fml*) projecting from its dorsal wall. The neck ends in a large thin-walled sac, or *bursa* (*Brs*), from which project a pair of crumpled hornlike pouches, the *bursal cornua* (*bc*). The bursa opens to the exterior by a wide orifice (*C, Phtr*) beneath the anus (*An*) and between a pair of small valvelike plates (*pv*). These plates and a still smaller pair (*lp*) at their outer angles are the only representatives in the honey bee of a large, often complex, external copulatory organ present in most other male Hymenoptera.

The mature spermatozoa are minute bodies with long vibratile tails. From the testes they pass down the vasa deferentia into the sperm vesicles, where they are temporarily stored with their heads buried in the soft cellular walls of the vesicles. In the mating season, spermatozoa are sent on down through the ejaculatory duct in a secretion from the mucous glands, and a mass of sperm and mucus now fills the bulb of the penis.

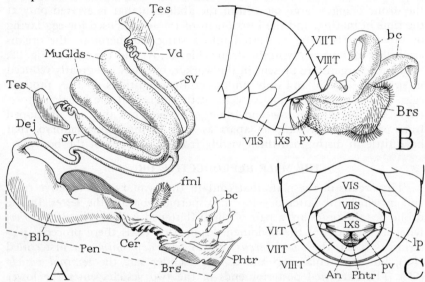

FIGURE 21. The reproductive organs of the drone.

A, general view of internal organs of reproduction as seen from left side. B, end of the abdomen of a drone with penis partly everted. C, end of drone abdomen, under surface, (penis not everted).

An, annus; *bc,* bursal cornua; *Blb,* bulb of penis; *Brs,* bursa of penis; *Cer,* neck (cervix) of penis; *Dej.* ejaculatory duct; *fml,* fimbriate lobe; *lp,* parameral plate; *MuGlds,* mucous glands; *Pen,* penis; *Phtr,* external opening of inverted penis; *pv,* penis valve; *SV,* seminal vesicle; *Tes,* testis; *Vd,* vas deferens; *VI S-IX S,* sternal plates of abdomen; *VI T-VIII T,* tergal plates of abdomen.

THE FEMALE REPRODUCTIVE ORGANS

In the female the primary germ cells are housed in the *ovaries,* and in these organs they undergo all but the last stage of development into eggs ready for fertilization. The ovaries of the queen bee (Fig. 22, A, *Ov*) are two huge, pear-shaped masses of slender, closely packed tubules, termed *ovarioles* (*B*). At the posterior end of each ovary the ovarioles come together in a *lateral oviduct* (A, *Odl*) and these two ducts unite in a short *common oviduct* (*Odc*). The last is continuous with a wide terminal sac, the *vagina* (*Vag*), which opens to the exterior by a median orifice (*VO*) in a depression of the body wall at the base of the sting. At the sides of the genital orifice are two other openings (*PO*) which are the mouths of two large pouches (*P*) embracing the sides of the vagina. Lying on the dorsal wall of the vagina is a spherical body (*Spt,* shown turned to one side in the figure), which is the female receptacle for the spermatozoa and is hence termed the *spermatheca.* The spermatheca is connected with the vagina by a short duct (*SptDct*). A pair of tubular *spermathecal glands* (*SptGld*) open into the distal part of the duct.

INSEMINATION OF THE QUEEN AND
FERTILIZATION OF THE EGGS

At the time of mating, the sperm mass in the penis bulb of the drone is discharged by eversion of the penis into the vaginal pouch of the female. It has been supposed that the male organ is first anchored in the female by the eversion of its lateral cornua (Fig. 21, A, *bc*) into the

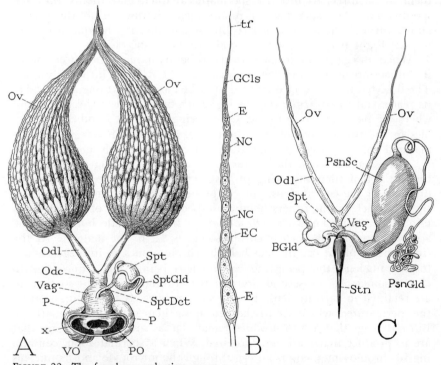

FIGURE 22. The female reproductive organs.
A, ovaries, genital ducts, and genital pouches of the queen. B, single ovariole, diagrammatic, showing succession of egg cells and nurse cells. C, reproductive organs of a worker, together with shaft of sting, sting glands, and poison sac.

BGld, "alkaline" gland of sting; *E,* egg; *EC,* egg chamber; *GCls,* undifferentiated germ cells; *NC,* nurse chamber; *Odc,* common oviduct; *Odl,* lateral (paired) oviduct; *Ov,* ovary; *P,* lateral genital pouch; *PO,* opening of lateral pouch; *PsnGld,* poison gland of sting; *PsnSc,* poison sac; *Spt,* spermatheca; *SptDct,* spermathecal duct; *SptGld,* spermathecal gland; *Stn,* shaft of sting; *tf,* terminal filament; *Vag,* vagina; *VO,* opening of vagina; *x,* cut edge of body wall around genital openings.

lateral genital pouches of the queen (Fig. 22, A, *P*), but apparently this plausible idea has not been verified by observation. Furthermore, some investigators say that the entire penis is turned inside out, while others claim that only the end pouch is everted.

Whatever may be the facts concerning the copulatory process and the extent of the penis eversion, when the mating queen finally separates herself from the drone, only the penis bulb remains in her genital tract, the male organ having been torn apart at its weakest point between the bulb and the penis neck. The spermatozoa discharged by the drone are first stored in the distended lateral oviducts. As soon as the remains of the male organ and the mucus are removed from the vagina, by muscular contractions the female forces the spermatozoa into the vagina. Here they are stopped by a valvelike fold of the vaginal wall, which causes them to be directed into the spermathecal duct, and finally into the spermatheca. The spermatozoa retain their vitality within the spermatheca throughout the productive life of the queen. The queen on her nuptial flight may mate with several drones in succession.

When an egg in the ovary is ready to be discharged, the lower end of its follicle opens and the egg passes down the oviduct into the vagina. The deserted follicle shrivels and is absorbed as the next one above takes its place, and the ovariole regains its length by growth at the upper end where the new eggs are forming. Considering the great number of ovarioles in the two ovaries of the queen bee, it is clear how eggs may be matured continuously and take their places consecutively in the vagina.

As the eggs descend the oviducts and enter the vagina they undergo the last act of their maturing process. This consists of two consecutive divisions of the egg nucleus, one of the new nuclei becoming the definitive egg nucleus, the others being absorbed. The nuclei of all cells contain small bodies known as *chromosomes*. In the female honey bee the accepted number of nuclear chromosomes is 32, in the male 16. At the first division of the egg nucleus half the chromosomes go into each newly formed nucleus, the persisting egg nucleus being thus reduced to 16 chromosomes. At the second division the chromosomes split so that 16 are retained in each nucleus. The eggs are now ready for fertilization by the spermatozoa, which are discharged upon them from the spermatheca. But only eggs that are to produce female larvae are fertilized; eggs that are to produce males are not fertilized. When a spermatozoon, containing 16 chromosomes, enters an egg through the micropyle and its nucleus unites with the egg nucleus, containing also 16 chromosomes, the fertilized egg will contain 32 chromosomes, and consequently develops into a female bee. On the other hand, an unfertilized egg remains with only 16 chromosomes in its nucleus and can develop only into a drone. The eggs finally are discharged from the vaginal orifice at the base of the sting. Whether the fertilized egg becomes a queen or a worker now depends on the feeding of the larva.

CHAPTER VI

SOURCES OF NECTAR AND POLLEN

by H. B. Lovell*

HONEY PLANTS ARE restricted to certain regions of the country although many species, such as the clovers, are planted in nearly every state. Many native species of former importance are no longer so because of the clearing of extensive tracts of wild lands.

Examples of important honey plants with restricted range are *Clethra* in eastern Massachusetts, blueberry in southeastern Maine, sourwood in the southern Alleghenies, gallberry in southern Georgia and adjacent Florida, tupelo in northwestern Florida, saw palmetto in northern Florida, black mangrove along the seashores of southern Florida, Spanish needles in the central states particularly in Arkansas and southern Missouri, rattan in southern Louisiana and adjacent Texas, huajillo in a narrow band south from Uvalde, Texas, to the Mexican border, white brush in the Big Bend Country of Texas, mesquite throughout the Southwest, sage and wild buckwheat in California, fireweed in Washington and other states bordering Canada east to Maine, and raspberry in Michigan and other lumbering states. These are all native wild plants.

Several areas are famous for the honey of cultivated species; all the northeastern states are in the alsike-clover belt, and the states south of the Ohio River depend largely on white clover supplemented in the Deep South by crimson clover. Buckwheat is the leading honey plant in New York and Pennsylvania. In many areas west of the Mississippi River, sweet clover is the chief honey plant. In the mountain states, alfalfa is the number one producer. In many southern states, from the Carolinas to California, large crops of cotton honey are produced locally. In Florida and California orange trees are leading producers.

MIGRATORY BEEKEEPING

With improved roads and trucks, many beekeepers practice migratory beekeeping, some moving from the northern states to Florida or Texas, or from the mountain states to California; others move short distances to catch the blooming of a specific flower. Particularly in some of the southern states, such as Florida and Texas, and in California, it is possible to obtain four or more crops by moving apiaries a few miles. In Florida, for example, beekeepers get tupelo and orange, then gall-

---

*Harvey B. Lovell, Ph.D. Professor of Zoology, University of Louisville, Louisville, Kentucky. Authority on American honey plants. Author of many articles on honey plants and pollination.

berry honey, followed by saw palmetto and black mangrove, by moving their bees only a few miles. In Texas, however, the distances are much greater and the honey crops are often several hundred miles away. Horsemint and Hubam sweet clover, mesquite, huajillo, white brush and cotton, with rattan in extreme eastern Texas, are some of the crops for which up-to-date beekeepers strive. By keeping bees in several areas, a beekeeper may obtain a crop in one place when others are a failure. The advantages of traveling from the far North to the Deep South are the saving in winter stores and the early spring build-up.

THE CAUSES OF NECTAR SECRETION

Nectar secretion consists primarily of the production of a sugar solution secreted from special organs of the plant known as nectaries. These organs are located in various parts of the flower or even on the stem, leaf, node, or bract of the plant; they are known as extra-floral nectaries when they occur elsewhere than in the flower.

Nectar is primarily a solution of sugars together with various mineral elements, certain enzymes, coloring material, and aromatic substances which give to honeys their characteristic flavors. Nectars vary in chemical composition with the plant sources, as well as environmental conditions. The amount of nectar secretion varies not only in different species of plants but also between members of the same species according to the vigor of the plant and such environmental factors as rainfall, temperature, amount of light, altitude, soil type, and minerals.

In order that a nectary may secrete nectar, its cells must be distended with water, or a solution of water and sugar. The nectar must exert a strong pressure outward, distending the elastic wall of the cell. If, owing to dry weather, there is not sufficient moisture in the soil, the leaves and young stems of plants will wilt or droop. They are rigid only when the cells composing them are distended or swollen (turgid). If the cells are flaccid no nectar is secreted.

Secretion in all probability begins by forcing of the nectar through the relatively thin and easily permeable outer wall or membrane of the nectary. As soon as the nectar has reached the external surface it evaporates and forms a solution more dense than within the cells of the nectary, and in consequence more nectar is drawn outward by osmosis. But during secretion turgor pressure manifests itself whenever the inflow of water exceeds in quantity the outflow of nectar. It is a widely-held opinion that pressure is an important factor in beginning nectar secretion.

Numerous instances have been recorded where a heavy shower at night has stimulated the nectar flow the next day, especially in the case of white clover. Rain in the fall will bring about a surplus the following year from this plant with very little or no crop following a year of drouth.

A cold rain, with a sudden drop of temperature often brings a nectar flow to an abrupt close. A drop of 10 or more degrees checks the conversion of starch into sugar and renders the outer membranes of the nectary less permeable. If the nectar is unprotected it may be washed away, and no longer drawn outward by osmosis.

Fog is an important factor in production of honey on a 20-mile wide strip of land in California, extending from Santa Barbara to San Diego County, where it prevails from May through July. Too much sunshine causes the lima beans under cultivation to droop and checks the flow of nectar, and best results are obtained in the fog area. Fog also is an important factor in the nectar secretion of the common huckleberry (*Gaylussacia baccata*) in southern Maine. The flowers were practically nectarless and almost devoid of insect visitors on a series of hot sunny days; on a morning when a dense fog lasted until noon, nearly every flower was filled with nectar and insect visitors were numerous.

Wind may also play a part in nectar secretion. In the Southwest of the United States, a hot dry wind may greatly injure the honey crop by causing the leaves to droop and the flowers to wilt. There have been instances in California where a desert wind has caused the blossoms of orange trees to turn brown and fall to the ground.

The character of the soil and its ability to retain moisture affect the quality and quantity of the nectar of plants. Some do well on acid soils while others do better on lime soils. In the Imperial Valley of California, where the soil is heavy, alfalfa consistently gives larger honey yields than on the light soils. Alfalfa honey is lighter in color on sandy soils and darker in color on heavier soils. Trace elements of minerals also affect nectar secretion. Holmes showed that the addition of boron, and possibly other trace elements, will quickly restore conditions which attract bees to blossoms of alsike clover and raspberry.

Temperature exerts a greater influence on the functions of plants, including nectar secretion, than does light, humidity, or rainfall. In general, high temperatures in the daytime favor nectar secretion since the membranes of the nectary are more permeable, the solvent power of water is increased, and chemical changes in the plant take place more rapidly.

Cool nights followed by warm days are better for nectar secretion than a uniform temperature. Nectar secretion is more rapid in the Northern States when the days are warm and the nights cool to cold. The days are longer with more intense sunlight; higher altitudes have the same effect, especially on alfalfa which secretes best in irrigated areas above 1000 feet.

QUALITY OF HONEY

The quality of honey depends upon a number of factors, of which the color is often overemphasized. The lighter and clearer the honey the higher it grades. While on the average, white honeys are milder and lack unpleasant odors and flavors, there are numerous exceptions. Some connoisseurs of honey find the extra white honeys too mild and tasteless, and prefer the more distinctive flavors of dark honey. Dark honeys have more minerals and other ingredients. There is an increased realization that each kind of honey has its own superior qualities (for additional information on quality of honey, see Chapter XIV entitled "Honey").

In New York the very strong, dark honey of buckwheat is preferred by many local residents, who find all other honeys insipid and tasteless. One large packer in Arkansas blends his honey to obtain a golden yellow color for his top grade, insisting that yellow is the ideal color for honey as it is for butter. Unfortunately, in many areas it is hard to get enough honey for blending a yellow color; this is particularly true in the West, and in the sweet clover-alfalfa belt. Some honeys, notably horsemint, spearmint, and thyme, have a minty flavor which is highly esteemed by many in the areas where these honeys are produced.

DISPLEASING FLAVORS

A few honeys have disagreeable flavors and odors which render them virtually unsalable.

Bitterweed *(Helenium tenuifolium)* is a common fall species in the states bordering the Gulf Coast and northward into southern Kentucky (Fig. 1). The honey is light yellow and very bitter. The bitter flavor is due to the pollen grains which can be removed by modern filtration

FIGURE 1. Bitterweed is a source of a bitter honey but is helpful to southern bee and queen producers

FIGURE 2. Mescal or century plant is a source of an unpalatable honey in the Southwest and in Mexico.

methods. This honey is especially useful to bee and queen breeders, several of whom state that the bitterweed flow makes their business possible, as their colonies fill up on bitterweed in the fall and have enough surplus to start brood rearing in the spring.

Chinquapin *(Castanea pumila)*, a shrub or small tree common in the Southeast from New Jersey to Florida and Texas, produces a most nauseating honey. E. R. Root stated that it is the worst honey he had ever tasted having a flavor of cayenne pepper and quinine.

A number of other honeys are said to be unpalatable. Privet *(Ligustrum)*, widely grown for hedges throughout the South, produces a honey of bad flavor. Bittersweet *(Celastrus scandens)* yields a strong honey which often flavors milder honeys. Ragwort *(Senecio)* produces a honey with a bitter flavor. Heartsease *(Polygonum Persicaria)* or smartweed honey has a strong, unpleasant odor and much good clover honey is damaged by it in the central states. Snow-on-the-mountain *(Euphorbia)* produces honey which stings one's throat. Mescal or century plant *(Agave americana)* produces such a strong honey that it is unpalatable. Beekeepers in the Southwest speak of being "mescaled up" when bees fill the hives with this honey (Fig. 2).

Cajeput or punk tree *(Melaleuca leucadendra)*, a tree much planted for ornament in Florida, produces honey with such a bad odor and flavor that it ruins much Florida honey. The Florida Honey Co-operative at Umatilla is waging a campaign to destroy all the punk trees in the vicinity of the orange groves.

In the Deep South, the coralvine *(Antigonum leptopus)* is a popular garden plant. If bees are kept near towns, they often produce a nearly black honey which damages other honeys.

POISONOUS HONEY PLANTS

There are two ways in which honey may be poisonous: 1. to the bees themselves, and 2. to man. Luckily, there is very little poisonous honey (for additional information on plants poisonous to bees, see Chapter XX, "Injury to Bees by Poisoning").

California buckeye *(Aesculus californica)* is poisonous to many bees in California when the buckeye is in flower. There is some disagreement over the cause. Is it the honey or the pollen which kills the bees? Late research by Eckert attributes the poisonous properties to the pollen.

Mountain laurel *(Kalmia)* is the only honey which has been proved poisonous to man. An alkaloid *(andromedotoxin)* has been extracted from it which is definitely poisonous. People eating the honey often fall unconscious in a few minutes, but no deaths have occurred. Bees rarely visit the *Kalmias*.

Jasmine *(Gelsemium sempervirens)*, a common vine in the Southeast, has been suspected of poisoning bees. It blooms in the winter when bees are not very active and little damage has been done.

Summer titi honey produces purple brood, a disease not uncommon in southern Georgia and northern Florida. Considerable brood is killed in some seasons.

Cultivated Plants of Importance

Sweet clover (*Melilotus alba* and *officinalis*) for a long time was considered a noxious weed by farmers who objected to the beekeepers spreading the seed (Fig. 3). The common varieties are biennials and die out after blooming, although they often reseed themselves. Sweet clover yields so much nectar it has become known as the "bee plant" and beekeepers established their apiaries where it was most abundant. It needs a limestone soil, hot dry days, and cool nights. It is now recognized as one of our best soil builders and is extensively planted in run-down soils. The honey is water white and mild in flavor. Hubam, an annual variety, has been extensively planted in Texas and adjacent states.

Alfalfa (*Medicago sativa*) is extensively planted in the irrigated portions of the West (Fig. 4). Much of the honey crop of Utah, Nevada, and other Rocky Mountain states is from this source. In many areas alfalfa honey is mixed with that of sweet clover. Honey bees have difficulty tripping the explosive flowers of alfalfa and often obtain the nectar through a groove in the sides of the flowers. Honey bees

FIGURE 3. The blossoms of sweet clover are a welcome sight to many U.S. beekeepers who depend upon it for their honey crop.

FIGURE 4. Alfalfa is the leading honey plant in irrigated parts of the West and in the Plains States west of the Missouri River.

FIGURE 5. White Dutch clover is the commonest clover in the U.S.A. In many of the southeastern states it is a leading honey plant.

do not like to work alfalfa and will usually leave it for an easier-to-work species when it comes into bloom. In order to get alfalfa adequately pollinated it is often necessary to bring in new hives of bees every few days. Alfalfa honey is mild and water white when gathered pure, but since bees often desert it for other flowers, the honey is sometimes diluted with a darker blend, leading to the opinion that alfalfa honey itself is dark. East of the Mississippi River, alfalfa honey is rarely obtained except when there is a wet spring followed by a very dry summer. In Lake Champlain Valley beekeepers often harvest alfalfa honey.

White clover (*Trifolium repens*) is often called white Dutch clover (Fig. 5). It is one of the commonest clovers used in grass-seed mixtures and usually grows luxuriantly in lawns, where it reseeds itself. It has a long blooming season, from late April to the middle of July, and reblooms in a few days after a lawn is mowed. It is usually the leading honey plant east of the Mississippi River. It is shallow rooted and stops yielding if the weather becomes dry, which often happens in the central states 3 out of 4 years. The honey is white to extra light amber with a mild, delicious flavor. There were good yields in 1958 and 1961.

Alsike clover (*Trifolium hybridum*) has flower heads pink at the base, which led early observers to think it was a hybrid between white and red clover. The stem is trailing and many branched. As a result, alsike clover produces more heads and blooms longer than white clover.

It does better in the northern states where it is often the leading source of surplus. The honey is mild and light colored and usually mixed with that from white clover, whose honey it closely resembles.

Vetch *(Vicia* spp.), called hairy vetch, is being cultivated in increasing amounts in Arkansas and northern Texas as a cover and forage crop. It is escaping to the roadsides too. In spite of its long tube, honey bees can reach the nectar by probing between the overlapping petals. Large crops of a water-white honey are obtained from this vetch.

Cotton *(Gossypium hirsutum)* is one of the major farm crops of the southern states, but depletion of the soils seems to have been the cause of less cotton honey than formerly. Also heavy spraying for the cotton boll weevil has made beekeeping in cotton districts a hazardous occupation. A beekeeper in northern Louisiana lost 600 colonies from spray and one in southern Arkansas lost even more from the same cause. Most cotton honey is now produced on the black lands of Texas which are still very rich in soil nutrients. Cotton yields honey from extra floral nectaries on the leaves and on the bracts at the base of the flower. The honey is light colored and usually of a mild flavor.

Buckwheat *(Fagopyrum esculentum)* was formerly grown extensively in New York, Pennsylvania, Ontario, eastern Ohio, and parts of Michigan. It yields a purple to black honey with a very pronounced flavor much esteemed by residents of the buckwheat belt, who consider all other honeys insipid. At one time great surpluses of 500 pounds or more per colony were common from buckwheat but in recent years other crops have crowded out much of the buckwheat acreage. The nectar is secreted by eight conspicuous orange nectaries in each of the white flowers. There is said to be over a million-pound shortage of buckwheat honey in New York City, where Hebrews use it in ceremonial cakes on religious holidays.

FIGURE 6. Orange blossoms, the only fruit bloom that is a major source of honey.

FIGURE 7. The blossoms of grapefruit, also a leading honey plant wherever citrus is grown.

Orange, grapefruit, and other citrus crops *(Citrus* spp.) are a major source of honey in Florida, Texas, Arizona, and California (Figs. 6 and 7). The flow is heavy as the trees produce a large number of flowers, each of which secretes nectar very freely. In Florida, beekeepers move their bees to the orange groves and produce large surpluses of a mild, white honey with the delicate aroma of orange blossoms. The flavor is distinctive and often not liked by northerners brought up on clover honey. Florida orange honey often has a reddish tinge, the cause of which is uncertain. Some beekeepers ascribe this to the honey of white Spanish needles which bloom freely on the ground under the trees all winter, and others to something obtained from oak trees, probably honeydew.

Wild Plants of Importance

Black mangrove *(Avicennia nitida),* abundant along the coasts of Florida, produces a light honey with a thin body having a slightly brackish taste. Surpluses of 50 to 75 pounds are usual. Before the great freeze of 1885 surpluses of 500 pounds were common.

Raspberry *(Rubus* spp.) springs up after lumbering operations all through the northern states and southern Canada. Surpluses of 50 to 180 pounds of white honey with a delicious flavor are obtained.

Buckbush *(Symphoricarpos* spp.). In the hilly country of eastern United States the red-berried species, often called coralberry, yields a surplus of light-amber honey with a good flavor. It blooms after the clovers and so extends the season. In the Rocky Mountains, a white-berried species called snowberry yields a surplus of good honey.

Sumac *(Rhus* spp.). These shrubs are good honey plants. They produce a light-amber honey with an excellent flavor. Poison ivy and poison oak each produce a good nonpoisonous honey in small amounts.

Sweet pepper bush *(Clethra alnifolia)* is very abundant in southeastern Massachusetts where it blooms in August (Fig. 8). The honey is light yellow with a mild flavor and odor of the bloom. The honey is marketed under the scientific name *Clethra.*

White brush *(Aloysia ligustrina* also called *Lippia ligustrina)* is a shrub of the arid Southwest where it blooms in great thickets after a good rain. The honey is white with a very heavy body and a mild flavor. The Hatch Brothers sometimes get 300 pounds from a single colony in west Texas.

Basswood or linden *(Tilia americana)* was formerly a leading honey tree but the valuable wood has caused the tree to be all but exterminated in many regions. The honey is extra white and has a slight bite when pure, but is usually mixed with that from clovers. It is a late bloomer which increases its value.

Catsclaw *(Acacia* spp.). This thorny shrub is an important honey plant in the Southwest, where it produces a white honey.

Chinese tallow tree *(Sapium sebiferum)* has been extensively planted along the highways of east Texas, where it blooms for 6 weeks in May and June. Large surpluses of light, mild-flavored honey have been obtained.

Wild cucumber *(Sicyos angulatus)* is a fall blooming vine with spiny fruits common in the Ohio Valley. In southern Indiana L. R. Stewart produces up to 100 pounds of a mild, table-grade honey from this source.

Dandelion *(Taraxacum officinale)* is a very common weed blooming in early spring when it yields both nectar and pollen so important for early spring buildup (Fig. 9). Parson Pile, in Montana, once produced 6,000 pounds of surplus dandelion honey. The honey is yellow with a pronounced, often bitter, taste and is best left with the bees.

White sage *(Salvia apiana)* is very common in the foothills of California from 3,000 up to 7,000 feet elevation. **Black sage** *(S. mellifera)*, or ball sage, is considered to be the source of most sage honey. It is perhaps the best honey plant in California. It grows from Mt. Diablo southward in southern California.

Purple sage *(S. leucophylla)*, or silver sage, grows in the Santa Monica and San Fernando mountains and in the San Joaquin Valley, and also is a good honey plant. Other species of sage are too local to be very important. The rapid growth of population in southern California is destroying much of the range where the sages grow.

Mesquite *(Prosopis juliflora)*. This tree of the Southwest spread northward in historic times throughout much of Texas, and into Oklahoma, New Mexico, Arizona, and eastern California (Fig. 10). It blooms several times some years and is an important source of surplus of good honey. The honey is light amber to white and is usually mixed with that from catsclaw, soap brush, and other chaparral plants. The

FIGURE 8. The bloom of sweet pepper bush is found in southeastern Massachusetts.

FIGURE 9. The common dandelion is familiar to everyone and provides spring buildup.

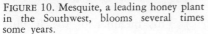

FIGURE 10. Mesquite, a leading honey plant in the Southwest, blooms several times some years.

FIGURE 11. Goldenrods are important fall plants to beekeepers in northern states and eastern Canada.

destruction of native plants to improve the range land has destroyed much of the honey-plant flora of most of Texas.

Goldenrod *(Solidago* spp.). Particularly in the northern states and eastern Canada, goldenrods are important fall honey plants and produce a rich yellow honey locally much esteemed (Fig. 11). In southern Maine, for instance, the white and alsike clover flow continues until the goldenrod flow starts. In the Southeast there is a big gap from the end of the white clover flow in July and the beginning of the goldenrod flow about the first of September. In this area goldenrod honey is generally mixed with a wide variety of fall plants, particularly aster, golden honey plant, bitterweed, ironweed, Spanish needles, and sunflower.

Aster *(Aster* spp.). Different species of asters are abundant in various parts of the country, which probably accounts for the divergent accounts of the quality of aster honey. White top *(Aster pilosa,* formerly *A. ericoides)* appears to be the more important species south of the Ohio River. Aster blooms very late in the season; bees often working it in Kentucky until the end of October on every warm sunny day. Bees often fill a shallow super in October. The honey, when being gathered, has such an unpleasant odor that beekeepers often call the inspector to check for foulbrood. This odor disappears when the honey is well ripened, but coming so late in the fall the unripe honey is said to be poor for wintering, often causing dysentery among the bees. The honey is usually light amber with a pronounced flavor. Farther north aster honey is lighter in color with a good flavor, and mixes well with goldenrod honey.

Spanish needles *(Bidens aristosa* and spp.) or tickseed sunflower (Fig. 12). This beautiful flowering plant with its numerous clusters of large yellow flowers grows in swampy places throughout the central states, from Maryland to Georgia, and west to Missouri and Arkansas. The honey is a golden yellow. One large packer in Arkansas purchases large quantities of Spanish needles honey and blends it with white honeys of clover and vetch to obtain a mild golden-tinted honey which is very popular. Spanish needles honey has a pronounced flavor which is highly esteemed in areas where the plant is abundant.

Tulip tree *(Liriodendron tulipifera)* or yellow poplar. The tulip tree is the chief honey plant in many parts of the South Atlantic Coast States. The trees are very beautiful, especially when in bloom, and grow very fast; the lumber is also valuable. The large tulip-shaped flowers secrete nectar freely but so early in the season that colonies often are not strong enough to take full advantage of the flow. The honey is red amber but has an attractive flavor generally liked in the tulip-tree area.

Black locust *(Robinia pseudoacacia)*. This member of the legume family is extensively planted for erosion control on worn-out land. The fragrant pea-shaped blossoms yield only in good weather. The honey is extra white and of very high quality, but locust blooms even earlier than tulip tree and special planning is necessary to get the colonies ready for so early a flow.

Tupelo *(Nyssa* spp.). There are four species, all valuable for bee-keeping. *(Nyssa ogeche)*, sometimes known as Ogeechee lime, is the leading honey plant of parts of south Georgia and western Florida, especially along the rivers and in swampy areas. It blooms in March and April and secretes nectar so abundantly that tons of honey are gathered. The honey is mild in flavor and light amber in color, and if pure never granulates.

Gallberry *(Ilex glabra)*. A low shrub common from the Carolinas southward into Florida and along the Gulf Coast. The honey is light amber with a pleasant aromatic aftertaste which is much esteemed in the area where it grows. The honey never crystallizes, hence is especially desirable for chunk comb honey. A related species, highbush gallberry *(Ilex coriacea)*, blooms in the same area and adds to the crop. Gallberry produces so much nectar that the late J. J. Wilder wrote that he never knew of a gallberry location to be overstocked by bees.

Horsemint *(Monarda* spp.). Chiefly in Texas, horsemint is an important honey plant producing large crops of white to light amber honey with a minty flavor and odor which is often very strong. Horsemint grows north to New York and east to Florida. There are several related species (Fig. 13).

Sourwood *(Oxydendrum arboreum)*. This low tree is common in the southern Alleghenies from West Virginia and southern Pennsylvania to

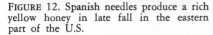

FIGURE 12. Spanish needles produce a rich yellow honey in late fall in the eastern part of the U.S.

FIGURE 13. Horsemint is an important honey plant chiefly in Texas but grows over an extended area north and eastward.

northern Georgia. It has a long blooming period in June and July and produces a water-white honey with a mild delicious flavor. The combs are so white and delicate that the honey cannot be extracted, so the honey is sold as comb honey or as chunk comb honey. Experts generally agree that this is the most delicious honey in the eastern states. The honey brings premium prices and is nearly all sold in the mountains where it is produced. A great deal of honey is sold as sourwood honey even though mixed with other kinds. It is often darkened by tulip tree honey.

Saw palmetto *(Serenoa repens)* grows in pinewoods and elsewhere from South Carolina to Florida and along the Gulf Coast to Texas. The petioles of its fan-shaped leaves are sawtoothed. It is the chief source of palm honey, a rich yellow honey much esteemed in the Southeast. Many Florida beekeepers consider this the best honey in the state.

Blue vine *(Ampelamus albidus)* or climbing milkweed. This fast-growing vine is a serious weed in cornfields. The honey is white but cloudy. Tons of blue vine honey were formerly produced in Missouri, southern Illinois, and southern Indiana as late as 1954.

Blue thistle *(Echium vulgare)*, is a prickly weed, widespread in the Northeast and especially common in northern New York, where good surpluses of a mild white honey are obtained.

Purple loosestrife *(Lythrum salicaria)*. Great patches of this honey plant grow in marshes in New England, New York, and Ontario, where extensive surpluses of an amber honey resembling motor oil in appearance are produced. The flavor varies according to the habitat. It is planted extensively in many other areas. Loosestrife blooms in late summer.

OTHER SOURCES OF NECTAR AND POLLEN

TABLE 1.   Flora east of the Mississippi River, usually including the
first tier of states west

Plant Name	Color of Honey	Flavor
American holly *(Ilex opaca)*	white to extra light amber	strong
Blueberry *(Vaccinium* spp.*)*	white	good
Boneset *(Eupatorium* spp.*)*		
Buttonbush *(Cephalanthus occidentalis)*	white	mild
Canada thistle *(Cirsium arvense)*	white	good
Chickweed *(Stellaria media)*	white	fair
Chicory *(Chichorium intybus)*	yellow	bitter
Cigar tree *(Catalpa speciosa)*	white	fair
Clematis *(Clematis virginiana)*	extra light amber, yellow	good
Cranberry *(Vaccinium macrocarpon)*	light amber	good
Dead nettle *(Lamium purpureum)*		
Dogbane *(Apocynum androsaemifolium)*	white	mild
False indigo *(Amorpha fruticosa)*	extra light amber	fair
Golden rain tree *(Koelreuteria paniculata)*		
Hawthorne *(Crataegus* spp.*)*	amber	strong
Hercules'-club *(Aralia spinosa)*	light amber	bitter
Ironweed *(Vernonia* spp.*)*	amber	fair
Joe-pye weed *(Eupatorium purpureum)*	amber	fair
Leatherleaf *(Chamaedaphne calyculata)*		
Leucothoe *(Leucothoe* spp.*)*	light amber	
Magnolia *(Magnolia* spp.*)*	amber	strong
Mountain mint *(Pycnanthemum tenuifolium)*	light amber	minty
Parsnip *(Pastinaca sativa)*	light amber	very bitter
Persimmon *(Diospyros virginiana)*	light amber	fair
Prickly ash *(Xanthoxylum americanum)*	light amber	very bitter
Redbud *(Cercis canadensis)*	extra light amber	good
Serviceberry *(Amelanchier* spp.*)*		
Sumac *(Rhus* spp.*)*	light amber	excellent
Sweet pepper bush *(Clethra alnifolia)*	white, yellowish	mild
Wild cherry *(Prunus* spp.*)*	reddish amber	bitter
Wild cucumber *(Sicyos angulatus)*	light amber	mild
Yellow flower *(Heterotheca subaxillaris)*	yellow	strong, pungent
Yellow hop clover *(Trifolium procumbens)*	yellow	mild
Yellow rocket *(Barbarea vulgaris)*	yellow	strong

TABLE 2.   Flora of Florida, Georgia, and the Gulf States

Plant Name	Color of Honey	Flavor
Bush mint *(Hyptis mutabilis)*	amber	strong
Cabbage palmetto *(Sabal palmetto)*	yellow amber	fair
Crotalaria *(Crotalaria* spp.*)*	light amber	fair to strong
Dwarf palmetto *(Sabal minor)*		
Gopher apple *(Chrysobalanus oblongifolius)*	amber	good
Manchineel *(Hippomane mancinella)*		
Partridge pea *(Cassia fasciculata)*	extra light amber	poor
Pennyroyal *(Satureja rigida)*	light amber	minty
Poisonwood *(Metopium toxiferum)*	light amber	good
Rattan vine *(Berchemia scandens)*	amber	good
Red bay *(Persea borbonia)*	light amber	fair
Sea grape *(Coccoloba uvifera)*	amber	good
Sea myrtle *(Baccharis halimifolia)*	(fall stores)	
Spring titi *(Cliftonia monophylla)*	light amber	strong
Summer farewell *(Kuhnistera pinnata)*	white	good
Wonder honey plant *(Penstemon hirsutus)*	extra light amber	good

TABLE 3.   Flora west of the Mississippi River

Plant Name	Color of Honey	Flavor
Antelope brush *(Purshia tridentata)*	amber	strong
Blackberry, dewberry *(Rubus* spp.*)*	white to light amber	good
Buckwheat vine *(Brunnichia cirrhosa)*	light amber	poor
Grapes *(Vitis* spp.*)*	red amber	good
Leafy spurge *(Euphorbia esula)*	amber	strong
Madrona *(Arbutus menziesii)*	light amber, yellow	good
Miner's candle *(Oreocarya virgata)*		
Muscatel *(Ampelopsis cordata)*	light amber	good
Mustard *(Brassica nigra)*	light amber, yellow	good
Oregon holly grape *(Mahonia aquifolium)*		
Pepper vine *(Ampelopsis arborea)*	reddish	fair to good
Rabbit brush *(Chrysothamnus* spp.*)*	amber	strong, unpleasant
Rocky Mountain bee plant *(Cleome serrulata)*	white, greenish	good
Rosinweed *(Grindelia squarrosa)*		
Russian knapweed *(Centaurea repens)*	amber	poor
Sainfoin *(Onobrychis viciaefolia)*		
Siberian peatree *(Caragana arborescens)*		
Snowberry *(Symphoricarpos* spp.*)*	light amber	good
Tornillo *(Prosopis pubescens)*	white	good
Vervain *(Verbena* spp.*)*	white, bluish tinge	mild
Yellow cleome *(Cleome lutea)*	white, yellowish	good

TABLE 4.   Flora of Texas, New Mexico, and Arizona

Plant Name	Color of Honey	Flavor
Agarita, wild currant *(Berberis trifoliolata)*	light amber	fair
Anaqua *(Ehretia elliptica)*	white	mild
Arrowweed *(Pluchea sericea)*	light amber	good
Balloon vine *(Cardiospermum halicacabum)*	light amber	good
Brazil bush *(Condalia obovata)*	amber	good
Broomweed *(Gutierrezia texana)*	yellow amber	strong to bitter
Cactus *(Cereus giganteus)*	white	good
Chamisa *(Adenostoma fasciculatum)*	light amber	pleasant
Coma *(Bumelia lycioides)*	light amber	fair
Creosote bush *(Larrea tridentata)*	bluish yellow	odor of creosote
Horehound *(Marrubium vulgare)*	amber	horehound flavor
Huajillo *(Acacia berlandieri)*	white	mild
Huisache *(Acacia farnesiana)*	(pollen only)	
Indian blanket or marigold *(Gaillardia pulchella)*	yellow amber	fair
Joint fir *(Ephedra* spp.*)*	greenish amber	strong
Paloverde *(Cercidium torreyanum)*	light yellow	good
Pink mint *(Stachys Drummondi)*	light amber	minty
Prickly pear *(Opuntia* spp.*)*	amber, reddish	fair
Retama *(Parkinsonia aculeata)*	amber	fair
Sensia *(Leucophyllum frutescens)*	light amber	good
Soapbush *(Porlieria angustifolia)*	white	mild
Soapberry *(Sapindus Drummondi)*	light amber	fair
Sotol *(Dasylirion texanum)*	yellow amber	strong
Tamarisk *(Tamarix* spp.*)*	amber	poor
Yaupon *(Ilex vomitoria)*	white (extra light amber)	good
Yerba dulce *(Baccharis angustifolia)*	light amber	

TABLE 5. Flora of California to Oregon along the west coast

Plant Name	Color of Honey	Flavor
California laurel *(Umbellularia californica)*	amber	spicy
Cascara buckthorn *(Rhamnus purshiana)*	amber	pleasant
Cat's-ear *(Hypochaeris radicata)*	light amber, yellowish	fair
Century plant *(Agave americana)*	amber	very strong
Chamisa *(Adenostoma fasciculatum)*	light amber	pleasant
Coffeeberry *(Rhamnus californica)*	white to light amber	good
Jackass clover *(Wislizenia refracta)*	white	good
Jagger weed *(Centromadia fitchii)*	yellow	strong
Leafy spurge *(Euphorbia esula)*	amber	strong
Leatherbreeches *(Amsinckia lycopsoides)*	light amber	
Manzanita *(Arctostaphylos manzanita)*	white to extra light amber	slightly bitter
Mountain mahogany *(Cercocarpus montanus)*	light amber	sharp to bitter
Mountain misery *(Chamaebatia foliolosa)*	amber	fair
Napa thistle *(Centaurea melitensis)*	light amber	good
Povertyweed *(Iva axillaris)*	amber	strong
Salal *(Gaultheria shallon)*		
Snowbush *(Ceanothus velutina)*	light amber	sharp to bitter
Spikeweed *(Centromadia pungens)*	yellow	strong
Tarweed *(Hemixonia fasciculata)*	amber	strong
Toyon *(Photinia arbutifolia)*	amber	strong
Wild buckwheat *(Eriogonoum fasciculatum)*	extra light amber	fair
Wild lilac *(Ceanothus cuneatus)*	light amber	good
Yellow star thistle *(Centaurea solstitialis)*	white to light amber	good
Yerba dulce *(Baccharis angustifolia)*		
Yerba santa *(Eriodictyon californicum)*	amber	spicy

REFERENCES ON FLORA FOR BEES

Arnold, Lillian. 1954. Fla. Agr. Expt. Sta. Bull. **548.** 47 pp.

Eckert, J. E., and Frank R. Shaw. Beekeeping. The Macmillan Co., New York. 536 pp.

Holmes, Frances O. 1960. Am. Bee J. **100:**122-123.

Howes, F. N. 1945. Plants and beekeeping. Faber & Faber, London. 224 pp.

Lovell, Harvey B. 1940. Rhodora. **42:**352-354.

----------------- 1956. Honey plants manual. The A. I. Root Co., Medina, Ohio. 64 pp.

Lovell, John H. 1924. Am. Bee J. **64:**280-283.

----------------- 1926. Honey plants of North America. The A. I. Root Co., Medina, Ohio. 408 pp.

Ordetx, Gonzalo S. 1952. Flora de la America tropical. Editorial Lex., Havana, Cuba. 334 pp.

Oertel, Everett. 1939. U.S.D.A. Circ. **554.** 64 pp.

Pammel, L. H., and Charlotte M. King. 1930. Honey plants of Iowa. Ia. Geol. Survey Bull. **7.** 1192 pp.

Pellett, Frank C. American honey plants. 4th ed. Orange Judd Pub. Co., New York. 476 pp.

Scullen, H. A., and G. H. Vansell. 1942. Ore. Agr. Expt. Sta. Bull. **412.** 63 pp.

Vansell, G. H. 1949. Utah Agr. Expt. Sta. Coll. Circ. **124.** 28 pp.

Vansell, G. H., and J. E. Eckert. Univ. Calif. Expt. Sta. Bull. **517.** 75 pp.

White, J. W., Jr., M. I. Reithof, M. H. Subers, and I. Kushnir. 1962. U.S.D.A. Tech. Bull. **1261.** 124 pp.

CHAPTER VII

FIRST CONSIDERATIONS IN KEEPING BEES

by G. H. CALE*

ENTHUSIASM IS THE keynote which induces a person to start bee-keeping. This enthusiasm often persists for years. From the ranks of the beginners, come the hobbyists, side-liners and full-time commercial honey producers.

The beginner soon finds that beekeeping offers him more than financial gain. It brings contact with the out-of-doors and many phases of nature. It may mean improved health, diversion from ordinary affairs, and satisfaction entirely beyond dollars and cents.

The beekeeper must have a thorough knowledge of his occupation. He must know the habits of the bees. He must learn what to do with them to serve best his own interests. He should be familiar with the plants from which the bees secure both nectar and pollen. He must acquaint himself with their blooming time in order to have his colonies ready for the honeyflow. He should be patient with details because beekeeping consists of many small duties carried out systematically to accomplish definite objectives.

The beginner acquires experience and knowledge as he continues his pursuit. He may seek the advice of friendly beekeepers or he may work with them until he has acquired enough knowledge to continue beekeeping on his own. It is advisable for the beginner to attend bee-keepers' meetings where he can learn considerable from those present. He can attend short courses in beekeeping at colleges and universities. He should become familiar with the literature about bees. Many good books are available, and bulletins are issued by the various states and by the U. S. Department of Agriculture. The beginner should read the current publications about bees and beekeeping. Those currently published are the *American Bee Journal* and *Gleanings in Bee Culture*.

It is advisable to start beekeeping with more than one colony. Many of the operations in the care of colonies depend upon the interchange of combs. When a colony becomes weak from queen failure, lack of food, or other causes, brood and bees and combs of honey may then be obtained from another colony. Having a number of colonies also pro-

---

*Gladstone H. Cale. Editor of the *American Bee Journal*. Formerly assistant professor of economic zoology, University of Maryland, and an associate in the U. S. D. A. Bee Culture Laboratory. Many years' experience in honey production in the apiaries of Dadant & Sons and operator of his own apiaries.

vides a means of making increases in their number when conditions are right.   Therefore, a start with about five colonies is advisable.

On the other hand, it is better not to expand beekeeping too rapidly. It is wiser to gain experience and to make the bees pay as they go. If the beginner lives in a community where there are regulations against the keeping of bees, he may arrange to place them on a near-by farm of a relative or friend, making frequent attention to the bees possible. Until the returns from beekeeping warrant the extra expense of outyard operation, it is advisable to keep them close to home.

KIND OF HONEY TO PRODUCE

Formerly, the beginner was advised to start with the production of section comb honey (Fig. 1). However, this requires skill, patience, and experience which the beginner usually has not acquired. The production of bulk comb honey is possible for the beginner since it is easier to produce than section comb honey. In spite of a somewhat greater investment in equipment, most start with the production of extracted honey (Fig. 2). The management of the colonies does not require as much skill and more honey can be produced with a less amount of work. Of course, the production of extracted honey requires the equipment needed to uncap the combs and to remove the liquid honey from them.

KIND OF BEEHIVE TO USE

The beehive most commonly used is the 10-frame Langstroth hive (Fig. 3). Used much less extensively are the 11-frame Modified Dadant hive and the 10-frame Jumbo hive, both of which contain frames deeper than the Langstroth, and the 8-frame Langstroth hive. For additional information on types of beehives, see Chapter VIII, "Beekeeping Equipment."

It is now generally accepted that a single 10-frame Langstroth hive body is not large enough to accommodate the brood of a good queen, so two bodies are employed together in what is called the two-story Langstroth hive. Sometimes a third body is added for additional brood expansion or for storage of honey and pollen as a food reserve during winter. Some beekeepers prefer the Modified Dadant hive with its deeper brood chamber, and accommodate the egg laying of superior queens by providing a super on top which also serves as a food chamber in winter.

Many beekeepers prefer to use shallow supers for honey storage rather than to use full-depth hive bodies because they are not so heavy to lift when full of honey. In spite of this, most use the Langstroth bodies in multiple units both for the requirements of the colony and also for honey storage.

The equipment required for the production of 100 pounds of extracted honey by a single colony, usually accepted by beekeepers as a paying crop, is two or perhaps three Langstroth hive bodies for the brood chamber, and two or three bodies for the storage of honey, in

FIGURE 1. A small display of section comb honey packaged in this manner finds a ready consumer demand.

FIGURE 2. Two glass containers of crystal-clear, extracted honey, attractively labeled, invite the customer to buy.

addition to the bottom board and cover. When shallow supers are used, four to five are required for honey storage. This amount of equipment will accommodate 100 to 150 pounds of honey.

Directions for assembling the hive equipment are supplied by the manufacturers but many details of the work will be learned only by experience. Hive bodies and supers should be assembled and firmly nailed at each corner. Frames should be assembled squarely with the V-edges of the end bars positioned against the flat edges of adjoining frames. It is advisable to buy equipment that is made accurately so that it will fit when assembled. Well made equipment of good clear lumber is the best investment.

KIND OF BEES AND HOW TO SECURE THEM

There are two races of bees available in this country: Italians and Caucasians. The Italian bees are available so generally that, when the name of the race is not mentioned in an advertisement, one may assume that they are Italians. Caucasian bees are available from only a few sources. Both races are suitable for the beginner.

Hybrid bees, produced from genetically controlled lines by artificial insemination, are now as generally available as the common-stock Italians. These hybrids present bees that are superior in honey production while having other desirable characteristics such as good temper, less swarming, better wintering, and a degree of resistance to disease. The breeding of superior strains of hybrid bees offers to beekeeping of the future increasingly higher honey production, disease resistance, and bees bred for special purposes such as comb honey production and the pollination of crops.

The purchase of package bees with queens is the procedure usually followed by the beginner in starting with bees. The production of package bees is a well established industry in the South, and in California and neighboring states, offering a reliable source from which to secure new bees. In this manner, the beginner is able to start beekeeping and to increase the number of his colonies as he desires (Fig. 4).

Some beginners start with a swarm they have secured in some manner, or they may obtain an established colony from a beekeeper friend. The hiving of a swarm of bees is a job for a specialist in many cases and, unless a large one at the beginning of the honeyflow, its management is not easy. The buying of established colonies likewise presents the problem of determining if they are free from disease, have good queens, and are properly provisioned.

If it is decided that the best way to start is with package bees, they should be ordered well in advance of the time they are wanted. They

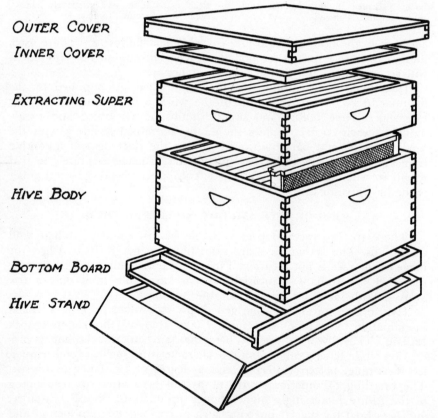

OUTER COVER

INNER COVER

EXTRACTING SUPER

HIVE BODY

BOTTOM BOARD

HIVE STAND

FIGURE 3. Diagram of the various parts that comprise the beehive, in the order in which it is assembled.

FIGURE 4. A small apiary provides diversion and profits for the amateur. Look at the grin on this beekeeper.

should arrive between April 10 and May 10, depending upon the latitude or how early spring comes. They should be installed in hives in time to take advantage of early bloom, and to allow 8 to 10 weeks for the colonies to build to good strength before the main honeyflow.

Equipment for package-bee colonies should be assembled well in advance of the arrival of the packages. For further information on the production and types of package bees, see Chapter XVII, "The Production of Queens, Package Bees, and Royal Jelly."

Upon arrival, the packages of bees should be installed in their hives as soon as possible. Methods of doing this are discussed in detail in Chapter X, "Management for Honey Production." When possible, it is advisable to install package bees on fully drawn combs containing some honey and pollen. When packages are installed on frames containing comb foundation, they should be fed sugar sirup and carefully managed until they are fully established. A properly cared-for package colony may secure surplus honey from the main honeyflows; they should at least become full colonies before winter.

HOW TO AVOID BEE STINGS

If it was not for the fear of bee stings, honey bees would be much more common on the farm and around the home. The penetration of the sting is always felt, no matter how many years are spent with the bees, but the swelling and irritation becomes less as time goes on, until the operator actually acquires an immunity. The seasoned beekeeper thinks no more of a sting on the hand or the arm than a woodsman thinks of a slight scratch from a thorn.

To avoid being stung, a good bee veil fitting snugly about the collar and shoulders should be worn. The shirt sleeves may be rolled down and a pair of gauntlet gloves can be worn. Avoid wearing dark-colored or woolen clothing; white or light-colored smooth material is best. To prevent bees from crawling up the legs, the pants can be stuffed inside white socks; some prefer to wear high-top boots. Women should wear similar clothing.

In an attempt to sting, the bee takes a firm hold with its claws. On feeling this, the beekeeper often is able to brush off or kill the bee before the sting penetrates the skin (Fig. 5). If the bee has managed to insert her "stinger," it should be removed as quickly as possible by scraping it off with the thumb nail. One should not attempt to pick it off with the fingers because that will squeeze the poison sac, causing the poison to be injected into the wound. If itching or swelling results, the application of cold cloths seems to be the best treatment.

FIGURE 5. This bee has been induced to sting by being held against the arm. In an attempt to remove its barbed sting, the worker bee suffers severe damage to itself and usually dies as a result.

Since the odor of the sting seems to infuriate other bees, the operator should beat a retreat if stings affect him seriously. Fortunately, the number of individuals so affected are few in number. If the skin becomes blotched and the breath shortens, a doctor should be called immediately. Adrenalin, administered by a physician, is a specific antidote when bee stings cause a systemic reaction. Ephedrin is also a remedy when the help of a doctor cannot be obtained.

The temper of honey bees varies with weather conditions, the time of day, the season of the year, the way the operator goes about his tasks, and by honeyflow conditions. An exceptionally cross colony is almost unheard of among common stock available today, and the hybrid stock is noted for gentleness.

The judicious use of smoke in working the bees has much to do with whether the bees are inclined to sting. Smoke causes bees to fill themselves with honey, not only in anticipation of the disaster which smoke suggests, but also due to their instinct to do this when disturbed by any means. Langstroth stated: "A honey bee when heavily laden with honey never volunteers an attack, but acts solely on the defensive." Thus, no one need have fear of keeping bees if wearing a bee veil and attired in suitable clothing, and if they are managed properly.

HOW TO USE A BEE SMOKER

A cool smoke puffed gently and used only when necessary will be found to be most effective. Unnecessary or excessive smoking actually may increase the tendency of bees to sting. A hot smoke containing sparks causes them to act similarly.

FIGURE 6. A gentle puff or two of smoke at the entrance before starting to open the hive.

Many amazing materials are used as smoker fuel—corn cobs, decaying wood, tree bark, sumac bobs, fallen leaves, hay wisps, dry grass, cloth and burlap—each beekeeper has his favorite fuel material. Any material that will supply a cool, clean source of smoke and remain ignited between infrequent puffs of the smoker is suitable. Usually, some of the fuel is lighted and placed in the bottom or fire pot of the smoker where the air from the bellows causes it to blaze before the balance of the fuel is added to produce the smoke.

In time, the bee smoker will become coated inside with a black tarlike formation. The smoker should be kept clean by daily scraping the inside with a hive tool before relighting. This is important because soot and tar should never be blown onto the combs to contaminate them. Cared for properly and kept dry, the smoker should last for years.

When the smoker is no longer needed, the lighted fuel should be emptied into a metal can and covered, or buried before leaving the apiary. This will eliminate the possibility of a grass fire, often destructive to the colonies. For obvious reasons, a lighted smoker never should be placed in a car or truck when leaving the apiary.

HOW TO OPEN A HIVE OF BEES

In opening a hive of bees, do not hurry or make sudden nervous movements. Nervousness apparently contributes to secretions of the skin and bees seem to resent the resulting odor. This may explain why some beekeepers are stung more than others.

The hive should be approached from the side; some prefer to work on the right, others on the left of the colony. Do not work in front of the hive interfering with the flight of bees to and from the entrance. A small amount of smoke should be puffed into the entrance (Fig. 6); a large volume of smoke is not necessary and may have harmful effects.

Next, remove the outer cover and puff a little smoke along the cracks or any opening at the top of the hive. Pry up the inner cover with the straight end of the hive tool and smoke gently (Fig. 7). Some prefer to use a fabric cover over the combs such as oil cloth or canvas. The cloth may be rolled back to any distance for examination and does not disturb the colony as much as the removal of the wooden inner cover.

First remove the nearest outside comb, setting it on the ground on your side of the hive. Sometimes two combs are removed before examination of the brood begins. When there is danger of robbing, the combs should be covered with a cloth (see robbing in Chapter X, "Management for Honey Production"). The remaining combs may be separated from each other with the bent end of the hive tool, opening a sufficient space for their removal without crushing or disturbing the bees (Fig. 8). Handle the combs quietly and easily, without jerky motions. These combs usually are not set outside the hive but are returned to their original positions (Fig. 9).

A little puff of smoke is required from time to time if the bees become excited, running over the combs and flying out in an attitude suggesting they are ready to sting. Do not jar the hive needlessly and do not strike at any cross bees.

When examining a comb of bees, hold it over the hive, not over the ground. Then, if by chance, the queen drops from a comb being examined, she will fall into the hive, and not be lost or accidentally killed. Handle each comb gently and easily. If a few bees drop off the comb, the colony will not become excited. Return the combs carefully and close the hive quietly. If the work is done in the sunny part of the day, particularly on calm, clear days when the bees are busy in the fields, little difficulty will be experienced.

FIGURE 7. A little smoke puffed over the tops of the frames after the inner cover has been removed.

FIGURE 8. The frame containing the comb is carefully raised without crushing the bees.

HOW MANY COLONIES CAN ONE PERSON KEEP

The number of colonies of bees that one person can care for will depend on the kind of honey he intends to produce, the extent of his experience, the time he has available, the nearness of his outapiaries, and whether they are close to abundant sources of nectar and pollen throughout the season, making their moving unnecessary.

In the production of extracted honey, a skillfull beekeeper can care for 500 to 700 colonies without employing permanent help. During the removal of the honey and its extracting, while moving colonies, and possibly when packing the colonies for winter, he will find it advisable to employ temporary help. There are many beekeepers who keep anywhere from one to several thousand colonies and find it necessary to employ permanent help if the family does not provide this.

In the production of bulk comb honey, one person cannot care for as many colonies as in the production of extracted honey, due to the more exacting system of management. Management for the production of section comb honey is even more exacting and intensive (see Chapter XII, "The Production of Comb and Bulk Comb Honey"). Generally, one person producing section comb honey can care for about half as many colonies as in the production of extracted honey, while in the production of bulk comb honey about three-fourths as many colonies can be kept.

FIGURE 9. This is the way the frame containing the comb of brood is manipulated to examine the brood and bees.

THE COST OF PRODUCING HONEY

The cost of producing honey varies considerably. Nevertheless, the average profits obtained from beekeeping compare favorably with those from other agricultural pursuits. Four chief factors largely determine the cost of producing honey: the yield of surplus honey, the cost of labor and materials, transportation costs, and the upkeep and investment in equipment.

The beekeeper should keep careful records to determine the costs of production so that he can know how profitable is his enterprise. If you sell your honey at retail, you need to add the cost of selling and distribution. If you sell your crop to a wholesale buyer, you can expect to receive less for the honey but you are spared the cost of sales and distribution. The wholesale price for extracted honey has varied over the years from a low of about 5 cents a pound to as high as 25 cents. The average price has been about 10 cents a pound, although there have been many years when extracted honey brought from 12 to 15 cents in quantity at wholesale.

To judge the possibility of income from the production of extracted honey, commercial producers base their figures on an average crop of 100 pounds to the colony each year. The cost of operating a single colony will vary from $5 to $6 to as high as $8 to $10, depending on the number of colonies operated, the cost of labor and materials required, and the efficiency of the operator. Considering the average long-range wholesale price with a low operating cost and a crop of 100 pounds or more for each colony, good returns may be expected.

LAWS RELATING TO BEEKEEPING

There are laws or regulations affecting beekeeping in most states, the chief purpose of which is to prevent the spread of serious bee diseases (see Chapter XIX, "Disease and Enemies of the Honey Bee").

Some states will not allow bees on combs to come in from another state or empty combs that have been in use. To undertake beekeeping in those states requires that new or sterilized hives and hive parts be used equipped with frames containing sheets of comb foundation. Other states require certificates of recent inspection and a permit of entry before the beekeeper can bring in bees on combs. The beekeeper should become familiar with the laws that are in force in any state in which he may wish to move his bees.

Some states require that apiary sites be registered and beekeepers are not permitted to move in unless locations are available that do not encroach upon other beekeepers. In California, the movement of bees within the state is regulated and apiaries must be registered because of laws pertaining to the use of pesticides harmful to bees (see Chapter XX, "Injury to Bees by Poisoning"). Other states have laws regulating the cleanliness of honey houses and laws of this kind are apt to become more widespread in the future.

Municipalities often have regulations against the keeping of bees within the corporate limits because of complaints that bees are a nuisance. The best way out of such possible difficulty is to locate the colonies behind high fences or vegetation so they fly high in going to and from the bee yard making it unlikely that people or animals will be stung. The gift of a reasonable amount of honey to your neighbors will silence most protests.

A swarm of bees is considered as being wild in nature and becomes the property of whoever captures and hives it. Once in the air, the bees cease to be the property of their former owner unless he can keep them in sight with the intent of hiving them. Bees in a tree or building, once fully established as a colony, become the property of the man who owns the tree or building. When bees are located so as to constitute a public menace and the beekeeper, through negligence, does not alleviate the situation, he is liable to prosecution.

CHAPTER VIII

BEEKEEPING EQUIPMENT

by H. C. DADANT*

IT IS A REMARKABLE fact that many valuable discoveries concerning the life history and activities of honey bees were made before the development of modern methods and equipment. Although the early hives were comparatively inconvenient, they permitted some movement of the combs and inspection of the bees, making possible valuable discoveries. For a description of these hives and their development, the reader is referred to previous editions of this book.

Through the use of modern equipment, the beekeeper is now the master while formerly it was the bees. It is no longer necessary to endure loss of time and crop by breaking into receptacles containing bees, cutting the combs away with a knife, and guessing at the condition of colonies. On the contrary, every colony can be well judged and controlled. A good honey crop can be readily harvested during a season of abundant nectar supply, but no one can make a success from year to year without knowledge of the behavior of honey bees, proper and timely attention to the colonies, and the use and efficient manipulation of modern beekeeping equipment.

In 1851, Langstroth discovered the bee space and invented his movable-comb hive (Fig. 1) and, in 1853, he published his book which gave a detailed description of its management. The frames were constructed so that they could be suspended in the hive, leaving a space of one-fourth to three-eighths inch, called a bee space, between all surfaces, permitting combs to be removed without crushing the bees. Additional bodies for rearing brood or for the storage of surplus honey could be added on top and removed easily. The principles of his hive are incorporated in all modern hives.

About 1843, Gottlieb Kretchmer[4] produced a comb base and Johannes Mehring made comb foundation on a flat press in 1857. Then, in 1865, Franz von Hruschka invented the honey extractor. Comb foundation and crude homemade extractors soon were in use making it possible to produce quantities of honey and remove it from the combs.

With the bee journals beginning to disseminate information, the first controversies on the size of the frame and the size of the hive began. J. S. Harbison of California, had introduced the four-piece honey section in 1857, and a marked trend toward the Langstroth frame and a smaller brood nest followed. In 1883, G. M. Doolittle reduced the

---

*Henry C. Dadant, Inventor of crimp-wired foundation and copartner of Dadant & Sons, manufacturers of bee supplies. Specialist in the study of comb building.

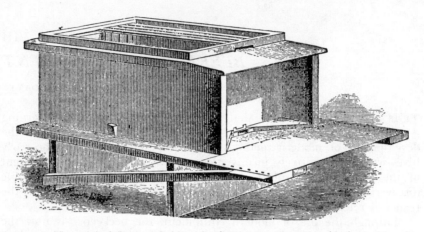

FIGURE 1. The original Langstroth hive, the first top-opening, movable-frame hive that provided a bee space between frames and other hive parts, making possible the present extent of beekeeping.

Gallup hive to nine frames, 11¼ inches square, and then to six frames. By 1885, Heddon and others reduced the Langstroth ten frames to eight, and even to five frames by the use of two "dummies" which occupied the space of three frames. Others contended that the brood nest should be divided horizontally, and the Bingham, Danzenbaker, and Heddon hives resulted. This period of contraction of the brood nest, 1876 to 1906, is known as the *Comb Honey Era,* and resulted in materially reduced crops of honey.

Foremost among the defenders of large hives were Charles Dadant and C. P. Dadant (Fig. 2). After lengthy experiments with hives containing eight, ten, eleven, and up to twenty frames, the original Dadant hive was adopted. It was on the Langstroth principle but contained eleven frames of the Quinby size, having an inside dimension of 10 by 17⅞ inches. In his contention for the large brood nest, C. P. Dadant often quoted Langstroth[5] who wrote: "Many hives cannot hold one quarter of the bees, combs, and honey which, in a good season, may be found in my large hives; while their owners wonder that they obtain so little profit from their bees."

Although highly efficient, the original Dadant hive did not become popular in America due to its high cost, heavy weight, and odd size. Pellett and others encouraged the Dadants to produce a large hive of economic construction similiar to the 10-frame Langstroth hive, hence the Modified Dadant hive was brought out in 1920. It is the same length as the Langstroth hive but contains eleven frames of the Quinby depth, spaced 1½ inches apart. This makes it possible to use Langstroth bodies on it as supers, although the 6⅝ inch Dadant super usually is used. It completes the large-hive idea of a large brood nest with shallow supers.

FIGURE 2. Charles Dadant (left) and his son, C. P. Dadant (right), recognized leaders in beekeeping throughout the world and originators of the large Dadant hive.

Modern Hives and Hive Parts

The beekeepers of America are fortunate in that only two sizes of hives are in general use: the ten-frame Langstroth and the Modified Dadant hive. In fact, the two standard hives have not been superseded after many years of use, and methods of management that insure success have been adopted in each case. Each type can be adapted to accommodate larger colonies of bees and greater crops of honey.

The ten-frame or standard Langstroth hive (Fig. 3) is used most universally and contains ten frames, 9⅛ by 17⅝ inches, spaced 1⅜ inches center to center.

The eight-frame hive is the Langstroth hive reduced to eight frames of the above dimensions and spacing. The eight-frame hive is not used extensively today.

The Jumbo hive contains ten frames of the Quinby depth, 11¼ inches, and the Langstroth length, 17⅝ inches, spaced 1⅜ inches from center to center. This hive sometimes is called the Quinby hive but differs from the original Quinby which had eight frames 18½ inches in length. The Jumbo hive is not used extensively today.

The Modified Dadant hive contains eleven frames of the Quinby depth and the Langstroth length, but the spacing is 1½ inches center to center (Fig. 3). This spacing, which was recommended by Quinby,

FIGURE 3. The two standard hives of America: the 1½ story Modified Dadant hive (left) and the 2-story, 10-frame Langstroth hive (right).

facilitates removal of combs, allows more room for clustering of bees in winter, and provides for better ventilation as an aid in swarm control. The Modified Dadant hive ranks second to the ten-frame hive in its use by beekeepers; its popularity in commercial production is increasing.

The modern beehive consists of a bottom board, a sufficient number of bodies containing the frames and combs of the brood nest, supers for the honey crop, the inner cover, and an outer cover. White pine is the wood generally used for beehives, although cypress, spruce, and basswood sometimes are used. Parts that tend to rot quickest, should be protected by "rotproofing" compounds that have pentachlorophenol as their basic material. The outer cover should be protected with galvanized iron sheeting and well painted.

Mitchener[8] showed that two coats of good white paint applied to galvanized roof covers provides a temperature within the hive which is about 5° F. lower than when aluminum or other kinds and colors of paint are used. It is the usual practice to allow galvanized iron covers to weather for a year or two before painting so that the paint will adhere. If it is desirable to paint them when new, they should be washed with vinegar before they are painted. All parts of the hives that are exposed to weather should be protected with paint.

Although the hive stand is not used often in commercial beekeeping practice, it is desirable because it prevents the bottom board from rotting, keeps the hive off the ground where grass and weeds obstruct the entrance, reduces dampness within the hive, and usually serves as an alighting board for incoming field bees. Hive stands made of concrete are ideal for permanent locations.

The bottom board usually is reversible, permitting an entrance ⅞ inches deep and the width of the hive, or a shallow entrance of ⅜ inch. It can be removed readily in order to clean it of dead bees and debris. By the use of an entrance block, the entrance can be kept small in winter or early spring, or enlarged to a full opening by its removal for crowded conditions or during warm weather.

The frames, as made by most manufacturers, are of the "Hoffman" style which touch each other along the upper third of their end bars, thus providing self-spacing. The width of the top bar usually is 1-1/16 inches, permitting more than a bee space between the frames. The underside of the top bar is cut away to make a wedge which is nailed into place to hold the foundation. The end bars contain holes through which wires may be threaded and fastened for holding the comb foundation. The bottom bar may be solid, grooved, or two-piece to provide for insertion of foundation used by the beekeeper.

The top of the hive is protected with an inner cover and an outer cover. The inner cover contains an oblong hole for receiving a bee escape and serves as an escape board when removing honey. The outer cover is usually of the type that telescopes over the top of the hive to a depth of an inch or more, and is covered with galvanized iron or aluminum sheeting. It is commonly called the "metal cover." The Excelsior cover is made entirely of wood with the top sloping slightly to each side and the ends telescoping over the front and back of the top of the hive.

The brood compartment usually consists of two 10-frame Langstroth bodies or one Modified Dadant with one super serving as a food chamber. The supers for the storage of surplus honey either are full-depth bodies, often preferred with the Langstroth hive, or shallow supers. Shallow supers for the 10-frame hive are 5 11/16 inches deep and take a 5⅜ inch frame. Shallow supers are always used with the Modified Dadant hive and are 6⅝ inches deep and take a 6¼ inch frame.

Shallow supers are used for the production of section comb honey and bulk comb honey. The standard comb honey super is approximately 4¾ inches deep and contains one tier of sections (see Chapter XII, "The Production of Comb Honey and Bulk Comb Honey"). The comb honey super can be used for producing extracted honey by using the 4½ inch frame. Some prefer the 5 11/16 inch or 6⅝ inch shallow supers for producing bulk comb honey.

Comb Foundation

Comb foundation is a sheet of pure beeswax embossed on both sides with the bases and the beginnings of the cell walls of the comb of the honey bee. It is inserted in a frame and placed in the hive where it becomes the midrib or base of the comb which the bees complete. It is astonishing as well as pleasing to see how quickly a colony of bees will build its combs from foundation.

The cells of comb foundation are ordinarily made of worker-bee size, as a sufficient population of drones is provided by a few small areas of drone cells which the bees usually construct along the bottoms and corners of the combs. Inasmuch as the bees draw out the foundation according to the size of cell embossed on it, a large force of worker bees is obtained. In fact, when frames are furnished with full sheets of worker-size comb foundation, colonies can be induced to abandon their natural trait of building one-fourth or more drone-size cells.

The proper use of comb foundation has many advantages (see Chapter X, "Management for Honey Production"). Straight combs are obtained which permit easy and rapid manipulation of the colonies. The removal of honey from the supers is greatly facilitated. At least half of the honey and much of the labor required by the bees in the construction of combs is saved. These advantages, plus the control of a desirable population of worker bees, makes commercial honey production possible.

A few sheets of drone-cell foundation may be used to advantage in queen-rearing yards where a large force of drones of selected stock is desired. There has been some contention that, due to the larger cells, drone comb facilitates storage, rapid evaporation of nectar, and greater ease in removal of honey from the cells when extracting. The difficulty of excluding the laying queen from large areas of drone comb, however, discourages its use. In any case, a large number of drones is a detriment to the colony because they do no work and consume large amounts of nectar and honey.

MANUFACTURE OF COMB FOUNDATION

Only pure beeswax should be used in making comb foundation. Microcrystalline wax, paraffin, ceresin, carnauba, hydrogenated castor oil, and others have been added to beeswax. With the exception of paraffin, these materials tend to harden the comb foundation and to raise the melting point. If the addition is considerable, the bees notice the difference and show a decided preference for pure beeswax foundation. This is emphasized in times when nectar is not being gathered in quantity by the bees.

The most serious objection to the adulteration of beeswax in the manufacture of comb foundation is the unknown composition of the wax derived from the resulting combs. Since the combs of the honey bee become a major source of pure beeswax, comb foundation should never be contaminated with the addition of other waxes or waxlike compounds which are inseparable. Chemical and physical tests can detect the impurity of these unknown mixtures.[9] Buyers of crude beeswax either pay a lower price for them, or even refuse to accept shipment, because of the expense and difficulty in determining their composition. All manufacturers of comb foundation in this county have signed an agreement to make comb foundation *of pure beeswax only*.

In the manufacture of comb foundation, the beeswax is sorted into two grades. The deep-yellow and brown shades are used for making comb foundation for brood and extracting frames. These darker shades of beeswax mainly come from the rendering of frame scrapings and old combs. The light-yellow shades are used for making foundation for comb honey sections and bulk comb honey frames. The light-colored beeswax is obtained from cappings and new combs.

The beeswax is carefully refined (Fig. 4) until free of all separable materials. It is then made into sheets which are run through milling rolls which emboss the sheets of wax. Brood foundation is made on a mill which makes foundation having a thick base and a deep cell wall which the bees draw into combs more readily. Comb honey foundation is made on a mill which makes the bases and walls so fragile that the foundation will not stand the weight of the bees in a full-size frame.

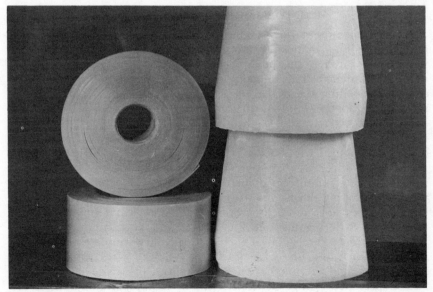

FIGURE 4. Cakes of fully refined pure beeswax are melted and extruded by a Weed-process sheeting machine in the form of a pliable sheet of pure beeswax which is rolled up, as above, for ease in handling.

GRADES OF COMB FOUNDATION

The best weight of comb foundation for use in the brood nest or for extracting frames of brood depth, averages seven to eight sheets per pound in the Langstroth size, 8 by 16¾ inches. The eight-sheet weight, with vertical wires included, provides only seven sheets per pound. Sheets of comb foundation for the large-size Dadant or Quinby brood frames are made heavier, six sheets to the pound in the size 10 by 16¾ inches and, with vertical wires included, five sheets to the pound. The above weights of comb foundation are known as *medium brood*. Lighter weights known as *light brood* are seldom used. Although there are one or two more sheets in each pound, combs built on them frequently are distorted, having imperfect cells unfit for brood rearing.

Comb foundation for bulk comb and section comb honey is made very light. One pound of *bulk comb foundation,* sometimes called cut comb foundation, size 4½ by 16½ inches, contains 20 sheets and has heavier walls and bases than comb foundation for section comb honey.

Comb foundation for section comb honey must be made as light as the finest machine can make it to avoid what is called the "fishbone," a heavy central rib of wax found in honeycomb built on foundation that is too heavy. Comb foundation for section comb honey is known as *thin surplus* and in size 3⅞ by 16½ inches is made 28 to 29 sheets per pound. An extra thin grade has 32 sheets per pound. Comb is not built as readily on it because the bees have to add more of their own beeswax.

REINFORCING COMB FOUNDATION

Plain comb foundation should be reinforced in brood frames with four longitudinal, malleable tinned wires of 28 or 30 gauge. The wire is threaded through the holes in the end bars of the frame, pulled tight, and fastened. The foundation then is inserted in the frame and secured by nailing the wedge in place in the top bar. Then, with the sheet of foundation underneath, the wires are embedded by an electrical device or by a spur embedder.

In 1921, Dadant & Sons perfected a method of wiring which consisted of vertical crimped wires woven into the foundation by machinery (Fig. 5). Crimped wires are better than straight ones, for the shoulders of support radiate reinforcement between the wires and prevent the beeswax from slipping downward when soft from heat. Nine or ten vertical crimped wires are ample to prevent sagging. When only seven wires are used, a little sagging sometimes is noticed between the wires.

When proper care is taken in handling and assembling the foundation and when the hives are level, the vertical wires alone may be sufficient to hold the foundation in the central plane of the frame and also to prevent sagging. Generally, two to four longitudinal wires are used in addition to the vertical support to prevent the foundation from swinging in the frame. This double wiring results in as rigid and

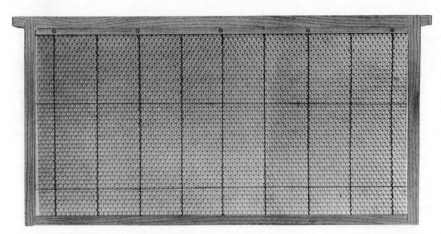

FIGURE 5. Crimp-wired comb foundation in a frame with two longitudinal wires electrically embedded provides a perfect foundation for a good comb.

straight combs as it is possible to get (Fig. 6), and permits rapid handling and hauling long distances with little or no damage to combs, even though newly built and heavy with honey.

In 1923, the A. I. Root Company brought out a three-ply foundation in an effort to prevent the sagging of combs. This product consisted of two outer layers of pure beeswax with an inner layer of beeswax hardened by the addition of carnauba wax. In 1943, the Root Company patented a similar foundation the center ply of which contained from 30 to 50 per cent hydrogenated castor oil. The addition of other waxes or waxlike materials to beeswax in the manufacture of comb foundation was discontinued by the Root Company January 1, 1959, when the manufacturers' agreement became effective. Since then, they have manufactured a three-ply comb foundation of pure beeswax, claiming it to be superior because of its method of manufacture.

Several attempts have been made to substitute other materials for beeswax in making comb foundation and even artificial combs. Most attempts have been unsuccessful because the bees instinctively attempt to remove any foreign material in comb building. A recent product has been an aluminum-base comb foundation—a sheet of aluminum foil coated on each side with beeswax and then embossed like foundation. Because aluminum is a good conductor of heat and cold, its use in the brood nest is questionable, but it offers the potential of a super comb difficult to throw out if properly installed.

Currently on the market is a plastic-base comb foundation introduced and patented by Dadant & Sons. Extensive tests have shown that bees accept it as readily as foundation made from pure beeswax. Because the plastic is a poor conductor of heat and cold, its use in the brood nest is

FIGURE 6. A straight comb wiithout sag or bulge and containing nearly all worker-size cells is ideal for both honey and for brood rearing.

as acceptable to the queen and the bees as its use in the supers. When properly installed in the frame, it results in a perfect comb that is practically indestructible. When such a comb is emersed in boiling water, the plastic shrinks greatly and separates from the beeswax.

CARE AND STORAGE OF COMB FOUNDATION

If properly stored, comb foundation will last for years. When cold, it becomes brittle and the least handling will crack it. If handled roughly in shipping containers when cold, the jarring of the boxes will crack the sheets of foundation imperceptibly and, although they may appear perfect, when handled they will fall into numerous pieces. Too much heat causes the foundation to become too soft and ductile. The bees can manipulate the beeswax best at about 90° F. This also is a good temperature for embedding wires with a spur embedder, although a few degrees lower will not be injurious.

The Honeycomb

It may appear strange to discuss natural combs, and comb construction when comb foundation is used, in a chapter on beekeeping equipment. A study of the construction of natural or virgin comb and the behavior of bees in comb building provides a sound basis for an understanding of what constitutes good combs in the beehive. Good combs are a requisite to successful beekeeping because they provide the inner home where the young bees are reared and where their two foods, honey and pollen, are stored. Because of this, the honeycomb as well as its construction is closely associated with the equipment required to care for the bees.

NATURAL COMB

Natural comb always is built of pure beeswax secreted by the bees. The wax employed usually is secreted fresh for the purpose by the worker bees and may be recognized by its white color (see Chapter IV, "Activities of Honey Bees"). Darker wax, carried from older combs which have become discolored through use, or from comb foundation supplied by the beekeeper, sometimes is employed.

The construction of natural comb usually starts at or near the top of the abode (Fig. 7) and is built downward. The attachment of the comb is extensive at the top while the lower corners often hang free. The comb is built heavily at the point of attachment, the bases of the cells being an eighth of an inch or more in thickness in order to sustain the weight of the rest of the comb, the bees, brood, pollen, and honey. The thickness of the bases gradually diminishes for a distance of about 2 inches where the midrib becomes very thin throughout the remainder of the comb. At the bottom edge, natural comb diminishes to a V-edge of empty, shallow cells.

While there does not appear to be any system or organization in the comb-building process, construction ordinarily proceeds by building one rhomboid base on which two cell walls are started. This is followed by a second rhomboid base and two more cell walls, and later the third rhomboid base and the last two cell walls. Much of the comb is started and partly built before any of it is finished to full depth. A heavy rim of wax is constantly supplied around the outer rim of the cells, affording the bees a working supply of beeswax and protecting the fragile cell walls underneath.

Ordinarily, the thickness of the combs is about 1 inch and their distance apart, from center to center, is $1\frac{3}{8}$ to $1\frac{1}{2}$ inches, thus providing a passageway or bee space of about three-eighths of an inch between the combs. The surface of natural comb is seldom a true plane, nor are the rows of cells straight for more than a few inches. Variations are partly due to the lack of a true guide for their start at the top of the abode, and to irregularities in the walls. Because honey bees are social insects which work in groups during comb building, it is perhaps understandable how their apparent lack of co-ordination results in wavy and irregular combs.

Under normal conditions, more than one comb is started and, as the size of the colony grows and its prosperity increases, several more are begun. The combs usually are of a broad U-shape when first built (Fig. 8), obviating excessive weight on the upper part of the comb while it is still fragile. They are arranged side by side giving compactness to the colony for protection against invaders, such as robber bees and moths. The number of combs, their size, and their shape depend on the space in which they are constructed, the season of the year, the strength of the colony, and the food at hand.

FIGURE 7. A colony in nature, not being able to find a hollow tree or other suitable abode, elects to build its combs in the branches of a tree. Lacking a true guide for starting the combs, they are constructed in a wavy and irregular manner. *(Photo by Alvard Bishop)*

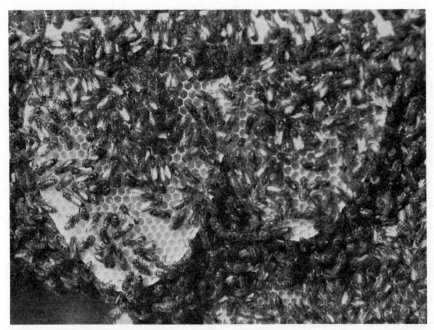

FIGURE 8. Natural-built, U-shaped combs, with the worker bees busily building the cells and hanging in festoons while secreting beeswax. The combs will be extended until they completely fill the frame.

The prosperity afforded by a large honey crop induces the bees to fill their abode with combs, although some recesses are always found near the entrance. The combs of a colony often occupy several feet in a hollow tree or inside the walls of a building. In comparison to this, the space occupied by combs in a two-story Langstroth hive is about 3 cubic feet with a comb area of about 36 square feet on both sides of the combs. In a 1½-story Modified Dadant hive, the space for combs and the comb area are about the same as the 2-story Langstroth.

Certain comb constructions, known as brace and bridge combs, are constructed between the large combs or between them and parts of the abode. They possess some value for they serve as braces to hold the combs in position, as bridges for the bees in passing to other parts of the abode, and as temporary storage places for nectar during the honey-flow and for water in excessively hot weather. When plentiful, they may interfere with ventilation. Burr combs usually are built on flat surfaces of the abode and are burrlike in appearance. They may be the beginnings of bridge combs or they may be surplus beeswax secretions deposited in this way. The tendency to build these comb formations varies with individual colonies, as well as with strains of bees, some building very little.

COMB BUILDING

The first requisite for the secretion of beeswax is a stomach well filled with nectar or honey. It is an intesesting fact that comb building and honey gathering proceed simultaneously and that when one stops the other stops also. As soon as the nectarflow slackens to a point where the consumption of nectar or honey exceeds the surplus, bees cease to build new combs even though large portions of their abode are un-filled. Langstroth has said: "When honey no longer abounds in the field, it is wisely ordered that they should not consume in comb building the treasure which may be needed for winter use."

There is evidence that the secretion of beeswax is involuntary during the honeyflow. But, although the amount of beeswax secreted may exceed that required for extending the cell walls and capping the cells of the combs, wax scales seldom are wasted in noticeable quantities about the hive. Usually bees secrete beeswax in proportion to their needs. A swarm responding to the necessity of building new combs has a supply of wax scales ready for the purpose. If hived on fully drawn combs, some of the wax scales may be wasted and wax secretion di-minishes rapidly. If hived in an empty box or on full sheets of comb foundation, the bees immediately make use of the beeswax they are secreting and continue to secrete more until a sufficient number of combs have been constructed for use by the colony.

If the beekeeper is neglectful in providing room as needed during the honeyflow and if bees are instinctively responding to the nectarflow by secreting beeswax, it is not surprising to find them with more wax scales than they can use. An abundance of burr and brace combs built during the honeyflow is an indication of plentiful secretion of beeswax. If there is no storage space available, bees may cluster on the outside of the hive where lumps of wax scales can be found later, or they may build combs there for honey storage. At such times, a small oversupply of wax scales occasionally is found where the wax scales were dropped on the bottom board or the tops of frames. If an abundant supply of nectar or honey is lacking, sugar sirup fed to bees will induce them to secrete beeswax (see "Comb Building" in Chapter IV).

Combs consist of two distinct sizes of cells known as worker and drone, and these are of a size to accommodate the rearing of worker and drone bees. Accommodation cells, usually odd-shaped, are found at the borders of combs while transition cells are built where a change from the worker-size to the drone-size cell occurs (Fig. 9).

Colonies hived without comb foundation in the frames build combs in an irregular manner as though occupying a plain box. The use of full sheets of comb foundation will result in straight worker combs, easy to handle if well reinforced in the frames.

The primary needs of a new colony are to increase its population and to provide ample stores of honey and pollen. An ample amount of

FIGURE 9. Worker and drone cells showing many odd-shaped transition cells in between. About actual size.

combs consisting of worker-size cells from which to rear a greater working force first is built. This continues as long as the queen keeps all cells filled by her capacity to lay eggs. Apparently, when her laying capacity is accommodated by an ample supply of worker comb, drone comb then is built. The building of drone cells also is promoted by the instinct to swarm, particularly at the beginning of a good honeyflow, bringing with it a need for drones for mating with the new queen.

Drone cells may be found scattered throughout the combs in a hive and many of them will be used for storing of honey during the honeyflow. There seems to be no regularity as to the position of the drone comb although much of it is outside or adjoining the brood area. Some drone cells always will be built, particularly at the margins of combs. The quantity of drone cells, with the use of comb foundation and proper care, can be held to about 5 per cent. Combs containing more drone cells than this should be used in the supers for honey storage or be discarded.

Supplying full sheets of comb foundation will not always ensure the best combs. Conditions favorable to comb building must also exist. Previous to the main honeyflow, when brood rearing should be proceeding without interruption and when comb building is necessary, ample feeding of sugar sirup often is resorted to for satisfactory wax secretion. Otherwise, comb foundation, whether in brood frames or in extracting supers, may be damaged beyond repair. Bees may tear down unoccupied foundation to employ the wax on combs already in use. In extreme cases, they may secure needed wax by gnawing unoccupied drawn comb. Sometimes, they appear to damage good combs or build undesirable ones as if in pure mischief.

At the time the combs are being drawn out from full sheets of comb foundation, the frames should not be spaced farther apart than 1½ inches from center to center. When fully drawn, it is common practice to space super combs as much as 1¾ inches center to center, resulting in thick combs of honey which facilitate uncapping and extracting.

Combs drawn from foundation in the brood nest often do not extend to the bottom bars, particularly near the entrance, thus providing space for ventilation. When a space of an inch or more is provided between the floor of the bottom board and the bottom bars of the frames, the bees are more likely to extend the combs to the bottom bars, the same as they build full combs in the supers.

If not reinforced by vertical or longitudinal wires, combs may stretch or sag in hot weather, resulting in considerable distortion. Because this is a serious handicap to the progress of colony strength, the wise beekeeper takes precautions to see that all combs are well built of worker cells, and amply reinforced with wires to preserve their shape. Combs that are wavy, misshapen, or broken from various causes should be melted up. There is little loss sustained by the beekeeper because the comb contains about twice the quantity of beeswax required for a sheet of comb foundation.

About 5 to 10 per cent of the combs can be replaced profitably each year, even though they have been properly reinforced and originally

FIGURE 10. An excellent comb of worker-size cells fully utilizing the space within the frame is a good thing for the bees and, therefore, for the beekeeper.

built under favorable conditions. Fifty per cent or more of the combs in many old hives that have not received proper attention should be culled. If poor combs are replaced with frames containing full sheets of foundation with the best system of vertical and horizontal wiring, the amount of comb culling from year to year will be reduced. The result obviously will be an increase in worker bees that produce the crop with a reduction in drones that are detrimental to a maximum crop.

During spring and early summer, the tendency of a normal colony to build comb is very dominant. Comb may be partly drawn on comb foundation even though the food supply is not sufficient for the secretion of new wax. The bees thin down the bases of the cells of the foundation and draw out the cell walls as far as available wax will permit. Medium brood foundation contains enough beeswax in the cell bases and partial cell walls to enable the bees to produce at least half the depth of the finished comb by their thinning process.

SIZE AND SHAPE OF THE CELLS

Races of bees such as the Italian, Carniolan, and Caucasian build cells of practically identical size, and accept standard comb foundation readily. Standard comb foundation usually is made on dies providing 857 cells per square decimeter, but the resulting cells may vary from this and usually are larger due to stretching of the wax in manufacture. The native-German black bees, according to European records, build smaller cells.

The small bees of India and other countries of the Far East (*Apis cerana syn. indica*) and a similar small bee of Africa (*A. mellifera adansonii*) build combs with smaller cells which accommodate their needs. The large, vicious bee of the Far East (*A. dorsata*) builds a single large comb having cells about the size of the common races of bees but twice as deep.

TABLE 1.   Approximate Number of Cells on Both Sides
of the Comb, Worker Size

Race of Bees	Cells per Square Decimeter	Cells per Square Inch
Italian	857	55.3
Caucasian	857	55.3
Carniolan	857	55.3
Italian (Drone)	520	33.5
Native German	897	57.9
Apis indica	1243	80.0
Apis dorsata	787	50.8
Apis mellifera adansonii	1000	64.4

The cell of the honeycomb is a hexagonal-shaped tube, consisting of six walls each of which forms a proportionate part of another cell, closed at its base by three rhomboids which form an inverted pyramid. Each of the three rhomboids forms a third of the base of a cell on the opposite side of the comb.

While combs are built vertically, or practically so, the cells are not built at a right angle to the vertical but slope upward from the central plane of the base. The angle of the upward slope varies from 9° to 14°. This sloping apparently tends to prevent the larvae from sliding out the mouth of the cells before they are sealed and to aid in containing the food placed there by the worker bees.

Measurements of new natural comb, built entirely by the bees, reveal that the central or thinnest part of walls and bases are about double the thickness of fine tissue paper, which is 0.001 to 0.002 of an inch in thickness. The average of cell walls measures about 0.001 of an inch thinner than the bases. This may be due to the fact that the bases are smaller and most difficult to build thin.

TABLE 2.   Average Thickness of Cell Bases and Walls, in Inches, Before and After Comb Foundation is Drawn Out

	Natural Comb	Brood Foundation		Surplus Foundation	
		Before	After	Before	After
Cell bases	0.0035	0.025	0.008	0.011	0.005
Cell walls	0.0025		0.0025		0.0025

These measurements indicate that when comb is built on foundation the cell bases are always thicker than natural comb, whereas the cell walls are identical in thickness. This may be due to the ease with which the two mandibles of the bee can be applied on each side of a cell wall like a pair of scrapers and also to the need for more beeswax in the midrib of the comb.

REDUCTION IN CELL SIZE

Brood cells become reduced in size with use and age. There is a slight thickening of the cell walls and bases due to the accumulation of cocoons and cast-off larval and pupal skins, and to the treatment given the cell in preparation for the next cycle of brood. However, it has been observed that the thickening due to this accumulation is principally in the base of the cells and that over a period of years, bees thin down the cell walls and extend them to compensate for this. The corners of the hexagonal cell appear to be gradually rounded. No objection to the rounded cell has been noted, although reduction in the size of the cell may render combs less suitable for brood rearing.

It would require the thickening of the cell walls only 0.004 to 0.005 inch in order to reduce the normal cells of the Italian bees to the size built by the smaller German or black bees. Michailov[6] has shown that after 16 to 18 generations the diameter of the cells is reduced 5.89 per cent and that this reduction caused a significant reduction in five physical characters of the exoskeleton.

Beekeepers frequently have reported that combs have been in use 20 to 30 years with no noticeable reduction in the size of the bees. It is probable that the thinning down of the cell walls and their extension, plus variation in cell size due to the downward stretching or sagging of combs and due to faulty making of foundation, may compensate for the thickening of the cell walls over many years.

THE LARGE CELL CONTROVERSY

Investigators in Europe have advanced the idea that worker bees reared in large-size cells were larger; possessing an increase in tongue length, wing size, and nectar-carrying capacity. They further claimed that a greater crop per colony was obtained by these bees in comparison with that obtained by bees in the same apiary reared in normal cells. They experimented with comb foundation having 760, 700, and 640 cells per sq. dec. (49.0, 45.2, and 41.3 cells per sq. in.) and their contentions resulted in foundation having larger cell bases being marketed in Belgium and France since the beginning of the century.

A study[3] of the influence of size of brood cell upon the size and variability of the worker bee, using foundation having 857, 763, and 706 cells per sq. dec. (55.3, 49.2 and 45.5 cells per sq. in.), showed that the size of the worker bee is affected and that significantly larger bees are obtained. But the excessive claims of Baudoux,[1] of Belgium, were not substantiated. Baudoux had reported an increase in tongue reach of 11.9 to 25 per cent as compared to a maximum increase of only 2.07 per cent obtained by Grout.[3] The increase in tongue length, accompanied by a corresponding increase in the dry weight of the bee and the size of wing, as determined by Grout, corresponded with data obtained by Michailov.[7]

Recent work in Russia by Glushkov[2] substantiates the work of both Michailov and Grout. Glushkov showed that the bees from larger cells carried 34 per cent more nectar per load. Over an 8-year period in tests involving 1600 colonies, those on large-cell foundation produced 17 per cent more honey than was normally expected.

The theory has been advanced in this country that the use of comb foundation having 706 cells per square decimeter in supers discourages the queen from laying eggs in the larger cells, and that worker bees store less pollen in such cells. It is true that the queen prefers to lay eggs in regular-size cells but, if she does not find them, she will lay eggs in the larger ones. As for less pollen being stored, this needs further study.

Apiary Equipment

The Bee Smoker. This is a necessity in handling bees (Fig. 11). Smoking causes the bees to rush to cells of nectar or honey and to gorge themselves, resulting in their being less apt to sting. The smoker consists of a metal funnel for directing the puff of smoke, a metal fire pot, and a bellows for blowing air into the base of the fire pot and out of the funnel of the smoker. A good volume of cool smoke often

FIGURE 11. The bee smoker is made in several sizes and is necessary equipment when working the bees.

FIGURE 12. The bee veil is made in a number of ways, but the important things are vision, protection, and ventilation.

is desired. Suitable fuel materials are decayed wood, coarse wood shavings, corn cobs, burlap, and corrugated paper.

The Bee Veil. This also is essential in handling bees (Fig. 12). It should either fit snugly around a hat or cover the top of the head, and should fit particularly well around the neck and shoulders. Bee veils are made either of panels of black screen wire with the top and bottom of an airy, meshed cloth material, or of meshed tulle veiling preferably having a silk-tulle face for better vision. Wire veils are preferred by many because they do not blow against the face and are more durable.

Bee Gloves. Gloves are a desirable protection for those who are not accustomed to stings. Usually, they are made with gauntlets reaching to the elbow. Few experienced beekeepers wear them because they tend to impede the handling of frames, but every wise beekeeper has a pair handy for use when working an exceptionally cross colony.

The Hive Tool. A hive tool of some kind is necessary in keeping bees. It is made of steel, having one end straight and sharpened to permit it to slip readily between supers or bodies in order to separate them. The other end, bent at a right angle and sharpened, is used for prying the frames apart. Usually, it has a V-shaped hole for pulling nails. Either end can be used for scraping combs or propolis from the hive parts, cleaning the bottom boards, and for many other purposes.

The Bee Brush. This usually is a thin horizontal brush having light bristles about 2 inches long. It is used to brush the bees from the combs and from hive parts.

Feeders. When there is an insufficient amount of honey in the hive for food for the bees, it is necessary to feed them honey or sugar sirup. The feeding of sugar sirup is preferred because it usually is more economical, there is no possibility of transmission of disease, and it is less likely to incite the bees to robbing. Often the sirup is placed in a 5- or 10-pound friction-top pail having several small holes punched in the lid. The feed pail is inverted over the open hole of the inner cover above the brood nest, an empty super or hive body is placed over the inner cover and the outer cover is placed on top. The Doolittle division-board feeder is a container the size and shape of a frame containing floats or a U-shaped piece of screen wire to enable the bees to take the sirup without drowning in it. It is placed in the hive, usually on one side, and is popular in queen-rearing yards in the South and when installing package bees or rearing nuclei.

Wiring and Embedding Device. This consists of a board and a spindle; the board holds the frame in place and the spindle supports a spool of 28- or 30-gauge frame wire. The wire is threaded through the holes in the end bars of the frame, fastened at one end, stretched tight, and secured at the other end. The sheet of comb foundation is made secure in the frame by nailing the wedge in place, or by means of a wood or "V" metal wedge inserted in the groove of the top bar. The longitudinal wires then are embedded usually by means of electric current which heats them, causing the wires to melt their way into the beeswax of the foundation.

Queen Excluders. The queen excluder is a sheet of perforated metal or a metal grill placed between two bodies, or between a hive body and a super, to prevent the queen, but not the worker bees, from going from one body to another. Originally it was made by cutting slots in flat pieces of zinc. The newer excluders are of round wire bars with metal crossbars welded to them and contained in a wooden frame. The distance between the bars should be 0.163 inch permitting the passage of worker bees but not that of the queen or the drones.

Moving Equipment. When moving colonies, it is necessary to fasten the parts of the hive together so they can be picked up and trucked to a new location. Two-inch hive staples are preferred to nails; they hold well and are easily removed when the hives are relocated. Another effective way is to use two bands of strap iron around the entire hive, fastened with special clamping devices. In hot weather, moving screens placed over the top of the hive and even over the entrance are desirable. Modern beekeepers use hive lifters or hoists, consisting of a long boom mounted on the bed of the truck which supports the hive lifter or cradle, to move colonies of bees. The boom swings to enable the operator to pick up the colony and the hive is automatically lifted for positioning on the truck, and works in a similar manner when unloading. The hive loader enables one man to load or unload 2- or 3-story colonies.

Bee Escapes. This device permits bees to escape from supers of honey or from other places where they are not wanted, such as a honey house. When used in removing supers of honey, the bee escape is fitted into the oblong hole in the center of the inner cover. This combination sometimes is called an "escape board." It is placed under the supers which are to be removed; the bees go down through the escape but cannot return to the supers. This use of the bee escape is preferred by some over other methods of taking off supers of honey because it allows time for the bees to clean up the dripping honey in the interval before they leave the super. A special type of bee escape is available for installing at the top of screened openings, permitting bees to escape from buildings.

The Fume Pad. This is a wooden rim the size of the top of the hive, varying in depth from an inch to that of a shallow super, covered on top by a sheet of metal under which is a "pad" of cloth or other absorbent material. It is used with propionic anhydride or perhaps carbolic acid in driving bees out of supers when removing the honey crop; it can be used similarly in the control of bee moth with ethylene dibromide; and it also can be used as a simple cover over stored stacks of supers of combs (see Chapter X, "Management for Honey Production").

The Observation Hive. The beginner, the student, and even the experienced beekeeper will derive much pleasure from an observation hive. It is made with glass sides and can be placed indoors with an entrance through a window, or can be set outdoors. Established in the spring with a comb of brood, bees and a queen, the activities of the bees and many of the intricacies of the bee colony may be watched during the season. Super space may be added if necessary. The single-frame width is preferred because the activities of the queen and the bees can be observed at all times.

REFERENCES CITED

1. Baudoux, U. 1927. L'Apiculture Rationelle. 11:57-58.
2. Glushkov, N. M. 1962. XVIII Intern. Beekeeping Congr. Madrid. *Rev. in* Gl. Bee Cult. 90(2):93.
3. Grout, R. A. 1937. Iowa Agr. Expt. Sta. Bull. **218**.
4. Kretchmer, E. 1878. Am. Bee J. 14:427-428.
5. Langstroth, L. L. 1883. A practical treatise on the hive and the honey-bee. J. B. Lippincott & Co., Philadelphia. 4th ed. p. 329.
6. Michailov, A. S. 1927. Opitnaja Paseca. pp. 246-249.
7. ----------------- 1927. Rev. Russe. Ent. 21:151-162.
8. Mitchener, A. V. 1941. Am. Bee J. 81:323-324.
9. White, J. W., Jr. 1960. J. Offic. Agr. Chem. 43:781-790.

CHAPTER IX

THE APIARY

by M. G. DADANT*

THE FIRST CONSIDERATION in choosing the location of an apiary is whether or not there are sufficient sources of nectar and pollen near. Bear in mind that honey bees obtain most of their nectar and pollen within a half-mile radius, but can gather at distances of 1 to 2 miles, depending on the ruggedness of the country and to some extent on the prevailing winds. Even in the heart of large cities, there are often sufficient sources of nectar and pollen to provide for a limited number of colonies, and even to produce surplus honey. A city lawn, a back yard, a flat roof, a pasture on a farm, a grove of trees—all will be satisfactory locations as the occasion demands. For convenience in working the bees, the apiary site should be as level as possible.

In all instances, the neighbors' rights should be considered. The beehives should be placed so that the line of flight is away from roads, sidewalks, or line fences where the bees might interfere with the neighbor or his stock. When this is not possible, the line of flight to and from the hives may be deflected upward out of possible difficulties by obstructions such as shrubbery, trees, or even chicken-wire netting.

For winter protection, windbreaks in the form of fences, shrubs, woods, or natural slopes are desirable (Fig. 1). While the bottom of a hollow with a north slope for wind protection in winter might seem ideal, there likely would not be sufficient air drainage to prevent excessive humidity. A preferred location is a slope having a south exposure and providing good drainage of water and movement of air. The beehives should be placed with their backs to the north as protection against the prevailing winter winds, and with their entrances to the south permitting the maximum amount of sunshine on the front of the hive.

Clean, fresh running water should be available in the apiary or nearby to prevent the bees from visiting the neighbors' watering troughs, fish ponds, and bird baths, and to preclude their visiting undesirable, contaminated moisture sources, particularly during drought periods. Because stagnant watering places are believed to be a contributing factor in the spread of certain adult bee diseases, it is not advisable to locate colonies where drainage is poor.

Shade is desirable (Fig. 2), but too much shade will hinder early and late daily flights. Trees and shrubs may be so dense that they prevent easy passage of the bees to and from the hive. They also may restrict

---

*Maurice G. Dadant. Business manager of the *American Bee Journal*. Author of *Outapiaries* and many articles on beekeeping. Manufacturer of beekeepers' supplies.

FIGURE 1. A fence of this kind makes an excellent windbreak; the trees behind the fence furnish additional wind protection.

ventilation in summer. Thus apiaries located in groves or woods should be placed in clearings. This will not only give the desired sunshine, but will direct the flight of the bees upward where they will not interfere with passers-by or with livestock. Shade boards placed on top of the hives may serve as a substitute for tree shade. Trellises and arbors provide good shade but conditions restricting flight and ventilation should be avoided. In the arid regions of the Southwest, shade often is provided by a "ramada," a long covered arbor under which the hives are placed in rows (Fig. 3).

Apiary sites along rivers and streams should be on elevated ground to eliminate the possibility of floods. Grass and weeds in the apiary should be cut to minimize possibility of fire and to aid in ventilation of the colony. Grass in front of the entrances may be kept down by use of cinders, old roofing paper, boards, or similar materials, thus giving the bees an unobstructed entrance for flight and for ventilation. The use of chemical weed killers, principally 2,4-D (see Chapter XX, "Injury to Bees by Poisoning"), will destroy most weeds found in the apiary.

In some sections of the South, Argentine ants are most annoying and destructive. They attack all kinds of food and are particularly fond of sweets and meats. In sections where they occur it is necessary to keep the beehives off the ground on platforms with legs which rest in cans of oil (Fig. 4). Except in the very North, termites occur throughout the United States, and are particularly numerous in the South. They burrow in and consume as food the wood of bottom boards and other hive parts. Some of the common ants are such pests that at times they constitute a major problem, affecting apiary locations and honey houses, as well as individual colonies. For additional information concerning these insects and their control, the reader is advised to refer to Chapter XIX, "Diseases and Enemies of the Honey Bee."

ARRANGEMENT OF COLONIES

The arrangement of colonies in the apiary depends largely on the kind and amount of space available. The hives should be placed far enough apart to allow freedom for working between them. They should be set as level as possible from side to side but should incline slightly forward to permit moisture to run out of the entrance, and to enable the bees to remove dead bees and other objectionable matter more easily. Each colony may be numbered to make record keeping and management more efficient. To protect from losses due to theft, some bee-keepers mark hives and hive parts so they can be identified, often by branding with a hot iron.

Colonies may be arranged in groups of two, three, four, or more in a manner which permits working each colony and allows winter pack-

FIGURE 2. Trees furnish shade for the colonies and aid the bees in locating the position of their own hives. A clearing in a woods, such as this one, provides an excellent apiary site. *(Photo by R. M. Rahmlow)*

FIGURE 3. A "ramada" in the Southwest provides shade for colonies, as well as for the beekeeper. (*Photo by J. N. Porter*)

ing of the group as a unit. However, the hives usually are arranged in rows. The rows should be far enough apart so that a workman in one row will not interfere to any extent with the flight of the bees from the next row back. Placing the hives 6 to 8 feet apart in rows 10 to 12 feet apart helps to prevent drifting and allows the use of a truck between rows. In large apiaries, the rows of hives should not be arranged too uniformly in order to assist the bees in finding their way back to their home colonies. Occasional shrubbery or trees scattered through the yard are beneficial in this respect.

Painting of hives not only preserves them, but also helps in minimizing confusion resulting in drifting if different colors are used for alternating hives. Light colors are less absorbent of the heat from the sun's rays and thus desirable in exposed locations in summer.

OUTAPIARIES

A wise and careful approach to the keeping of bees on an increased basis is always recommended, whether in the case of the beginner, the expanding side-liner, or the commercial beekeeper. Most beekeepers begin in a small way, starting modestly and learning beekeeping as they go. Thus they are better able to meet the problems of outapiary management when the desire for such expansion comes.

Much the same factors determine the success of the outapiary location as those which affect the home apiary. However, due to the additional expense of trips that will have to be made in the management of bees, greater care must be exercised in selecting a site which will afford a maximum honey crop. Also more important are minor sources of pollen and nectar for proper buildup of the colonies before the main honeyflow and for maintaining them after the honeyflow.

Thus, before one finally decides on an outapiary site a study of the rainfall, temperature, soils, natural flora, cultivated crops, and crop rotation practices becomes of prime importance. A variation in location may mean the difference between a 50-pound and a 150-pound crop and similarly between obtaining a fine white honey or a darker grade. Especially if outapiaries are to be established permanently a very thorough study of all pertinent factors should be made.

While inspection measures and disease laws are tending to bring bee diseases under control, the advantages of locating in a disease-free territory are to be considered seriously. The beekeeper should learn as accurately as possible from neighboring beekeepers, and from apiary inspection sources, the prevalence of bee diseases in the territory under consideration. The cost of disease eradication can be an appreciable item of expense aside from the loss of crops from those colonies which may have to be destroyed. In the interest of disease control, regulations in many states forbid bees on combs to enter from outside, while other states require a certificate of recent inspection before bees on combs may be admitted, or before bees may be moved from one part of the state to another location. Before attempting to move bees to a new location, one should become acquainted with the regulations which apply. A letter to the state apiary inspector, or to the inspection department of the state to which one wishes to move, will bring the desired information.

FIGURE 4. Colonies in the South often are kept on platforms as a protection against floods and ants. *(Photo courtesy Garon Bee Company)*

In choosing apiary sites, consideration should be given to overstocking. No matter how fine the location, there always is the possibility of placing more bees in a territory than it can support profitably. Some of the irrigated sections have become so overpopulated with bees that the honey crops doubtless have been reduced. In a few states, regulations have resulted requiring a beekeeper to obtain a permit before occupying a territory with a given number of colonies. In most areas, there is no specific law against moving bees into a section already amply stocked, but common sense and courtesy strongly suggest that no beekeeper do this. Co-operation with other beekeepers will always pay big dividends.

If the beekeeper is just expanding to the extent that his home yard is insufficient for his colonies, his problem is somewhat different from that of the established beekeeper who is seeking a location for another of his outyards. In the former case, it is likely that he will want his first outapiary location close to his home yard to keep at a minimum the cost of transportation to and from the outapiary. Thus he may be content with a smaller crop, although a paying one, in order to fit the operations of his outyard into that of his home apiary.

The established beekeeper will select locations which fit best into a plan of operation from one or more central points and give the largest possible crops of good quality honey, produced at the lowest cost. Other than selecting a suitable place to live, he may sacrifice all else to honey production. In some cases it is necessary to make an intensive study of a large section of a state to determine the best locations. With good roads and truck transportation one need not restrict operations to a small territory. Especially in heavy-yielding sections where the cost of production will permit additional travel, apiaries may be as much as 50 miles from the central operating point. However, most apiarists restrict their apiary system to a radius of 20 or 30 miles.

If at all possible, the apiary should be accessible over good roads, thus making it possible to reach it under all weather conditions. In spring it is often necessary to get to the bees for feeding or for supplying supers. It is exasperating and costly when impassable roads necessitate the carrying of feed and equipment by hand. One such experience usually suffices to prevent a recurrence.

Apiaries, particularly permanent ones, should be located on the property of congenial and friendly people who understand the advantages of having bees on their farms to pollinate legumes, garden crops, fruits, and berries. Usually a farm owner is to be preferred to a renter because the former is more permanently located. Where possible, the apiary should be located near the farm home so that the farmer can watch out for the bees, such as protecting from theft and replacing covers blown off by storms.

When livestock is present, the outapiary usually should be fenced. A low woven-wire fence will suffice for hogs and sheep, but a higher fence, consisting of several strands of barbed wire or one or more strands in addition to a low woven-wire fence, is required for cattle and horses.

In the mountains of the West, the cutover timber country of the North, and near the swamps of the Southeast coast, bears are often destructive in robbing hives. Formerly, it was necessary to erect stockades around apiaries in these places, in addition to hunting and trapping the bears. However, in most cases, the electric fence has proved more effective and economical. At least four strands of barbed wire are recommended with the first and third strands from the top connected to the controller and a six-volt, hot-shot battery, and with the second and fourth strands attached to the ground wire. Some prefer six strands with every other strand connected to the controller and battery. In dry locations, some charge all the wires, placing a strip of chicken-wire netting at the base of the fence to be sure that the bear makes a good contact with the ground to complete the circuit.

The charged wires should be insulated at the posts and care taken that limbs of trees, shrubs, and weeds do not touch them, causing short circuiting, particularly in wet weather. The battery should be a dry-cell, weatherproof, 6-volt unit which should serve continuously for 3 months. However, a wet storage battery having a rating of 90 ampere hours or higher is satisfactory and will last about the same length of time. Due to the possible danger to people, the fence should be marked conspicuously with signs to warn passers-by that the wires are charged.

A universal question concerns the number of colonies to be kept in an apiary. This can only be determined by the abundance of floral sources of nectar and pollen. In the eucalyptus regions of Australia, 200 or more colonies may be kept in one location without serious reduction in the average colony production. Years ago, when E. W. Alexander was keeping bees in the buckwheat region around Delanson, N. Y., he had as many as 700 colonies in his home yard. The same location today probably would not support more than 10 per cent of that number, due to a reduction in the buckwheat acreage. In good seasons, sweet clover sections of the Midwest may provide maximum colony production for as many as 100 colonies. In northern Georgia, as in many areas where only a moderate amount of flora is found, the number of colonies in an apiary should not exceed 50.

Permanent apiaries should contain the maximum number of colonies which the territory will support in poor years. As mentioned previously, minor sources of nectar and pollen play an important part in the total honey crop. It is desirable to regulate the number of colonies in the permanent apiary to the number which can be built to peak strength on the minor floral sources previous to the main honeyflow. For the aver-

age location, about 50 colonies are usual, with the number varying either
way depending on the number which can produce a maximum crop
of honey at a minimum expense of operation.

Nectar and pollen availability and the contour of the country likewise determine how close apiaries may be placed to each other. With a
profuse supply of nectar in a hilly country, apiaries may be placed 2 to
3 miles apart; in open country, perhaps 3 to 4 miles would be better.

APIARY RENTALS AND CONTRACTS

Farmers are friendly and co-operative people. Certainly this has been
evident to beekeepers. Nevertheless, it is always advisable that there be
a definite and written contract covering rentals, locations, and related
matters. In spite of this, nothing more than a verbal agreement is made
with the farmer in 95 per cent of the cases. The rental charge varies:
most beekeepers settle with the farmer for enough honey to satisfy his
family, usually a case of six 5-pound jars. Others have a rental basis of
a pound of honey for each colony of bees.

More and more, farmers are coming to realize that they must depend upon honey bees for adequate pollination in order to obtain
maximum fruit and seed yields. As a consequence, honey bees are being
sought and growers are even paying beekeepers to place bees on their
property. In such a case, the beekeeper must carefully consider the
possibilities of making a honey crop and also what losses he may incur
from programs of insect control. Colonies located for pollination purposes should be as close to the crop to be pollinated as possible. For
further information on pollination of crops, see Chapter XVIII, "The
Honey Bee as a Pollinating Agent."

WORKING BEES ON SHARES

Occasionally the apiarist finds it necessary to rent all or part of his
bees on a share basis to another beekeeper, or he may wish to add to his
income by keeping bees for another owner on a share basis. It is good
business practice for the agreement to be detailed and in writing so
that misunderstandings may not occur when the final settlement is
made. Usually, the owner furnishes the bees, hives, supers, honey house,
extracting equipment, and the containers for his share of the crop. The
share worker furnishes the truck, all of the labor, and the containers for
his share of the crop. On such a basis, the honey and beeswax crop
usually is divided half to the owner and half to the share worker. The
circumstances affecting each agreement naturally will be somewhat
different in each case, particularly with regard to who should pay apiary
rentals, who should pay for necessary feed, how swarms or increase
should be apportioned, and many other matters. Consequently, a written
agreement should always be made between the two parties, even though
it is necessary for a lawyer to prepare it.

CHAPTER X

MANAGEMENT FOR HONEY PRODUCTION

by G. H. CALE*

Success in beekeeping depends upon a proper exercise of the knowledge of colony organization, growth, and behavior in relation to environment as affected by seasonal changes and the occurrence of nectar- and pollen-bearing flora. In beekeeping it is not possible to use fixed rules or exact routines. No two seasons are ever alike and the beekeeper who has the truest understanding of the habits and activities of bees and of the fundamental reaction of the colony to its environment is the one who is most likely to succeed.

In the intelligent management of a colony of bees there are practices which do not come in any natural succession throughout the season, but may be necessary to employ when conditions require their use. Each of these practices is important and vital to the well-being of the colony and to the production of a maximum crop.

HOW TO PREVENT ROBBING

Colonies of bees have little respect for each other when it comes to the possession of honey. Nature teaches honey bees to search for food and any that they can find by fair means or foul they consider their own property. As soon as bees begin to fly in the spring, their quest for food starts. They not only seek honey stores but often will turn their attention to sirups, sugar, fruit juices, and any other similar sweet material that is within easy access. They will try to rob another colony whenever there is a chance, particularly when there is little nectar in the field. Often strong colonies with the largest stores are the most apt to prey upon the possessions of weak colonies.

When supers of extracting combs still sticky with honey are given to colonies at the beginning of the honeyflow, it is likely to cause robbing. Therefore, it is best to arrange to have such supers dried of all honey each year before they are stored, so that the excitement which occurs when wet supers are returned to the colonies may be avoided. For information concerning the care and storage of empty supers, see Chapter XI, "Extracting the Honey Crop." Only when there is a good honeyflow and the field bees are gathering nectar freely do they disregard

---

*Gladstone H. Cale. Editor of the *American Bee Journal*. Formerly assistant professor of economic zoology, University of Maryland, and an associate in the U.S.D.A. Bee Culture Laboratory. Many years' experience in honey production in the apiaries of Dadant & Sons and operator of his own apiaries.

exposed honey. Even then, at certain times of the day or when conditions change, robbing may be resumed.

Sometimes it is difficult to distinguish between the physical appearance of robber bees and others, although robbers eventually become
smooth, shiny, and almost black. They have an air of roguery and a
nervous and guilty agitation. They do not alight boldly at the entrance
of another colony, nor do they face the guards without fear. They seem
to try to glide by the sentinels without touching them. When robbers
are caught by the guards, they try to pull away. If these marauders
attack a strong colony, they have difficulty in escaping with their lives.
On the other hand, a bee that loses its way and alights in front of a
strange hive behaves differently, shrinking to a corner, bewildered and
submitting to any treatment her captors may exact.

The beginner may mistake the play flights of young bees for robbing.
Young bees circle around to mark the location of the hive but there
is no fighting or disturbance. These play flights occur in the middle of
the day, especially on warm sunny days in the brood-rearing period.
Frequently an apparent case of robbing proves to be bees coming out
of the entrance and flying around their own hive to clean up honey or
sirup which may be leaking through cracks. This soon is accomplished
and the disturbance ends.

Some robbing is carried on so secretly that it escapes notice. The bees
do not enter the hives in large numbers and no fighting is seen. Yet
strange bees actually are entering the hives and carrying off the honey
constantly. They sneak in at corners and cracks, pass the guards one at
a time, and are observed by the beekeeper only on close scrutiny. This
kind of robbing, called *progressive robbing,* is difficult to control and
usually no attempt is made to do so.

Robbing, however, is seldom a menace to the careful beekeeper. He
will do everything in his power to prevent it, particularly in times of
dearth. If it becomes essential to manipulate colonies when robbing is
dangerous, he will proceed with caution, opening the hives carefully,
doing work speedily, and never leaving combs of honey exposed. He
will cover the tops of the combs in the hive with a cloth moistened with
water, sometimes containing a small amount of carbolic acid or propionic anhydride. Similar cloths may be used to cover combs or bodies
of combs which need to be removed from the hive when working the
bees.

When robbing is prevalent, the entrances of colonies should be reduced and cracks or openings in the equipment through which robbers
might gain entrance should be closed. In addition to reducing the
entrance, it sometimes helps the colony if a broad board is laid across
from one side of the bottom board to the other. This forms a sort of
porch or tunnel through which the robber must pass and in which the
hive bees congregate and defend themselves. In serious cases of robbing,

the porch or tunnel may be further protected by piling green grass over it. Repellents, such as kerosene, gasoline, propionic anhydride, and carbolic acid, used about the cracks and the entrance will help discourage robbers to some extent.

Poorly established or weak colonies should be kept in an apiary by themselves. Entrances should be kept reduced and these colonies worked with extreme care as a precaution against robbing. If colonies must be fed, the feed may be given when the weather is inclement, in the evening, or in the early morning, and then the feed should always be placed inside the hive, never outdoors.

When bees are flying vagrantly about hunting at all corners and cracks of hives, the experienced beekeeper knows that the colonies should not be opened unless it is absolutely necessary. When robbing gets out of control, the bees are apt to sting fiercely without apparent reason, especially when they have exhausted the supplies they have been plundering. Even a hardened beekeeper will shrink from the punishment that awaits him until robbing is reduced.

When robbing occurs among a few colonies in the same yard as a natural consequence and not from any disturbance caused by the beekeeper, it is usually best to allow it to continue without making any attempt to stop it. It is seldom disastrous and the bees discontinue it voluntarily. On the other hand, when robbing occurs between two apiaries some distance apart, it may result in the loss of many colonies that are being robbed, and all the colonies in the robbing apiary will participate in the destruction of those colonies.

If a single, well-established colony is being badly robbed, it may be removed to a new location in the apiary and the entrance reduced and some grass thrown over it. Another hive with a single comb containing a little honey is then placed at the location where the robbing was taking place. A tablespoonful of calcium cyanide is placed on the bottom board. The robbers will continue to come but never leave because they are killed by the cyanide gas.

HOW TO FEED BEES

It is necessary to feed colonies in the fall that do not have enough stores to carry them through the winter and into spring. It also is necessary to feed some colonies in the spring even though an abundance of honey was left with them in the fall. When new colonies are being installed, such as package bees, nuclei, or divisions, feeding usually is necessary.

The best feed for a colony of bees is a super full of honey. Too often beekeepers are unwilling to leave a full super of the season's crop with the colonies for winter. For further information on winter food requirements, see Chapter XIII, "The Overwintering of Productive Colonies."

Except during the winter period when a large amount of stores is required, a colony should have from 30 to 40 pounds of stores at all times. When a colony is short of food, there will be little honey in the combs and the hive will be light in weight. When there is no sealed honey, the bees may be approaching starvation.

When hives are full of bees with an immense amount of brood to feed, the stores must be watched closely. Bees are most apt to starve in the period of brood rearing before the beginning of the main honeyflow. Even in a period of honeyflow, when nectar is unavailable for any duration because of weather, the bees may require feeding. There also may be intervals in summer between honeyflows when colonies need feed to support them. If stores are reaching the point of exhaustion, bees will carry larvae and pupae out of the hive entrance. They also will drive the drones from the hive where they die from exposure.

When honey is not available, the best food is sugar sirup made from pure cane or beet sugar. Sugar sirup is easy to make. Usually a mixture is made of 1 part sugar to 1 part water by volume, the sugar dissolving readily in hot water. The water is brought to boiling and removed from the source of heat, and the sugar is then added, stirring until it is dissolved. Heating the sugar and water together is satisfactory if the mixture is stirred constantly. However, the sirup should not be boiled over direct heat as it will caramelize slightly and will not be satisfactory as feed for bees. Sometimes sirup made in this manner will crystallize in the containers. This may be prevented by adding to the prepared sirup a tablespoon of tartaric acid for each 100 pounds of sugar used.

Those having a steam boiler use steam to heat the water. The sugar may then be added at once to the water and boiled vigorously without danger of caramelization because the steam agitates the solution. When the sirup is cool, it is ready for use.

When there is no nectar available, the amount of feed that bees will take is almost unlimited. Colonies will store the sirup just as they do nectar, even swarming at a time when there is not sufficient nectar from natural sources for a livelihood. Obviously, such overfeeding is a waste. On the other hand, beekeepers may feed too little and use feeders of small capacity which do not give the bees enough feed.

The best feeder is a 10-pound, friction-top pail (Fig. 1), or a screw-top jar of large capacity, having two or three holes punched in the center of the lid. Some beekeepers punch holes over the entire lid for faster feeding but, if such feeders are not placed exactly level, the last of the sirup may leak out.

When filled with sirup, the feeder is inverted over the open hole in the center of the inner cover or, if an oilcloth is used, the feeder may be placed at one corner with the oilcloth turned back. An empty hive body or super is used to surround the feeder and the hive is then covered. In early spring or late fall, the feeder may be inverted directly over the combs above the cluster of bees with a packing of cloths around it. If the sirup is warm (not hot), it will be taken more easily and quickly.

Many prefer to use the division-board feeder (Fig. 2) which holds about as much sirup as the 10-pound pail. It is made the size and shape of a hive frame, supported at the top by projections like the ends of the top bar of the frame. The sides of the feeder are made of plywood, pressed wood, or similar material, or the feeder may be made entirely of metal. In any case it should be watertight; melted paraffin may be used if necessary to coat the inside of the feeder. The division-board feeder is hung in the hive at one side; sometimes it is left there permanently where it is always ready for use. The feeder is open at the top to provide entrance for the bees, and contains floats or a V-shaped piece of screen wire to enable them to take the sirup without drowning in it. There are other types of feeders, but the 10-pound pail and the division-board feeders are used most commonly.

In the spring, unless a colony of bees is on a starvation basis, a 10-pound feeder of sugar sirup at one time is enough, and this amount should last at least a week. When nectar sources become available to augment the feed, a 10-pound feeding may last as long as 2 weeks. A colony on a constant feed basis usually does not require over three feedings in spring before the beginning of the main honeyflow.

When taking feed to outyards, large containers, such as steel drums provided with a faucet for filling the feeders, are ideal and are easily carried in the truck. Sixty-pound cans are satisfactory but less substantial.

When bees fly freely and the weather is warm, it is often possible to feed them dry sugar (Fig. 3) which may be spread on the inner cover with the hole open or on the oilcloth with one end turned back. Five pounds of sugar will last longer than 10 pounds of sirup, particularly when bees have access to minor sources of nectar before the honeyflow.

FIGURE 1. A 10-pound friction-top pail with several small holes punched in the lid makes a handy feeder.

FIGURE 2. The division board feeder at the side of the hive is convenient to use and holds 10 pounds of sirup.

FIGURE 3. Honey bees are being fed dry granulated sugar in a special feeding device with entrance at the rear. The inner cover with the escape hole open will serve the same purpose.

For spring feeding, the Behlows, of Montana, use feed rims which consist of a sheet of Masonite, or hard board, the size of the top of the hive with a wooden rim of inch lumber glued to it. The feed is made by this formula: 200 pounds of sugar, 30 pounds of honey, 2½ gallons of water, 1 cup of vinegar, and sulfathiazole at the rate of ¼ teaspoonful per gallon of feed. The feed is heated in a double-jacketed cooker to 240° F. and the temperature maintained for 2 hours. When partially cooled, the feed is poured into the feed rims which are stacked criss-cross until the feed solidifies in them. Each feed rim contains about 6½ pounds.

At the apiary, the outer cover and inner cover are removed, the feed rim inverted over the colony and the covers placed on top. The surface of the feed is like a thin icing which the bees easily pierce to work on the main portion which is something like caramel. Unlike sirup, the bees consume it only as needed so they have no reason to store it in the combs, nor is it wasted as sometimes happens when feeding dry sugar. One rim of feed usually will last 2 to 3 weeks.

PROVIDING WATER FOR BEES

Honey bees use quantities of water to dilute the brood food and to aid in cooling the hive by evaporation. It may some day become apparent in practice that water should be given bees in a feeder inside the hive where they may obtain it without having to fly in search of it in inclement weather.

Particularly in the South, large amounts of water are gathered by bees and placed in convenient, temporary storage places in the combs, especially in burr combs and other comb constructions between the hive parts and along the top bars. This water is used to cool the hive through evaporation.

The need for water in substantial amounts for brood-rearing purposes is so great that the bees will obtain water from any outside source, frequently going to stock watering tanks, pumps, bird baths, lily pools, or similar places where they often become bothersome. This is particularly true in the spring and during periods when nectar is not plentiful in the fields. Bees may collect water from undesirable sources as well as from sources of clean water. Often they prefer salty water.

If colonies are not located near natural sources of water, some sort of watering device becomes a necessity. It is best to provide water that does not stand in a container with a still surface but rather drips from a container onto a sloping board or trough where it is collected by the bees as it flows along. There is a strong suspicion that the spread of nosema disease is often aided by water sources which may become stagnant, such as low seepage places in the vicinity of an apiary.

HOW TO MAKE INCREASE

A common source of increase is the swarms which issue from the colonies in the apiary. Swarming, however, is not desirable because it creates a division of the working force of the colony. Neither the swarm nor the colony from which it came will produce as much honey as the original colony would have done. Nevertheless, a swarm successfully hived does constitute a new colony.

There are ways to secure increase from the bees on hand without depending on swarming. In spring, colonies that are not as strong as others and which may be spared from honey production can be divided into two-comb nuclei and each nucleus given a new queen. It is best to move the newly made colonies beyond flying distance of the apiary in which they are formed so that field bees will not return to their old location, thus depleting their flying force. These nuclei will build to colony strength during the season. Each division may be helped greatly by giving them additional combs of brood and bees when the opportunity presents.

Those who keep bees in 2-story Langstroth hives frequently make increase by separating the hive bodies when both of them are occupied with brood. The queenless hive is given a new queen. In most seasons neither part will produce as large a crop as the undivided colony. However, if there is a long period between the time the division is made and the beginning of the main honeyflow so that there is a large increase in the population of each part, both divisions may make a good crop. They also may need feeding.

FIGURE 4. Two beautiful combs of worker brood—the kind to use when making increase.

A slow but convenient and relatively sure way to make increase is to shake most of the bees from one colony into a hive with combs, leaving the queen and some of the young bees with the original combs. Put the original hive in the place of any other strong colony in the apiary, moving the strong colony to a new location. The bees shaken from the first colony are then placed in the original location and provided with a new queen. Thus, from two colonies, a new one is obtained.

Before the honeyflow when colonies are at their peak in population, it is possible to remove combs of brood and bees from strong colonies without impairing their strength. Combs of emerging brood are preferable (Fig. 4). The addition of empty combs or foundation to these strong colonies, to replace the combs of brood that are taken for increase, frequently reduces the tendency to swarm. In removing combs of brood for this purpose, never reduce the strength of colonies sufficiently to impair their ability to gather a maximum honey crop.

Toward the end of the summer honeyflow when the major part of the crop has been gathered and there is still a period of about 3 months in which nuclei can grow to colony strength, colonies that are not doing well in gathering a crop of honey may be divided into nuclei. The supers, which may be on these colonies, are removed and given to other colonies. Each of the selected colonies is broken up into two or three nuclei. Each nucleus is hived in a transport box, removed to a new location, and a new queen is introduced. Later the nuclei may be transferred into hives. If these divisions are made sufficiently early in the year, they will make full colonies by late fall.

Package Bees

The sale of bees by the pound has grown to large proportions and package shippers in the South and in California have developed an extensive industry. Package bees are shipped either by express or parcel post; when five or more packages are involved, express is somewhat less expensive. Northern beekeepers also drive south in their own trucks to obtain package bees, taking them north in the spring.

Two, three, or more pounds of live bees are shaken into wood and wire cages each of which is provided with a queen in a small shipping cage with candy or a small container of sugar sirup for food on the trip. Strange as it may seem, in the North where there is a long buildup period previous to the main honeyflow, the 2-pound package is preferred. However, in localities where the period before the flow is short, the 3-pound package is more popular. For further information on package bees, see Chapter XVII, "The Production of Queens, Package Bees, and Royal Jelly."

Where winter conditions are severe and there is difficulty in wintering bees except at high cost, as in the far North, many commercial beekeepers prefer to kill their bees at the end of the producing season and to replace them with packages the following spring. Such practice has the advantage of a short working season, nearly all of the honey may be extracted, the hives may be stored away out of the weather where they can be placed in condition for the next season, and the combs can be sorted better.

PREPARING TO RECEIVE THE PACKAGE BEES

To determine the number of packages which will be needed in the spring, estimate the number of colonies that ordinarily may be lost in winter. Add that figure to the number of empty hives on hand in the fall to make a total count that can be ordered from the package-bee producer in early fall or winter. This makes it possible to obtain packages from preferred breeders and to choose a shipping date to suit one's conditions.

Package bees should arrive 8 to 12 weeks before the beginning of the first main honeyflow. It is also desirable to have bees arrive during a time when nectar is being gathered from minor sources, such as fruit bloom, so that the conditions for hiving packages will be ideal and they will be started into colony life with the least attention and trouble.

It is good practice to set aside combs containing pollen and honey from healthy colonies for use in starting packages the succeeding year. These combs may be distributed in the hives intended for the packages and the remaining space filled with empty drawn combs or with frames containing full sheets of comb foundation.

When outyards are operated, it is sometimes better to hive packages near home where they can be cared for with the least expense. Here they can be managed carefully so they will reach full strength together, when they may be moved to the outyards just before the main honey-flow. Weak or indifferent colonies can either be united, or left behind for further attention.

Package bees are shipped by parcel post and express. If the shipment is over five packages, express usually is used and parcel post is recommended for smaller shipments. When the packages arrive, they should be examined carefully to determine whether or not there has been loss in shipment. Packages in which the bees are dead and those in which the percentage of dead bees is high should be reported on the express receipt or a bad order receipt should be obtained from the postmaster or carrier. This should be sent immediately to the supplier from whom the packages were ordered with a request for replacement or refund. The shipment should always be accepted, however, because refusal complicates matters. Serious losses in shipment are infrequent.

Many beekeepers drive their own trucks south to obtain package bees for replacement or for increase of colonies (Fig. 5). Arrangements should be made with the package-bee producer well in advance of planned arrival so that he can have the packages ready. The packages should be placed on the truck in such a way that each of them gets good ventilation although too much ventilation under cool conditions is not desirable. The greatest danger in trucking package bees is over-heating and most loads are equipped with thermometers on this account. If overheating occurs, it is advisable to stop along the way and wet

FIGURE 5. A load of package bees leaving California for southern Idaho—600 two-pound packages with Italian queens.

down the load. Most loads of packages are driven straight through to their destination.

It is best to hive packages in the late afternoon or toward evening so that the bees will not fly too freely before the end of the day, but will become established to a certain extent overnight. Cool, cloudy weather with a temperature even as low as 32° F., particularly without wind, is ideal for hiving package bees.

Unless conditions are ideal for hiving packages on their arrival, it is good practice to store them in a dark, quiet place with a temperature of 50° to 60° F., such as a cool basement. Before placing them in storage, the packages should be fed heavily with sugar sirup brushed or sprayed on the wires of the cage.

INSTALLING PACKAGE BEES

A satisfactory procedure for hiving the package bees is to set the individual pail of feed and a package behind each prepared hive. A good plan is to provide each hive with five combs leaving the remaining space empty, arranging the combs at one side of the hive. In the Dadant apiaries, an oilcloth, or similar material, over the frames of the hive is preferred, even when using an inner cover.

The entrance of each hive should be reduced. A good entrance reducer is a thin slat with a two-beeway opening in the center which is lightly filled with green grass. If a top entrance is used, the lower entrance should be closed and the top entrance lightly filled with grass. As the grass dries, the bees gradually remove it. If they are not disturbed, package bees will not fly freely until they have become accustomed to their new quarters.

Before the bees in the package are hived, it is a great help to spray or sprinkle them with warm water so the bees are not able to fly freely. It takes several hours for them to dry in the hive, and this gives them plenty of time to become organized.

When everything is in readiness, the bees in each package are shaken down into the bottom of the cage (Fig. 6) and sprayed with warm water, the feeder can is removed (Fig. 7), and the queen cage taken from the package (Fig. 8). The feeder can then is set over the hole in the package while the queen cage is prepared for introduction.

Some prefer to allow the bees to release the queen from the cage in which she is shipped. With this method of queen introduction, the usual procedure is to remove the paper cover over the hole of the candy compartment and either to hang the queen cage with the candy end up between the combs, or to lay the queen cage face down on the top bars of the frames or face up on the bottom board. The hive bees later will eat out the candy and effect the release of the queen.

When package bees are hived on combs, it is more satisfactory to release the queen at once. The cover over the open end of the queen cage is removed and the cage is placed screen side up under the bottom bars of three of the combs in the hive, the remaining two combs being pushed aside to provide a space into which to shake some of the bees from the package onto the bottom of the hive (Fig. 9) where they will quickly find the queen cage or the queen as she comes out. The two combs, temporarily placed at one side, are then pushed up close to the others, a piece of wood or a stick is laid on the bottom board in the empty space at the side of the five combs, and the package with the remaining bees is placed there with the feed hole up (Fig. 10).

The cloth cover or inner cover is then placed over the top of the hive and the feeder pail inverted over the hole so that the bees have ready access to the feed. An empty super or hive body, or a special rim, is placed on top (Fig. 11) and the hive is closed. If the combs contain considerable pollen and honey, often only this one feeding is necessary. Should the feed in the combs become exhausted, feeding must be resumed or combs of honey must be supplied until the colony is able to gather sufficient nectar and pollen to provide for its food requirements.

MANAGEMENT OF PACKAGE BEES

There comes a critical time in the progress of the package colony, usually about 3 weeks after it is hived, when the new brood produced from the eggs of the queen reaches a relatively high point in proportion to the number of adult bees. Many of the bees that came with the package will have died and no young bees will have emerged. It is often at this time that supersedure of the queen occurs, probably because the population is out of balance. This can be largely overcome by giving the package colony a comb of emerging brood and bees from a healthy colony, placing this comb next to the brood combs in the package colony. This should be done about 2 weeks after the package is installed; colonies so treated will gain surprisingly in strength.

When packages are hived on drawn combs with plenty of food and with a favorable season, they will often develop into full colonies in time to gather some surplus honey the first season. In the North, packages will produce good crops during the first season due to the long build-up period.

Supersedure in package bees is often a critical problem. Sometimes supersedure occurs because of too frequent handling of the new colony and sometimes because the queens are inferior or because they are infected with nosema disease. Because of the possibility of nosema infected queens, it is recommended that package colonies be fed sugar sirup medicated with Fumidil-B. For further information on this, see Chapter XIX, "Diseases and Enemies of the Honey Bee."

Breeding stock also is a factor in queen losses inasmuch as some queens are not as good as others in the quantity or the quality of their brood, and thereby influence the amount of surplus honey secured.

FIGURE 6. This hive with reduced entrance is ready to receive its package of bees. This one is being hived on frames of comb foundation.

FIGURE 7. The cage is jounced on the ground, the lid is pried off, and the feeder can is then removed from the cage.

FIGURE 8. Next the queen cage is removed, shaking the bees clinging to it gently back into the package cage.

FIGURE 9. Shake about half the bees between the frames where the queen cage is suspended and carefully push the frames together.

FIGURE 10. Now place the package cage with the remaining bees upright in the empty space beside the frames of comb foundation.

FIGURE 11. Invert the feeder pail over the frames, place an empty super on top, and the hive is ready to be closed.

A heavy annual replacement of queens suggests that each apiary should have a reserve supply of laying queens in nuclei ready to replace those which show signs of being inferior, thus making it possible to prevent interruptions in brood rearing during the active season.

If the combs on which the package is hived do not contain an abundance of pollen in the cells or if foundation is used in hiving the package, it is a good plan to make sure that the bees have access to a pollen supplement or a pollen substitute unless natural pollen is available in abundance and the weather is such that bees can gather all the pollen they need. For further information on pollen supplements, see Chapter XIII, "The Overwintering of Productive Colonies."

Haydak and Tanquary[1] have given a number of formulas for the preparation of pollen substitutes. A good formula consists of a mixture of 3 parts by weight of brewer's yeast, of the type fed to animals, and 6 parts of expeller-processed soybean flour, moistened with sugar sirup made of equal parts sugar and water. Mix this with the hands until the material is of a soft, pasty consistency. Cakes of this pollen substitute may be placed over the top bars of the frames directly over the brood (Fig. 12). Feeding pollen substitute every 10 days for as long as the bees will take it, will help the packages grow materially. The bees take the substitute as long as they need it. When natural pollen is available they will not take it readily; frequently they will not take it at all.

FIGURE 12. A cake of pollen supplement or pollen substitute given in this manner helps the colony to grow. (*Photo by Laidlaw and Eckert*)

The chance of shipping package bees from diseased colonies in southern locations is slight. Inspectors in the South are active in checking the apiaries of package shippers and every precaution is taken to be sure that bees are taken only from healthy colonies. There have been instances of disease in the apiaries of shippers but such apiaries are quarantined until a clean bill of health is available. A good method of prevention of disease in package-bee colonies is the feeding of ¼ teaspoon of soluble sodium sulfathiazole in each 10-pound pail of sirup given to the packages at the time they are hived.

Combs or frames of foundation should be added to the new colonies as they continue to grow. The entrances should be enlarged as the colony needs additional ventilation and is able to defend itself from marauders. Each colony also should be kept supplied with an abundance of food until it is able to obtain sufficient food from natural sources. When the new colonies have reached sufficient strength to occupy completely the hive bodies, they are capable of occupying supers and of storing surplus honey whenever there is a honeyflow. Their management thereafter will be the same as that of any other established colonies.

Queen Management

It would be difficult to discuss the queen bee and all of her relationships to the colony in a single subject division. Consequently, the methods of finding and marking the queen, ways of judging and introducing the queen, and methods of using two queens in colony management are discussed separately. Probably no phase of beekeeping is more frequently discussed than the management of the queen nor have so many different ways been devised to conduct management successfully. In the following pages are given those methods which are used most frequently and with the greatest degree of success.

HOW TO FIND THE QUEEN BEE

It is much easier to find queens in the early part of the season when the population of the colony is not large and the amount of brood is small. Choose a time when there is sufficient nectar available to prevent robbing. When brood rearing is expanding in the spring, the queen is apt to be in the upper body of a 2-story colony. During the honeyflow, she is usually in the lower body. At this time, considerable labor is required to reach the brood nest because supers must first be removed, and there are so many bees present that it is difficult to find the queen. In the latter part of the fall honeyflow when most of the supers have been taken off and the colony is not so large, it again is relatively easy to find the queen.

When trying to find the queen, easy motions and the use of as little smoke as possible are advisable. The queen will be so occupied with her duties that she will pay little attention to the operator. Remember that the queen is seldom on combs which contain little or no brood. Remove one or two such combs and begin to work slowly toward the center of the brood nest, or separate the combs in the middle and work either way from the center. When removing a comb from the hive, look quickly for the queen on the side of the comb next in view within the hive before examining the one which has been removed. Two people working together on opposite sides of the hive usually find the queen more quickly.

The queen is usually on combs containing young brood and eggs (Fig. 13) and it is unlikely that she will be found on combs of sealed brood or honey unless she has a tendency to run from the operator. Bees of some colonies accompanied by the queen tend to travel away from the operator, even to the point of reaching the hive walls or the bottom board where the queen will remain hidden in a cluster of her own workers.

When there is little chance of robbing, combs may be set outside the hive in their proper order after they are examined, and they should be returned in the same order when through. Watch carefully. Do not try to see the whole surface of the comb but look only for the queen. She will usually be found on the first examination. If not, the brood combs may be put back into the hive in separated pairs, the hive closed for a few minutes, and then reopened. Each pair of combs may then be examined in succession, looking first for the queen between each pair of combs.

FIGURE 13. Here the queen is searching for cells in which to lay her eggs. This good queen on a newly drawn comb should have no difficulty in doing this. *(Photo by Donald Barber)*

It is sometimes necessary to use special methods to find the queen. Perhaps the easiest way is to set the hive body of brood and bees to one side, place a hive of empty combs on the bottom board, cover it with a queen excluder, and place an empty hive body on top of the excluder. Shake the bees from the combs of the original hive into the empty body on top, replacing the combs in the hive from which they came. After all the bees are in the empty body, the workers will run through the excluder onto the combs below but the queen, unable to pass through, will eventually come into view above the excluder. A similar method is to place a strip of queen-excluder zinc over the entrance of the hive, shaking the bees in front of the hive.

In looking for the queen in a 2-story colony, put a queen excluder between the two bodies, examine the upper body first, and then the lower one. The queen cannot go from one hive body to another because of the excluder. Sometimes the two bodies are set apart quickly and then covered, each one being worked separately to find the queen.

It is not necessary to see the queen to know that she is present in the hive. If there is brood in all stages of development in satisfactory quantity and arrangement and the colony's adult population is well maintained, there is seldom any reason to search for the queen.

Queen bees which are marked in some manner are found more readily than those which are not marked. Queens of the Caucasian and Carniolan races are more nearly the same color of the worker bees and are difficult to locate unless the queens are marked.

Marking fluid may be placed on the center of the thorax of the queen between the two wings. A good material to use is nail polish or a quick-drying enamel. The fluid is applied with a small brush while holding the queen with the fingers, and it is well to allow the material to dry to some extent before releasing the queen. Red, green, orange, and bright blue are satisfactory colors. Some use colors to designate years, source of stock, or other factors. The bees apparently pay little attention to the marking which usually lasts during the lifetime of the queen.

Although it does not help in finding the queen, the most common way of marking the queen is to clip her wings on one side of the body (Fig. 14). Usually the wings are clipped on the right side if the queen is introduced in an even-numbered year and on the left side in an odd-numbered year. If a queen is found later with unclipped wings, it is known that she is a supersedure queen or that the queen originally introduced was not accepted.

HOW TO JUDGE A QUEEN BEE

Like any other animal, the queen bee has definite physical characteristics. Inasmuch as the queen bee lays the eggs, she is the mother of the colony, and her physical conformity must provide for this im-

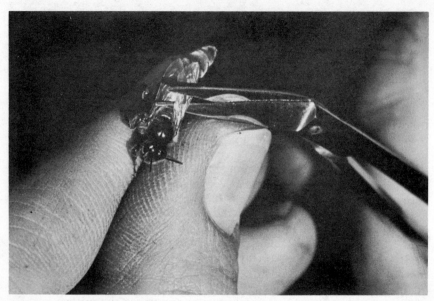

FIGURE 14. The queen is carefully held between the thumb and the index finger while clipping the wings on one side. *(Photo by Laidlaw and Eckert)*

portant responsibility. Not only may she be judged by her physical qualifications for the work she is expected to do, but also by the results of her labor.

The queen should have a gently tapering abdomen particularly large and full along the sides. She should be evenly colored and have a large thorax. Such a queen usually has good egg-laying capabilities. A queen that is short, stubby, off-colored, erratic in movement, or whose body tends to fall away from the hips in a "rat-tailed" shape with a point at the end of the abdomen is not desirable.

Sometimes a queen with good body conformity, however, does not lay well. When a queen has established three or four combs of brood, the efficiency of her work may be determined. If the combs are well occupied with concentric circles of brood of similar age (Fig. 15), the queen should be satisfactory. The queen that lays steadily, producing brood of an even character throughout the season and until late in the fall, is a good queen.

Virgin queens frequently mate more than once, sometimes as many as six to eight times. Frequently a queen bee, during the course of her life of laying, shows variability in the worker bees that she produces due to the different matings. So a queen that may be satisfactory at one time may be judged unsatisfactory at another time for this reason. This should be considered when judging the behavior of a laying queen.

It takes a large population of field bees to gather a crop of honey. Queens that fill the cells of the combs rapidly several weeks before the beginning of the honeyflow and maintain their egg-laying rate through the honeyflow period will produce a maximum number of bees to gather the crop. Queens that lay slowly before the flow may later develop a maximum colony but they will do it on the honeyflow rather than before, and the colony will gather less surplus honey.

A good queen will place her eggs in the exact center of the cell bottom, each egg usually slanted in the same direction. The eggs will be laid symmetrically, starting usually a little above the center of the combs and spreading out evenly in all directions.

A good queen may also be judged by the behavior of her progeny. The colony should be a good honey producer and not inclined to swarm. The bees should be gentle and evenly marked. Colonies should winter well and should provide themselves with an abundance of stores of honey and pollen placed properly in the combs.

Replacing poor queens in early spring and fall is a valuable practice. Queens introduced in the spring will provide vigorous mothers for the production of large colonies before the honeyflow. Those introduced in the fall will provide the colonies with many young bees for winter and will be able to carry the colonies successfully through the honeyflow the succeeding season.

Some beekeepers contend that queens should be replaced each year but it seems foolish to replace queens on a calendar basis. Under some

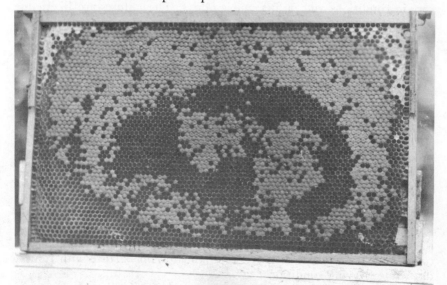

FIGURE 15. An example of the concentric circles of brood common to the egg laying of a good queen.

conditions, queens cannot possibly exhaust their powers of egg laying in a single season. Under other conditions, queens will actually wear out in preparation for and during a single honeyflow period. The best way to practice requeening is to replace poor queens whenever they are found. Poor queens may be noted when one works with colonies and the hives marked so that those colonies may be requeened at the first favorable opportunity.

The age of the queen does not determine her performance. Young queens are often poor from the very start of their egg laying; sometimes queens lay well for several seasons in succession. The bees apparently know when a new queen is needed. They may supersede the old queen by their own efforts and the beekeeper may not know that the old queen has been replaced. Some colonies will replace their queens several times a year, others may not replace them more than once in several years.

It is not unusual for the beekeeper to find two queens in the same colony at one time, one of them the aged mother and the other the supersedure daughter. If the beekeeper sees only the old queen and judges her by physical appearance, he may try to introduce a new queen to a colony which already has a young laying queen. This will result in the loss of the queen that is being introduced.

HOW TO INTRODUCE THE QUEEN

The proper method of introducing queens is a much discussed subject. There are many methods used, most of them working under certain conditions and failing under others. The failures are likely due to an incorrect understanding of the basis for successful introduction. The theory of colony balance in relation to queen introduction was defined first by Sechrist.[2] According to this theory, the queen to be introduced must be in about the same condition with respect to egg laying as the queen which is to be removed. This appears to be the requirement for ready acceptance of new queens, and when this balance is provided introduction is easy by almost any method. If the balance between the two queens is not equal, introduction will usually fail.

In the natural processes of brood rearing, the colony will have little brood in the spring and as the colony grows the amount of brood increases until it reaches a large amount just before or in the beginning of the honeyflow. Brood rearing will taper off between flows, and in the fall it is at a low point. Young queens, therefore, may be introduced easily in a nectarflow in the spring or in the late fall when egg laying is at a minimum without any special attention being paid to whether the new queens may have begun their egg laying. The queen of the colony and the young queen are approximately in balance with respect to their egg-laying condition.

If a queen must be introduced when there is considerable brood in the colony, and the queen of the colony is daily depositing eggs to the best of her ability, then the young queen to be introduced should also be laying eggs daily to be in balance with the queen in the colony. Thus, the new queen must begin her egg laying elsewhere before introduction. This may be accomplished by first introducing the queen into a nucleus where she may be kept until she is laying well.

The queen also may be placed in a reservoir while still confined in her cage where she is fed by the worker bees and stimulated to fitness. A reservoir for conditioning queens and for holding them until they can be used in requeening can be made by establishing a nucleus of several combs of brood and bees without a queen in a convenient hive or in a transport box. A colony of bees also may be used as a reservoir without removing the queen.

Whether using the queenless nucleus or the queenright colony for a reservoir, the attendant bees are removed from the cages containing the new queens and the cages placed in a frame adapted for the purpose of holding them. One should make sure that the candy compartments are protected so that the bees will not eat their way into the queen cages. During confinement, the new queens will be fed by the bees, and they will increase in size and begin to lay eggs about their cages. The queens may be kept in the reservoir a week or two before they are used, and the reservoir should be kept in condition by frequent additions of brood and bees. The reservoir can be carried from one yard to another when requeening, and brought home each night.

When the time comes to introduce the new queen into the colony to be requeened, the introduction ordinarily is made by using the shipping cage containing the young queen, whether she is introduced directly upon receipt from the breeder or taken from a reservoir or nucleus. First, remove the old queen from the colony that is to be requeened. The safest plan when using the queen-mailing cage is to remove the attendant bees, providing this already has not been done, and to remove the paper cover over the candy hole of the queen cage. The cage then is inserted between two brood combs in the colony (Fig. 16). If the weather is cool, the bees will cluster about the cage and the queen will not be chilled. In time, the worker bees will eat through the candy and release the queen.

The behavior of the queen when she is released by the bees, influences the conduct of the bees toward her. If she is rapid in motion, she may not be accepted as readily as a queen that is quiet and slow in movement, ready to lay at once and eager for food.

Many beekeepers are overly anxious to determine whether or not the queens have been accepted after their introduction. Frequent examination of the colony, or examination in inclement weather, may result in the loss of the new queen through being balled by the worker bees. Balling occurs when the worker bees cluster tightly about the queen and pull at her legs and wings until she is badly injured and frequently killed. When a colony is examined to make sure the new queen has been accepted, if eggs are seen, the queen is there. The hive should be closed and the colony left alone.

During a honeyflow when it is desirable to keep colonies up to full strength to maintain their field force, a new queen, before being introduced into a colony to replace one that is not doing well, first must be brought into egg-laying condition in a nucleus. The old queen should be removed from the colony along with as many combs as there are combs in the nucleus. Then the nucleus with the new queen is placed in the center of the colony, the bees of both the nucleus and the colony being sprinkled with sugar sirup.

Inasmuch as the egg laying of the old queen and the queen that is being introduced are in about the same balance, introduction usually is assured. The new queen will carry the colony forward without loss of honey and sometimes with considerable addition to the crop. It is suggested by Farrar (see reference No. 3 in this chapter) that a satisfactory number of nuclei to maintain in each yard is at least 10 per cent of the number of colonies in the yard. Thus, for a 50-colony apiary at least five nuclei would be established with good queens, and used in replacing queens in producing colonies when they show signs of failure during the honeyflow.

Introducing the new queen in her mailing cage directly to emerging brood and young bees is a method which seems to work under all circumstances. To accomplish this, combs of emerging brood are placed in a hive body on top of a colony, first shaking the majority of the bees

FIGURE 16. The queen cage is suspended between the frames with the paper removed from the candy hole and with the candy end of the cage up. (*Photo by Milledge Murphey, Jr.*)

off the combs so that those which remain are young bees. The upper hive body is separated from the colony by a screen, and the brood is kept warm by the heat of the colony below. The new queen is introduced by suspending the cage between these combs, as previously described, or by releasing her on the combs where she will be readily accepted by the young bees. Later, the new queen and the combs may be given to a colony to be requeened, or the nucleus can be moved to a new location and built up by the addition of more brood and bees to form a normal-size colony.

An adaptation of this plan that is generally suited to queen introduction is the use of the so-called "push-in" cage (Fig. 17). A 4-inch square of ordinary screen wire is bent along each edge and the corners clipped to form four sides, making a wire cage which can be pushed into the face of the comb. The cage should be pushed into an area of emerging brood, preferably where there are a few cells of honey for feed. It should be inserted deep enough into the face of the comb so that the bees cannot readily gnaw through the comb to reach the new queen. The new queen is released inside of the cage without any bees other than those which are emerging. A few days later the cage is removed. In the interval, the queen will have been accepted by the emerging bees inside the cage and subsequently by the bees of the colony.

HOW TO USE TWO QUEENS

It is not uncommon in nature for a colony to have two queens. If both queens are laying before the honeyflow, it may account for

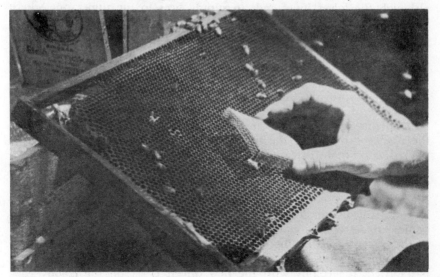

FIGURE 17. The push-in cage is about to be placed over the queen, before pushing it into the comb. It is recommended that the cage be placed over an area of emerging brood.

the extra-large population of a colony and the harvesting of more than the average amount of surplus honey. A number of attempts have been made to use two queens in colony management in order to take advantage of the maximum field force obtained.

Farrar[3] is perhaps the most ardent advocate of the two-queen system of management for honey production. Strong colonies are selected early in the season and divisions are made from them, as soon as available pollen will permit uninterrupted brood rearing for the purpose of introducing a second queen. The old queen is confined by means of an excluder to the lower brood chamber containing a reserve of honey and pollen and half the brood. Two supers of drawn combs are added above the excluder, an inner cover with the escape hole covered with a screen is placed above the supers, and a hive body containing the rest of the brood is placed on top to form an upper brood nest. The upper brood nest should contain combs of emerging brood, plenty of pollen and honey, and over half of the original population. An auger hole in the upper hive provides an entrance. Some of the bees will go back to the lower hive but there will be enough left to maintain a satisfactory population above. A young queen is introduced in the upper hive body, preferably a laying queen from a nucleus.

As soon as the queen in the top hive body has a well-established brood nest, the screened inner cover may be removed, and the bees in both brood nests should be sprayed with sugar sirup. As populations increase, it is necessary to provide more room for brood. Super room is given immediately above the brood nest of either queen as needed, although the lower hive tends to supply bees to the upper one where honey storage is dominant.

The colonies should be united back to a single-queen condition about 4 weeks before the end of the flow. It is not necessary to locate the queens; just set one colony on top of the other and put the supers on top, one queen being disposed of by the bees. In the fall, it may be necessary to provide these colonies with three stories to insure an abundance of honey and pollen for wintering.

Dunham[4] recommends a modified two-queen system which involves the use of two queens during spring and before the honeyflow, and the reduction to a single-queen system at the beginning of the honeyflow.

A modification of the two-queen system which often works is accomplished by wintering the colony in two hive bodies. These are reversed in early spring so that the queen establishes brood in both bodies. During fruit bloom, or 6 to 8 weeks before the main honeyflow, the two bodies are set apart, one behind the other, and a queen is introduced to the queenless half. The two colonies are left until the beginning of the main honeyflow, supers often being added to both. When the flow has started, the colony with the new queen is set on the colony containing the old queen and the supers of both are placed on top.

There are many modifications of two-queen management, but it should be remembered that if the management materially increases the costs they must be weighed against the crop obtained. In general, any new procedure should be aimed at reduction rather than increase in costs. Thus, the increased crop obtained under a two-queen system should more than offset the cost of the additional management to be profitable.

The Swarm

Swarming is an instinctive part of the annual life cycle of the honey-bee colony. The tendency to swarm is usually greatest when the bees increase their population rapidly in the period before the honey-flow. However, if a colony reaches a period of steady daily intake of a major honeyflow with a well-balanced population, the bees usually will concentrate on nectar gathering and show no indication of swarming.

Colonies with queens one or more years old, whose egg-laying powers are diminishing, swarm more readily than colonies with young laying queens. The failing of the queen will not be so evident in early spring, but as the colony approaches the honeyflow her ability to lay eggs will be taxed to the utmost. Daily the old queen lays fewer eggs, her laying is less systematic, and the bees become eager to replace her with a young and more efficient queen. Then the bees raise queen cells for the purpose of superseding the old queen. Eventually, they induce the old queen to lay in them and then they guard them well until the young queens are available.

Inasmuch as supersedure is most apt to occur during the period just before the honeyflow, swarming and supersedure may be carried out together. Usually, supersedure swarms issue with one or more virgin queens, the old queen remaining with the parent colony to be replaced in turn with a young queen.

However, the supersedure impulse is not the cause of many swarms. The cause may be a crowded and unbalanced brood nest, displaced nurse bees, or "living room" not adequate for colony needs (see Chapter IV, "Activities of Honey Bees"). Inasmuch as swarming occurs most often before a honeyflow, there may be one or more swarming periods each year. Some colonies reach large proportions and do not swarm; others swarm without apparent reason.

When the cells built in the hive in preparation for swarming are reaching maturity and when there are few field bees leaving a strong colony on a clear, warm day when other colonies are busily at work, you may look for a swarm unless conditions change rapidly. The usual time for a swarm to issue (Fig. 18) is from 10 o'clock in the morning until 2 o'clock in the afternoon, the majority of swarms issuing when the sun is within an hour of the meridian. However, in sultry weather a swarm will leave the hive as early as 7 o'clock in the morning, and occasionally a swarm ventures out as late as 5 o'clock in the afternoon.

When the swarm leaves the hive with the old queen, it is called a "prime" swarm. Half or more of the bees may go out with the swarm. The bees seem to be of all ages, although the majority have been found to be those that have not yet taken up field duties. With their stomachs full of honey, they quickly forget their old location. The swarm soon will settle after its flight from the hive, often nearby.

In very populous colonies, about a week after the prime swarm leaves, more bees may swarm out with virgin queens, apparently when the virgins take their mating flights. There may be several virgins in each of these swarms and this swarming may continue until the population of the colony is reduced to a low point. Anywhere from one to several new colonies may be established by this process.

HOW TO CATCH A SWARM

If the swarm clusters on a low shrub or limb, it can be obtained without difficulty. However, the swarm may alight on a fence post, the wall of a house, a woven-wire fence, or some other place from which it is more difficult to remove. Usually, the quickest way to secure them is to set a nucleus box or hive with combs underneath the swarm (Fig. 19), brushing off all the bees in front of the entrance. The bees should be smoked vigorously to drive them into the entrance, making certain that the queen goes in with the bees. When the bees are all in, the nucleus or hive is taken at once to the spot where it is to be located permanently. If a nucleus box is used, the bees may be transferred to a hive whenever the operator desires.

FIGURE 18. A swarm starting to issue—one of the most thrilling sights within the compass of rural economy. This is Nature's way of expanding the number of colonies.

FIGURE 19. A swarm of bees about to be hived in a clean cool hive. This swarm obliged the beekeeper by landing on a near-by low limb of a tree.

Too often the swarm prefers to cluster in a tall tree out of easy reach. If the swarm can be reached with a stout pole, a light box is fastened to the end of the pole and then placed in position underneath the swarm. The limb on which the bees have clustered is shaken to dislodge them. A rope thrown over the limb close to the swarm and given a quick pull will do the trick at times.

A nucleus box with combs also may be raised up underneath the swarm and tied in place until the bees find their way onto the combs. This is accomplished by throwing a rope with a weight attached to its end over the limb, and then raising the nucleus box to a proper position. Frequently, by climbing the tree, sawing off the limb on which the swarm is clustered, and carefully lowering it, the bees can be easily hived.

A cloth sack with its mouth sewed to a wire loop fastened to the end of a pole may be used for securing high swarms. The sack is lifted up until it surrounds the swarm, the limb jarred, and the mouth of the sack quickly turned to close the opening. After being lowered to the ground, the swarm is carried in the sack to where it is to be hived.

Some beekeepers use decoy hives to attract swarms. These are old hives or boxes containing combs and placed in the crotches of trees. The scouts sent out by the swarms to locate new homes may choose these places and the swarms later will enter them of their own accord.

HOW TO HIVE A SWARM

Because the swarm divides the population of a colony, resulting in a reduction in the field force and consequently the amount of honey the colony might have gathered, it is obvious that the swarm and its parent colony should be put back together to make the best use of the bees. Only if the swarm occurs considerably in advance of the main honeyflow will it or the parent colony build to strength and secure a satisfactory surplus crop.

One method of returning the swarm to the parent colony is to hive the swarm in a new hive on the old stand. If there were supers on the parent colony, they are placed on the swarm in the new hive. A queen excluder or an inner cover with the center hole open is put on top of the supers and, after having destroyed all queen cells, the parent colony is set at the top and left there until all of the brood has emerged. The population is thus brought back together and further swarming is unlikely, particularly if the old queen, which may have issued with the swarm, is replaced with a new queen at the earliest convenient time.

A variation of this method is to set the parent colony close beside the swarm which has been hived on the old stand. The entrance of the parent colony should be at a right angle to its former position. The field bees that leave the parent colony then will enter the hive of the swarm because it is on the old stand. All but one or two of the best queen cells, preferably those from which the virgin queens are not due to emerge for a few days, are removed from the parent colony. One of the virgins will mate and provide a queen for the parent colony. After about 10 days, move the parent colony to the other side of the swarm in a similar position. Thus the parent colony will steadily lose its field bees to the swarm. After its queen is mated and laying, the colony may be set in a new location as an increase in the number of colonies in the apiary. Inasmuch as the majority of the field force will have joined the swarm in this process, not much of the crop will be lost.

If a swarm is hived on a full set of drawn combs, the bees may soon fill the cells with nectar, restricting the egg laying of the queen. If the new swarm, however, is given supers in which the bees were working prior to swarming, a full set of combs may be used in the brood nest with little trouble. On the other hand, because a newly hived swarm will draw foundation readily when there is a good quantity of incoming nectar stimulating the secretion of beeswax, frames of foundation can be given to the swarm. The queen is able to use the newly constructed cells as fast as they become available. Space is thereby provided for her in a more satisfactory way than when all of the combs given to the swarm are drawn combs.

SWARM PREVENTION AND CONTROL

Because swarming is an instinctive habit which follows a natural sequence of conditions, the beekeeper must follow this sequence carefully to make certain that each colony is led away, step by step, from that culmination of circumstances which results in a swarm.

Populous colonies with the best queens (Fig. 20) are frequently unable to stand the congestion of the brood nest. This congestion throws the colony out of balance in population and queen cells are started in preparation for swarming. Therefore, the brood nest should be kept as free as possible at all times from any condition which will contribute to congestion. There should be plenty of worker combs containing empty cells for egg laying and with a minimum of honey and pollen in them.

The addition of more empty combs may be necessary at the sides of those occupied with brood so that the queen may use them, or room may be provided for the empty combs by removing those occupied with honey and pollen. Thus the queen is induced to expand her brood area to the sides. Additional bodies of combs may be placed on top into which the queen may go, expanding her brood area in an upward direction. Supers also can be added supplying an area for the storage of nectar and honey away from the brood area. This is the basic idea of a free brood nest by the provision of areas for definite use.

Any management that adds to the comfort of the colony will aid materially in the prevention of swarming. Colonies may be shaded, they may be given ventilation (Fig. 21), and adequate watering places

FIGURE 20. Big colonies like this one will swarm at the "drop of a hat." *(Photo by Laidlaw and Eckert)*

FIGURE 21. A big colony made comfortable by raising the entrance and staggering the top super for ventilation.

should be at hand inasmuch as the colony is kept cool in very warm weather through evaporation of water by the bees.

During the period when colonies are most likely to attempt swarming, an examination of a few selected at random throughout the yard, particularly the strong ones, will give the operator an idea of existing conditions. The brood bodies can be separated or raised from the bottom boards and the lower edges and sides of the combs examined to see if queen cells have been started. A thorough examination of the individual combs of a few of the strongest colonies at the same time will increase the value of the superficial examination already made. If there is little evidence of swarm preparation, further attention will not be needed.

Swarm cells are numerous and usually constructed along the lower edges of the comb (Fig. 22). The bees start one or two each day over a period of a week or more so swarm cells provide many young queens for the full expression of swarming. Supersedure queen cells (Fig. 23) are usually of about the same age and few in number. However, it is not safe to assume that the presence of only a few queen cells indicates for certain that supersedure is underway rather than swarming.

Special practices are often used to control swarming; among the well-known methods is the so-called Demaree plan of swarm control. This method may be used when individual colonies have swarm cells, or

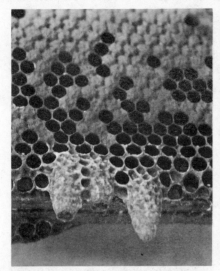

FIGURE 22. Swarm cells in their usual place along the bottom of the combs. They are often whiter than supersedure cells.

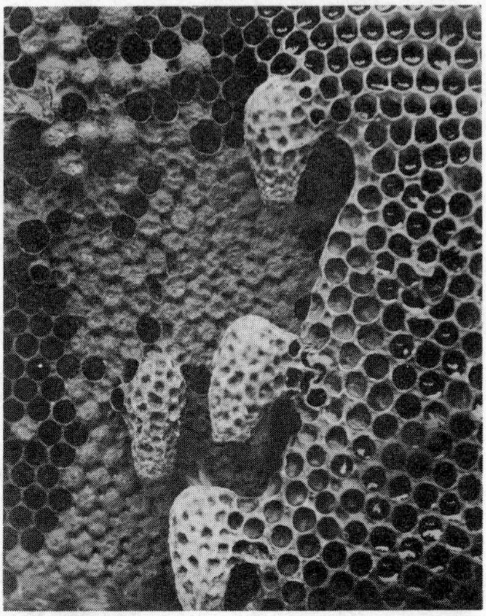

FIGURE 23. Supersedure cells are few in number, usually of about the same age, and constructed on the face of the comb.

it may be applied to all the colonies in the apiary at one time when it is apparent that most of them will develop cells.

The brood of the colony is examined and all queen cells are destroyed. The hive is then removed from its bottom board and a body containing one comb of unsealed brood, eggs, and the queen is put in its place with the remaining space filled with empty combs. A queen excluder is placed on top of this body. Supers are put above the excluder and the remainder of the brood and the bees are placed at the very top. The colony still has all of its brood, and the queen is in the lower body with a free brood nest.

In 10 days, examine the brood combs in the top hive body and remove all queen cells that may have been built in the interval. In 21 days, all of the brood will have emerged in the upper body and it will be used for honey storage, while bees will be beginning to emerge from new brood in the lower body, so that a continuous succession of young bees is maintained. Except in unusual seasons, it is seldom necessary to use the Demaree plan more than once.

Should a swarm be likely to result from supersedure, swarming may be prevented by removing the old queen and any queen cells which may have been started. Wait 10 days and again remove any cells that have been built in the interval. There will then be no brood left of an age suitable for queen cells. A young laying queen may now be introduced and it is seldom that the colony will attempt to swarm again that season. This method is particularly valuable in the production of comb honey.

A similar condition may be brought about by forced supersedure. When colonies are in a 2-story brood nest, a queen excluder is inserted between them 4 days before giving a new queen or a ripe queen cell to the queenless portion. It is not necessary to find the queen because, after the 4-day interval, the part with eggs and young larvae obviously is the one that contains the queen. This part is set aside and the queenless part left on the old stand and given a new queen or a ripe queen cell. A day later, a super of combs is placed next on top and an inner cover with its center hole covered with queen-excluder zinc is placed above the super. Finally, the brood body with the old queen is placed at the very top. The old queen is permitted to continue her laying for at least 2 weeks after the young queen below has started to lay, and then the old queen is killed and the excluder removed.

During a period when swarming is apt to occur, if bees are confined at intervals to their hives by rain or inclement weather and then have access to the fields in successive periods, this intermittency may stimulate swarming. To control its effect, a thin sugar sirup may be fed to the colonies. This feeding has the effect of an uninterrupted flow, restoring the balance of the colony and tending to avoid swarming. Another method is to place an empty super, containing no frames, on top of the colony, covering the tops of the brood frames with a cloth turned back so the bees can cluster in this empty space at will. Dry granulated sugar is placed in the center of the turned-back cloth. This simulates flow conditions; the bees may work on the dry sugar, cluster in the space, and return to outdoor work when weather allows.

The exchange of strong colonies with weak ones in the apiary, so that weak colonies are strengthened by the addition of the field force of stronger ones, and strong colonies lose strength to the weak ones, is a swarm-preventive measure that works satisfactorily and does not involve the exchange of combs or the use of additional equipment. In outyards, where the attention required by most swarm-control methods is difficult, a variation of the exchange plan, called relocation, has been developed.[5]

It is the practice in the Dadant apiaries to diagram the colonies as shown in the example (Fig. 24). The relocation of the colonies is indicated by arrows. Colonies are examined for queen cells and any found are destroyed. Such colonies are placed either in the location of weak colonies or in new locations at the front or back of the yard, or at the end of a row. By this exchange, the colony which had the swarm cells loses much of its population. The field bees of colonies that have been placed in spots previously unoccupied by colonies will return to their old locations, entering neighboring colonies and increasing their field forces. While the relocated colonies may continue to develop queen cells to carry out supersedure, they will not swarm.

Colonies whose strengths are too much alike should not be exchanged. Those in which virgin queens have already emerged cannot be helped by the exchange. When the virgin queen has emerged the swarm is as good as in the air.

Divides may be made of colonies in which virgins have emerged or from those containing swarm cells from which they will emerge within a few days. These colonies should be taken to another location at least 2 miles away and the brood and bees divided into any desired number of parts, giving each part a new queen or allowing a virgin to mate. This removes the colonies from the production of surplus honey and uses them for increase.

Various devices have been used to control swarming, such as placing a queen-and-drone trap over the entrance to screen out the drones in the belief that an excess of drones is the direct cause of swarming. The same device is used to keep laying queens from going with the swarm when it issues. However, when a queen has reduced her egg laying previous to the issuance of the swarm, she often is able to make her way through such traps. If the swarm is accompanied by a virgin queen, she can leave readily in spite of the device which is expected to prevent her flight. Such devices, therefore, are of little value.

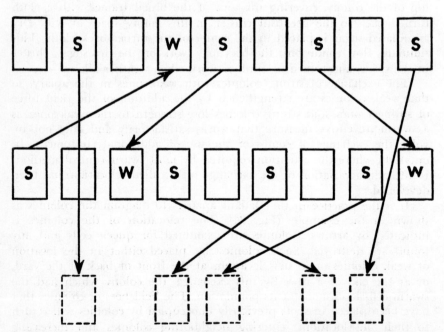

FIGURE 24. Diagram of "relocation" of colonies as a method of swarm control. Strong colonies are indicated by the letter "S," weak ones by the letter "W," and arrows indicate the possible relocation of the colonies.

Beekeepers sometimes clip the wings of queens to prevent them from flying away with the swarm; clipping will accomplish this. But, if the swarm has failed in an attempt to leave with the old queen, the bees will return to their hive and wait until virgins have emerged, and then issue with one or more virgin queens. So, clipping is, at best, only a temporary deferment of swarming. It does give the beekeeper time to do something about it provided he is able to determine the hive from which the swarm has issued and returned. However, clipping does not prevent the swarm occurring.

HOW TO MOVE BEES

If bees are to be moved only a short distance, such as across the bee yard, to a different position in the apiary or across a city lot, a simple way to accomplish the move is to change the position of the colony a little each day so gradually that the bees will not be confused by the new position of the entrance. A satisfactory distance may be judged by the tendency of the bees to drift to other colonies after each step in the move is accomplished. If there are no other colonies close to the one that is being moved, it may be moved farther at each move. Colonies may also be moved farther to the front or to the back than they can be moved sideways. If they find their own entrance readily, the distance is safe.

It is possible to accomplish a short move quickly by carrying the colony to the desired location late in the day after the bees have quit flying. A board should be leaned against the front of the hive so that the bees will be confused by this obstruction the next day and will mark the new place. A hive containing a set of combs can be placed on the old location to catch any bees that may go back to their former location. In the evening, when all of the field bees have returned, set the body in which the bees have been caught above a newspaper on top of the original colony in its new location, as in uniting.

If bees are to be moved a considerable distance, they should be moved at least 2 or 3 miles beyond the flight range of their former place. When this is done few bees will return to the old spot. It is preferable also to do the moving when the field bees are all in the hive, either late in the day or very early in the morning.

Make sure that any small cracks or openings between the hive parts are closed by filling them with paper, rags, or similar materials so that the bees will not find their way out during transit. The bottom boards and hive parts must be fastened securely. Hive staples are made for the special purpose of fastening the hive parts together. When using them, be sure that the two staples on each side used to fasten two parts, such as the hive and the bottom board, are slanted in opposite directions. Otherwise, they may shift position when raising and handling the colonies. In hot weather, the hives should be provided with a top-moving screen to provide a clustering space and air for the bees. It also is a decided advantage to use entrance screens.

The hive hoist or loader mounted on the bed of the truck certainly has been a boon to large beekeepers both for moving colonies and for taking off the crop (Fig. 25). Although some loaders are mounted on the rear of the truck bed, most are mounted at the front and have a long boom supporting the hive lifter or cradle. The lifting and leveling movements are performed by motors. With such a device, one man is able to load or unload 2- or 3-story colonies. The boom swings to enable the operator to position the colony where it is wanted.

When colonies are loaded on trucks (Fig. 26) or other vehicles, each layer of hives should be separated by wood strips to provide a space between for the free movement of air. Properly prepared colonies can be moved in the hottest weather. The truck should be kept moving, but if stops are necessary it should not be parked in the sun. It is a good idea to carry extra gasoline so stops do not have to be made at filling stations. There are always some bees riding along on the outside of the hives; they will fly when a stop is made and often cause trouble when left behind.

It is ideal to arrive at the new location so that the entrances may be opened and the screens removed just before dark. In any case, the truck should be stopped in a shady place, if possible, and all of the colonies should be unloaded and located before the screens are removed. By the time all are unloaded, the bees in the first colonies removed will have settled down considerably and entrances can be opened and screens removed. On a bright, hot day, it is helpful to spray the bees with water to prevent rapid flight and drifting.

FIGURE 25. The hive loader mounted on the truck bed makes it possible for one man to load or unload colonies or to remove supers of honey. (*Photo by Kopec Photo Co.*)

FIGURE 26. A truck and trailer load of colonies ready for a long journey. (*Photo courtesy of Rocke Apiaries*)

In the cool weather of early spring or late fall when bees are not flying, or after they have ceased flight for the day, colonies can be moved without any special preparation. The bees make little attempt to come out of their hives while the truck is in motion. If the weather is too cool for flight, the colonies may be left on the truck until morning before unloading. Sometimes conditions are such in early spring that hives can be moved when bees are flying. Smoke the entrances vigorously before loading. As the field bees return, they usually stay in the hive because of the smoke. A single colony or a hive full of combs can be left in the yard to collect the bees left behind, and this hive can be moved later. Some beekeepers move open colonies in warm weather but there is danger of loss if it is necessary to stop the truck. Sometimes trucks are covered with a nylon screen so bees will not fly out of the load if it becomes necessary to stop.

THE PREVENTION OF DRIFTING

The drifting of bees from one hive to another because of wind or confusion caused by other circumstances is common. A high wind may buffet bees coming in from the field until they find themselves in the wrong hives, even though they make their best effort to return to their own home. Drifting often is most noticeable at the ends of rows in the direction of prevailing winds which force the bees down the row until they come to the last two or three hives and rush in pellmell. These bees are always welcome because they come in laden with nectar, pollen, or water, and they are not robber bees.

If package bees are installed on a bright, sunny day and are permitted to fly too soon, they will drift in the same manner, causing serious losses in the population of some of them. Greater skill in hiving the packages would have prevented this (see "The Management of Package Bees").

The effects of drifting may be corrected by exchanging the positions of colonies that have become strong with those that have been weakened. This exchange should be made preferably when there is nectar available and bees coming in from the field enter the hives without being molested.

A frequent occurrence is the drifting of young bees in their play flights. Not having thoroughly learned the location of their own hives, they may drift into neighboring hives when affected by wind. The next day this drift may be corrected by changing winds.

The arrangement of colonies close together in straight rows encourages drifting in the apiary. Colonies should be placed 6 to 8 feet apart in the rows with 10 feet or more between the rows. If colonies are arranged in rows, with the hives in every other row placed so they are opposite the middle of the spaces between the hives in the next row, thus staggering the positions of the colonies, it will have a tendency to reduce the amount of drift. In windy and exposed places, a good windbreak will also reduce drifting.

Drones tend to drift about the yard more freely than worker bees and are welcome in almost any hive during summer. It is not infrequent to find drones of both light and dark color in every hive, even though they may originate in colonies where drones of one color predominate.

HOW TO UNITE BEES

The occasion frequently arises when it is necessary to put one or more groups of bees together, one colony with another or one nucleus with another nucleus or with a colony. Weak colonies in fall may not winter well; it is usually best to unite them with other colonies which will be strengthened by the union. Colonies with good queens which require strengthening may be united with small colonies having unsuitable queens, the poor queens being destroyed. This makes the better colony stronger and disposes of the weaker one.

It is frequently considered good practice to unite weak colonies just previous to the main honeyflow. Such colonies should be permitted to grow until that time. Then, any that are unsuitable for the flow can be united with other colonies that thus will be benefited. It should be remembered, however, that weak colonies with exceptionally good queens may grow rapidly into populous colonies.

If uniting is necessary during summer when little nectar is available and robbing is apt to occur, it is advisable to set the colony that is being united above the other colony on top of a single thickness of newspaper with one or two small holes punched in the center. The bees gnaw away the paper and gradually mingle together as time goes on, and so unite peacefully without excitement. After a large portion of the newspaper has been removed by the bees, the remainder may be removed by the beekeeper, and any extra combs resulting from the union can be disposed of as desired. It is not necessary to find either queen unless there is a preference for one of them. Then the undesirable queen may be found and disposed of before the colonies are united.

A quick way of uniting is to kill the poorest queen of the two units that are being united, and to place most of the brood of both colonies in one hive with the remaining queen and part of the bees. Then shake all of the remaining bees from both colonies in front of the hive, sprinkling them with sugar sirup and smoking the entrance. Bees returning from the field will enter the hive at once, and there is so much confusion that there is seldom any fighting.

Another quick and easy way is to set the best colony with its queen above an excluder over the lower colony which has been made queenless. The excluder checks rapid mingling of the bees, there is usually little disturbance, and the bees of both hives unite peacefully.

In early spring or in late fall, colonies often may be united by merely placing them together. Whether one is set on top of the other, or whether the combs of each are placed together in a single hive, makes little difference. During a honeyflow when bees are busy in the field, two colonies may be put together by placing one immediately above the other, or they can be placed together in the same hive without special preparation. In the fall, it is often possible to shake the bees off the combs of a colony in front of the hive of another with which they are to be united. When there is no brood and the weather is cool, the bees enter peacefully and mingle together without any fighting.

In uniting bees, one will be reminded that some of the field bees will fly back to the parent stand, while the young bees will stay with the union. However, the loss of some of the field bees is not important because they usually drift into neighboring colonies without hesitation.

HOW TO TRANSFER BEES

Sometimes it is necessary to transfer bees from one kind of equipment to another, or to move them from houses, trees, or other natural lodgings. Many colonies are still housed in log gums, box hives, and various other domiciles in which the combs are crooked or run crosswise. Such colonies should be transferred to modern equipment because they cannot be managed properly and they produce only a small amount of surplus honey.

In buying bees which need to be transferred, the cost of the work should be considered in the purchase price. The combs usually are worth only the value of the wax in them, the bees are worth no more than the price of a package of bees, and often the hive is of little value.

The best time to transfer bees, particularly if it requires exposure of combs that may incite robbing, is in a period of honeyflow. An ideal time is during fruit bloom in spring; the amount of brood and bees in the colony then is relatively small and the work is easier.

To transfer bees from a house, a tree, or similar abode, a nucleus is made containing two or three combs of brood and bees and a new queen. The nucleus is placed on a temporary shelf so that its entrance is turned at a right angle to the entrance the bees have been using (Fig. 27). All entrances which they may have been using, except the main entrance, should be closed. A cone of screen wire is then made with the small end of the cone reduced to leave a space sufficient for only one bee to enter or leave the cone at a time. The large end of the cone is fastened to the old entrance so that bees go out through the small end of the cone, but have difficulty in finding their way back through the cone entrance. Gradually, the bees will then join the nucleus. When the population of the old colony has reached a low point, the remaining bees may be killed with cyanide or chlordane, the old entrance stopped up, and the bees in the nucleus removed to a new location.

Bees in box hives or containers in which the combs are crooked and crosswise also may be transferred. A good way is to turn the old hive over, remove the bottom board, set a new hive body with frames of foundation or combs over the open bottom of the colony, and close tightly any remaining spaces between the hive bodies so that the bees may come and go only through the entrance of the top hive. Then, with a stick in each hand, drum the bees from the bottom hive into

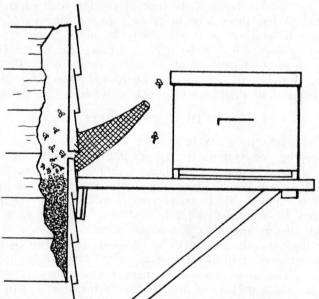

FIGURE 27. Diagram of transferring a colony of bees from a house by means of a screenwire cone. (*Drawing courtesy of J. E. Eckert*)

the hive above, rapping continually on the sides of the old hive. This causes the bees and queen to run up into the new hive. The drumming should be continued for some time; if it is possible to smoke into the old hive, this also helps to cause the bees to move upward.

Finally, a queen excluder is slipped under the bottom of the new hive to keep the queen confined to that body. The worker brood in the body below will have emerged within 21 days and in the meantime the colony will have established itself in the new hive. The excluder can then be removed, the bees on the old combs can be shaken in front of the new hive which by then is setting on a bottom board on the ground, and the old equipment and combs can be taken away and disposed of as desired.

Should a prime swarm issue from a colony that needs to be transferred, the swarm is hived in a new location in a modern hive containing a full set of good combs or frames containing comb foundation. The old hive with the bottom board removed is placed over an inner cover with the hole open and above the supers of the new colony. An entrance is not provided for the upper hive and any openings should be closed. When the virgin queens emerge in the upper hive, they will find their way down to the lower colony where they will be killed. When all of the brood has emerged from the combs in the upper body, the old combs and equipment can be disposed of as desired.

In transferring from small hives to larger ones when both contain removable combs, such as transferring an 8- or 10-frame Langstroth colony to a Modified Dadant hive, take two or three brood combs with the queen from the small hive and put them directly into the large hive, filling the rest of the space with full-sized combs or frames containing comb foundation, of the Modified Dadant size. A queen excluder is put over the top of the large hive, the small hive is set on top, and the open spaces at the sides are closed. The queen below will gradually work over to the larger frames, and the smaller frames can then be returned to the small hive body above the excluder. When all of the brood has emerged, the small hive can be removed, used as a super, or disposed of in some manner.

SUPPLYING VENTILATION

It is often necessary to ventilate the hive in order to cool it on warm days so the colony will be more comfortable, and to aid in the evaporation of nectar. Ventilation is accomplished by bees fanning their wings at the entrance and within the hive on the bottom board, the extent of fanning being determined by the need for ventilation (see Chapter IV, "Activities of Honey Bees").

If the entrance to the hive in warm weather is small, bees may not be able to set up sufficient currents of air for ventilation. Should the entrance become clogged from one cause or another, it is not uncommon for the combs of the colony to melt down and for the bees to perish. This often occurs when hives are located where it becomes extremely hot in summer and there is insufficient ventilation throughout the colony. The top combs of honey melt first, the melted wax and honey finally running out of the entrance and partially or completely suffocating the entire colony. It is not unusual for bees under such circumstances to stop their field work and cluster on the outside of the hive until conditions improve.

The beekeeper can help ventilation by keeping the bees in partially shaded places, using shade boards on top of the colonies, and cutting away weeds and brush in the apiary to allow circulation of air.

It sometimes is advisable to give additional ventilation by offsetting the top cover. Some stagger the supers slightly forward and backward (Fig. 21), although this is not advisable when producing comb honey. Frequently, it is good practice to raise the front of the hive body at the bottom board with small blocks, or the hive can be raised in this manner at all four corners. Later in the season, special ventilation spaces should be closed because of the possibility of robbing and because of the approach of cool fall weather.

SECURING GOOD COMBS

The ideal time to secure good combs is during a honeyflow, and the best combs are obtained from frames of foundation placed in hive bodies or supers immediately above the brood nest. Then the bees will build combs out fully, from one end bar to the other and from top bar to bottom bar. They will be composed largely of worker-size cells and are the very best that can be obtained for brood rearing and for honey storage. If they are left with the colony and used for honey storage during the honeyflow, they can be extracted and later used in the brood nest when they are needed. It is a good practice to draw new combs in this way each year for use the following season. Poor combs should be removed from the colony at every opportunity until all the combs of the colony are as nearly perfect as can be obtained.

The best way to remove combs that are no longer suitable (Figs. 28,29) is to take them from the brood nest of the colony during the honeyflow and to replace them with good drawn combs. In a good flow, it is possible to remove two or three at a time from a strong colony and to replace them with frames containing full sheets of comb foundation, though this is not as desirable as replacing them with fully drawn combs. The poor combs may then be placed in hive bodies and set on top of any colonies over inner covers with the center hole open. The brood will emerge and the bees will not store honey in the combs, but even will remove the honey from these combs, storing it below in the supers. If the undesirable combs contain only honey, they can be extracted and later melted into beeswax.

FIGURE 28. This comb has sagged causing a bulge at the bottom which contains a few drone cells in a distorted way.

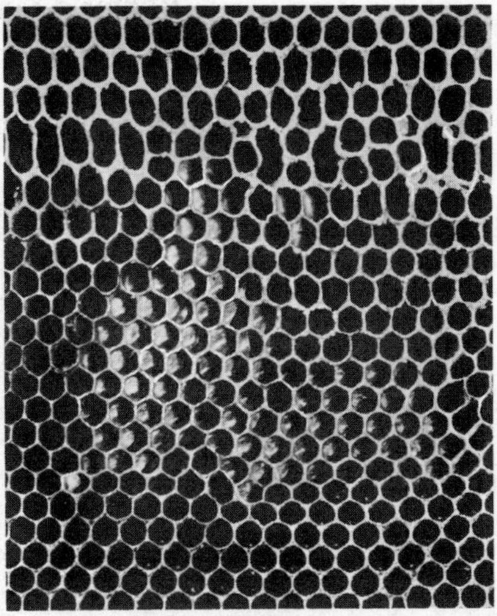

FIGURE 29. Sagging at the top of this comb has resulted in many stretched cells used for rearing drones.

THE CARE OF EQUIPMENT

There seldom is time to concentrate on the care of equipment when it is necessary to think about colony development in spring, harvesting the crop, and preparation for winter in the fall. Nevertheless, equipment represents a greater investment than the bees. Inasmuch as it is possible to replace bees at relatively less expense than it is to replace equipment, it is good sense to keep equipment in first-class condition—repaired, painted, and damaged or worn-out parts replaced. This task can be done best in the off season in a suitable workplace where it is comfortable to work.

Supers and hive bodies should be renailed if they are not firm. Inasmuch as they spend much more time out of doors than inside, a good coat of paint will help to preserve them and to prolong their life. Cracks in equipment should be filled with plastic wood, and holes should be plugged or covered. Bottom boards deteriorate faster than other equipment especially when set on the ground. Even when hive stands are used, bottom boards are subject to more moisture and insect damage than hive bodies, supers, or covers. They will last longer if painted with a wood preservative or dipped in creosote and dried in the sun before they are used. This should be repeated every 3 or 4 years. Modern beehives are now manufactured from wood that has been treated to prevent rotting. The penetration of the rot-proofing material is a fourth inch on flat surfaces and up to 3 inches at dovetails. This treatment considerably prolongs the life of beehives.

KEEPING USEFUL RECORDS

Individual colony records are an aid in bringing colonies that are not normal into good condition as rapidly as possible. They are especially valuable in keeping a record of the queens, so their ages, behaviors, and possible supersedures may be known. Individual colony records may be marked on the top of the cover or on the sides or the back of the hive. The markings may be made with a crayon or a water-proof ink pencil, or by some marking system, such as bricks or sticks in different positions on top of the hive.

Operation records are more important than colony records. These may be kept in a book carried by the beekeeper in which he sets down the cost of labor, mileage, the materials used, and the attention required on the next visit. Thus, the cost of operation and the frequency of visits are recorded, and the beekeeper knows whether his beekeeping is paying or not. Pertinent notes may be added about variations in the honeyflow, the season, extent of the crop, weather, and other significant factors. When it is possible to establish a scale colony in the home yard, the recording of the seasonal fluctuations is a valuable addition to record keeping.

Usually, each beekeeper has a pet method of keeping records which he finds best for his own purposes. Some use a printed form on which notations are kept. At the end of a year, a summary is made of profits and losses and a study made to determine how operation costs may be reduced. It is often possible through such a study to learn how to combine work so that fewer visits to the yards are necessary or to accomplish work in a shorter time, cutting costs to the lowest point. There is something fascinating about going back over the past to measure significant facts and to broaden one's memory by the history which records reveal.

Seasonal Management

The major portion of the total honey crop of the United States is harvested from May to September, although in the South and in California crops are produced as early as March and April. It is likely that at least half of the total crop of the country is produced before July 1. It follows, therefore, that the inactive, preflow, honeyflow, and afterflow periods occur at about the same time over most of the country. Although this discussion of seasonal management is based on beekeeping in the Midwest, beekeepers in other areas will be able to apply the same procedures.

The honey-bee colony must come through winter and into early spring with enough of the winter population of worker bees remaining to support the queen in her egg laying and to care for the brood, so that the colony will increase in population until it reaches a high point at the beginning of the main honeyflow. This is a matter of timing and expert fall management has much to do with it. Farrar (see Chapter XIII, "The Overwintering of Productive Colonies") states that each colony must be conditioned in the fall, if it is to be the best in the spring.

When the food reserves of honey and pollen are sufficient for winter, many colonies with capable and efficient queens will begin brood rearing in the latter part of winter, and will add enough young bees to replace their winter population in early spring. Colonies with insufficient stores or with less satisfactory queens will have little, if any, winter brood. They may not start brood rearing until spring is at hand, and often they are unable to build to peak strength by flow time.

EARLY SPRING

All colonies should be given a quick examination as early in spring as possible. It is not necessary to wait until bees fly freely every day. If the colonies are in two or more full-depth bodies or if they are in one hive body with a shallow food chamber, pry up the top body and tip it back without removing the cover on top. Look closely among the combs to see if there is brood present. If there is no brood, the colony is most likely queenless. If the queen has failed and has become a drone layer, that will be shown by the predominance of drone brood.

A colony with a strong cluster of bees and a normal amount of worker brood needs little attention unless it is light in stores. This may be determined by lifting the hive at the back. If it is light in weight, the colony should be opened and the combs examined for stores of honey and pollen. If lacking in honey stores, the colony will need to be fed sugar sirup or given combs of honey. If there is little stored pollen, the colony should be fed pollen substitute or pollen supplement, especially if early spring sources are not available or weather is not satisfactory for daily flights.

Hives in which bees have died in winter should be removed from the apiary; the combs should be examined carefully for the possible presence of disease. If the combs are free of disease, the hives should be cleaned and made ready for future use. Weak or indifferent colonies may be removed from the outyards to the home yard where they can be managed with less expense or disposed of later. If a queenless colony has an abundance of bees, it should either be given a new queen obtained from a southern breeder or should be given a comb containing eggs or very young brood, with the hope that the bees will raise a new queen which will mate and provide the colony with a laying queen.

Any work in early spring must be done quickly and with care, stopping if robbing becomes apparent. See that the entrances of the colonies are clear of obstructions so the bees will have free flight, and reduce all entrances so that the colonies will be able to guard against intrusion by robber bees. The bee yard should be cleaned of rubbish and trash ahead of the working season, and all hives that are out of position should be leveled. Bees have greater need for water for brood rearing in spring than at any other time; if an abundant natural source is not at hand, watering places will have to be provided.

Colonies that have been wrapped with tar paper or similar material and those that have been lightly packed can have their protective covering removed in early spring. If the colonies have been heavily packed for winter, the packing should be left on until the season has advanced to a daily maximum temperature of about 60° F. These colonies expand their brood area in late winter or early spring over a greater comb surface than those with light packing. Early removal of the heavy packing may cause loss of brood by chilling because of the inability of the bees to keep all of the brood warm. Heavily packed colonies should be amply provisioned with stores of honey and pollen in the fall so that it will not be necessary to remove the packing before warm weather occurs.

Colonies in spring often lose adult bees faster than newly emerged bees can take their place. This is frequently referred to as *spring dwindling*. This is usually present in most colonies, but it is serious only in those that lose so many old bees in proportion to the emergence of young ones that the colony reaches a low point in population before there are enough young bees to balance the loss. It is more apparent in some colonies than in others, and it is more severe in some springs than in others. Colonies with an abundance of reserve honey and pollen in late fall and with a strong winter population begin brood rearing in late winter and are able to replace their loss in adult population. Some colonies may even show an increase in the number of bees when winter is over.

When the population of the colony in early spring steadily declines, it may also be due to the failure of the queen. In such cases, the old queen should be removed and replaced with a new one, introduced in a mailing cage or in a push-in cage during a period of early bloom. Additional combs of brood and bees from colonies that can spare them will help bolster the colony.

The loss of adult bees in early spring may also be due to nosema disease, a disease of the adult honey bee that is general throughout the country. The losses of adult bees often are not easily detected. Careful scrutiny may detect bees crawling about on the ground in front of an occasional colony in the apiary. In some seasons, nosema disease may cause such extensive losses that many colonies are unable to reach producing strength by the time of the honeyflow. For additional information on adult bee diseases, see Chapter XIX, "Diseases and Enemies of the Honey Bee."

The antibiotic, fumagillin, has been found effective in keeping down nosema infection. Treatment is with Fumidil-B, a water-soluble form of fumagillin together with several agents which protect the fumagillin. When nosema is indicated in the colony, a feeding of a 10-pound pail of sugar sirup containing Fumidil-B (a rounded teaspoonful of Fumidil-B per gallon of sirup) may be of great benefit.

Both American foulbrood and European foulbrood may be prevented if colonies in spring, between the beginning of brood rearing and the start of the honeyflow, are given a dust treatment of terramycin and sulfathiazole. A satisfactory formula is a quarter teaspoonful of Terramycin (TM-25 poultry formula), a quarter teaspoonful of sodium sulfathiazole, and 1½ teaspoonfuls of powdered sugar. This mixture should be dusted over the tops of the brood frames three times before the flow.

When early bloom, such as dandelion or fruit bloom, is sufficient to provide colonies with nectar, they may be opened and examined more freely and thoroughly than previously. A careful examination of the brood nest is advisable to make sure that the queen in each colony is satisfactory, that food is present in sufficient quantity, and that there is no disease of the brood.

THE PERIOD BEFORE THE FLOW

When brood rearing begins in late winter or in early spring, the brood area is usually to be found in the upper portion of the brood nest at the time of the first thorough examination of the colony. The brood area will mainly be in the top hive body when two or more bodies are used for wintering the colony, or in the super and the top of the brood combs of the hive body when the colony has been wintered in a single hive body with a shallow super used as a food chamber. Inasmuch as the tendency of the colony is to expand the brood nest upward, the queen will not readily move down to empty combs. Therefore, it is good practice to set the top hive body or super on the bottom board, setting the bottom hive body on top, thus reversing the parts. This reversal brings most of the brood to the lower position (Fig. 30) with a less amount of brood at the top. It also breaks the circle of the brood, placing the two segments in inverse positions. The queen then moves upward readily, first into the empty portions of the brood area and then into the empty combs above. At the same time, the house bees rearrange the stores of the colony around the new brood area. This stimulates the colony to greatly increase its population. With a good queen in a populous colony, it may be necessary to reverse the brood bodies again before the flow occurs.

Before the beginning of the main honeyflow, the bodies that earlier were placed on the bottom boards in the reverse position will have become empty through the emergence of the brood and the rearrangement of the stores of honey. They then should be returned to their original positions. When the flow begins, they will be used for storing the first part of the flow. At the end of the season, these bodies will be well provisioned with honey and pollen and should be left on the colonies as food reservoirs for winter. During the flow, supers needed for storage of surplus honey are added above these food chambers.

The period just before the main honeyflow is usually when colonies are most apt to exhaust their reserve stores. In the earlier season, relatively few colonies may have needed feed, but there will be some colonies that will require feed at this time even though an abundance of stores was left with them the previous fall. It is not unusual for populous colonies, with a large amount of brood to feed, to use up all of the available food supply and even to die of starvation. In this period when not enough nectar is available to supply the food requirements of the colony, the careful beekeeper will make sure that all colonies have an ample supply of food so that brood rearing can continue without interruption.

When the development of the colony starts with the beginning of brood rearing in late winter or early spring, with a vigorous young queen, an abundant supply of food, and sufficient comb area for brood rearing, the colony's peak of population may occur at the start of the honeyflow, and the ideal in management has been attained. It usually requires 8 to 10 weeks between the time that spring begins and the start of the honeyflow to bring about this favorable occurrence. In other words, a fortunate conjunction of the peak in colony population and the beginning of the main honeyflow makes honey production relatively easy. Either too long a period before the flow or too short a time, makes beekeeping more difficult.

FIGURE 30. Diagram of reversal of a colony wintered in one hive body and a shallow food chamber. In spring, the food chamber is placed under the hive body, and reversed to the position at right just before the honeyflow. The supers on top of the food chamber have been added for the flow.

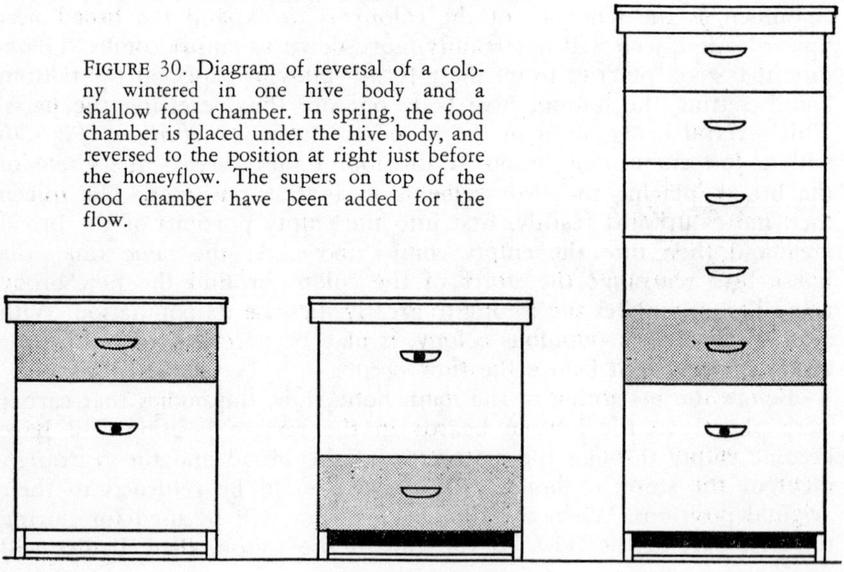

If the honeyflow occurs in less than 8 to 10 weeks from the beginning of spring, there is often too little time for the colony to reach proper strength without the most expert care. It requires prolific young queens, an ample supply of food, and effective intelligent management—plus ideal conditions of weather, an abundance of honey and pollen plants, and freedom from diseases—to produce a maximum honey crop. If conditions are not ideal, it may be necessary to bolster colonies with queenless packages or to unite colonies prior to the honeyflow.

When the honeyflow occurs 12 weeks or more after the beginning of spring, the colony may have reached its peak of population before the start of the flow. It either will swarm before the main honeyflow or lose its colony morale and decline in its honey-gathering ability. To delay the peak of population in a long period before the honeyflow, colonies may be divided during the time of early flow from dandelion, fruit bloom, or other sources. A new queen is given to the queenless part and each division is allowed to grow until the honeyflow begins. The two parts may then be united or may be operated individually, if there has been time for each part to achieve a satisfactory population of field bees for the flow.

This period before the honeyflow is also the time when many colonies follow a natural instinct to divide their populations through swarming. Because neither the parent colony nor the swarm will gather as much honey as the original colony, swarming should be prevented or controlled by proper management.

THE HONEYFLOW PERIOD

It will now be assumed that we are entering the honeyflow with populous colonies that have not swarmed and are headed by queens able to maintain colony strength through the honeyflow period. There is little else that may be done to improve the colony; it is ready for the honeyflow.

Now is the time when supering colonies for the surplus honey crop must be carried on in earnest. When the nectar is brought in from the fields by the field bees, it is given to house bees who first may place it in temporary storage in the cells of combs in the brood nest. Later it is removed and the house bees evaporate its water content and invert the complex sugars, and place it in more permanent storage in the super combs.

Most beekeepers regard the super as merely a shallow or full-depth body containing a set of combs in which surplus honey is stored, but it is more than that. The super is one of the most significant pieces of equipment in the apiary. It is the place where bees congregate when working the nectar being brought in from the fields. It serves both for storage of honey and for distributing the population of the colony in that the bees are not confined to the brood area. The congestion of the brood area is one factor always present in swarming. Supering, therefore, becomes of greater significance than is often realized.

Supering the Colonies.   The importance of giving supers early enough to provide room for the bees to congregate while they are working the nectar that is being brought in daily from the fields cannot be stressed too much. Supering extends throughout the honeyflow period, and the way in which the beekeeper supplies additional supers is important inasmuch as it influences the morale of the colony and, in turn, the size of the crop.

On the other hand, if supers of drawn combs are given when nectar is not available, it is an invitation for the queen to use the combs for brood rearing, particularly if the supers are full-depth hive bodies. Some beekeepers use queen excluders to prevent the queen from using the supers for brood rearing. However, the use of the queen excluder is often considered an impediment to the bees during the honeyflow period.

When shallow extracting supers are used, the tendency for the queen to produce brood in them is less than when full-depth supers are used. When it becomes necessary to supply super room for colony expansion previous to the honeyflow, the addition of one shallow super is usually sufficient. If the shallow combs are used by the queen, they become occupied with honey as soon as the brood emerges, and the queen returns to the full-depth brood combs below.

The first supers given above the food chambers in the start of the flow should be supers of drawn combs. When the combs along the tops of the frames in the food chamber or the brood nest are whitened with freshly secreted beeswax, any delay in supering is bound to bring on swarming conditions. If possible, supers should be added just before this whitening of the combs.

As the bees require more room, the addition of supers of drawn combs may be made on top of those already in use. When the bees occupy the top super, storing nectar and honey in it freely, it is time to give another one on top. This *top supering* is continued until the flow begins to taper off and no further room is considered necessary.

If supers of drawn combs are not available, it is necessary to use supers containing frames of comb foundation. It is a good plan to replace one or more of the frames of foundation with drawn combs to induce the bees to start to work the foundation more readily. The adding of drawn combs in this manner is referred to as *baiting* the super.

The supers containing comb foundation may be added next to the brood nest during the heaviest part of the honeyflow where they will be quickly drawn into combs for honey storage. They will not be drawn as readily higher up in the stack of supers above the brood nest, particularly at the very top. Nevertheless, when supers of drawn combs are added for an immediate requirement for room for honey storage, it often is a good plan to put the super of foundation one or two positions above the brood nest. Here, it will be occupied by the bees in a good honey-flow and partly drawn into combs. On the next visit, it may be placed below the supers of drawn combs, and another foundation super added in its former position. This may continue as long as the bees will draw foundation into comb.

Another way to have foundation drawn into combs is to select a few colonies that are effective comb builders, and to remove most of the supers of drawn combs from them, adding foundation supers in their places. When these foundation supers are partly drawn, they can be removed and used on other colonies. The supers of combs that were first removed from the colonies can then be returned.

The use of foundation supers is sometimes an aid in the prevention of swarming. At the beginning of the honeyflow, bees sometimes secrete more beeswax than they can use. If supers of drawn combs are given to the colonies, the bees may not have sufficient opportunity to use the wax which they are secreting. The giving of supers of comb foundation affords them ample opportunity to use this wax, and at the same time removes these bees from the brood nest. At such a time the foundation is quickly drawn into combs and the colony seems to be content to remain at work, and is less apt to initiate swarming.

When bees will no longer draw foundation and all the comb supers are in use, and yet more room is needed for honey storage, it becomes necessary to remove supers which have been completely filled with honey and the cells sealed. These are then extracted and the supers of empty combs returned to the colonies, thus providing room for the balance of the crop.

At this time of the year, it is sometimes difficult and occasionally impossible to get over roads with truck loads of supers. To avoid this, supers may be stored in advance on platforms at the yards, and the stacks of supers made bee tight, fumigated, and covered to keep them clean and dry. They are then available when needed in spite of road conditions. Sometimes, a few more supers are taken to a yard than are needed for immediate use. These supers can be stored above some of the colonies over the inner cover with the center hole open and the outer cover placed on top.

It is difficult to judge how much room to give colonies when the flow is at its best. Colonies on scales have registered gains of from 10 to 25 pounds of unripe honey in a single day. Twenty-five pounds of nectar, as stored temporarily by the bees in a heavy flow, is sufficient to fill an average shallow super of combs and to fill partially a second one. The gain in 2 days often will completely fill a shallow super with ripe honey. Thus the importance of giving sufficient room well in advance of need is demonstrated.

It is usually good practice to keep colonies supplied with at least one super ahead of their needs. Frequently, two or more supers are given to strong colonies at one time, particularly in an exceptionally heavy and fast honeyflow. However, it is easy to give colonies more supers than they need toward the latter part of the honeyflow, and the period may end with honey distributed through a large number of combs instead of being concentrated in a few.

Toward the end of the flow when it is doubtful that bees will need additional room for honey storage, a super of combs can be placed over the inner cover with the center hole open, or over the oil cloth with one corner turned back. If the colony really needs this additional room, they will go up through the space provided to store honey in the super; otherwise they will remain below, finishing the supers there. This plan also is useful when the beekeeper is not sure that he will be able to return to the yard in time to give additional room, and colonies already have considerable comb space partially filled with honey.

In estimating the number of supers that may be needed for each colony during the honeyflow, figure the number required in an average flow, determined by experience over a period of years. In most locations, three or four supers to the colony are sufficient. In years when the honeyflow is more abundant than others, and more room is required, supers of honey will have to be extracted and the empty combs returned to the colonies. This practice is referred to as *rotating* the supers. In years of light honeyflows, supers containing empty combs must be stored in the honey house, or other place, and protected from damage by the larvae of the wax moth, or by mice and other rodents (see Chapter XIX, "Diseases and Enemies of the Honey Bee").

REMOVING THE EXTRACTED HONEY CROP

The beekeeper who has managed supering correctly will have most of the supers well filled and ready to remove during the last of the honeyflow period before robbing has become prevalent. Usually, it is possible to remove all but one or two supers at this time leaving the balance on the colonies for the bees to use in storing the rest of the nectar which may be gathered. Thus, the intense robbing, which occurs when all supers are left and removed after the flow has ceased, is avoided. The few remaining supers may later be removed quickly so that robbing does not impose a serious problem.

When the supers are taken from the colonies, a well-filled super with an abundance of pollen and honey should be left with each one. Usually, this will be the food chamber which was returned to its position above the brood nest before the beginning of the flow.

Many beekeepers still remove supers of honey by shaking and brushing the bees off the individual combs of honey, returning the combs to the supers, and loading them on trucks or carrying them into the honey house. Some insert bee escapes in the hole in the center of the inner covers and place the inner covers under the supers to be removed. When equipped and used in this manner, the inner cover sometimes is called an *escape board.* If there are cracks or holes opening into the supers of honey above the escape boards, they must be closed tightly in some way. Pieces of cloth, paper, or even mud may be used to close these openings. This will prevent robbers from reaching the honey while the escapes are in use. As soon as the supers are free of bees they may be removed from the colonies. In exceptionally hot weather, the escape boards should be placed on the colonies the afternoon before the honey is to be removed; if left on for too long in very warm weather, the combs of honey will melt or break down in the supers. In cool weather, a longer time is required for the bees to find their way to the brood nest below.

When removing honey in cold weather, supers may often be taken from colonies without any preparation of this kind. The bees will have left most of the super combs and will have clustered below in the brood nest and in the first super or food chamber. If there are a few bees remaining in the supers, they can be shaken off the combs.

REMOVING SUPERS OF HONEY WITH REPELLENTS

There are two chemicals used to drive bees from the supers of honey—carbolic acid or phenol and propionic anhydride.

Carbolic acid has been used effectively for this purpose for the past decade or more, but the question of its possible absorption by honey in view of present Food and Drug regulations has resulted in a search for a substitute. Misuse of the chemical further contributed to the problem.

Consequently, the Bee Culture Investigations of the U.S. Department of Agriculture, in 1961, recommended the use of propionic anhydride, and designed a "fume chamber" equipped with a smoker bellows for driving the fumes down among the combs. Because beekeepers have experienced both success and failure with the recommended use of propionic anhydride, and also because it still is not known whether the slight absorption of carbolic acid in honey is harmful to human health, both methods of removing supers of honey are given here.

Removing Supers with Carbolic Acid. The use of chemically pure carbolic acid in removing supers of honey is swift, effective, and economical. However, **it must be said forcibly that carbolic acid is a dangerous chemical.** It burns flesh severely and rapidly; a drop of acid in the eye could result in blindness. Containers of acid should be labeled conspicuously and never placed where children can reach them. The effects of the acid can be neutralized with grain or denatured alcohol, and a bottle should be carried along whenever carbolic acid is used. If alcohol is not available, thorough washing with water will minimize its effects. When distributing the acid on the fume pad or board, it is wise to wear rubber gloves and to have goggles to protect the eyes.

FIGURE 31. The top super, which the bees have left, is being removed from the colony. The handy V-shaped block holds up the front of the super until it is lifted off.

Equipping the acid bottle with an ordinary clothes sprinkler top provides a good way of dispensing the liquid. To prepare the fume pad for use, shake the sprinkler over the cloth pad, wetting it well but applying only enough to produce strong fumes. Never use so much that drops of acid will fall on the frames or combs of honey.

The outer cover and the inner cover are removed from the colony and the prepared fume pad is placed over the hive with the cloth side down. The pads are added in this manner from hive to hive until all of them are in position. Anywhere from five to ten pads may be used at one time; the number used is determined by those required to make it possible to take supers away in steady succession without having to wait for the bees to leave the supers.

The heat from the colony and the sun volatilizes the acid. During a hot, quiet day of full sunshine, the bees leave the supers quickly (Fig. 31). Never leave the fume pads on long enough to drive the bees out of the hive and into the air. When the weather is cool or when the sun is under a cloud, the use of acid often is unsatisfactory. Supers of honey removed with acid should be ventilated thoroughly in some manner to remove the fumes of carbolic acid as quickly as possible.

Removing Supers with Propionic Anhydride. Propionic anhydride is less apt to injure the operator than carbolic acid and its fumes are not injurious to honey. However, it can be irritating to the eyes and it also affects the breathing if the fumes are too strong. Consequently, it should always be handled with care and the precautions on the label followed.

Most have abandoned the use of the recommended fume chamber with the smoker bellows and now use a fume pad or board which is a modified acid board. It consists of a 2½-inch wood rim the size of the top of the hive covered with a somewhat thick absorbent cloth pad with a black tin on top.

Propionic anhydride is used much as carbolic acid in the removal of supers of honey. The original recommendation was to use equal parts of propionic anhydride and water mixed together at the time of application to the fume pad. The main difficulty encountered in its use was that, under certain conditions, it stupified the bees before they were driven from the supers of honey. Because of this, some have used lower concentrations of propionic anhydride; others have placed the fume pad at an angle on top of the hive. Most agree that propionic anhydride works well under most conditions when removing shallow supers of honey, but others have experienced difficulties in removing full-depth bodies of honey. The use of propionic anhydride in the removal of supers of honey needs further study and experimentation.

It is surprising how rapidly the supers of honey can be removed from the colonies and delivered to the honey house when the methods and equipment are suitable for the job. Several loads of honey thus may be brought to a central extracting plant in a day's time (Fig. 32).

CARE OF BEES IN THE FALL

Now that the season's crop of honey has been removed from the colonies leaving a full supply of stores for winter, we have reached the fall period.

FIGURE 32. Loading the truck with supers of honey. Notice the inclined walkway at the rear of the truck—a good method for the small and medium-sized beekeeper.

This is the time of year when the influence of the queen is greatly felt. Some queens continue egg laying until late in fall, even after the beginning of cold weather. There also is a marked difference in the rate at which queens lay their eggs. Some queens reduce egg laying at a much quicker rate than others, although there may be some brood in the colonies throughout the entire fall period.

The ideal queen is one whose egg-laying rate is high and continues well into late fall, thus furnishing a populous cluster of young bees for winter. The stronger the colonies are with respect to a population of young bees before winter, the better they will be able to survive the winter period. A large colony of relatively young bees, well supplied with stores of honey and pollen, also will be able to rear brood in the latter part of winter and in early spring. Such colonies will usually come through the following spring with little spring dwindling, and, with proper management of their steadily increasing populations, can be brought to the honeyflow in optimum condition for gathering a maximum crop.

It is of utmost importance, therefore, to make sure that each colony has a queen which is able to give an ideal performance. New queens should be introduced early enough to begin egg laying in late summer and early fall. Queens introduced late in the season are unable to produce a desirable population of young bees for the winter cluster.

It is also important in the fall to make sure that each colony has an abundance of reserve stores of honey and pollen. When storing pollen, particularly toward the end of the season, bees seldom fill the cells more than two-thirds to three-fourths full. The bees then often finish filling these cells with honey and seal them with wax cappings, so that the comb appears to be full of honey. When the food chamber and brood nest are properly provisioned with both honey and pollen, and the colony has a young queen and a strong winter cluster, the colony is in ideal condition for winter.

Colonies that are not in first-class condition for winter, should be united with other colonies. Those that are in poor condition should have their bees shaken from the combs in front of other colonies, and the equipment should be removed from the yard and placed in storage. The equipment should be carefully saved and filled again with bees the following season.

REFERENCES CITED

1. Haydak, M. H., and M. C. Tanquary. 1943. Univ. Minn. Tech. Bull. **160.** 23 pp.

2. Sechrist, E. L. 1944. Honey Getting. Am. Bee J., Hamilton, Ill. 128 pp.

3. Farrar, C. L. 1946. U.S.D.A. Circ. **E-693.** 12 pp.

4. Dunham, W. E. 1943. Am. Bee J. 83(5):192-194.

5. Cale, G. H. 1944. Am. Bee J. 84(5):155-156.

CHAPTER XI

EXTRACTING THE HONEY CROP
by Roy A. Grout*

THE HARVESTING OF extracted honey is completed in the extracting plant, commonly called the honey house. Here the liquid honey is thrown from the cells of the honey comb by centrifugal force.

The honey house of today, as well as the equipment it contains, is largely the result of the ingenuity of beekeepers, and has become the center of beekeeping operations. Sechrist,[4] who wrote extensively about extracting the crop, has said, "As the queen bee is the heart of the colony, so the honey house is the heart of the apiary. Into it, through it, and out of it flow all the currents of beekeeping activity throughout the season."

The removal of liquid honey from the combs is accomplished by the honey extractor. The invention of the honey extractor ranks in importance with the invention of comb foundation, and is accredited to Major Franz von Hruschka, an Austrian, in 1865. Hruschka noticed that honey was thrown from the cells of a comb which his son playfully swung around in a basket. Langstroth was the first American to recognize the importance of the discovery and, as early as 1868, constructed a centrifugal extractor similar to Hruschka's.

Charles Dadant, Moses Quinby, A. I. Root, H. O. Peabody, and others contributed to the early development of the honey extractor. According to Pellett,[1] T. W. Cowan appears to have been the first to build an extractor of the radial type, while Root,[3] attributes the building of the first practical radial extractor to Arthur Hodgson.

The invention, development, and use of the centrifugal extractor greatly influenced practical beekeeping. Methods of separating the honey from the combs by heat, often resulting in discoloration and injury to flavor and aroma of honey, could be abandoned. Combs of honey no longer needed to be crushed to obtain strained honey. Moreover, when the empty combs were returned to the bees, greater yields of honey could be obtained.

The advent of the radial extractor, trucks, and all-weather roads brought into use the central extracting plant or honey house. Here the extracting, storage of honey and equipment, wax rendering, and the workshop could be located under one roof for efficiency and economy. Today's honey house is the result of the development of ideas and inventions of many beekeepers, plus improvements by manufacturers of extracting equipment.

---

*Roy A. Grout. Production manager of Dadant & Sons, Inc. Associate editor of the *American Bee Journal.*

In areas where summer temperatures are hot enough to result in injury to combs and loss of honey if hauled to a central extracting plant, beekeepers have resorted to portable extracting plants which extract the honey at the outapiary. The extracting equipment is installed in a trailer or buslike vehicle where the honey is extracted and either pumped into a tank in the vehicle or into a storage tank on another truck. The emptied supers can be returned to the same colonies, minimizing transmission of disease and immediately providing additional storage space for the bees. The portable extracting plant is relatively less expensive than a permanent building and saves the trips to and from an apiary. Their use is limited to hot climates.

The Honey House and Extracting Honey

The honey house should be efficiently arranged, designed for cleanliness, and of ample size to accommodate the requirements of the beekeeper. A simple structure with the equipment compact, well arranged, and everything sanitary is better than the finest building with expensive equipment poorly arranged. Trucks and good roads have made it possible for the beekeeper to build and maintain a central extracting plant, workshop, and warehouse. Federal food regulations require that the honey house be clean and sanitary. Some states now are enforcing honey house sanitation laws, and the future will see more of this.

Insurance should be carried on the honey house and its contents. Locations having fire protection will, of course, have a much lower rate. The type of structure, its arrangement, and the surroundings will influence the premium rate. A fluctuating type of insurance can be obtained with the premium based on the contents of the building. When the supers are on the bees and much of the equipment is out of the honey house, the premium is reduced.

Labor is a very important consideration in the design, arrangement, and equipment of the honey house. During the extracting, the large beekeeper often depends upon unskilled or inexperienced labor. The small beekeeper may have just as important a problem because he does not depend upon bees for his entire livelihood and often must extract his honey quickly and efficiently.

For some, a co-operative plan of operating a honey house may be a solution. The cost of the building and equipment, as well as the overhead and operating expenses, can be shared, and those involved can work together to their mutual benefit. Custom work may help solve the problem of others. A neighbor may own and operate the extracting equipment, doing the extracting for a fixed fee. Combs can be rendered and sugar sirup for feed can be prepared on a similar basis.

Sechrist has given the following requisites for a good honey house: it should be large enough, but compact and well planned for its particular requirements; the building should be bee tight, well ventilated, and capable of being kept thoroughly clean; the floors should be as nearly perfect as floors can be made and should be strong enough to carry heavy loads and be free from vibrations; and the building should be planned so that the honey, when brought into the building, goes in a continuous and direct line of travel to the storage tanks and shipping room. To this might be added that the building should be well lighted and its construction as fireproof or fire resistant as circumstances will permit.

In all cases, the honey house should have a warm area for the full supers as they are brought in from the apiary, a room for uncapping the combs, and an area for the storage of liquid extracted honey. Often the honey house serves as the truck garage, although a greater fire risk is involved. Usually the steam supply and heating plant are located in the honey house, but such equipment may be placed in a small separate building to minimize fire hazard. In such a case, wax melting and rendering equipment could well be included in the separate building for the same reason.

TYPES OF HONEY HOUSES

The most common type of honey house is the one-story structure used by both large and small beekeepers (Fig. 1). The construction is simple and has the advantage of all operations being on the same level, making supervision of work easier. Its principal disadvantage is that it is not readily adapted to gravity handling of honey, but proper use of honey pumps can overcome this.

FIGURE 1. This fine honey house was built by Don Barrett of Michigan. Everything is on one level except for the lower driveway for the truck.

The two-story honey house may have two stories above the ground or one story above the ground with a full or partial basement underneath. The two-story honey house constructed on a foundation above the ground presents the problem of building a ramp or driveway to the second floor for loading and unloading trucks (Fig. 2). On sloping ground, the type with a basement underneath is found to be quite practical. When built on level ground, this type of honey house makes it necessary to build a depressed driveway into the basement which may cause a drainage problem.

In the two-story honey house, the supers of honey can be unloaded at the upper level where the extracting plant is located. Here the honey is extracted and flows by gravity to storage tanks below. However, with modern honey pumps, the extracting can be handled as readily in the one-story honey house. Either type is adaptable to the ideal system of handling honey in which, from the time the trucks drive in with supers heavy with honey until they drive away with the extracted honey, no unnecessary manual lifting need be done.

CONSTRUCTION FEATURES

Foundations and footings should be deep enough to prevent upheaval by frost, usually about 3 feet. They should be constructed of concrete, stone, brick, or cement block. Footings should extend beyond

FIGURE 2. An example of a honey house constructed on two levels so that supers of honey can be unloaded on the upper level, extracted, and the honey flowing by gravity to the lower level.

the width of the foundation wall on each side, being approximately twice as wide as the wall, and should be as deep as the wall is wide. If of concrete, a mixture of 1 part cement, 2 parts sand, and 4 parts gravel, properly mixed and handled will make an impermeable concrete.

Walls and floors beneath the surface of the ground should be of concrete. The 1-2-4 mixture will be suitable if well mixed and puddled. It is well to remember that concrete is only as good as the workmanship in preparing and forming it. Walls and floors should be completely poured at one time or water will eventually seep through where stops are made in pouring. To obtain a floor surface which is smooth and will stand heavy wear, concrete should be mixed in the proportion of 1 part of cement to 2 parts of sand, and well troweled. Plenty of slope toward each drain should be allowed to permit quick exit of water when floors are flushed and scrubbed.

When not possible to have concrete floors, a well-laid hardwood floor or one covered with ceramic tile is recommended. In general, honey house floors should be of a kind that can be kept clean easily, will stay smooth under cleaning and trucking, and strong enough to carry heavy loads and minimize vibration of machinery.

The walls and ceilings of the extracting plant should be of a type that can be kept spotlessly clean. They should be painted or covered with a light-colored material that will withstand repeated washings. As much care should be taken in handling honey to obtain a clean wholesome product as with any other food.

Lighting and ventilation should be given careful consideration in the planning of the honey house. To a certain extent, electricity must furnish light, so the building should be wired for lights and motors in a manner that will pass the inspection of fire insurance companies. But the main source of light, as well as ventilation, is the windows. Consideration should be given to a sufficient number of windows placed high in order to give the maximum amount of light and ventilation.

The roof of the honey house should be gabled high to form a loft in which light equipment may be stored. A steep roof is easier to maintain and is less subject to leaks because water gets away quickly. A fire-resistant type of roofing always should be used.

Above all, the honey house should be bee tight. It is desirable for trucks to be driven into the honey house and doors closed to prevent the troublesome presence of robber bees. This portion of the honey house should be partitioned or screened from the extracting area. All openings should be screened and equipped with escapes to allow exit for bees brought into the building. Some use electric bug killers over windows or in the building to kill such bees. Nothing will make the extracting task more annoying to inexperienced help, the honey house more unsightly to customers, or the production of a clean product more difficult, than the presence of bees in the honey house.

THE STEAM SUPPLY

If steam is required only for heating one or two uncapping knives or planes, the 1- or 2-gallon copper steam generator heated by a gas or electric burner will be sufficient. But when steam is used to heat the honey or to melt the cappings, in addition to the uncapping equipment, a larger steam supply will be needed. Many will find the 8-gallon steam generator large enough, but commercial beekeepers will find a steam boiler necessary.

A boiler of about 5 horsepower capacity will perform all of the tasks for most, even for heating the extracting area. Others use boilers having a capacity of 10 horsepower. The flueless type of boiler is most common and is economical and easy to maintain.

The steam gauge and water-level glass should be placed where they can be seen at all times. Most boilers are gas or oil fired and are automatically controlled as to the steam pressure and a water injector makes sure that a proper water level is maintained at all times. Boilers of this kind are available in sizes of 5 horsepower and larger.

CARE AND STORAGE OF SUPERS OF HONEY

In handling the supers of honey, the use of the single hauling board or tray makes the extracting work easier and prevents honey from dripping on the floors (Fig. 3). These boards are the size of the bottom of the supers, resembling a telescoping outer cover, and with two heavy cleats nailed lengthwise underneath. Often they contain a galvanized iron tray which can be removed for washing and cleaning. They can

FIGURE 3. Stacks of supers placed on hauling boards enable the beekeeper to move them readily.

FIGURE 4. This platform holds two stacks of supers and can be moved easily with a hydraulic lift truck.

be placed on the truck bed and supers piled on them as they are removed from the colonies. When unloading at the honey house, an ordinary warehouse truck with an extension on its front can be shoved under each stack and wheeled to any part of the building. After extracting, the supers can be stacked on them for further handling. They also can be used to cover stacks of supers.

Some use more expensive lift trucks capable of handling skids or platforms holding two to four stacks of supers (Fig. 4). Like the hauling board, the skid can be covered with a metal tray to catch the dripping honey. A departure from the single hauling board is the dolly, a low platform holding one or more stacks of supers, supported on casters enabling them to be rolled about the honey house. The dolly works well only on smooth floors and is not suited for trucking. The requirements of each beekeeper will dictate which is best for his use.

When none of these methods are in use, supers of honey should be set on clean paper whether on the truck or in the honey house. The papers can be gathered up and burned and can save much scrubbing and cleaning. A number of pans about 4 to 6 inches deep, into which a number of supers can be stacked, are useful. Sometimes accidents occur; a super is dropped or a stack is upset. Placing these supers in the pans eliminates much cleaning and the honey which drains from the broken combs can be saved.

The average beekeeper has comparatively few colonies and economy dictates that the supers be placed in or near the extracting space, as the honey usually is extracted soon afterwards. In cool weather, when it is desirable to warm the honey in the combs, it also is necessary to heat the extracting area.

Many large beekeepers find it desirable to place their supers of honey in a warm room, especially in cool weather, and to leave them there for a day or more before extracting the honey. The combs of honey should not be left in the warming room for more than 2 to 3 days at temperatures above 70° F. because higher temperatures may result in discoloration of the honey. It is advisable to circulate the air in the room with a fan to prevent the top supers from becoming too warm while those near the floor may be cool.

In regions where the humidity is high, supers of honey can be placed in a warm room, stacked crisscross or alternately spaced so that warm, dry air can be circulated through them. Some also use dehumidifiers to speed the lowering of the moisture content of the honey. The temperature should not exceed 100° F. and a sufficient time should be allowed for the combs to warm slowly. Higher temperatures may soften the wax of the combs, causing damage to them in extracting.

When supers of honeycombs are stored for more than a week before extracting, it is necessary to fumigate to prevent damage by the larvae of the wax moth. For methods of fumigation, see Chapter XIX, "Diseases and Enemies of the Honey Bee." Whenever practical, supers of honey from different plant sources should be kept separate and extracted separately. This will prevent dark-colored or strong-flavored honeys from mixing with the light-colored or mild-flavored honeys, resulting in honey of an inferior quality usually lower in price. When honeys of different floral sources are mixed in the supers, it seldom is possible to separate them. This may be due to the neglect of the beekeeper in not removing supers of one kind of honey and replacing them before another kind of nectar is gathered, but there are conditions when this is unavoidable.

UNCAPPING THE COMBS OF HONEY

To extract the honey from the combs, it is necessary to cut away the cappings from the surface of the comb. A warm comb can be uncapped with a sharp, cold knife such as T. F. Bingham invented. Such a knife, when heated by placing it in hot water, also can be used when the combs are not warm. In 1912, the A. G. Woodman Company, Grand Rapids, Michigan, purchased Bingham's uncapping knife and bee smoker business. It was after this that the steam-heated uncapping knife was developed which lead to the introduction of the electrically heated knife (Fig. 5), and the steam and electrically heated uncapping plane. Although the uncapping plane served well its purpose in the hands of a skilled operator, the uncapping knife is generally preferred.

FIGURE 5. This producer is uncapping with an electrically-heated knife.

FIGURE 6. The Woodman vertical-mounted, power-driven uncapping knife.

FIGURE 7. The "Sioux Bee Automatic Uncapper" removes the cappings from as many as nine combs a minute, greatly speeding up the extracting operation for the large producer. *(Photo courtesy of Max Cook)*

The power-driven, steam-heated uncapping machine, with the knife in a horizontal position, has been in use for a long time. About 1955, A. G. Woodman mounted the knife in a vertical position with a rest to support the frame of honey while uncapping. This made the handling of the combs of honey less laborious and thus expedited the operation (Fig. 6).

Machines have been built which automatically carry the combs of honey between two steam-heated knives to uncap them. Other machines used revolving knives or flails of various kinds to remove the cappings from each side of the honey comb. The automatic machine in common usage in this country was developed about 1945 by Bogenschutz Brothers, of New York State, and now has been taken over and further perfected by the Sioux Honey Association. It is marketed under the trade name of "Sioux Bee Automatic Uncapper" (Fig. 7). Revolving knives remove the cappings from both sides of the honeycomb as the frames are fed through the machine at the rate of nine frames a minute. Equipment of this kind will keep four or even more large radial extractors supplied.

TREATMENT OF CAPPINGS

While the large automatic uncapping machines are equipped with tanks to catch and hold the cappings and the honey removed with them, most will uncap over a receptacle into which fall the cappings. The next step is to separate the cappings from the honey without injury to its color, flavor, or aroma. Two general methods are in use: 1. draining by gravity, centrifugal force, or pressure, and 2. melting the cappings so that the liquid wax separates from the honey and rises to the surface. Frequently, a combination of the two methods is used. A few beekeepers have devised ways for letting the bees clean the honey from the cappings after they have been drained but most prefer not to do this because of the possibility of bee diseases.

Draining by gravity is accomplished by allowing the cappings to fall onto a screen held above the bottom of a container, sometimes a tall container but often long shallow boxes or tanks large enough to hold a day's cappings. The cappings should be stirred and broken up with a wood paddle to facilitate draining of the honey. In all cases, the cappings should be allowed to drain in a warm room for at least 24 hours before further treatment. The drained honey is not injured in any way and can be added to the balance of the crop.

When cappings are drained by centrifugal force, the beekeeper either uncaps directly into a specially constructed centrifugal drier while it is running (Fig. 8), or he may uncap into baskets constructed to fit into a centrifugal drier or his centrifugal extractor. At the end of the drying, the cappings are removed and stored for further treatment.

FIGURE 8. The machine at left is a centrifugal cappings drier made in Canada. It spins the cappings dry.

FIGURE 9. This centrifugal machine separates the honey from the beeswax cappings. *(Photo courtesy of Max Cook)*

When cappings are drained by pressure, they first are allowed to fall into a container where part of the honey drains by gravity before pressing. Usually the basket-shaped container is constructed so that it can be placed directly under the screw of the press. Some have used heavy springs between the follower board and the jack screw, permitting continuation of the pressure for a long time. When removed, the cappings are in the form of a compressed cheese which can be stored for later treatment.

Compressed cappings frequently contain as much as 50 per cent honey by weight. Cappings that have been well stirred and drained by gravity over a screen in a warm room for a sufficient time contain no more honey than cappings that have been dried by centrifugal force or by pressure.

Those using the large automatic uncapping machines are presented with a real problem in separating the honey from the cappings because of the large volume of material to be handled daily. Most have resorted to transferring the cappings and the accompanying honey into trays with screened bottoms, transporting these into warm rooms for prolonged drainage and further melting or treatment. A recent development is a centrifugal machine developed and perfected by Max Cook, of Nebraska, which takes the honey and cappings from the Sioux Bee Automatic Uncapper and automatically separates the honey and dries the cappings (Fig. 9).

MELTING THE CAPPINGS

Cappings melters function in two ways: 1. to melt the cappings after the excess honey has drained from them, and 2. to melt the cappings and separate the honey at the time the combs are uncapped.

Drained cappings are either melted over an excess of hot water or in a steam or electrically heated device of some kind. Granulation of the honey contained in the cappings often occurs before this operation which adds to the problem of obtaining beeswax and honey of good quality. There is no equipment on the market today that can separate the honey while melting such material without serious injury to the color, flavor, and aroma of the honey. Such honey should not be added to the remainder of the crop. For further information on melting of cappings, see Chapter XVI, "Production and Uses of Beeswax."

The first device used generally for melting the cappings as they fell from the knife was the Peterson cappings melter. The sloping surface of the heated bottom melts the beeswax and heats the honey. This results in overheating the honey which also comes into contact with the beeswax refuse. Such honey is unsuitable for adding to the remainder of the crop or for marketing as table honey.

The Brand cappings melter is an outstanding development in American beekeeping. It employs the principle of floating the cappings

FIGURE 10. The Brand cappings melter separates the beeswax and honey from the cappings in one melting operation. The extracting equipment includes a "Merry-Go-Round" comb rack and a 50-frame radial extractor.

on the surface of the honey removed with them until they touch a steam-heated grill suspended above them. The cappings fall onto the heated surface of a hopper at one end of the melter (Fig. 10) and slide underneath the melting unit. As the liquid wax collects at the level of the melting unit, it is run off into molds. The level of the honey is maintained several inches below the heating grid, and the excess honey overflows during the operation. The melting grid can be raised for cleaning and the refuse can be skimmed off from time to time. If properly operated, the honey will be affected only slightly in color and flavor and may be added to the rest of the crop without injury to its grade. At the end of the workday, the beeswax is in the form of a cake suitable for marketing, and the problem of storing the cappings and later melting is eliminated.

EXTRACTING THE HONEY

After the combs are uncapped, they usually are placed in a device which catches the honey that drips from them until they are put into the extractor. Some use two extractors, filling one while the other is in operation. But most find it desirable to have some means for holding the uncapped combs. Many use a comb rack set conveniently between the uncapping point and the extractor (Fig. 10). The revolving rack, called the Merry-Go-Round, is an ideal piece of equipment when the radial extractor is used. It provides for racking 10 combs in each of five divisions, making it possible for the beekeeper to return the same combs, when empty, to the supers from which they were removed.

When the Sue Bee Automatic Uncapper is used, the uncapped combs are carried automatically above a tank, which contains the cappings and the honey removed with them, until they are placed in radial extractors.

THE HONEY EXTRACTOR

The small beekeeper has a choice of the basket-type extractor in which the combs are reversed by hand (Fig. 11), and the reversible-type in which the baskets swing to reverse the combs. Both types are made in either a two- or four-frame size. Circumstances will dictate whether equipment of this kind should be used or whether the more expensive radial equipment (Fig. 12) should be employed. It is reported that the four-frame extractor is capable of extracting a thousand pounds of honey in a day when operated by one man.

In the central extracting plant of today, the radial extractors are in general use. They are available in 30-, 45-, and 50-frame sizes. Depending

FIGURE 11. This is the type of extractor used by the small beekeeper. The combs are reversed by hand and the extractor is manually turned.

FIGURE 12. The large 50-frame radial extractor equipped with Rosedale winged comb supports to minimize comb breakage in the extracting process.

upon the temperature and the density of the honey, the time required for extracting a loading of combs is from 15 to 30 minutes, with the average about 20 minutes. The larger extractors will put out about 5,000 to 7,000 pounds of honey in a day. The shaft speed should be about 300 revolutions per minute for the smaller sizes and about 275 for the larger ones. The friction drive allows for gradually increasing the speed of the reel until it is turning at approximately the same speed as the drive shaft. Difficulty is sometimes experienced in breakage of new combs, particularly when they are warm, so care should be taken when starting the extractor to increase the speed gradually. The use of the Rosedale winged comb supports (Fig. 12), which clasp both sides of the uncapped comb, minimizes breakage.

The pivotal-reversible extractor is preferred by some to the radial, and usually is in the 8-frame size. The combs are contained in baskets which reverse automatically, resulting in little or no breakage regardless of how thick the honey may be. It is claimed that this equipment will extract as fast as the radial when the honey is heavy in body.

PUMPING THE HONEY

From the extractor the honey flows directly into a honey sump where the coarser foreign materials are removed. Here the honey is contained until it either is pumped or flows by gravity through the heating and straining processes. Honey draining from the uncapped combs and the cappings may be introduced at this point. The sump is provided with a coarse wire-mesh basket or screen to catch the particles of beeswax and larger foreign materials. Hardware cloth having ¼- to ½-inch mesh should be used for this purpose. Some sumps have one baffle plate extending from above the surface of the honey to near the bottom, under which the honey flows before leaving the sump. The purpose of the baffle plate is to separate the lighter foreign materials from the honey.

The honey pump should be suitable for handling viscous materials, should be geared to run slowly, and should have large inlets and outlets. The honey pump should remove the honey from the sump or reservoir, but should not be allowed to run until the pump sucks air. A float attached to an automatic switch, which turns the pump on when the honey level reaches a fixed height and off when the lower level is reached, is a timesaver to the beekeeper and eliminates incorporation of air with the honey. Available on the market is a combination honey pump and reservoir tank with automatic controls of this kind.

When the honey pump is not of the right kind or is operated carelessly, air is incorporated into the honey. The air bubbles that rise in the straining and settling equipment cause foam to form on top of the honey which is troublesome to handle. Smaller air bubbles remain in the body of the honey, along with small particles of suspended wax and other foreign materials causing a permanent cloudiness. Pipe lines carrying honey from the pump to the other equipment should be large (from 1½ to 3 inches in diameter) to avoid excessive friction, which can result in air incorporation.

Heating, Straining, and Clarifying Honey

Sechrist[5] has said that honey should never be heated unless it is absolutely necessary, and then it should be heated only as much as is necessary to give the desired results; that it should be heated quickly and cooled as soon as possible. Phillips[2] and others had favored methods which avoided heating honey in the extracting process, at least until impurities had been removed. He pointed out that there is a marked variation in honeys with respect to their abilities to withstand heat damage. Most mild-flavored, light-colored honeys may be heated to a higher temperature for a longer period of time without damage than can the dark honeys and those with pronounced flavors.

However, to facilitate straining and clarification, most have found it advisable to heat honey, especially if cold or of heavy body. For most, it is not necessary to heat honey beyond 90° to 100° F. for these purposes and the honey should be cooled as quickly as possible. Townsend and Adie,[6,7] who developed the O.A.C. Pressure Strainer and Continuous-Flow Honey Pasteurizer, recommend heating to higher temperatures when followed by quick cooling (Fig. 14).

METHODS OF HEATING HONEY

A simple way of heating honey is to allow it to run quickly down the inclined surface of a shallow pan, about 2 inches deep, 2 feet wide and 4 or more feet in length. It should be jacketed on the bottom to contain hot water heated by some appropriate means. As the honey flows onto the upper end of the pan, some means for spreading it out over the surface, such as baffles, is desirable (Fig. 13). The temperature of the honey should be carefully controlled by a thermometer at the lower end. This arrangement is simple and economical but open to question from a pure-food standpoint unless effectively done.

Another simple and effective method of heating is performed in conjunction with a gravity separator (Fig. 13). The honey flows from the pipe line into a water-jacketed tank, baffled to retain impurities and lighter substances. The honey flows quickly under and over the baffles, or even through straining screens, and out of the other end of the separator. The temperature of the honey leaving the separator is determined by the speed at which the honey flows and the temperature

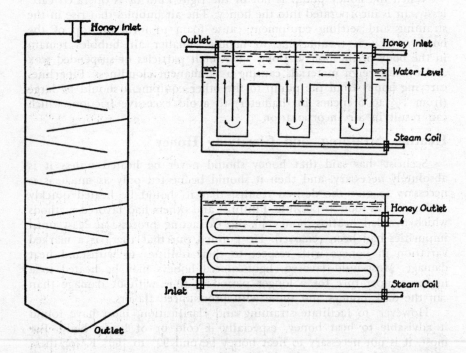

FIGURE 13. Diagram of methods of heating extracted honey. At left, heating honey while it flows by gravity down the baffled surface of a shallow pan. At top right, heating honey and gravity separation combined in one efficient piece of equipment. At lower right, heating honey in a coil immersed in a bath of hot water, a common method called "flash heating."

of the water jacket. This type of separator accomplished in part the task of gravity separation or clarification while heating the honey.

Flash-heating of honey usually consists of causing the honey to flow quickly through a coil contained in hot water (Fig. 13). The success of the operation depends largely upon the rate at which honey flows continuously through the coil and the amount of honey exposed to the heating surface. It has, as do most other methods of heating honey, the objection of overheating honey when the flow diminishes or stops before the temperature of the heating surface is reduced.

STRAINING AND CLARIFYING HONEY

The gravity separator allows the lighter foreign materials to rise to the surface where they are removed, while the heavier particles are allowed to settle. This often is accomplished in a tank containing one baffle, the heated honey entering at one side, flowing under the baffle,

FIGURE 14. The so-called package unit consisting of the honey sump, pump, the heat exchanger, and the pressure strainer, has a capacity of 300 pounds of honey per hour. (*Photo courtesy of Dr. G. F. Townsend*)

and overflowing at the top of the opposite side. Others have used a series of tanks, the honey flowing from a point near the bottom of one through large piping to the top of the next tank, thus accomplishing both separation and settling.

Before the honey enters the settling or storage tanks, it usually is run through some type of strainer to clean it further. A common method of straining honey is through a cloth supported by the top of the settling tank. To prevent incorporation of air, the honey should not fall from a height into the settling tank. This can be accomplished by allowing the honey to fall on a float, where it disperses, or by causing the honey to flow down an inclined plane to the bottom of the tank.

Several thicknesses of cheesecloth are often used for straining cold honeys. For warm honeys, sugar-sack toweling, muslin, or other materials having sufficient nap to the threads are suitable. Some prefer to use bolting cloth and others prefer metal screen of a fine mesh.

Many use a bag-type strainer made by sewing the full width of a material to form a bag, often as long as the depth of the tank in which it is suspended. The mouth of the bag is attached to the pipe from which the honey flows. As the bag fills, the honey strains through it and gently flows down the sides. If large enough to take care of a day's extracting, it can be raised above the level of the honey for draining, and replaced by a clean bag the following day.

The box-type strainer usually contains a number of vertical screens through which the honey passes before overflowing at the opposite end. The screens fit into slots in the sides and are removable for cleaning or replacing.

In the O.A.C. Pressure Strainer (Fig. 14), the particles of wax and other refuse are trapped and held in a layer of gravel placed above a screen of suitable mesh for straining. For normal extracting conditions, when granulation has not occurred, the honey must be approximately 110° F. If granulation has occurred, the temperature should be increased to 120° F. For day-to-day operation, the strainer must be kept hot overnight by means of an electric wrap-on cable, preferably insulated and with a thermostatic control. A flow of 300 pounds an hour at 120° F. is considered normal.

After straining, the warm honey should be allowed to stand in the settling tank until it is clear. A good plan is to have two or more settling tanks, extracting into one while the others are settling and clarifying. The tanks should be covered at all times to keep the honey clean. While it is common practice to let the warm honey settle overnight or longer, this is apt to result in some injury to the color, flavor, and aroma of some honeys. The honey should be drawn into shipping containers as soon as possible, sealed, and the containers set apart for cooling as quickly as possible.

COOLING THE HONEY

Seldom are sufficient precautions taken to cool the honey after heating. Some have installed coils in a bath of cold water for this purpose. The Continuous-Flow Honey Pasteurizer, referred to previously, is ideal for this purpose. The future should see increased use of such equipment in which the warm honey is cooled quickly without exposure to air. Treatment of this kind prevents injury to color, flavor, and aroma and the honey goes into shipping containers with less likelihood of granulation.

Care and Storage of Empty Supers

When the combs of honey have been extracted, they are returned to the supers. The supers then are either taken to the permanent storage place, usually in the honey house, or returned to the bees to be refilled or dried of adhering honey.

The permanent storage space for empty supers should be large enough to contain upwards to four supers for each productive colony. Compared to the extracting area and other parts of the honey house, it should be much larger. Wherever the wax moth is a problem, it is necessary to fumigate the stored combs as needed to prevent damage by the larvae of the greater wax moth. Thus, provisions must be made for proper fumigation of combs, and the storage space should be mouseproof and bee tight. For information concerning fumigation for wax moth, see Chapter XIX, "Diseases and Enemies of the Honey Bee."

Many beekeepers prefer to return the wet supers to the bees to clean them of adhering honey. When disease is prevalent, it is advisable to return them to the same colonies from which they were removed. Because of the effort required to do this, some stack their supers high over a few colonies, or have arrangements whereby a single colony finds access to a number of stacks of supers. Both of these methods present the possibility of spreading disease. Drying the combs minimizes the possibility of granulated honey in the combs inducing granulation later on. When dry supers are returned to colonies, the bees are not incited to robbing as often happens when wet supers are taken into the yards.

Care and Storage of Honey

It is often necessary to store the extracted honey in bulk containers before it is sold. It is desirable that this be in a dry place at a temperature as near 70° F. as possible. If stored where there is moisture, the 60-pound cans rust, although the larger drums are little affected. Oiling the outside of the cans with a thin coat of fine oil will prevent, or at least retard, their rusting in storage. If stored over long periods of time at temperatures higher than 70° F., discoloration and lowering of the quality will result. Storage at lower temperatures is inducive to granulation.

The beekeeper usually will find it advisable to dispose of his crop soon after extracting, thus minimizing the problems of storage, and eliminating such work as reliquefying, packaging, and marketing. The temperatures of most honey houses in winter are ideal for granulation of honey (50° to 65° F.). The possibility of loss through fermentation when carried over until warm weather presents another problem. For additional information concerning storage temperatures and their effects, see Chapter XIV, entitled "Honey."

Summary of Recommended Measures

Because honey is extracted and processed in contact with air and the surface of the equipment, as much care should be taken to produce a clean, wholesome product as with any other food. The extracting plant and its equipment should be kept freshly painted and spotlessly clean. The equipment preferably should be of stainless steel or other metal approved for food handling. Bees and other insects, as well as rodents, never should be permitted in the honey house.

The honey to be extracted should be well ripened, and honeys from different plant sources should be extracted separately whenever possible. All honey removed from diseased colonies, or from apiaries where disease is prevalent, should be kept separate and extracted after all other honeys; after which the equipment should be thoroughly cleaned and sterilized.

Honey should be heated only to facilitate its handling and to prevent or retard granulation and fermentation. Honey should be heated quickly with care and cooled as quickly as possible. Honey from cappings melters should be added to the rest of the crop only when it has not been injured in quality. The honey should be strained thoroughly to clean it, and allowed to settle until it is clear. It should be drawn into containers, sealed while hot, and the containers set apart for cooling. It always should be kept in mind that a fine, wholesome, natural food is being prepared for human consumption.

REFERENCES CITED

1. Pellett, F. C. 1938. History of American beekeeping. Collegiate Press, Inc., Ames, Iowa. p. 73.

2. Phillips, E. F. 1939. Gl. Bee Cult. **67**:146-148.

3. Root, E. R. 1947. ABC and XYZ of bee culture. A. I. Root Co., Medina, Ohio. p. 264.

4. Sechrist, E. L. 1937. Am. Bee J. **77**:121-123.

5. _____. 1938. Am. Bee J. **78**:216-218.

6. Townsend, G. F., and A. Adie. 1954. Ont. Agr. Coll. Circ. 216. 7 pp.

7. _____ 1955. Ont. Agr. Coll. Circ. 218. Rev. 4 pp.

CHAPTER XII

THE PRODUCTION OF COMB AND BULK COMB HONEY

by CARL E. KILLION*

C OMB HONEY IS ONE of the most beautiful agricultural products in
the world. It is a wonderful and wholesome food. Words cannot
describe it; honey in the comb tells its own story. The building of
the fragile hexagon-shaped cells of wax, filling them with pure, sparkling, fragrant nectar, and transforming it into honey with a particular
blossom flavor is certainly one of nature's masterpieces.

Not all areas are suitable for producing section comb and bulk
comb honey. Regions where nectar-producing plants are plentiful,
ensuring a fair to heavy flow, are the best areas for these types of
honey. These plants should produce honey which is slow to granulate
or crystallize, because the sale of comb honey which has crystallized is
next to impossible. Areas that have overlapping honeyflows of light
and dark-colored honeys are not good; areas that have an abundance
of clovers are the best.

The clovers include white Dutch, alsike, yellow sweet, and two
varieties of white sweet clover. One variety of white sweet clover is
known as Ohio Evergreen. This is a late variety and helps prolong
the honeyflow over a longer period. In most years, it is a heavy yielder
and the honey is of excellent quality.

Some of the heavily wooded areas are not suitable because the
bees gather an excessive amount of propolis, which requires a great
amount of labor to remove from the honey sections when preparing
them for market.

There has been a steady decline in comb honey production since
World War I. This has been caused by a variety of reasons. Beekeepers
themselves appear to dislike the extra work and details of preparing
sections and cutting the foundation. Swarm control methods used for
extracted honey production are found inadequate when producing comb
honey. The production of comb honey is all handwork and cannot be
benefited by mechanical equipment. The cost of equipment and special
packaging materials have advanced far more than the price of comb honey.

Our best market for comb honey would appear to be the large
modern supermarkets with thousands of food items packaged in their

---

*Carl E. Killion, Sr. Superintendent of the Division of Apiary Inspection, Illinois
Department of Agriculture for the past 25 years. Senior partner in Killion and Sons
Apiaries, Paris, Illinois. Specialist in the production of both section comb and bulk
comb honey.

best "Sunday dress." However, most of these large markets refuse to handle comb honey because of past experience in damage by breakage, and honey smeared on their shelves and tables. A limited amount of chunk honey can be found in these markets in glass containers; sometimes one can find a small amount of cut comb honey.

For those who live near large cities it is reasonable to assume that they may find it quite profitable to service large markets with properly packaged comb honey. Remarkable interest is shown in comb honey at state fairs and when demonstrated in food markets. Sales are excellent at such places and people often remark that they cannot find comb honey elsewhere.

To succeed in beekeeping, one must produce and market a crop of honey at a profit. The marketing of honey is a continuous program with sudden changes in consumer and buyer demands. The producer must be ever on the alert to have the best quality of honey packaged in the finest way to attract consumer attention, and priced competitively. For further information on marketing of honey, see Chapter XV, "Marketing the Honey Crop."

Comb Honey Equipment

The 10-frame Langstroth hive is used more than any other today in the United States. It is safe to assume that most consider it best for the production of either section comb, bulk comb, or extracted honey. Years ago some of the old master comb honey producers used 8-frame equipment exclusively with outstanding results. Dr. C. C. Miller, of Marengo, Illinois, used the 8-frame hive, and supply manufacturers at that time featured the 8-frame instead of the 10-frame hive.

Dr. Miller made improvements and even designed equipment to best suit his own ideas. Much of this equipment has been used in the Killion apiaries for almost 40 years, and found to be excellent. However, any beekeeper can produce fine quality comb honey with his present equipment, although slight changes may be desirable to obtain the best possible results.

In the Killion system of beekeeping, the 10-frame hive body is used with only nine frames, spaced their regular distance apart, and follower boards are used, one on each side next to the wall of the hive (Fig. 1). The follower boards are a necessary part of the equipment and are used for more than one reason. An apiary inspector hears numerous complaints about difficulty in removal of the first frame from a hive containing ten frames. The follower board solves this problem as it can be removed much easier than a frame, and permits the removal of the first comb with ease and each comb can be replaced before the next one is removed. If both follower boards are removed, it makes room for a division-board feeder or, in queen rearing, the cell-bar frame can be placed where desired in the brood chamber, preferably as near its center as possible.

The follower boards also permit better ventilation and provide insulation for the brood. One can expect more brood in the nine frames than would occur if all ten frames were used. By actual experience it has been found that a queen does not like to lay in the combs next to the walls of the hive, the reason perhaps being the sudden changes in temperature. When ten frames are used, the result usually is eight combs of brood instead of ten.

It is to the beekeeper's advantage to have proper ventilation in the comb honey colony during the honeyflow. If the equipment is designed to furnish the necessary ventilation without personal manipulation by the beekeeper, it eliminates considerable work. Extracted honey producers may slip the supers sideways to provide openings at the sides for ventilation in hot weather, or raise the cover at one end. It is best not to follow this practice with section comb or bulk comb colonies because the bees do not finish the comb properly near these openings. Additional ventilation may be supplied by the Miller bottom board which is 2 inches deep, having a slatted arrangement which prevents the bees from building comb beneath the frames.

COMB HONEY SUPERS

The comb honey super most generally used is the one having wooden beeway section holders and scalloped separators. The section holders provide protection to the bottoms of the sections and split sections may be used.

 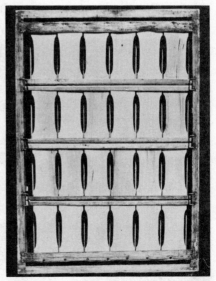

FIGURE 1. The hive contains nine frames with a follower board on each side. The removal of both provides space for a feeder.

FIGURE 2. An inverted T-super showing how the T-tins support the rows of sections in the ventilated super.

The T-super, although not widely used, has been preferred by some of our leading producers of comb honey, including Dr. C. C. Miller and Charles A. Kruse. Improvements have been made on the T-super since it was first shown to Dr. Miller by D. A. Jones, of Beetown, Ontario, at the North American Beekeepers' Convention in Toronto, Canada, in 1883. The super received its name from the fact that the sections were supported by tins bent in the form of an inverted "T." (Fig. 2).

Beeway sections are used in both types of supers but split sections cannot be used in the T-super. The ventilated passageways at the sides and ends of the T-super prevent sudden temperature changes around the sections because of the continuous passage of bees at work. The T-super uses plain separators without scallops and the inside super parts can be cleaned of propolis much easier than when section holders and scalloped separators are used.

Both types of supers use a square section 4¼ x 4¼ x 1⅞ inches. There are other sizes of sections but they are used only to a limited extent. These are plain, without beeways, and slatted separators, or fences as they are sometimes called, are used with them. For many years, beekeepers preferred white basswood sections (Fig. 3). Due to the scarcity of basswood today, they accept whatever is available.

Only the clearest and lightest colored grade of foundation should be used either in sections or shallow frames. This grade is known as thin super or thin surplus. When the 4¼-inch square split sections are used, a full sheet of foundation size 4⅛ x 17 inches can be inserted through the groove of the four sections. One advantage of this is that it results in the foundation being installed properly with the rows of

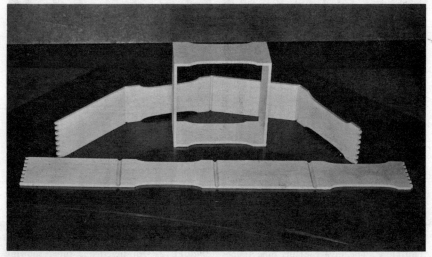

FIGURE 3. The beeway section, scalloped along the top and bottom for vertical passage of bees, is used by many.

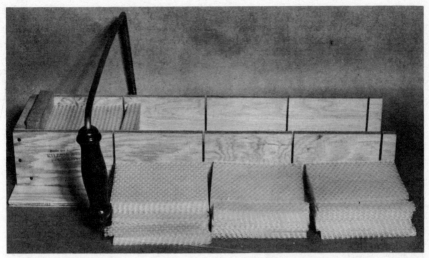

FIGURE 4. The cutting box and scalloped slicing knife. The foundation has been cut into squares, and the block has been inserted into the box at the closed end for cutting the bottom starters.

cells running horizontally with the hexagons pointing vertically. Inasmuch as the rows of cells run horizontally in brood foundation and in shallow frame foundation, it is only natural for them to run the same direction in sections.

Manufacturers have been guilty of not making the proper size of foundation for the square unsplit sections. The size of foundation should be 3⅞ x 15⅜ inches, and not 16½ or 16¾ inches in length. The 15⅜-inch length may be cut into four equal parts that will fit inside the sections. To use the 16½-inch length, the foundation must be placed in the sections with the rows of cells vertical, unless one wastes the extra foundation.

CUTTING FOUNDATION FOR SECTIONS

A box for cutting foundation the desired size may be purchased from a bee supply house or made in any beekeeper's workshop. For 3⅞-inch foundation, the box is about 2 inches deep, 4 1/16 inches wide, and the sides and bottom 16½ inches in length. The box can be nailed to a piece of plywood or masonite somewhat larger than its base in order to fasten it to the worktable while cutting (Fig. 4). There are four saw kerfs in the sides, but the one near the open end is not used except when the foundation is longer than 15⅜ inches.

A thin knife, such as a scalloped slicing knife, is used with a sawing motion to cut the beeswax foundation. A better one can be made by mounting a blade from a bread slicing machine in a hack saw or similar frame. A temperature of near 70° F. is about correct for cutting;

if the temperature is too cool, the foundation will shatter along the cut edges.

The cutting box can be filled within a quarter inch of the top. The foundation, held lightly by the left hand, is cut into squares. The squares are removed and a small block, which is the width of the bottom starter (5/8 x 2 x 3 7/8 inches), is inserted against the closed end of the box. This block causes the foundation squares to extend beyond the saw kerf the exact width of the bottom starter, or 5/8 inch. As each stack of foundation is picked up to be placed in the cutting box again, it should be turned at right angles to its original position. This allows the foundation, when placed in the section to have the rows of cells running horizontally.

FASTENING THE FOUNDATION

A most satisfactory and efficient method for fastening the foundation in the sections is the use of the multiple-block board and hot plate (Fig. 5). The twelve blocks, three deep and four wide, are 3 5/8 inches square, 7/8 inch in thickness, and spaced 11/16 inch apart. Before using the board of blocks, it should be painted with linseed or paraffin oil. When used in warm weather, a small amount of vaseline smoothed on each block allows the foundation to slide across easily.

Aluminum is the best material for the hot plate. The blade of the hot plate, 3 7/8 inches broad and 2 1/2 inches deep, is heated by a small kerosene stove. The blade should be heated enough to melt the wax sufficiently for the foundation to adhere to the wood section properly. If the blade is too hot, the wax and section may be discolored. If the room temperature is from 55° to 65° F., better and swifter fastening will result because the foundation starters are stiff and handle more readily.

As the folded sections are placed on the blocks, the tops of the four sections in each row should be farthest away, with the bottoms having the dovetails nearest the operator. The entire board is then given a one-quarter turn counter-clockwise and the board tilted to slide the sections to the right, making openings between the blocks and the bottoms of the sections. Twelve of the small bottom starters are then placed in proper position on the blocks. The heated plate, held in the right hand, is lowered into the opening between the block and the section, and at the same time the left hand guides the foundation against the plate. The plate is withdrawn quickly and the foundation is forced against the wood of the section with a slight pressure to fasten the bottom starter.

The board is now turned clockwise until the bottom of the sections are to the left and the board tilted to cause the sections to slide to the right, making openings between the blocks and the tops of the sections. The larger top starters are then fastened in a similar manner (Fig. 6).

FIGURE 5. The multiple-block board with the hot plate at top, ready for fastening the foundation into the sections.

FIGURE 6. The three rows of sections with the foundation fastened in place, resting on the multiple-block board.

Each row of four sections is then lifted off the block, turned upward in the correct position, and placed in the super. The blocks are now ready to receive twelve more sections. Drops of wax which collect on the blocks and the board must be removed from time to time or they will interfere with the sliding of the sections and the starters.

One may finish all fastening of the foundation before starting to assemble the sections in the comb honey supers. When using section holders in the standard comb honey super, the sections are placed in the section holders, and together these are placed in the super with a separator on each side and between each row of sections. End blocks and super springs are used to hold the sections compactly within the super. Directions for assembling the sections and super parts are supplied by manufacturers.

When the T-super is used, a small wooden strip is inserted between each crossrow of sections to compensate for the width of the T-tins and to hold the sections perfectly square. Separators are used on each side and between the rows of sections, as before, and super springs are inserted on both sides to hold the sections firmly within the super. The rows of sections should present a perfectly smooth surface on top to prevent propolizing by the bees. When this is done, the sections are ready for painting with paraffin.

PAINTING SECTIONS WITH PARAFFIN

The tops of all sections should be painted with hot paraffin before the super is placed on the hive. If the ventilated super is used with sections exposed on the bottom, these should also receive the painting. An electric hot plate with a temperature control has been found ideal for heating the paraffin. A 5-pound honey pail may be used but a container without seams in the bottom or sides is best. A stiff piece of wire should be used across the top to wipe the brush so the excess amount of hot wax will fall directly into the pail and not run down the outside. A candy thermometer is used to control temperature from 320° to 330° F. Some waxes have lower melting point than others. If the wax is too cool, too much wax will be used and, if too hot, there is always the danger of fire. Every precaution should be used when painting supers. Extra fire extinguishers should be placed within easy reach; the garden hose may be connected to the waterline as an extra precaution in case of a fire.

A brush about 2 to 2½ inches wide is used for painting. A wire hook, which can be placed over the rim of the paint bucket, is fastened to the handle of the brush so its bristles will not rest on the bottom of the pail. The super to be painted is upended on the table, and holding the top with one hand it can be tilted slightly backwards and the sections painted one row at a time with up-and-down strokes. The purpose of painting the exposed surfaces of sections is to permit easier removal of any propolis and to keep dust or stains from discoloring the wood.

BAIT SECTIONS

For many years it was a common practice to prepare one bait-section super for each colony to be used in the production of comb honey. One section containing empty comb, free of honey, was placed near the center of the super, the rest of the sections containing foundation. These bait-section supers were to be the first used, serving to entice the bees to enter the sections and start comb building. If bait sections are used, they should be plainly marked so they may be set aside and melted or used for feeding some colony. They should never be marketed with the rest of the crop; the comb is much tougher and in most cases has a dark line in the comb. Some producers do not use bait sections and find that bees enter the supers quite readily without them.

Spring Management

There is not much difference in the spring management of colonies up to the time the honeyflow starts. Only the strongest colonies should be used for the production of either comb honey or bulk comb honey.

These colonies should reach their peak of strength as near the beginning of the honeyflow as possible. Weaker colonies should be used for the production of extracted honey, or united with other colonies. During the honeyflow, management for section comb and bulk comb honey is quite similar.

A large number of producers use the double brood chamber during the spring buildup period, and some even use the two bodies through the honeyflow. This is good practice when producing extracted honey or bulk comb honey as it helps reduce swarming and eliminates some work. Previous to the honeyflow, these double bodies should be reversed as often as needed. This can be determined by examination and, in most cases, the best brood conditions will be observed in the upper body. The reversing gives both bodies a more uniform brood pattern and should delay swarm preparation.

The use of two hive bodies is not recommended during the honeyflow when producing section comb honey by the Killion system. Regardless of whether colonies are in two or three bodies at the start of the honeyflow, **each colony is always reduced to a single hive body when the first comb honey super is given,** either for section comb or bulk comb honey. With the latter, a queen excluder is used but they are not used on section comb colonies. If a producer finds that better results are realized by using two hive bodies, then he should by all means use them.

After the flow starts and fresh nectar is plentiful in the bodies (when the combs are heavy and the nectar drips freely), one hive body of brood, bees, and the queen is left on the bottom board and given one super either of sections or shallow frames. In most cases the upper body is used. Most of the bees are shaken from the combs of the removed hive body, leaving only enough bees to take care of the unsealed brood. This body and the brood it contains can be used to strengthen some weaker colony. It may also be used for increase, adding other bodies until it is as strong as needed. Two days later a young queen or a ripe queen cell can be given. These colonies are used to produce surplus stores that can be distributed in the fall to needy colonies.

The manipulation of supers is almost identical for either the production of honey in sections or shallow frames. When the first super is given, the bees should start drawing the foundation immediately. The first super should be one-half or two-thirds full before the second super is added. When a new super of foundation is given, it should almost always be placed on top of the other supers already on the hives. For some reason known only to the bees themselves, they prefer to work a little better in the back two-thirds of the super. Storing honey in the sections or frames toward the front of the hive will be a little slower. Each time a super is manipulated on the hive, this condition should be noted and supers reversed, putting the lesser filled combs toward the back. This reversing makes the entire super uniform in fullness. On the next trip the second super should be placed next to the brood, and the first super placed on top. When the colony is ready for a third super, it is placed on top of the other two supers. Before giving the third super, the first super should be nearly full and the second one at least half full. In an exceptionally heavy flow, the third super can be given before the second is half full, but it is better to crowd the colony just a little than to give it super room too far in advance. One serious mistake made by many beekeepers is to add comb honey supers too fast or too many at one time.

If the next trip reveals that the third super is being drawn rapidly, it is placed next to the brood with the second super above it, and the first super on top. If the fourth super is needed, it is added on top. As soon as a super is completely capped over or finished, it should be removed. This is to eliminate all unnecessary travel stain on the cappings, and to avoid the handling of the super with each colony manipulation. The next visit may necessitate the giving of the fifth super and the removal of the first one. The proper order of supering is shown in Figure 7. It should be remembered that comb honey supers cannot be staggered, leaving openings for additional ventilation, as practiced with extracted honey supers. Such practice will cause the bees to leave sections unfinished near these cracks or openings.

Swarm Control Measures

When strong 2-story colonies are reduced to a single hive body and only a single super, it is an invitation to swarm. Some of the preventive measures practiced by extracted honey producers, such as giving abundant room with empty drawn combs, cannot be used. The comb-honey colony must be forced to continue to work in this crowded condition if the best possible results are to be realized. Therefore swarm control methods must be more drastic and complicated. A few days after the colonies are reduced to a single hive body, queen cells will be found in some colonies and these should be destroyed. It is a good plan to check comb-honey colonies at least every 3d or 4th day. On the second examination many cells may be found and, at this time, the queen should be killed and all cells destroyed. About 4 days after killing the queen, each colony is examined again and all freshly built queen cells destroyed. On the 8th day after killing the queen, every cell is destroyed, and either a ripe queen cell or a young laying queen is given. This queen should be one that is just starting to lay and not one that is a few weeks old. To find all the queen cells on the combs it will be necessary to shake the bees off and look very carefully. If one single cell is missed and another is given the colony, it is an invitation for them to swarm. If one cell is left and there is no unsealed brood, **the colony will not swarm.**

Care should be used in shaking bees from combs at this time since the fresh nectar will spatter out if the comb is shaken too hard. Most beekeepers soon learn a technique of shaking gently with a trembling motion. After this brief period when brood is not being reared and the young queen starts laying, no amount of crowding will induce the colony to swarm. During this requeening process one must continue adding supers and reversing them end to end as shown in Figure 7.

Care of Comb Honey

It must be remembered that section comb or bulk comb honey cannot be handled too carefully to prevent damage. It is the appearance of comb honey that determines much of its sale value. After the supers are removed and brought to the honey house, they should be fumigated against damage by wax moth. The supers may be stacked about 15 high leaving no cracks for fumigant to escape. One of the best fumigants is carbon disulfide, but it is highly inflammable and extreme caution must be used at all times or a serious fire or explosion may result. Other types of fumigants are discussed in Chapter XIX, "Diseases and Enemies of the Honey Bee." One well-known fumigant, paradichloro-benzene (PDB), should never be used as the odor will permeate the cappings and ruin the flavor of the honey.

MOISTURE REMOVAL

Those who produce section comb and bulk comb honey in areas of high humidity have a problem of fermentation (Fig. 8). As soon as possible (24 hours or so) after fumigating, the honey should be tested for moisture content. If the moisture is above 18.6 per cent, plans should be made to remove the excess moisture as fast as possible. The quicker this is done, the better will be the flavor of the honey. Delays will allow yeast cells to multiply and to damage the flavor.

The first requisite for moisture removal will be a room as airtight as possible. The smaller the room, that will hold the necessary supers and equipment, the better. Supers should not be placed directly on the floor but on strips of wood to allow free passage of air beneath the stacks. The supers should be criss-crossed in such a way that air can

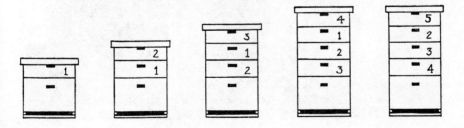

FIGURE 7. Diagram showing the method of supering. The supers are numbered in the order in which they are given to the colony.

circulate through and around them. A dehumidifier must be used to lower the humidity in the air around the combs before it is possible to draw the moisture out of the honey. There are a number of dehumidifiers on the market, but it is best to get one larger than needed than one too small. For circulation of air a large pedestal fan or a window exhaust fan may be used. The direction of the fan may be changed at times to ensure ventilation of all parts of the room.

During the period of moisture removal, the room temperature must be relatively high, 80° to 85° F. The air will thus be warm and moisture will condense in the dehumidifier. As soon as the moisture content of the honey is lowered to the desired amount, the dehumidifier, fans, and extra heat should be turned off; to continue the dehydration process would make the honey too thick and taffylike. Storage temperatures may vary with different packers but a careful check over a period of several years shows that a temperature of near 74° F. has been excellent. If either types of comb honey are held in storage for a long period, it may be necessary to increase the humidity in the room from time to time to prevent the honey from becoming too thick.

PREPARATION FOR MARKET

The preparation of section comb honey for market is a very simple task after the supers reach the honey house. The removal of the propolis from the sections requires the most labor. The paraffin may be

FIGURE 8. Six sections of comb honey ruined by fermentation. All are a total loss to the producer.

FIGURE 9. Beautiful sections of comb honey being inserted into polyethylene bags with an inserting device, makes sure there will be no sticky packages.

scraped off the tops and bottoms with the blade of a single-edge safety razor. The sections must then be picked up individually and the propolis scraped from edges and corners. A small short-bladed knife is best for this.

The comb honey is now ready for sorting or grading, weighing, and packaging. The sections may be placed directly into a window carton, or wrapped in cellophane. Some dealers now sell a polyethylene bag; the section is placed in the bag, heat sealed, and then inserted into a window carton (Fig. 9). This method ensures the producer that regardless of damage to the comb the handlers will not have a dripping, sticky package with which to contend.

Before marketing any type of honey, the producer should make sure that all packages meet state and federal regulations. "U.S. Standards for Grades of Comb Honey," effective August 1933, may be obtained from the Agricultural Marketing Service, U.S.D.A., Washington 25, D. C. The net weight of the section of comb honey should be stamped on the section and on the end of each case of honey, as required by some states. Illinois will not permit the words "100 per cent pure" to be used on the package.

The Production of Bulk Comb Honey

Bulk comb or shallow frame comb honey is usually produced in shallow supers. The foundation used in the frames is similar to that used in sections. The section of comb honey weighs less than 1 pound, while shallow frames will weigh from 3 to 5 pounds depending upon the thickness and depth of the comb.

During the honeyflow, the management for section comb and bulk comb honey production is very much alike. Any method that produces perfect comb of desired thickness, depth, color, and pattern of cappings is the one to use. If a single brood chamber is used, it will be necessary to place queen excluders under the shallow frame supers. The queen will enter shallow frame supers more readily than section supers. Some producers claim excluders are not necessary when using the new 706 cell size foundation.

The frames should not be filled with foundation too far in advance of the honeyflow as the foundation will become wavy or crack and break loose from the top bars. Only full sheets of comb foundation should be used. If starters are used, the comb will be drawn slower and will be uneven and, in most cases, of drone-cell size.

Three types of top bars are used in the production of bulk comb honey: the wedge top bar, the grooved top bar, and the slotted top bar. Since it takes more time to fasten the foundation by nailing in the wedge of the wedge top bar, most either prefer to use the hot wax method of fastening the foundation in the groove of the grooved top bar, or use the slotted top bar which permits fastening the foundation by bending and pressing it over where it extends above the slot of the top bar.

Fastening the foundation by the hot wax method is described below. The author has drawn freely here from the writings of Newman I. Lyle in Chapter XIII, "The Production of Bulk Comb Honey," in the 1949 edition of "The Hive and the Honey Bee."

Form boards are a great convenience in inserting the sheets of foundation into the frames. They are the size of the inside of the frames and of a thickness that just reaches to the back edge of the cut-out portion of the wedge top bar, or the groove of the top bar, when the frame is laid over the board. Four or more of these form boards may be fastened to a reel for speed and convenience (Fig. 10). Frames are then placed over the form boards, each frame being held in position on the reel by a cleat parallel to the form board, and by a spring pressing against the outside of the frame end bar.

The foundation which is to be waxed into the frames should have been kept in a warm place for a time so that it is slightly pliable. A sheet of the warm foundation is placed on the lower form board of the reel and the edge of the foundation pushed into the groove of the top bar or into the corner of the wedge top bar.

Liquid beeswax is used to fasten the foundation in the frames. The beeswax may be melted in a gallon honey bucket on a grate in the bottom of a 12-quart bucket, the latter serving as a water jacket. Any type of portable stove may be used for heat. When the beeswax is melted and the water in the outer container is boiling gently, the temperature of the wax is correct. A teaspoon, having its tip pinched

FIGURE 10. The reel holds four frames and is turned to facilitate waxing in the sheets of special bulk comb foundation.

together to form a pouring spout and the handle bent up nearly at right angles to the bowl of the spoon, serves to convey the beeswax from the melting container.

The reel is turned so that one end of the frame is slightly higher than the other. A spoonful of the liquid wax is poured into the groove of the top bar, or into the corner of the wedge top bar, at the highest end and allowed to run down the length of the top bar. When the liquid wax reaches the lower end of the frame, the reel is turned quickly so that the frame is level. A few drops of wax then are placed at the corners of the foundation to reinforce the attachment to the top bar. When the wax has been applied, all the fingers are used quickly to push the sheet of foundation firmly into the groove and to hold it in position until it sets solidly in place. The wax must still be liquid when this is done or the operation will have to be repeated. If the foundation is not fastened solidly in place, the sheets are liable to come loose before the bees have a chance to build combs. There is no worse mess than combs constructed on foundation which has come loose and fallen out of position in the frames.

The slotted top bar frame has been found satisfactory by many producers, and the foundation can be assembled more quickly. This is especially true if the thin top bar is used. To determine the proper width of the foundation to be used in the frame, measure from about 1/8 to 3/16 inch above the bottom bar to about 5/16 inch above the top bar. When the comb foundation is inserted through the slot of the top bar, it will extend above the top bar, and this part can be pressed over and down with an electric heat sealer (Fig. 11).

A form for holding the frames when inserting the foundation should be placed at a convenient working height. A piece of metal is placed on the form so that the foundation remains above the bottom bar at least ⅛ inch. When fastened at the top bar, the foundation hangs freely away from the bottom bar and buckling is eliminated.

PACKAGING AND MARKETING BULK COMB HONEY

Some beekeepers prefer to sell their crop of bulk comb honey to a large packer or market it through a co-operative. The comb honey is delivered in the supers; after packing the honey, the empty supers with frames are returned to the producer. When taking supers of honey across state lines, it is best to check with the Apiary Inspector for any possible law violation due to transporting used bee equipment.

A few producers sell the entire frame of comb honey to their customers. The frame of honey either is wrapped in wax paper or cellophane, or placed in a special window carton.

However, bulk comb honey is usually sold as chunk honey in a glass container surrounded with liquid honey, or as cut comb honey wrapped or packaged in various sizes and types of containers. In order to pack either type, it is necessary to cut the comb honey from the frames and then into desired sizes and shapes.

FIGURE 11. Plywood support for holding the frame with the foundation extending up through the slotted top bar to be bent over with the electric sealer.

FIGURE 12. Special extractor made by the A. G. Woodman Company for drying the cut edges of the comb honey before packaging either in glass as chunk honey or in packages as cut comb honey.

The usual procedure is to cut the combs either on a board or on hardware cloth resting above a tray. Knives used for this purpose must be heated to cut the comb easily without tearing the cells. Some utilize a special kind of paring knife, using two in this operation, heating one in hot water while the other is being used. Others have a specially constructed knife with multiple blades for making two or more cuts at one time. Some of the multiple-blade knives are heated with hot water and others are heated with steam.

When packing either chunk honey or cut comb honey, the cut edges of the comb must be drained of the liquid honey. The cut pieces of comb either are placed on hardware cloth above trays, or put into a special extractor (Fig. 12) and drained by centrifugal force. If the edges are not drained of the liquid honey, it will cause granulation later both in the jars of chunk honey and the packages of cut comb honey.

CHUNK HONEY

When packing chunk honey, the pieces of comb are placed directly into the size of glass jar or tin pail required by the trade. The containers are then filled with extracted honey which previously has been heated to 150° F. and allowed to cool to 120° by the time of filling. The extracted honey should be run down the insides of the containers to prevent incorporation of air bubbles. As fast as the containers are filled, the lids are placed on tightly and the containers laid on their sides so the comb will not be crushed by its own buoyancy in the warm honey. After cooling thoroughly, the containers may be packed in shipping cases.

After packaging, chunk honey should not be stored for a long time as granulation may ruin its sale. The surface of the comb honey tends to hasten crystal formation. Freshly packed chunk honey should be delivered to the store in small lots where it may be sold and consumed before granulation occurs. If the storekeeper has an oversupply and the honey granulates, it should be replaced immediately with freshly packed honey.

The returned containers of honey may be placed in a warm oven at a temperature just under the melting point of beeswax (approximately 145° F.) until the granulated honey is entirely liquefied, when it can be placed again on the market. The containers also may be placed in hot water, and the comb melted and the contents emptied into a tank where the beeswax can be separated from the honey after cooling. This process may darken the honey causing it to be of inferior quality.

Consumers who like both comb honey and extracted honey usually will pay a higher price for this extra fancy product which has both kinds of honey in the same package. Also, some who are suspicious of honey purity will buy honey when it has a piece of comb visible in it. The glass package usually is preferred by the discriminating buyer.

To maintain a reputation as fancy honey, the chunk honey package must look its best. The honey must be of good flavor and comb must be white, free from pollen, and cut neatly to a length that will extend from the top to the bottom of the container, and to a breadth that will permit it to slip readily through the mouth of the container. Because of this, glass containers for chunk honey are all made with large openings. The liquid honey surrounding the comb honey should be of good flavor and exceptionally clean and clear. This is a picture package—the comb is the picture; the liquid honey and an attractively labeled glass container, frame it.

CUT COMB HONEY

Cut comb honey is bulk comb honey cut into pieces varying in size from the 2-ounce individual serving to larger ones weighing nearly a pound. The cut pieces of comb honey are drained as previously described and either wrapped in cellophane or placed in polyethylene bags, heat sealed, and then packaged in containers of various styles with suitable labels.

CHAPTER XIII

THE OVERWINTERING OF PRODUCTIVE COLONIES

by C. L. FARRAR*

THE HONEY-BEE COLONY has a remarkable capacity to adapt itself to great extremes in climatic conditions when allowed to develop without restriction, if amply provisioned with honey and pollen. The beekeeper often employs management practices that so restrict the populations of honey-bee colonies as to prevent them from surviving the winter in good condition.

Langstroth[1] effectively stated the essential requirements for wintering of the honey-bee colony when he wrote:

> If the colonies are strong in numbers and stores, have upward ventilation, easy communication from comb to comb, and water when needed—and all the hive entrances are sheltered from piercing winds, they have all the conditions essential to wintering successfully in the open air.

That Langstroth understood the basic problems better than many who have written on wintering will be evident in the following considerations of the winter cluster, the causes of winter loss, and the principles of wintering.

The colony should be viewed as the living organism representing the honey-bee species *Apis mellifera* L.; the individual bees (queens, workers, and drones) are merely cells of the organism that are continually being regenerated. In nature the species reproduction is through the process of swarming. The beekeeper needs to concern himself with the conditions, functions, and requirements of the colony—not of the individual bees—in his management to increase its productivity, either in honey and wax or in the pollination of crops.

The honey-bee colony can survive in nature from the tropics to the northernmost regions that permit a pollen- and nectar-producing flora adequate for its food supply. The colony adjusts to seasonal extremes of climatic conditions that may be either humid or arid, and where temperatures may exceed 120° or −50° F.

Environmental factors important to the honey-bee colony are those that influence the flora. Of course, weather conditions must be favor-

---

*Clayton L. Farrar, Ph.D. Bee Management Investigations Leader, Apiculture Research Branch, Entomology Research Division, Agricultural Research Service, U.S. Department of Agriculture, in cooperation with the University of Wisconsin Agricultural Experiment Station; also Professor, Department of Entomology, University of Wisconsin. Specialist in the study of colony behavior and its seasonal management.

able for flower visitation by the bees during periods when pollen and nectar are yielded in copious quantities. The natural instinct of honey bees is to store large food reserves, honey and pollen, for use during dearth periods, whether these be from rain, drought, or extreme cold.

The behavior of queen, worker, and drone honey bees as individuals has been the center of more research than the behavior of the colony as an organism. The behavior of the whole is no less important than the behavior of its parts.

At the close of brood rearing in October, the normal unrestricted colony consists of approximately 30 thousand physiologically young bees. These may consume 10 to 15 pounds of honey and decrease in numbers by perhaps 3,000 to 5,000 before egg laying commences in January. With ample pollen and honey within the winter cluster, brood rearing will increase both the daily food consumption and mortality of bees. However, continuous emergence of young bees 20 days after brood rearing starts will eventually replace the bees which die, so that the colony should again have about 30,000 bees and 30,000 cells of brood in all stages of development by the time the first spring flowers bloom. Under favorable conditions in spring, brood rearing expands and the population will increase to a maximum of 50,000 to 60,000 within 5 to 7 weeks.

There are also fundamental concepts important in considering the problem of overwintering colonies. These are the relationship of populations to egg laying and brood rearing, the production efficiency of the bees, and the nectar supply. During the active season the queen reaches her highest rate of egg laying in colonies of approximately 40,000 bees. However, the percentage relationship between the number of cells of sealed brood and the total population is highest in a colony of approximately 10 thousand bees and lowest in a full-strength colony of 60 thousand bees. This relationship decreases about 12 to 14 per cent for each increase of 10,000 bees. Thus, colonies of 10, 40, and 60 thousand bees may have 85, 56, and 30 per cent as many cells of sealed brood as they have bees or 8,500, 22,400, and 18,000 cells respectively. Honey storage per unit number of bees increases with increased colony populations because smaller colonies have a higher ratio of brood to bees than larger colonies. The small colonies require a larger proportion of their bees to care for the brood, whereas the large colonies have a much higher proportion engaged in gathering nectar. Experiments have shown that full-strength colonies of 60,000 bees will usually produce one and one-half times more honey than four colonies, each of which has but 15,000 bees. It is also important to recognize the difference between nectarflows and honeyflows. The nectarflow represents the relationship between flowering plants and their environment, whereas the honeyflow represents the ability of the colony to gather the nectar supply. The nectarflow may be intense and the supply abundant, yet differences in colonies may cause them to reflect either a light, medium, or heavy honeyflow.

The condition of overwintering colonies has a great influence on the time and food factors essential for colonies to reach their maximum production potential for a particular period of abundant pollen and nectar resources.

Efficient overwintering requires that the colonies be free of disease and headed by well-reared queens of superior genetic stock. Their hives must be abundantly supplied with both pollen and honey to permit full colony development independent of weather conditions. More comb space is needed than is often supplied to accommodate adequate food reserves, the bees, and their normal brood rearing.

Honey bees are highly socialized in their colony organization, and they possess fixed instincts. The colony is active throughout the year, but the type and rate of activity is influenced by climatic factors and the available food supply. The maximum population is limited by the number of eggs the queen can lay, the time required for the bees to develop from the egg to the adult, and the length of life of the adults. In the fall when plant life approaches dormancy, brood rearing and field activity decline until they cease entirely.

The Winter Cluster

RESPONSE TO TEMPERATURE

When the air temperature falls below a certain point, the winter cluster becomes well defined. Actually, the colony maintains a cluster throughout the year designed to regulate its internal temperature and humidity environment. The heating and air-conditioning capacity of the colony rivals that obtainable by man's most efficient engineering developments.

The winter clustering temperature was determined by Phillips and Demuth[2] to be approximately 57° F. Subsequently, winter-cluster temperatures have been studied by a number of investigators. Although no one has ever recorded a temperature below 57° F. in the active center of the normal colony, it is now known that all the bees do not become a part of the cluster until the air temperature surrounding the bees in the hive is approximately 43° to 46° F. (also see "Activities of Bees in Winter" in Chapter IV).

The winter cluster is formed by the grouping together of all the bees to fill empty cells within the area of their food reserves (Fig. 1).

The bees on the surface form an insulating shell varying in depth from 1 to 3 inches but the bees within, which are much less compact, generate heat through metabolic processes. An inner temperature is produced which permits heat to be conducted to the surface bees so that their temperature will not fall below 43° to 46° F. As the outside temperature falls, the cluster draws together which decreases its size,

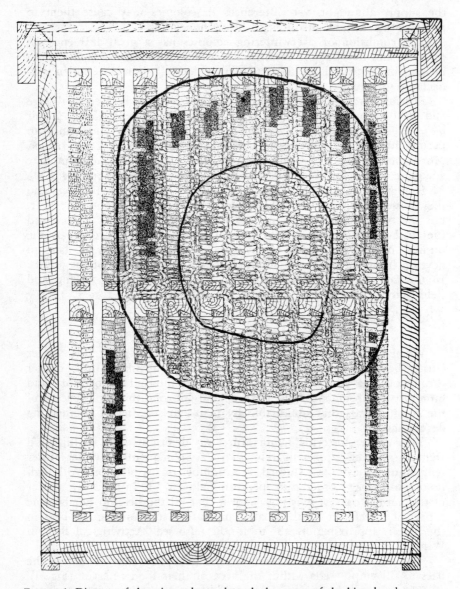

FIGURE 1. Diagram of the winter cluster through the center of the hive, based upon an examination of several colonies. They were killed when the temperature was approximately 0° F. during the latter part of December and before brood rearing had started. The cluster covers 20 to 30 pounds of reserve stores. The much greater concentration of bees in the periphery demarks the insulating shell from the active center. The dark bands of pollen covered with honey indicate an accumulated reserve before the honeyflow. The pollen shown illustrates the optimum reserve more than the quantities found in the average colony. *(Photo U.S.D.A.)*

and, therefore, reduces the surface exposed to heat radiation. This contraction of the cluster concentrates more bees within to generate heat. Conversely, the cluster expands as the air temperature rises.

The temperature of the periphery of the cluster is fairly constant, but within the heat-producing center (not necessarily the geometric center) the temperature rises as the outside temperature decreases. The contraction or expansion of the cluster is the principal mechanism used by the bees in maintaining a favorable temperature environment under winter conditions. At a given low temperature, small clusters tend to maintain higher inner temperatures than those of large clusters.

As the winter season progresses, the cluster temperature rises until it reaches a brood-rearing temperature of 93° to 96° F. some time in January. At this temperature, the queen will commence egg laying and, if pollen is available, brood rearing will be proportional to the cluster's capacity to maintain the proper temperature. The level of brood rearing is influenced by the size of the colony population, available pollen, and by external temperatures. Of course, the colony must have honey at all times.

The following four pages of photographs of a winter cluster (Fig. 2) show how the normal cluster orients to its brood and food supplies. These illustrations will give the reader a clearer picture of how the normal colony adjusts to severe conditions than further word descriptions. The all-shallow 4-story hive is not significant since the style of hive is for the convenience of the beekeeper in his management operation; it is what is in the hive that is important to the survival of a good colony capable of producing next year's crop. The 4-story shallow 10-frame hive has 17 per cent less comb space than a standard 3-story hive (20″ vs. 24″ in total depth of comb since the two sizes of frames have 5″ and 8″ of comb, respectively).

AGE OF BEES

By marking most of the bees emerging the last 6 weeks in the fall, it has been determined, by recording the daily mortality during the broodless period, that bees of all ages are lost in small numbers proportional to their total numbers. Since the daily rate of brood rearing decreases during the fall, the number of bees in any age group making up the winter cluster varies considerably. A bee that emerges on October 1 is just as likely to die on January 1 as one emerging September 1. Colonies killed instantly with a high charge of cyanide have shown a random distribution of marked bees within broodless winter clusters, an indication that although these vary in age as measured by time, they are all of a similar physiological age.

THEORIES PERTAINING TO WINTERING

Hive protection has long been considered a requisite for wintering honey-bee colonies. Protection has been provided by placing colonies

5   5a

6   6a

7

7a

8

9

10   11

FIGURE 2. A series of 14 pictures taken on January 16, 1962 at a temperature of 0° F. showing each plane of combs in sequence within the hive, which define the normal cluster in relation to its brood and food supply. The mean winter temperatures were subnormal for the area (minimum −17° F.). On January 4, two combs of bees, including one of sealed brood, were raised from the center of the third to the center of the fourth chamber and a cake of pollen supplement added. It was 0° F. when the colony was killed at 10:00 a.m. with a heavy charge of cyanide. The nails from two corners of the four hive bodies were replaced in the fall to permit removal of the comb from one side without jarring the cluster. (1) First plane of combs and cyanide flask used to kill the colony without breaking its cluster; (2) 2-frame cluster on honey; (3) 2-frame cluster on honey; (4) 2½-frame cluster on honey; (5) 3-frame cluster on brood and honey, also showing feeding channels in pollen cake; (5a) Bees removed from unsealed brood in top frame; (6) 3-frame cluster on brood and honey; (6a) Bees removed from 2 frames of sealed and unsealed brood; (7) 3-frame cluster on brood and honey; (7a) Bees removed from frame of unsealed brood; (8) 2½-frame cluster on honey; (9) 2½-frame cluster on honey; (10) 2-frame cluster on honey; (11) Bees of cluster estimated at 27,000 to 30,000 bees. The four frames of brood represented 10,000 to 12,000 young bees that would have emerged within 20 days and about 800 had previously emerged (see center of top brood comb 6a). *(Photo by Fritz Albert, University of Wisconsin)*

in cellars for 4 to 5 months or by insulating the hives out of doors. The purpose of protection, in whatever form, was to reduce the cluster activity and thereby conserve bee energy and honey stores. Thus the bees in the winter cluster were expected to live longer so they would be physiologically young in the spring. Disturbances caused by fluctuating temperatures, opening of the hive, accumulation of indigestible materials from honeys of low quality, and other means were believed to be responsible for winter losses.

Many organized experiments and thousands of practical tests have been made to test this theory of conservation of energy, but the results have not been consistent. Winter losses continue to tax the resources of the beekeeping industry, because rarely have all the factors essential to efficient wintering been satisfied. In the last 30 years there have been marked changes in wintering practices in northern regions. Where colonies were formerly wintered in cellars, they are now wintered out of doors; heavy packing has been reduced to light packing, or to wrapping for wind protection, and finally to no special hive protection. Changes in colony standards and food requirements for efficient wintering have paralleled this transition in methods.

Co-operative research on electrical hive heating was conducted over a period of years by the Agricultural Engineering and Entomology Research Divisions of the Agricultural Research Service, U.S. Department of Agriculture, and the Wisconsin Agricultural Experiment Station. Many of the experimental hives were equipped with 320 thermocouples (electrical temperature-sensing points) distributed at 1-inch intervals throughout the hives. More than 10 million temperatures were automatically recorded, and minimum winter temperatures ranged as low as −37° F.

The studies failed to show superiority of colonies surviving in insulated hives, or those insulated and electrically heated within temperature ranges of 55° to 25° F., over normal colonies in unprotected hives. Colonies in hives maintained at the lowest temperature (25° F.) were in better condition in the spring than those maintained at higher temperatures. In a severe test during August and September, both unprotected and insulated hives were subjected continuously to −50° F. for 50 days in a deep freeze and brought out alive. Colonies failed to survive for 6 months when placed in the freezer controlled to provide variable day and night temperature extremes characteristic of the most northern beekeeping regions. These colonies probably failed to survive because ice formed in the long entrance tubes leading through the freezer chest and thus shut off their air supply. This situation did not occur in the freezer tests on colonies under summer temperatures. The mechanical vibrations resulting from the cycling of the compressor could also have been a contributing factor.

Packing fails to conserve the energy of bees because the winter cluster does not attempt to heat the inside of the hive. Subzero temperatures have been recorded in both packed and unpacked hives. The size and position of the cluster determine the temperature in any portion of the hive for a given outside temperature.

As the air temperature decreases below the surface temperature of the cluster, there is a greater concentration of bees in the outer areas of the cluster which form the insulating shell to retain the heat generated by the more active bees within. Under falling temperatures the cluster contracts and raises the temperature within by increased activity of the bees inside. A balance is maintained between the internal temperature, the diameter of the cluster, and the depth of the insulating shell, so that heat conducted from within will equal the small amount of heat radiated from the surface at approximately 45° F. It is easy to understand why small populations have greater difficulty than full-strength colonies in maintaining this balance.

Starvation is the major cause of winter losses. It may result from inadequate stores or from their improper position; also, from populations too small to maintain contact with their stores. Management practices prior to the winter period may influence all three situations. Maximum food requirements rather than the average must be satisfied. Furthermore, studies over a period of years have shown that colonies, which consume more than the average, produce substantially more honey above what they consume than those that consume less than the average.

The viewpoint that winter brood rearing is normal was untenable under the conservation-of-energy theory. As long ago as 1852, Langstroth[1] observed brood in all stages on February 5, and demonstrated that pollen was necessary for continued brood rearing. Work done by the U.S. Department of Agriculture since 1932 has shown conclusively that winter brood rearing is both normal and beneficial to the colony. At no time have any harmful effects been observed from the inability of newly emerged bees to have an immediate flight when reared during the winter. The size and quality of surviving populations have been found to be directly proportional to the quantity of reserve pollen within reach of the winter cluster.

To provide every colony with optimum pollen reserves presents a major problem in apiary management. However, the practice of feeding trapped pollen supplemented with expeller-processed soybean flour provides a means of regulating the early development of colonies. Pollen reserves may be out of reach of the cluster during low temperatures. Supplemented pollen cakes placed over the center of the cluster permit the timing of brood rearing independent of climatic conditions.

WINTER LOSSES

Winter losses usually are reported as the percentage of colonies that die out. Beekeepers seldom recognize that a much greater loss results from colonies that survive in weakened condition and consequently with greatly reduced productive capacity. No other branch of agriculture could survive if it experienced annual losses suffered by the beekeeping industry. The tremendous reproductive power of bees makes this possible, but the economic loss is not minimized in the least.

Winter losses result from starvation, weak colonies, inadequate supplies of pollen, nosema disease, and queenlessness. These factors may operate separately or collectively either to kill colonies or to reduce their productive strength. Climatic conditions have only an indirect effect on winter losses. The type of climate will influence the standards that must be met to ensure the successful overwintering of colonies, but it is doubtful whether any region favorable for commercial honey production has such severe winters that normal, healthy colonies cannot survive in good condition if properly provisioned with honey and pollen.

FOOD REQUIREMENTS

Many colonies are lost from starvation because too little honey is left in the fall. Good colonies in most northern regions consume, on an average, 50 to 55 pounds of honey from the time brood rearing ceases in the fall until sufficient nectar is gathered in the spring to support the colony. Because the best colonies use more than the average, a minimum of 60 pounds should be present in late fall (Fig. 3). Additional honey may be required by exceptional colonies in the spring, or by all colonies when the weather is unfavorable for nectar secretion by early blooming plants. The practice of providing 80 to 90 pounds of honey in the fall reduces labor costs and ensures adequate food under practically all conditions.

The strength of overwintered colonies is directly proportional to the amount of honey consumed. Honey consumed by good colonies in

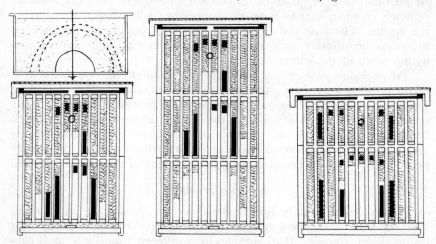

FIGURE 3. Diagrams of the most favorable organization of honey and pollen reserves for Langstroth and Modified Dadant hives at the close of brood rearing. The arrow drawn through the single frame above the 2-story Langstroth hive indicates the position of the section through the three hives. The auger hole in the top chambers and the entrance cleats would, of course, be in the front of the hives. The dark bands illustrating pollen indicate optimum rather than average reserves. By interchanging hive bodies, pollen reserves accumulated early in the season may be covered over with sealed honey. *(Photo U.S.D.A.)*

rearing bees is more valuable than the same amount of honey sold for human consumption. Populous colonies often will replace the honey consumed during the winter from spring nectar sources while small colonies may gather only enough to meet their daily needs. Furthermore, these large colonies will produce from two to ten times as much surplus honey as the retarded colonies. Honey, which is not consumed in winter, will reduce the amount the colonies must store to provide their reserves for the following winter.

The cluster must be able to encompass honey throughout the winter (Figs. 1 to 4). It will form in the top of the hive when there are dark brood combs containing a small open center that is free of honey, but it will avoid a top chamber containing all new white combs, or old dark combs if the latter are solid with honey. The top chamber of a Langstroth 10-frame hive should contain 45 pounds of honey at the close of brood rearing. This amount represents seven or eight full combs of sealed honey and the remaining combs two-thirds or one-half full. The chamber or chambers below should each contain 20 to 30 pounds of reserve honey, which the bees will move into the cluster under favorable temperatures either in the fall or spring.

FIGURE 4. Glass observation hive simulating the colony as it lives in nature; also, a primitive straw skep. The ⅜-inch plywood outer case serves mainly to exclude light from the glass hive. Both are populous colonies with abundant honey stores and capable of surviving in good condition under the most severe winter weather. (*Photo by Fritz Albert, University of Wisconsin*)

Too little honey in the top chamber may allow the colony to starve even though there is plenty of honey in the chamber below. Similarly, when the cluster fails to form in the top chamber because it contains new combs or dark combs that are solid with honey, the colony may starve even though there is honey above, if brood is present to hold the cluster in the lower chamber.

For year-round management, the 3-story Langstroth hive (Fig. 5) or its equivalent in hive space permits the colony to store ample honey reserves. In localities that provide good flows from plants producing off-flavored honey, special manipulations may be needed to concentrate such honey in the minimum number of combs for winter feed. Where disease is not a problem, this honey may be removed and stored until after the main honeyflow and then returned to the colonies for reserve food.

It is sometimes impossible to determine accurately each colony's need for reserve food. An occasional colony headed by an exceptional queen and containing large pollen reserves may become so strong through winter brood rearing as to require much more honey than the average good colony.

Robbing in an apiary may unbalance the stores between hives. There are two forms of robbing. One form is always recognized by beekeepers because of the tremendous bee activity and the complete destruction of the robbed colony, unless corrective measures are taken immediately. The other is described as progressive robbing. The bees from one

FIGURE 5. A 3-story colony wintered without hive packing. (*Photo U.S.D.A.*)

FIGURE 6. A 2-story colony wintered with hive packing. (*Photo U.S.D.A.*)

colony enter another hive to fill up with honey and return to their own without antagonizing the robbed colony or destroying it as long as it has food. Observations have shown that individual colonies subjected to progressive robbing sometimes require twice the normal amount of honey. Progressive robbing is fairly common and often accounts for the difference in apparent food consumption between otherwise equivalent colonies.

WINTER INSPECTION AND COLONY ADJUSTMENTS

The queens in most overwintered colonies commence egg laying early in January, and brood rearing will develop if pollen is available within the cluster even though external temperatures may go as low as $-20°$ to $-40°$ F. During the remainder of the winter, the organization of stores within the hive is critical to the survival of the colony whether only eggs are present or the colony engages in brood rearing. The cluster even will not leave eggs to maintain contact with its food reserves.

Excessive fall labor would be required if food stores were ideally organized in every colony. It is more economical to make sure all colonies are populous and have honey stores in excess of their maximum requirements and basically organized within the hive chambers as shown in Figure 3. The colonies should be inspected in January to make corrective adjustments that some colonies require.

These adjustments can be made at a temperature of zero though it is certainly more comfortable for the beekeeper if they can be made on a calm, bright day with temperatures above 20° F.

Lift the hive covers; if a quiet cluster is visible from the top and there is plenty of honey, no adjustment is required. When only honey is visible, an adjustment will be beneficial to the colony. Invert the hive cover and place it to one side of the hive; gently remove two combs of honey from both sides and spread the remaining combs at the center. Then set the top chamber on the inverted cover. Using a minimum of smoke, remove an outside comb from the chamber below if it contains the main cluster; then gently lift two combs of bees (including brood) from the center, placing these in the center of the set-off hive body. Crowd the combs covered by bees together at the center and fill the outside spaces with combs of honey. Replace the top chamber and crowd the combs together at the center and replace the remaining combs of honey at the outside.

The main cluster may be either in the middle or bottom chamber in a multistoried hive. If in the bottom chamber, it is necessary to locate any combs containing eggs or brood and place these in the center of the top chamber. It is essential to have all segments of the readjusted cluster in contact with each other to prevent stranded groups of bees from chilling.

All of these adjustments must be made without jarring the hive or the moved frame of bees. Any bees dislodged or separated from the cluster will be chilled and lost. When care is exercised, this loss will seldom amount to more than 50 to 200 bees. If the colony is re-examined within a few hours, the cluster will have moved up into the top chamber even though the combs of honey on either side of the elevated bees may have been at zero temperatures.

These adjustments are made to insure that brood in either the middle or bottom chamber does not prevent the cluster from encompassing abundant honey stores regardless of how cold the weather is during the remainder of the winter. Major pollen deficiencies can be met by feeding cakes of pollen supplement beginning 5 to 6 weeks in advance of the first pollen collections in the spring.

WEAK COLONIES

Weak colonies require less honey to survive than strong colonies, but they use more honey for the number of bees present. Small clusters are at a serious disadvantage in cold weather because of the low ratio between bees in the center generating heat and those in the insulating shell. The small cluster is unable to maintain brood-rearing temperatures over a sufficient area to rear the young bees necessary for replacing those worn out, or lost from chilling or disease. Small healthy colonies sometimes survive under severe climatic conditions but, because they seldom gain in strength during the winter, their productive capacity is low the next season.

Weak colonies result from restricted brood rearing during the summer. This restriction may be brought about by the use of small hives, crowded brood chambers due to manipulative practices or the lack of any manipulation, a scarcity of pollen, poor queens, queenlessness, disease, and/or poisoning either of insecticidal or plant origin.

A single brood chamber is too small to allow for optimum brood production during late summer unless special manipulations are used to keep it free of excess honey and pollen. In an unmanipulated 2-story brood chamber, brood rearing may be restricted by the use of a queen excluder or by top-supering if there is a substantial honeyflow at that time. If the honeyflow ends in midsummer this restriction may be beneficial, for there will be more honey in the brood chambers for winter. The restricted colony then will expand brood rearing sufficiently to develop a normal winter cluster, if it has a good queen and pollen is available. Without a concentrated honey reserve the colony would require additional feed for winter. Because the exact time or duration of honeyflows cannot be predicted, unrestricted brood rearing is more likely to provide populations that will yield maximum crops and normal clusters for winter. Unrestricted brood rearing requires more hive equipment to accommodate the colony and to provide space for reserve honey.

SPRING DWINDLING DUE TO INSUFFICIENT POLLEN

Insufficient pollen to support normal brood rearing during late winter and early spring is the basic cause of spring dwindling in otherwise normal, healthy populations. A pollen shortage that limits normal brood rearing also contributes to an increase in nosema infections within the population. Spring dwindling too often is attributed to seasonal conditions rather than to the colony. Colonies that are provisioned with plenty of pollen in a position available to the winter cluster will replace their fall populations with young bees and have a large brood nest when the first pollen becomes available from the field. Such colonies increase their populations rapidly, but colonies wintered without pollen lose bees rapidly when fresh pollen becomes available. Colonies that benefit from winter brood rearing frequently store more honey from early spring nectar flows than the honey they consumed in winter. Retarded colonies, on the other hand, wintered without pollen, may scarcely gather enough nectar to meet their daily food requirements under the same flow conditions.

Surveys of fall pollen reserves and normal colony requirements have been made in the Intermountain States, the North Central States, the Pacific Coast States, and in the package-bee producing areas in the South. In all these regions pollen reserves have been found inadequate for optimum colony development. The pollen problem is more acute in some localities and in some seasons than in others, depending on plant sources, seasonal conditions, and type of colony management.

In most northern beekeeping areas, colonies should enter the winter period with the equivalent of three to five well-filled pollen combs. A reserve of approximately 500 square inches (both sides of the comb estimated separately) of cells containing pollen is desirable for each colony. The amount of reserve pollen in the colonies of most apiaries may vary from none to a few hundred square inches. Few apiaries will average more than 100 to 300 square inches per colony, although an occasional colony may exceed 1,000 square inches. The occasional colony with an excess of pollen causes many beekeepers to conclude that they have no pollen problem.

Pollen reserves must be located within the cluster if they are to be utilized in winter brood production. It is impractical, however, to have 500 square inches of pollen located in the top chamber because too little room is left for honey stores. One or two good pollen combs in the top are advantageous, particularly if they also contain honey. Several combs containing bands of 30 to 60 square inches of pollen covered with honey are ideal, but the bulk of the pollen should be near the center of the chamber just below. Except under extremely low temperatures, strong colonies will occupy two chambers so that this pollen will become available for late winter and early spring brood rearing.

Pollen collection, like honey storage, is proportional to colony strength during producing periods. The accumulation of pollen reserves depends upon the amount collected and the amount consumed in brood rearing. Colonies that have failing queens, or are queenless when there is an abundance of pollen in the field, accumulate the largest reserves.

Some adjustments in pollen reserves between colonies may be made profitably, unless a disease problem precludes the exchange of equipment. If a super of dark brood combs is placed beneath the active brood nest during periods of heavy pollen collection, the bees will store pollen there. If this super can then be raised above the brood nest during a good honeyflow, the pollen will be covered with sealed honey, thus preserving it indefinitely.

There is no satisfactory substitute for pollen, but a pollen deficiency can be largely overcome by feeding trapped pollen supplemented with expeller-processed soybean flour (see "Pollen Supplements" in this chapter).

NOSEMA DISEASE AND WINTER DYSENTERY

Dysentery sometimes causes substantial losses among colonies wintered in the North where the bees are confined to the hive for months at a time. The presence of dysentery indicates an unhealthy condition of the bees, and few affected colonies survive to produce a profitable crop. Colonies are considered to suffer from dysentery whenever the bees discharge feces within the hive.

Dysentery usually has been considered to be due to the excessive accumulation of indigestible materials in the food stores. It also has been attributed to excessive moisture, either in the honey stores or in the hive atmosphere, which prevents the bees from excreting moisture rapidly enough to maintain a favorable balance in their bodies. More recent studies, however, indicate a pathological condition, due to nosema disease, to be the primary cause of dysentery. Nosema spores have been found in the majority of bees, and in the feces discharged within the hive, of every colony suffering from dysentery examined since the winter of 1940-41.

The accumulation of indigestible materials was presumed to be aggravated by unnecessary activity of the cluster resulting from insufficient hive protection, winter brood rearing, and low-quality honeys, namely, those high in dextrin and resins. Experimental tests and commercial beekeeping practices, however, have demonstrated that practically all well-ripened honeys are satisfactory for winter food if present in sufficient quantity.

Colonies have been wintered successfully at Madison, Wisconsin, in skeleton hives providing only a framework to support the two sets of combs and a cover (Fig. 7). These colonies lacked even the protection of single-walled hives.

Colonies have been wintered successfully at Laramie, Wyoming, when provided with 25 pounds of honeydew stores that contained 12 to 13 per cent dextrin. Although inferior to equivalent colonies that had clover honey, when supplied with pollen reserves they were superior to colonies provided with clover honey without pollen. Only two out of eight colonies wintered on honeydew stores suffered from dysentery, and it is probably a safe assumption, based upon recent studies, that these were heavily infected with nosema. At Madison, Wisconsin, during the winter of 1944-45, additional tests on honeydew stores verified these results.

The unfavorable moisture balance was presumed to result from poorly ripened stores, granulation of stores, inadequate hive ventilation, high humidity, and excessive activity of the winter cluster. The moisture content of most honey stores in the North Central States is at least 5 per cent higher than in drier regions, such as the Intermountain States; yet good colonies survive the winter in similar condition in both.

Nosema disease, caused by the protozoan, *Nosema apis,* has been recognized as a disease of the adult bees since the organism was named

FIGURE 7. Two good colonies housed in skeleton hives that survived a severe winter and produced a surplus above their 12 months' honey consumption equal to the Wisconsin state average in 1942. They were exposed to 9 days of subzero temperature (—5° F. to —22° F.) under an average wind velocity of 17 miles per hour in screened skeleton hives protected only by the hive covers. Such extreme exposure, of course, is not recommended. (*Photo U.S.D.A.*)

by Zander in 1909. The disease was known to be present throughout the world, but it had been considered relatively unimportant in North America until about 1940. Spring dwindling will result from nosema disease because infected bees do not support normal brood rearing and their own lives are materially shortened.

When the percentage of nosema-infected bees in the colony is high at the beginning of winter, dysentery will become evident after a relatively short period of confinement, and the colony has little chance of survival. Even with a low incidence of the disease in the fall, long periods of confinement increase the infection and serious loss may result. Whenever the weather is such that the bees are stimulated to take cleansing flights, many of these infected bees drop to the snow and are lost. Loss of these bees is generally beneficial because it helps to reduce the infection potential in the colony.

Nosema disease seems to be the most certain of the three suggested causes of winter dysentery, and infected bees very likely increase the activity of the cluster. If the quality of stores is poor, the bees consume more honey and thus accumulate more waste material. Because the water metabolism of infected bees is probably not normal, it is possible that both the accumulation of indigestible material and unfavorable moisture conditions could hasten a condition of dysentery in the infected colony.

The most effective control for nosema disease in overwintered colonies is to provide all the conditions essential for a high level of brood rearing throughout the preceding summer and fall, i.e., productive queens, strong colonies, ample pollen and honey, and plenty of hive space organized so as not to restrict the normal activity of the colonies. Unrestricted brood rearing will add healthy young bees to the population faster than the infection spreads within. Furthermore, a high level of brood rearing shortens the life of bees, causing infected bees to die sooner than they otherwise would. Under unfavorable conditions that adversely affect the colonies, the feeding of 2 gallons of sugar sirup (2:1) containing 200 milligrams of fumagillin (10 grams Fumidil B) to all colonies in the fall will greatly reduce the spread of nosema within the overwintering populations.

The infection of queens with nosema has been shown to be responsible for considerable supersedure in package colonies. Recovery of a large number of nosema-infected dead queens from queenless colonies in the spring suggests that nosema infection is often responsible for queens lost in overwintered colonies.

Although nosema infection and a lack of pollen are major causes of spring dwindling, other secondary causes may prove damaging to individual colonies or to an entire apiary in certain locations. These secondary causes include failing queens, partial starvation of the cluster, severe drifting, arsenical poisoning, plant poisoning, sacbrood, European foulbrood, American foulbrood, and diseases of adult bees (see Chapter XIX, "Diseases and Enemies of the Honey Bee").

Colony Standards for Overwintering Productive Colonies

The consideration of the colony as a single organic unit, and an understanding of the formation and activity of the winter cluster, as well as the causes of winter losses, predicate definite colony standards for successful wintering. The problem of management is not how or where, but what kind of colonies are wintered.

The colony requirements during the nonproductive period of winter must be anticipated during the productive period when growing plants supply pollen and nectar. The so-called fall and winter management becomes principally a problem of making adjustments where colonies fall below optimum standards.

The normal productive colony should meet the following standards at the close of brood rearing in the fall and just prior to dandelion or similar bloom in the spring. The 2-story Langstroth hive should have a minimum gross weight of 130 pounds in the fall to ensure 60 pounds or more of honey; the 3-story hive provisioned with 90 pounds of honey will weigh 180 pounds. In the case of the 1½-story Modified Dadant hive, a gross weight of 140 to 170 pounds will provide food reserves within the range of 60 to 90 pounds.

FALL CONDITION AT CLOSE OF BROOD REARING

1. A productive queen
2. Bees covering 20 or more combs in a normally provisioned hive
3. 45 pounds of honey in top chamber in dark brood combs
4. 15 to 30 pounds of honey in lower chamber
5. 500 square inches of pollen divided between both chambers (this amount is desirable but seldom attained)
6. Reduced lower entrance and 1-inch auger hole in top chamber
7. Protection from wind
8. Maximum exposure to sunshine
9. Good air drainage

SPRING CONDITION AT THE BEGINNING OF DANDELION OR SIMILAR BLOOM

1. A productive queen
2. 15 to 20 frames of bees—8 to 10 pounds
3. 6 to 10 frames of brood
4. 15 pounds or more of reserve honey
5. Continuous supply of pollen or pollen supplement
6. Entrances adequate for free flight of bees
7. Hive organization permitting upward expansion of the brood nest
8. Storage space adequate for honeyflow

Colonies whose hives contain 90 pounds of honey are even better prepared for winter than those provided with a minimum of 60 pounds. The reader may ask why, in the literature on wintering, the recommended food reserve has increased from 20 or 30 pounds to 45, 50, 60, or 90 pounds. The hazards of wintering bees are reduced by increasing the food reserves, spring feeding is avoided, and larger and more certain crops are obtained. Colonies that consume less than 50 pounds, between the end of one productive season and the beginning of the next, seldom can be considered first-class colonies. It should be recognized, however, that gains by strong colonies from early nectar sources may obscure the true winter requirement. Since the early sources cannot be depended upon, an excess of honey stores is essential to efficient colony management.

Apiary Locations and Hive Entrances

Apiary locations should be chosen that provide maximum sun exposure, good air drainage away from the apiary, and protection from prevailing winds. A sheltered location is desirable when the bees are clustered and at temperatures when they can take winter flights. Snow coverage is not harmful, even if colonies become buried in deep drifts for weeks at a time (Fig. 8). Sunshine on the hives often permits an expansion or shift of the cluster; also, sunshine on an upper entrance adjacent to the cluster permits the bees to fly when they might not otherwise have an opportunity if they were obliged to pass over

FIGURE 8. A colony that was buried under a snowdrift from January 14 until March 15 when at least 1½ feet of snow was removed from the top of the hive. When the cover was removed, the large cluster shown had many newly emerged bees and brood in three frames. *(Photo U.S.D.A.)*

cold combs to reach the bottom entrance. General observations on several apiaries maintained in the same location for 25 years suggest that air drainage is even more important than protection from wind.

To winter a colony in the best possible condition, the bottom-board entrance should be reduced to an opening ⅜ by 1 inch and a 1-inch auger hole provided just below the handhold in the front of the top chamber. The auger-hole entrance is especially valuable in multistoried hives since the cluster is normally located in the top chambers; also, if the lower entrance becomes temporarily blocked with ice, snow, litter, or dead bees, the bees still can fly whenever they desire. The upper entrance has great value when hives are covered with deep snow (Fig. 8), since the top may be exposed to sunshine a week or more before the lower entrance is open. Colonies in this situation but without upper entrances may suffer severely or be lost because the bees are confined to a closed hive warmed by sunshine on top. The bottom entrance helps to prevent the growth of molds on the lower combs which are not covered by the bees. The hive should tilt slightly forward and have an entrance large enough to allow drainage of water from the bottom board and the removal of dead bees. The dead bees will dry up considerably even when it is too cool for the colony to clean them out. It is also good practice to place a piece of hardware cloth 3-mesh to the inch over the bottom entrance to exclude mice.

Hive Packing

Winter packing has more of a psychological value to the beekeeper than real value to the normal colony because it gives him a feeling of being kind to his bees. Packing will not make strong colonies out of those deficient in honey, pollen, or populations, or those having a poor queen or a heavy nosema infection. Strong, productive colonies will survive whether or not the hives are protected if provision is made for all the colony's internal requirements as shown in Figures 2 and 3.

Packing does provide a measure of protection to colonies from being pilfered. Two- or 3-story hives, heavy with honey, present temptation for stealing the honey from unprotected hives. The packed colony (Fig. 6), on the other hand, is not so easily provisioned with cakes of pollen supplement when pollen reserves are inadequate.

Packed hives or those wrapped with moisture-proof paper cool off slightly more slowly under declining temperatures than those lacking such protection, but conversely, they also warm up more slowly when temperatures rise. The gain in the first instance is counterbalanced by a loss in the second. It matters little how one winters his colonies, but it is very important that the colonies be strong, healthy, and abundantly supplied with food under conditions that will make these stores available to the cluster at all times under all conditions (Figs. 4 to 8).

Pollen Supplements

Pollen deficiencies may be largely overcome in the spring by feeding cakes consisting of trapped pollen supplemented with soybean flour mixed with sugar sirup. Soybean flour produced by the expeller process is superior to that refined by the chemical-extraction process. Feeding may be started a month or 6 weeks before pollen is collected from the field and continued through the spring when pollen collection is intermittent.

These cakes are prepared by mixing 1 part dry matter (1 part pollen and 3 parts of expeller-processed soybean flour) and 2 parts sugar sirup (2 parts sugar and 1 part hot water). Dry pollen softens readily in water but not in sugar sirup; therefore, the desired amount of pollen should be added to the water before dissolving the sugar.

Any number of cakes can be prepared in the proportions suggested above. For example, 32 cakes weighing 1½ pounds each can be made as follows: mix 4 pounds of dry pollen in 11 pounds of hot water, add 21 pounds of sugar and stir until in suspension, and finally add 12 pounds of soybean flour and mix until a doughlike paste is formed. This amount is sufficient to rear approximately 120,000 young bees, or a pound of bees in each of 32 colonies.

A 1½-pound cake is placed on the top bars directly over the center of the cluster and covered with wax paper to prevent drying (Fig. 9). The inner cover is reversed on the hive to provide space for the cake. A new cake should be added before the previous one is entirely con-

FIGURE 9. Colony feeding on a cake of pollen supplemented with soybean flour. The bees practically obscure the wax paper over the cake. The feeding channels are shown after the bees were smoked down, and the cake turned over. *(Photo U.S.D.A.)*

sumed, usually at intervals of approximately 10 days. Colonies with five to seven frames of brood may be given 2 to 4 pounds at one time.

When trapped pollen is not available, cakes made with the soybean flour alone may be fed advantageously to colonies in the spring about 10 days prior to new pollen collection when colonies have insufficient pollen and during periods when pollen collection is likely to be intermittent. Soybean cakes are not so effective as those containing pollen, but they do permit more brood to be reared when pollen is scarce.

TRAPPING POLLEN

Pollen for these cakes must be collected as the bees bring it into the hives, for there is no commercial source of bulk pollen. A pollen trap consists of a grid made from 5-mesh hardware cloth over a tray covered with 7-mesh wire cloth (Fig. 10). The bees pass through this grid as they leave or enter the hive and most of the pollen from their legs is scraped off and falls into the tray. The grid is fastened inside

FIGURE 10. Hive equipped with a pollen trap consisting essentially of a grid made from 5-mesh hardware cloth, a pollen tray with a 7-mesh cover, and a shield for attachment. The ventilating rim with screened openings has value during warm weather in preventing the bees from clustering over the grid. *(Photo U.S.D.A.)*

the top of a storm shield, which also supports the pollen tray and attaches the complete unit to the hive entrance.

Beekeepers are inventive by nature, so it is not surprising that many types of pollen traps employing these principles are now in use. The important thing is to gather enough pollen to build each colony to full producing strength before the honeyflow, regardless of spring weather conditions. Yields of trapped pollen obtained from good colonies may range from 20 to over 50 pounds, depending upon the flora in different geographic locations and the season. Trapped pollen, when properly dried, can be stored for years in closed containers without appreciable loss in its value for brood rearing. One to 2 pounds of trapped pollen is not too large a reserve to maintain for each colony or package, but, like honey reserves, the average requirement may be about 1 pound. The beekeeper should prepare for the most adverse season rather than the average.

The pollen trays should be emptied every day or two. For this reason pollen traps cannot be satisfactorily used in outapiaries. The pollen should be dried at about 110° to 120° F. and then stored in a closed container such as a 5-gallon honey can. It should be dried to a point where the pellets will not cake when squeezed in the hand. This usually means a loss of about 20 per cent of its original moist weight. Five gallons of dried pellets will weigh 28 to 30 pounds. Pollen may be dried rapidly in quantity in an improvised oven made of a large fiber carton by building in a framework to support cheesecloth trays on which to spread the pollen. Mazda lamps or resistance heating elements installed with due precaution against a fire hazard, may be used to supply the heat at the bottom to drive off moisture-laden air through an opening at the top (Woodrow[3]).

Wintering Surplus Queens and Double Colonies

Surplus nuclei that have good queens and four or five frames of bees may be successfully wintered above strong colonies. A screen is placed over the upper brood chamber of the normal colony, and on it is set a single hive body provided with an auger-hole entrance. The nucleus is placed in the center of this body plus additional full frames of honey and pollen in dark brood combs to provide food.

The two clusters will winter in direct contact but separated by the screen. If both the normal colony and the nucleus have auger-hole entrances, some bees from the colony below will drift into the nucleus, and it may be the stronger unit in the spring. To reduce this drifting it is well to provide the lower colony with an auger-hole entrance in its lower chamber instead of the upper. When the normal colony is wintered in three stories, this entrance should be in the middle chamber.

Two full-strength colonies may be wintered by the same method, except that each should have normal honey and pollen reserves. Four

Langstroth hive bodies are required for these double colonies, and, to minimize drifting, auger-hole entrances should be placed in the bottom chamber of the lower colony and in the top body for the upper colony. Demareed colonies that happen to have two queens, or colonies managed under a two-queen plan, may be wintered as double colonies, if the beekeeper has plenty of reserve honey and pollen and desires increase. Beekeepers who have followed this procedure on a considerable scale believe that the double colonies consume less honey than when they are wintered separately.

The Relation of Wintering to Productive Management

To provide for the optimum requirements of the normal colony during the nonproductive season, the beekeeper must apply skillful management during the productive season. The strong colony requires more hive space, which must be properly organized for expansion in brood rearing and honey storage, to prevent the colony from swarming. Queens wear out faster in colonies that are provided with pollen or pollen supplements because they rear a larger amount of brood in late winter and early spring. Honeyflows may develop from plants formerly thought to be only of minor importance because colonies were not strong enough to make gains. Temporary increase made by dividing strong colonies and introducing young queens may be necessary and profitable as a swarm-control measure prior to the main nectarflow. However, when the main flow develops it is often more profitable to reunite the divided colonies, because strong colonies produce more honey for a given number of bees than small colonies. Such uniting is an efficient method of providing each producing colony with a young queen during the honeyflow.

Colony standards have changed since Langstroth's time, but the principles he outlined cover the requisites of wintering and we need only to assign the necessary values. A colony "strong in numbers" now means 30 thousand young bees, which represents a normal population of an unrestricted colony. A colony "strong in stores" now has 60 to 90 pounds of honey and 500 square inches of pollen. Although Langstroth recognized the need for pollen, 75 years elapsed before the significance of the pollen supply in controlling colony development was understood. The upward ventilation he recommended has been readopted by the use of auger-hole entrances. Langstroth allowed communication between combs by cutting holes through the center, while today the same objective is accomplished in hives of more than one story by the space between the sets of combs. The importance of water for spring brood rearing has been appreciated, but it is still left largely to chance. Protection from wind, whether obtained by utilizing the natural vegetation surrounding the location or by wrapping the hive, is considered beneficial to the colony. To Langstroth's principles may be added exposure to maximum sunlight, good air drainage, freedom from infectious diseases, and winter inspection to correct unfavorable cluster positions.

Langstroth, if living today, would be disappointed in the number of neglected colonies. Yet he would be surprised and equally pleased with the strength of colonies made possible through the use of larger hives, more honey, more pollen or pollen supplements, productive queens, and intelligent management. Such colonies produce correspondingly larger and more certain yields because many of the elements of chance have been eliminated by intensive management.

REFERENCES CITED

1. Langstroth, L. L. 1859-1871. 3d. ed. J. B. Lippincott & Co., Philadelphia. pp. 81,346.

2. Phillips, E. F., and George S. Demuth. 1914. U.S.D.A. Bull. **93**. 16 pp.

3. Woodrow, A. E. 1947. Am. Bee J. **88**(3):124-125.

SUPPORTING SUBJECT REFERENCES
BY THE AUTHOR

1931. 51-52 Ann. Rept. Ontario Beekeepers' Assoc. **1930-31**:126-130.

1934. Gl. Bee Cult. **62**(5):276-278.

1936. Am. Bee J. **76**(9):452-454.

1937. J. Agr. Res. **54**(12):945-954.

1941. U.S. Bur. Entomol. and Pl. Quar. Circ. **E-531** (rev. 1946).

1942. Gl. Bee Cult. **70**(11):660-661,701.

1943. Gl. Bee Cult. **71**(9):513-518.

1944. Gl. Bee Cult. **72**(1):8-9,35.

1944. U.S.D.A. Circ. **702**. 28 pp.

1947. U.S.D.A. Yearbook of Agriculture, **1943-47**:680-685.

1947. J. Econ. Entomol. **40**(3):333-338.

1952. J. Econ. Entomol. **45**(3):445-449.

1954. Am. Bee J. **94**(2):52-53,60.

1959. Am. Bee J. **99**(2):63.

1960. Am. Bee J. **100**(8):306-310.

SELECTED REFERENCES OF HISTORICAL INTEREST

Corkin, C. L. 1930. Wyo. Agr. Expt. Sta. Bull. **175**. 51 pp.

Hess, W. R. 1926. Ztschr. f. Vergleisch. Physiol. **4**:465-487.

Milner, R. D., and George S. Demuth. 1921. U.S.D.A. Bull. **988**. 18 pp.

Pirsch, G. B. 1923. J. Agr. Res. **24**(4):275-287.

Wedmore, E. B. 1947. The ventilation of bee-hives. Bee Craft, Lewes Press, Sussex, England. 115 pp.

Wilson, H. F., and V. G. Milum. 1927. Wis. Res. Bull. **75**. 47 pp.

CHAPTER XIV

HONEY

by J. W. WHITE, JR.*

WHEN PREHISTORIC MAN reached deep into a bee tree or a cleft in the rocks for a highly prized store of honeycomb, he must have felt that the prize was worth the price in stings from the outraged bees. Veneration of the bee and its products, honey and wax, can be traced through the entire span of man's record; honey has been an article of commerce for many thousands of years. As such, many definitions and standards have attempted to describe it. Honey is a sweet, viscous liquid prepared by bees from nectar collected from plant nectaries and stored by them for food. This definition excludes honeydew, which does not originate directly from nectaries (floral or extra-floral) but either from plant secretions (manna) or more commonly from the excretion of certain homopterous insects (aphids, leaf hoppers, scale insects). While feeding on plant sap, these insects excrete from the alimentary canal a sweet liquid that is sometimes gathered by bees and stored for food, during partial or total absence of a nectar supply. More will be said of honeydew later in this chapter; sufficient now to note that it differs in most of its properties from honey.

The Food and Drug Administration does not have an official definition of honey. The former definition, in force under the original Federal Food and Drug Act of 1906, held that "Honey is the nectar and saccharine exudation of plants, gathered, modified and stored in the comb by honey bees (*A. mellifera* and *A. dorsata*); is levorotatory, contains not more than 25 per cent water, not more than 0.25 per cent ash, and not more than 8 per cent sucrose." The Food, Drug, and Cosmetic Act of 1938, which supersedes the original law, provides for definitions and standards of identity for foods. It has none for honey. The older definition is still considered by the Food and Drug Administration as an informal description of what honey should be, though it has only advisory status. Feinberg[23] and White et al.[108] have noted that it is unrealistic in its limits for moisture (too high), sucrose (too high), and ash (too low). Many states follow the Federal definition for honey, though some vary in moisture content and density requirements. It is advisable to become familiar with state food and drug requirements for honey, as well as state grading requirements, before packing honey even on a small scale.

---

*Jonathan W. White, Jr., Ph.D. Head, Honey Investigations, Plant Products Laboratory, Eastern Utilization Research and Development Division, U.S. Department of Agriculture, Philadelphia, Pa. Specialist in the chemistry and utilization of honey.

Kinds of Honey

Honeys are classified by the principal sources from which the bees gathered the nectar. Although bees may work only one plant source at a time, the chances are that there is nectar from several plant types in most honeys. Ordinarily, honey is identified by one or more prominent floral-source names as "gallberry honey" or "alfalfa honey," or by two names, as "sage-buckwheat honey" (Fig. 1). Other less specific names are also used, such as "fall flower" and "spring blend." It has been held by the Food and Drug Administration (Herrick[33]) that honey may not be labeled with the name of a plant or blossom except where the particular plant is the chief floral source of the product.

Another system of classifying honey is by method of production and preparation for market:

1. *Extracted honey* (also known as strained honey) is honey that has been separated from the comb by centrifugal force, gravity, straining, or by other means. It may appear on the market in different forms:

a. *Liquid honey* is honey that is free of visible crystals.

b. *Crystallized honey* is honey that is completely granulated or solidified, including products known as "candied," "fondant," "creamed," or "spread" types of honey. Such crystallization may be natural, i.e. with no added fine-crystal "starter" honey, or produced by one of several controlled crystallization processes.

2. *Comb honey* is honey contained in the cells of the comb in which it is produced. It appears on the market in several forms:

a. *Section comb honey,* produced in squares $4\frac{1}{4}$ x $4\frac{1}{4}$ x $1\frac{7}{8}$ inches or rectangles 4 x 5 x $1\frac{3}{4}$ inches, called sections. Such novelty forms as circular sections may be seen.

b. *Individual section comb honey* is produced in small sections, usually one quarter the size of ordinary sections.

c. *Bulk comb honey* is comb honey produced in shallow extracting frames fitted with thin super foundation. These combs may be sold when filled as complete units.

d. *Cut comb honey* is bulk comb honey cut into pieces of various sizes, the edges drained or extracted, and the individual pieces wrapped in cellophane or polyethylene bags.

e. *Chunk honey* consists of cut comb honey packed in a container which is filled with liquid extracted honey. For U.S. Fancy and No. 1 chunk honey, not less than 50 per cent by volume of comb honey must be present in the container, if tin; if glass, no volume is required.

The United States Department of Agriculture has established voluntary grade standards for extracted and comb honey.* These standards

---

*Copies of grade standards for extracted honey (fourth issue, effective April 16, 1951) and comb honey (second issue, effective August 1933) may be obtained from the Processed Products Standardization and Inspection Branch, Fruit and Vegetable Division, Agricultural Marketing Service, U.S. Department of Agriculture, Washington 25, D.C.

FIGURE 1. Dr. White examines the color of some of the 490 samples collected by the Honey Investigations Unit for their extensive study of U. S. honeys. (*U.S.D.A. photo by M. C. Audsley*)

are designed to serve as a convenient basis for sales, for establishing quality control programs and for determining loan values. They also serve as a basis for the inspection of honey by the Federal Inspection Service. Standards have been established for extracted honey including crystallized honey, and for comb honey, including section comb, shallow-frame comb, wrapped cut comb, and chunk or bulk comb honey.

For extracted honey, there are four classes: U.S. Grade A or U.S. Fancy, U.S. Grade B or U.S. Choice, U.S. Grade C or U.S. Standard, and U.S. Grade D or Substandard. Factors considered in grading are flavor, clarity, absence of defects, and moisture content. The first of these, flavor, refers to the prominence of honey flavor and aroma and its conformity to that of the predominant floral source. Clarity is concerned with freedom from pollen grains, air bubbles or other suspended materials. Absence of defects refers to degree of cleanliness and absence of particles of comb, propolis, or other materials. To qualify for the top two grades, honey must contain not more than 18.6 per cent moisture; Grade C may contain up to 20 per cent.

Color of honey is not a quality factor. It is measured by means of the U.S.D.A. permanent glass color standards or by the Pfund honey color grader. In Table 1 are the seven color classes of honey as defined in the U.S.D.A. grades.

Comb honey is classified as U.S. Fancy, U.S. No. 1, U.S. No. 2, and Unclassified. The factors considered in grading are appearance of cappings, attachment to the section, uniformity of honey, and absence of pollen, granulation, honeydew, or off-grade honey.

TABLE 1. Color Designation of Honey and Range for Each Color

U.S.D.A. color standards	Color range U.S.D.A. color standards	Color range Pfund scale in millimeters	Optical density[1]
Water White	Honey that is Water White or lighter in color than Water White Color Standard	8 or less	0.0945
Extra White	Honey that is darker than Water White but not darker than Extra White Color Standard	Over 8 to and including 17	0.189
White	Honey that is darker than Extra White but not darker than White Color Standard	Over 17 to and including 34	0.378
Extra Light Amber	Honey that is darker than White but not darker than Extra Light Amber or Golden Color Standard	Over 34 to and including 50	0.595
Light Amber	Honey that is darker than Extra Light Amber but not darker than Light Amber Color Standard	Over 50 to and including 85	1.389
Amber	Honey that is darker than Light Amber but not darker than Amber Color Standard	Over 85 to and including 114	3.008
Dark Amber	Honey that is darker than Amber Color Standard	Over 114	

[1]Optical density (absorbance) $= \log_{10} (100 \div$ per cent transmittance), at 560 mμ for 3.15 centimeter thickness for caramel-glycerin solutions measured versus an equal cell containing glycerin.

PHYSICAL PROPERTIES OF HONEY

The hygroscopicity of a substance is its ability to remove moisture from the air. It is commonly expressed by the relative humidity of the air with which the substance is in equilibrium, neither gaining nor losing moisture. The exact degree of hygroscopicity of honey depends upon the specific composition of the sample, its sugar composition and moisture content. The variation among samples is not large; honey (17.4 per cent moisture) has been found by Martin[53] to be in equilibrium with air at 58% relative humidity. This honey would gain water if exposed to air of greater moisture content and lose water when exposed to air dryer than 58 per cent R.H. Moisture change would continue until the honey reached a moisture content in equilibrium with the ambient relative humidity. Martin[54] has determined the equilibrium moisture content of honey exposed to various atmospheres (see Table 3).

TABLE 2. Composition and Physical Properties of Extracted Honey*

One pound (453.59 g.) of average American extracted honey would contain the following materials:

Principal Components	Per cent		Grams	
Water (natural moisture)	17.20		78.0	
The sugars of honey				
Levulose (d-fructose; fruit sugar)	38.19		173.2	
Dextrose (d-glucose; grape sugar)	31.28		141.9	
Sucrose (common table sugar)	1.31		5.9	
Maltose and other reducing disaccharides	7.31		33.2	
Higher sugars	1.50		6.8	
Total sugars	79.59	79.59	361.0	361.0
Acids (gluconic, citric, malic, succinic, formic, acetic, butyric, lactic, pyroglutamic, and amino acids). Total acid calculated as gluconic acid.	0.57		2.6	
Proteins (nitrogen x 6.25)	0.26		1.2	
Ash (minerals: potassium, sodium, calcium, magnesium, chlorides, sulfates, phosphates, silica, etc.)	0.17		0.8	
Total acids, protein, and ash	1.00	1.00	4.6	4.6
Minor Components		2.21	10.0	10.0
Pigments (carotene, chlorophyll and chlorophyll derivatives, xanthophylls)				
Flavor and aroma substances (terpenes, aldehydes, alcohols, esters, etc.)				
Sugar alcohols (mannitol, dulcitol)				
Tannins				
Acetylcholine				
Enzymes:				
Invertase (converts sucrose to dextrose and levulose)				
Diastase (converts starch to dextrins)				
Catalase (decomposes hydrogen peroxide)				
Phosphatase (decomposes glycerophosphate)				
Inhibine (antibacterial substance)				
Vitamins (thiamine, riboflavin, nicotinic acid, vitamin K, folic acid, biotin, pyridoxine — in small and variable amounts)				
Totals		100.00		453.6

*The average of the analyses of 490 samples of honey, by Honey Investigations Unit, Plant Products Laboratory.

Specific Gravity 68°F. (20°C.) = 1.4225, corresponding to: 81.25° Brix at 60°F., 43.19° Baumé (Modulus 145) at 60°F., 84.6° Twaddell.
   1 gal. weighing 11 lb., 13.2 oz. average.
   I lb. having volume of 10.78 fl. oz. (318.9 ml.).
Caloric Value—1 lb. = 1,380 calories, 100 g. = 303 calories, 100 ml. = 432 calories, 1 tbsp. = about 60 calories.
Refractive Index—1.4935 at 68°F. (20°C.), 1.4924 at 77°F. (25°C.).
Vapor Pressure—Corresponding to atmosphere of 60% R. H. at 68°F.
Thermal Characteristics—Specific heat 0.54 at 20°C.
   Thermal conductivity at 21°C. 12.7 x 10^{-4} cal./cm. sec. °C.
   Thermal conductivity at 49°C. 13.6 x 10^{-4} cal./cm. sec. °C.
Sweetening Power—Honey sugars have approximately 25% greater sweetening power than cane sugar. Hence: 1 gal. average extracted honey (about 9 lbs. 6 oz. total sugars) is equivalent to about 11 lbs. 12 oz. granulated sugar.
   1 volume honey is equivalent to about 1.67 volumes granulated sugar.
   1 lb. average honey (containing about 17% water) is equivalent to about 0.95 lb. (15.25 oz.) granulated sugar.

TABLE 3. Approximate Equilibrium Points between the Relative Humidity and the Percentage Water Content of Liquid Clover Honey

Percentage Water in Honey	Equilibrium Relative Humidity
16.1	52
17.4	58
21.5	66
28.9	76
33.9	81

Martin noted that the surface layer of honey takes up moisture rapidly. Thus water diffuses more slowly into the depths of the container. When honey is exposed to dry air, it loses moisture more slowly because of the formation of a relatively dry surface "skin." This rapid thinning of surface honey as it takes up moisture can allow fermentation to proceed in honey, building up the level of yeast contamination rapidly as the moisture diffuses into the honey.

Lothrop[46] found honey to be more hygroscopic than invert sirup or corn sirup. Hygroscopicity of honey is a valuable property, however. It aids in keeping honey-containing baked goods and candies fresh and soft, and has been used to prevent excessive drying of tobacco products.

Excessive moisture content of honey can be reduced by exposing it to air of relative humidity lower than its equilibrium value. Killion[36] has used dehumidifiers to remove over 220 lbs. of water from 130 supers of comb honey in 23 days. A more common way, studied by Stephen,[79] to reduce the relative saturation of the air, is to warm it; forced circulation of hot air will reduce the moisture level of comb honey. Townsend and Burke[86] have removed 1 to 3 per cent moisture in 24 hours from 72 supers of honey in a 6½- by 7-foot room.

Even when packed in a screw-cap jar, honey can take up moisture if only a simple cardboard insert is present in the cap (Villumstad[91]). Nicol[64] found none of 22 screw-cap English honey jars to be gastight.

The viscosity of a material is simply its resistance to flow. The beekeeper calls it "body." A heavy-bodied honey has a high viscosity and flows only slowly. Like other physical properties, viscosity of honey depends upon its composition, especially the moisture content. Chataway[12] proposed the determination of moisture content of honey by a viscosity measurement. She used the time of fall of a steel ball in a special apparatus and claimed an accuracy equal to direct drying.

Oppen and Schuette[66] have improved Chataway's apparatus for this purpose. Many beekeepers feel that they can get an idea of the moisture content of honey by allowing a bubble to rise in it. This may be quite misleading, since viscosity is quite sensitive to temperature and protein content of honey.

Honey viscosity is of great practical importance to the beekeeper and honey processer. The high viscosity of honey makes it difficult to empty containers and to extract it from the comb. It retards the rate of straining and clarification, including "settling" and clearing of entrapped air bubbles. As all beekeepers know, the body of honey is reduced by heating; the use of some degree of warming greatly facilitates extraction, straining, settling, flow through pipes and emptying of containers. Munro[62] has shown that heating honey above 86° F. gives no further practical advantage in extraction and handling of most honeys, with the exception of especially heavy honeys of about 14 per cent moisture or lower.

No American honey has to any marked degree the property of *thixotropy*, which is a decrease of viscosity following stirring or agitation which then returns on standing. Heather (Europe) and manuka (New Zealand) honeys are markedly thixotropic. Pryce-Jones[71] found a protein to be responsible; the property is lost when the protein is removed. Clover honey becomes thixotropic when the heather honey protein is added to it. Pryce-Jones has written a comprehensive article on the viscosity and related properties of honey.

Mention should perhaps also be made of "spinnbarkeit" which might be termed "stringiness" or "spinnability." Some honeydews and honeys containing honeydew will form long hairlike threads when a rod is dipped into them and pulled away. Ordinary honey does not do this.

The density of a substance is its weight per unit volume. It usually is expressed as pounds per cubic foot, pounds per gallon, or grams per milliliter. The most familiar expression for honey is in pounds per gallon. Honey meeting the grading requirements for U.S. Fancy or Choice must have a density of at least 11 pounds, 12 ounces per gallon.

Specific gravity is the ratio of the weight of a volume of a substance to the weight of the same volume of water. The minimum density noted above for top-grade honey corresponds to a specific gravity of 1.4129. Density and specific gravity may be determined by weighing known volumes, by the use of a hydrometer, or by a specific gravity balance.

These attributes vary with the temperature of measurement and the moisture content of honey, hence temperature must be specified in tables relating moisture content and density, specific gravity, or solids content by hydrometer.

The variation of density of honey with moisture content is sufficiently large that a low moisture honey will tend to layer under a higher moisture honey in a tank unless especial care is taken to mix them. Honey exposed to moist air will absorb water and form a more dilute layer which will remain at the surface for a long time due to its lower density, as shown by Martin.[54] Diffusion of the water through the mass of material is very slow. Table 4 shows how the specific gravity and density of honey vary with its moisture content.

The Brix hydrometer is commonly used for measuring sucrose solu-

TABLE 4. The Relationship Between Various Hydrometer Scales and Refractive
Index to Moisture Content and Weight per Gallon of Honey*

% Moisture	Sp. Gr. (20°C.) 20°C.) at 20°C.	°Brix at 20°C.	Diff. between use of honey hydrometer tables and Brix tables in % H$_2$O	Lb. per Imp. Gal. at 20°C.		Lb. per U. S. Gal. at 20°C.		Ref. Index at 20°C.	% Moisture
				lb.	oz.	lb.	oz.		
13.2	1.4510	85.45	1.35	14	8	12	1	1.5035	13.2
14.0	1.4453	84.61	1.39	14	7	12	0.5	1.5015	14.0
15.4	1.4352	83.13	1.47	14	5.6	11	15	1.4980	15.4
15.8	1.4324	82.71	1.49	14	5	11	14.5	1.4970	15.8
17.0	1.4239	81.45	1.55	14	3.8	11	13.5	1.4940	17.0
17.4	1.4212	81.04	1.56	14	3.2	11	13	1.4930	17.4
18.0	1.4171	80.42	1.58	14	2.6	11	12.5	1.4915	18.0
18.6	1.4129	79.80	1.60	14	2	11	12	1.4900	18.6
19.0	1.4101	79.39	1.61	14	1.4	11	11.5	1.4890	19.0
20.2	1.4020	78.15	1.65	14	0.2	11	10.5	1.4862	20.2
21.0	1.3966	77.33	1.67					1.4844	21.0

*Condensed from more extensive tables by H. D. Chataway[13] with additions and slight changes. Printer's errors should be checked if the original tables are consulted. The original tables contain temperature corrections for various scales. The method of determination of moisture content by means of a refractometer and the tables have been adopted in Canada, and in the United States by the Association of Official Agricultural Chemists.

tions and is calibrated to read per cent sucrose directly. When used for honey the values obtained are too low by the amounts shown in the table. A honey hydrometer is commercially available.

The refractive index of a substance is actually the ratio of the velocity of light in the substance to that in air. This apparently abstruse and difficult measurement provides the simplest and possibly the most accurate method of determining the water content of honey. By use of the refractometer, a relatively simple instrument, moisture in honey can be determined with ease, compared with other methods. Equipment is expensive, however, and because of the small sample required (as little as a drop) care must be taken that the sample is representative. Table 4 relates refractive index to the moisture content of honey. Again the temperature of measurement must be known.

Color is an optical property of honey, inasmuch as it is the result of the different degree of absorption of light of different wave lengths by the constituents of honey. Honeys may vary from virtually colorless to deep red in color through shades of yellow, amber, and brown, with greenish or reddish tinges. A blue honey of unknown origin is produced in North Carolina. Most honeys also fluoresce (emit visible light) in various colors when illuminated by ultraviolet light.

Optical rotation, or rotation of the polarization plane of polarized light, is shown by many types of organic materials. The direction and extent of such rotation differs for various substances. The sugars of normal honey are such that it is levorotatory (left-rotating), while honeydews are sufficiently different in composition that they are largely dextrorotatory (right-rotating). Thus the measurement of optical rotation has been used both to analyze the sugars of honey and to detect the presence of honeydew. More reliable methods are available now for these analyses.

THE COMPOSITION OF HONEY

Moisture Content. The natural moisture of honey in the comb is that remaining from the nectar after ripening. Its concentration is thus a function of the factors involved in ripening, including weather conditions and original moisture of the nectar. The moisture content of honey may change after removal from the hive as a result of storage conditions after extraction. It is one of the most important characteristics of honey, having a profound influence on keeping quality, granulation, and body; yet few beekeepers trouble to measure it, relying instead on rule of thumb (Bauer[8]).

The Sugars of Honey. Since honey is above all a carbohydrate material, with 95 to 99.9 per cent of the solids being sugars, they have been studied for many years. Recently much new information has been published about the sugars found in honey.

Sugars are classified according to the size and complexity of their molecules. The simple sugars (*monosaccharides*) are the building blocks of the more complex types. The dextrose and levulose in honey are examples. The disaccharide sugars are made of two monosaccharides joined in various ways; many of these are known. Common examples are maltose (malt sugar), sucrose (table sugar), and lactose (milk sugar). Other kinds of sugars are still more complex, being made of three or more simple sugars (higher sugars).

Table 5 shows our present knowledge of the sugars of honey. Of the fifteen sugars therein, the first nine have been rigorously identified; the remaining six have been reported without extensive evidence. Many of these sugars probably do not occur in nectar but are formed during ripening and storage by effect of enzyme action and honey acids. The simple sugars, dextrose and levulose, predominate and give honey its sweetness, hygroscopic properties, energy value, and physical characteristics. In nearly all floral types of honey more levulose than dextrose is present; only very rapidly granulating types such as blue curl, dandelion, and rapeseed have more dextrose than levulose.

Acids of Honey. Because of its great sweetness, the acidity of honey is largely masked. The acids contribute to the honey flavor complex. Until recently it had been thought that citric acid was the predominating honey acid; Nelson and Mottern[63] isolated and positively identified citric, malic, and succinic acids in honey. Other acids reported were formic and acetic.

TABLE 5. Sugars Identified in Honey

Name	Components	Investigators
Monosaccharides		
Levulose	————	} Long known to occur.
Dextrose	————	
Disaccharides		
Sucrose	glucosyl fructoside ----------------	} Long known to occur.
Maltose	4-glucosyl glucose ------------------	
Isomaltose	6-glucosyl glucose ------------------	
Turanose	3-glucosyl fructose -----------------	} White & Hoban[103]
Maltulose	4-glucosyl fructose -----------------	
Nigerose	3-glucosyl glucose ------------------	
Kojibiose	2-glucosyl glucose ------------------	} Watanabe & Aso[92,93]
Leucrose	5-glucosyl fructose -----------------	
Higher Sugars		
Melezitose	glucosyl turanose -------------------	
Erlose	glucosyl sucrose --------------------	Goldschmidt
Kestose	fructosyl sucrose -------------------	and
Raffinose	galactosyl sucrose ------------------	Burkert[26]
Dextrantriose	glucosyl isomaltose -----------------	

Recently it was found (Stinson et al.[80]) that the most important acid in honey is gluconic acid, which is derived from dextrose. Other acids identified for the first time in honey, in addition to those listed above, were lactic and pyroglutamic. The inorganic acids, phosphoric and hydrochloric, are also present. Honey contains traces of amino acids, the building blocks of proteins. Komamine[40] has identified sixteen such acids in honey.

Minerals in Honey. The ash content of honey averages about 0.17 per cent of its weight, but varies widely, from 0.02 to over 1.0 per cent. Schuette and his students examined the composition of honey minerals rather extensively (see Table 6).

Although the mineral content of honey is not very high, honey added to the diet in place of sugar does increase the mineral intake and thereby adds to the other values for honey.

Calcium and phosphorous are the minerals present in the body in the largest amount; next in order come potassium, sulfur, sodium, chlorine, and magnesium. About 99 per cent of the calcium and 80 to 90 per cent

TABLE 6. Mineral Constituents of Honey (Parts per Million)*
(Rearranged from Schuette et al.†)

Element	Number of Samples‡	Light Honeys			Dark Honeys		
		Average	Minimum	Maximum	Average	Minimum	Maximum
Potassium	13, 18	205	100	588	1676	115	4733
Chlorine	10, 13	52	23	75	113	48	201
Sulfur	10, 13	58	36	108	100	56	126
Calcium	14, 21	49	23	68	51	5	266
Sodium	13, 18	18	6	35	76	9	400
Phosphorus	14, 21	35	23	50	47	27	58
Magnesium	14, 21	19	11	56	35	7	126
Silica (SiO$_2$)	14, 21	22	14	36	36	13	72
Silicon (Si)	10, 10	8.9	7.2	11.7	14	5.4	28.3
Iron	10, 10	2.4	1.2	4.8	9.4	0.7	33.5
Manganese	10, 10	0.30	0.17	0.44	4.09	0.52	9.53
Copper	10, 10	0.29	0.14	0.70	0.56	0.35	1.04

*The parts per million equal the milligrams per kilogram, or divided by 10,000 equal the actual per cent of the total honey composition.

†Schuette, H. A., and D. J. Huenink. 1937. Mineral constituents of honey. II. Phosphorus, calcium, and magnesium. Food Res. 2:529-538.

†Schuette, H. A., and R. E. Triller. 1938. Mineral constituents of honey. III. Sulfur and chlorine. Food Res. 3:543-547.

†Schuette, H. A., and W. W. Woessner. 1939. Mineral constituents of honey. IV. Sodium and potassium. Food Res. 4:349-353.

†Schuette, H. A., and K. Remy. 1932 Degree of pigmentation and its probable relationship to the mineral content of honey. J. Am. Chem. Soc. 54:2909-2913.

‡The first figure refers to the number of samples of light honeys, while the second figure refers to the number of samples of dark honeys.

of the phosphorus are in the bones and teeth; the rest is in the soft tissues and body fluids and is highly important to their normal function. Sodium and potassium are similar in chemical properties but differ in their location within the body. Sodium is largely in the fluids circulating outside the cells while potassium is mostly inside the body cells. They are vital in keeping a normal balance of water between the cells and the fluids. They are also essential for nerve response and muscle contraction and, with proteins, phosphates, and carbonates, keep a proper balance between the amount of acid and alkali in the blood. Magnesium is related to calcium and phosphorus in its location and function in the body, with about 70 per cent of the body magnesium in the bones, and the rest in soft tissues and blood, where it has several important roles.

Minerals occurring in very much lower amounts in the body are known as trace elements. Those required for growth of animals include copper, iodine, iron, magnesium, manganese, and zinc. Molybdenum and fluorine are also important. The table lists the amounts of four of these in honey. Iron is vital because it is a constituent of hemoglobin and also of several enzymes which are important in oxidative reactions. Manganese is also most important in many enzyme systems and is the primary metal for the enzymes of the citric-acid cycle, the scheme of metabolism wherein most of the final oxidation to carbon dioxide occurs. The details of the function of copper in humans are obscure. It is thought to be concerned with the oxidation of tyrosine and vitamin C and in the formation of melanin, the skin pigment. It is also involved in many aspects of iron metabolism.

It may be seen from Table 6 that, in general, dark honeys are richer in minerals than light honeys. This was noted by the Wisconsin group, and has been confirmed statistically in a recent survey of American honeys (White[99]).

Enzymes in Honey. Enzymes are complex materials formed in living cells that aid in carrying out the myriad reactions and processes of life. In their presence, processes are easily accomplished that man has not learned to duplicate in their absence. The most important enzyme in honey is undoubtedly invertase (also known as saccharase or sucrase) which converts the sucrose of nectar into the "invert sugars," dextrose and levulose, found in honey (*see* "Ripening of Honey"). Another important enzyme (for a different reason) is the diastase (amylase) found in honey. Its origin and function in honey are obscure; it has been stated to arise chiefly from the bee (Ammon[2]). Its importance lies in its ease of measurement and its instability to heat. Europeans, who prefer their honey essentially unheated, use the diastase level as an index of the heating history of a honey. Occasionally honey shipments are downgraded by German importers as being too low in diastase and hence useful only as commercial honey at a lower price. Some U.S. honeys are naturally low in diastase, but it is claimed this is due to climatic conditions. It is finally being recognized that the diastase content of an unheated honey can deteriorate in storage (White,[100] Hadorn and Kovacs[29]). Half of the diastase content can disappear in 17 months at ordinary temperatures (75 to 80° F.). Other enzymes reported to occur in honey are catalase and phosphatase. An enzyme producing acid has been reported (Cocker,[15] White[96]).

Vitamins in Honey. There is no doubt that honey contains small but measurable amounts of several vitamins. Using both chemical methods and bioassays, Haydak et al.[31] found thiamin, riboflavin, ascorbic acid, pyridoxine, pantothenic acid, and nicotinic acid, in low and extremely variable amounts, which they ascribed to the floral source and pollen content of the honey. They also noted that filtration of honey diminished its vitamin content. Kitzes, Schuette, and Elvehjem[38] assayed 40 samples from various parts of the country and of various ages for the B vitamins (riboflavin, pantothenic acid, thiamin, nicotinic acid, and pyridoxine). Their results for the latter two vitamins were much lower than those of Haydak *et al.* They found variation among samples to be large and also ascribed it to honey source and pollen content.

Viewed in the light of the recommended daily requirements of the various vitamins and the amounts of honey normally consumed, the vitamin content of honey is of little practical significance.

Honey Dextrins. In the earlier methods of analyses of honey, measurement was made of the amount of material thrown out of honey solution by the addition of strong alcohol. This material was called honey dextrin by analogy with similar behavior of starch sirup when mixed with alcohol. Starch dextrins are long-chain compounds of glucose formed by partial breakdown of starch. The so-called honey dextrins have been shown (von Fellenberg and Ruffy[24]) to be quite different from starch dextrins. The "dextrin" (or "higher sugar") content of honeydew is generally higher than of honey. The higher sugars of honey all contain levulose and can thereby be differentiated from the glucose-containing starch dextrins; in fact, admixture of corn sirup with honey can be detected in this way (White[97]).

Honey Colloids. Colloids are large molecules or aggregates of smaller molecules that exist in permanent dispersion in a liquid. They do not settle out and are too small to be filtered out by ordinary filtration media. They are intermediate between materials in true solution (sugars in honey) and in suspension (pollen grains, for example). Lothrop and Paine[47,48,49,67] have studied honey colloids extensively. They report them to be gummy, noncrystalline substances consisting of proteins, waxes, pentosans, and inorganic constituents. They have examined the influence of colloids on honey properties—foaming, color, and turbidity. Light honeys usually contain around 0.2 per cent colloidal matter while dark honeys may contain nearly 1 per cent.

Biologically Active Materials in Honey. In this category such entities as vitamins and minerals might be included insofar as they possess specific biological activity, i.e. a response by living material to their presence. Over the years honey has been examined for several kinds of biological activity. Such responses as root-promoting activity (Oliver[65]), amelioration of guinea pig joint stiffness (Church[14]), estrogenic activity (Dingemanse[17]), yeast-growth response (Lochhead and Farrell[44]), antibacterial action (Dold, Du, and Dziao[18]), cholinergic action (Marquart and Vogg[52]), and "appetite promotion" (Anon.[3]) have been reported in the scientific and lay literature. Some of these are presently under study; others appear to be well established. Cholinergic activity has been ascribed to the presence of choline and acetylcholine in honey. The antibacterial activity appears to be due to a heat-sensitive, light-sensitive material termed *inhibine;* little is known of its composition, though the effect has received considerable study.*

AROMA AND FLAVOR OF HONEY

The aroma and flavor of honey are its most important characteristics from the beekeeper's and consumer's point of view, yet relatively little

---

*Recent research has indicated that inhibine is actually hydrogen peroxide produced by natural glucose oxidase in honey. Am. Bee J. 102(11):430-431.

work has been done on them. When beekeeping and processing practices are considered, their effect on flavor is often ignored.

The delightful aroma and flavor of fresh honey are remembered with pleasure by all who experience this. Yet we may at times be disappointed by flavor (and off-flavor) of commercial honeys. There are as many different honey flavors as there are plant nectar sources. Many of these are of only local significance, and usually preferences are expressed for many honey types in their area of production that would not be especially welcome elsewhere. There are of course some kinds of honey that are unpalatable to humans though acceptable to bees as stores. Beekeepers are generally adept at avoiding the inclusion of such honeys in their salable product.

The delicate bouquet and fine flavor of honey are particularly vulnerable to heat and improper storage. In addition to loss of the more volatile aromas, excessive heat can alter honey flavors and introduce off-flavors from the effect of heat on the sugars, acids, and protein materials in honey. Heating can be applied to honey to delay granulation and avoid fermentation without danger of flavor damage if care is given to the duration as well as the amount of heat. Removal of heat after the desired treatment is essential to the best quality product. Flavor loss can also be serious during storage, as explained in more detail under "Storage of Honey."

Little is known of the specific materials responsible for honey flavor and aroma, other than sweetness. With new and extremely sensitive methods of analyses now in use, this situation should soon improve.

FLORAL TYPES OF HONEY

Of the hundreds of nectar-bearing plants which bees visit, relatively few are of commercial importance, though the taste and color characteristics of hundreds have been described (Pellett,[69] Lovell[50]). Each honey type has a characteristic flavor and color and can thus be identified. They also are relatively consistent in other characteristics—relative amounts of the various sugars, acids, nitrogen, and ash content. Table 7 shows how the average composition of 74 honey types and 4 honeydews compares with the average of all American honeys. In the table a plus sign means that the honey type is higher than the average in the listed characteristics, a minus sign means that it is lower, and no mark means that it is near the average. An "n" means that insufficient data were available to estimate. These data were obtained in a recent analytical survey of American honeys (White et al,[108]). In the same work it was shown that area of production has little effect on the composition of honey (Fig. 2) with cotton honey from three states, alfalfa honey from two areas, and orange honey from two states showing relatively little variation in composition (White[100]).

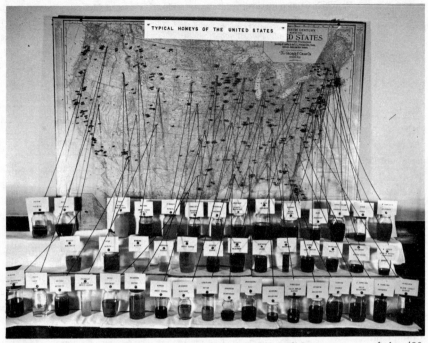

FIGURE 2. This is a display of typical honeys of the United States—a part of the 490 samples collected by Dr. White. (*U.S.D.A. photo by M. C. Audsley*)

Nectar and its Conversion to Honey

It has been said that to know the composition of nectar we need only to examine the components of honey, the only difference being changes in the water content and inversion of sucrose. This is over-simplification, since it is not clear which of the minor components (enzymes, vitamins, some nitrogen compounds, and acids) may have been added by the bee. Relatively less is known of the composition of nectar because of the difficulty of obtaining sufficient material for examination of the minor components. As long ago as 1886 (Planta[70]) it was found that nectar contained dextrose and levulose as well as sucrose. Recent quantitative work has shown that though the relative amounts of these three sugars vary widely, they may be relatively constant for a species (Wykes,[112] Maurizio,[56] Bailey et al.[7]). The ratios of levulose to dextrose show a much greater variation for nectar than found in honey. Other sugars have been reported in nectar. Wykes[111] found traces of maltose, melibiose, and raffinose; Taufel and Reiss[81] reported five unidentified sugars in nectar, and Furgala et al.[25] confirmed the presence of appreciable amounts (1 to 26 per cent of solids) of maltose. The solids content of nectar varies enormously among

TABLE 7. Characterization of Various Floral Types of Honey

	Color	Granulation	Levulose	Dextrose	Sucrose	Maltose	Higher Sugars	Undetermined	pH	Free Acidity	Lactone	Total Acidity	Lactone/Free Acid	Ash	Nitrogen	Diastase
Alfalfa		+		+	+		−	−					+	−	−	
Aster	+	−			−	+				+			−	+		n[1]
Athel Tree	+	+	+	+			−							+	+	n
Bamboo, Japanese			−		+											n
Basswood														−	−	
Bergamot	+		+								+	+				n
Blackberry	+	−		−		+	+			+			−	+		−
Blueberry	+					+				+						n
Blue Curls		+	−	+						−		+				n
Bluevine			−	−												n
Boneset	+		+	−								+		+		
Buckwheat	+	−			+					+		+				+
Canteloupe		+		+							+	+			−	−
Cape vine			−			−										−
Chinquapin	+	−	−	−		+	+	+	+		−		−			
Clover, crimson	−									−				−	−	
Clover, hubam	−			+					−					−	−	n
Clover, sweet yellow	−	+			+					−	−		+	−	−	n
Coralvine	+	−	−	−			+	+	+	+		+		+	+	n
Cotton		+		+	−	−			+				+			
Cranberry	+	−	−	−			+	+	+				+			
Gallberry		−	+							+				−		
Goldenrod				+	−	−			+		−		−			+
Grape	+	−	−	−		+						+			+	n
Holly	+	−		−		+	+			+						n
Horsemint				+	−					−	+	+	+			
Locust	−	+	−							−		−		−	−	−
Manzanita		+	−	+						−		−			−	n
Marigold				+			−			−	+		+	−		+
Mesquite		+	+	+			−					−			−	n
Mexican clover	+	−								+		+				+
Mint	−		+	+		−									−	
Mountain laurel	−	−	−	−	−	+	+	+	+	−	−	−	−			+
Mustard	+	−		−	+					+				+	+	
Orange									−			+	+	−		n

Characterization of Various Floral Types of Honey—*Continued*

	Color	Granulation	Levulose	Dextrose	Sucrose	Maltose	Higher Sugars	Undetermined	pH	Free Acidity	Lactone	Total Acidity	Lactone/Free Acid	Ash	Nitrogen	Diastase
Orange-grapefruit					+									−	−	−
Palmetto	−					+			+	−	−				−	−
Palmetto, saw	+									+	+	+	+		−	−
Pepperbush	+	−						+		+			+			−
Peppermint	+	+							+				−	+		n
Peppervine	+	−	−	−	+										−	−
Poison oak		−			−	+	+	+						+	+	n
Privet	+						−		−	+	+	+				n
Prune	+	+	−	−	+	−			+	−	−	−	−	+	+	n
Raspberry	+	−	−	−	+						+		+		+	−
Rhododendron	−	−	−	−	+		+		+	−	−	−			−	+
Sage		−	+	−												n
Snowbrush	+									+		+				+
Sourwood		−				−	+	+	+		−	−		−		
Spanish needle	+	−	+	−						+	+	+	+		+	+
Spearmint		+											+			n
Sumac	+	−	−				+	+	+	+		+	−	+	+	+
Sunflower	+	−						−		+	+				+	−
Thistle, blue	−	−								−		−		−		n
Thistle, star			−		+		+		−	+	+	+				+
Thyme	+								+					+	+	n
Titi	+						−		+	−	−	−	−	+	−	
Titi, spring	+	−	+	−				+	+	−	−	−	−			n
Trefoil	−									−				−	−	−
Tulip tree	+	−	−	−	+		+	+	+	+	−	+	−	+	+	
Tupelo		−	+	−						−	+	+	−			
Alfalfa honeydew	+	+	−							+	−	+	−	+	+	n
Cedar honeydew	+	−	−	−		−	+	+	+	+	+	−	+			n
Hickory honeydew	+	−	−	−	+		+	+	+	+	−	+	−	+		n
Oak honeydew	+	−	−	−	+			+	+	+	+	−	+		+	n

Near average in all above characteristics except diastase, which differs as shown in parentheses: Wild buckwheat (+); clover, alsike; clover, sweet; clover, white; crotalaria (−); cucumber; eucalyptus; fireweed; heartsease (n); palmetto, cabbage; pentstemon (n); purple loosestrife (n); rosinweed (+); vetch; vetch, hairy (−).

[1] "n" means insufficient data were availabe to allow valid comparison.

different plants with extremes of 3 and 76 per cent recorded. The average concentration range in species visited by the honey bee is 20 to 40 per cent; Wykes[110] and Park[68] have shown that only a very slight decrease in concentration takes place between the flower and the hive. As shown in Chapter IV, "Activities of Honey Bees," the solids content increases rapidly in the hive to full honey density.

Aside from this increase in body, the most obvious change is the conversion of nectar sucrose to dextrose and levulose. For many years it has been known that such action ("inversion") does not stop when honey is harvested, but continues slowly during storage if the honey has not been heated. It is brought about by the enzyme invertase added by the bee. With the sucrose inverted, honey can attain a much higher sugar concentration, with higher efficiency in storage and immunity from spoilage by ordinary yeasts and molds.

In a study of the action of yeast invertase on sucrose, English workers noted that the process was not a simple splitting of sucrose to dextrose and levulose but that several more complex sugars appeared during the process to disappear at the conclusion. A similar process was then found (White and Maher[105]) to take place when honey invertase acted on sucrose, with different, more complex sugars being formed.

One of these new sugars which was isolated, its structure determined, and named "erlose" by White and Maher,[106] has been found to be a common constituent of honey and honeydew (Goldschmidt and Burkert,[26] Maurizio[57]). Honey invertase has been shown to differ from other invertases (yeast, mold, and plant invertases) in its action on sucrose.

Thus in the nectar-to-honey transformation, some nectar sugars (dextrose, levulose, and maltose) become more concentrated; sucrose is largely split to dextrose and levulose, and such by-products appear as maltose, isomaltose, erlose and, according to Goldschmidt and Burkert,[26] traces of other complex sugars (kestose, dextantriose). Another source of the rare sugars in honey may be the action of honey acids on the concentrated simple sugars. In order to trace the source of the rare sugars found in honey, Taufel and Muller[82] studied the sugars of pollen finding, however, only sucrose, dextrose, and levulose.

Maurizio[56] has made an exhaustive study of the sugars of various nectars and the corresponding honeys. She points out that the sugar "spectrum" of a honey depends on the sugars present in the nectar and the influence of enzymes of the bee and of the nectar. She has classified various nectars and honeys on the basis of the dextrose-levulose ratio and the relative levels of sucrose and monosaccharides.

Relatively little is known of the origin of other honey constituents such as the acids and vitamins. Komamine[40] has suggested that a part of the amino acids of honey originate from pollen. Probably the bee

FIGURE 3. The jar of honey at left has granulated completely. The bubblelike formation toward the top of the jar is the result of fermentation after granulation. The jar in the center represents partial granulation with coarse crystals in the upper half and the lower part solidly granulated. The jar of honey at right shows natural partial liquefaction after complete granulation. Eventually, the sample may completely liquefy.

adds diastase, since sugar-fed honey shows diastatic activity, but some may arise from pollen, as a correlation between these factors has been shown (Vansell and Freeman[89]).

It may appear that at least some of the vitamin content of honey may be associated with pollen, since filtration has been reported to lower the content of several vitamins (Haydak et al.[32]).

Granulation of Honey

A supersaturated solution is one that contains more dissolved material than can normally remain in solution. Such solutions are more or less unstable and in time will return to the stable saturated condition with the excessive material coming out of solution. Many honeys are in this category with respect to their dextrose content and will equilibrate by crystallizing the excessive dextrose out of solution. Crystallizing tendency is related to honey composition and storage conditions; some honeys never crystallize while others will do so within a few days of extraction, or even in the comb (Fig. 3).

Granulation is characterized by firmness and by the fineness of the crystals or grain. A fine-grained crystallization is characteristic of an unheated honey, or one that has been "seeded" either naturally or intentionally with fine-grained honey. Such semi-solid honey, sold under various trade names, is of a fine nongrainy, nonrunning texture that facilitates its use at the table. It is susceptible to breakdown or softening of texture when stored at temperatures higher than 80 to 85° F., and also can soften and partly liquefy due to natural changes at lower temperatures (*see* "Storage of Honey").

When honey granulates slowly, either because of its composition or because natural "seed" crystals have been destroyed by heat, the size of crystals is much larger; such a product is of reduced commercial value. Careful heating will redissolve such crystals; the coarser they are, generally, the more difficult they are to redissolve (*see* "Processing and Storage of Honey").

Several attempts have been made to express the liability of a honey to granulate. The ratio of levulose to dextrose has been most used. Recently, White[102] has shown that the dextrose-to-water ratio first applied by Austin[5] is more closely related to the granulation tendency of honey than other indices are. D/W ratios of 1.70 or lower appear to be associated with nongranulating honey, and values of 2.10 and higher predict rapid completion of granulation.

Table 7, "Characterization of Various Floral Types of Honey," shows the granulating tendency of many honeys insofar as it deviates from the average. Honeys marked "minus" in the column under "granulation" are substantially nongranulating and those marked "plus" granulate rapidly. Even though a honey may be a granulating type, it can be maintained in the liquid state for considerable time. If the so-called "crystal nuclei" (very fine crystals of dextrose, dust particles, or possibly pollen grains) are eliminated and the honey is protected from subsequent contamination and storage temperatures favoring crystallization (50 to 60° F.) are avoided, honey will remain liquid for many months.

The most favorable temperature for honey granulation is 57° F., with both higher and lower temperatures being less effective. Storage of honey at very low temperatures (0° F. or lower) greatly retards but does not eliminate granulation, probably because the extremely high viscosity reduces the diffusion necessary to the increase of crystal size. Granulation does not take place at these temperatures. According to de Boer,[9] the most effective temperature for *initiation* of crystallization is lower, around 5 to 7° C. (41 to 45° F.); fluctuating temperatures in these ranges are particularly effective in promoting granulation.

Since the U.S. retail honey market largely favors liquid honey, some type of processing is necessary to maintain the liquid state, as many honey types will normally granulate, though some will not. This is most commonly done by straining, heating, or filtration. Heating must be done without damage to flavor or color. The most-used heating conditions appear to be 30 minutes at 140 to 150° F. In general, lower

FIGURE 4. This simple polariscope is a great aid in judging honey. (*U.S.D.A. photo by M. C. Audsley*)

FIGURE 5. Cleanliness and crystallization in honey are readily observed by the light. (*U.S.D.A. photo by M. C. Audsley*)

temperatures, even for much longer times, will not be effective. Higher temperatures may be used providing the time is sufficiently short and means are included for rapidly reducing honey temperature to 130° or less. Austin[4] recommended 170° for 5 minutes with rapid cooling.

After a honey is processed for destruction of crystals and nuclei, care must be taken to avoid re-contamination with dextrose crystals. Dextrose crystals, like yeasts, may actually float in the air in the honey house. Utensils, storage tanks, and pipelines may contain crystals.

Small crystals may be present in honey and induce granulation without being perceptible to the unaided eye. A useful device in examining honey for crystal traces (White and Maher[104]) is shown in Figure 4. This simple polariscope can easily demonstrate the presence of less than 0.004 per cent of fine-grained crystallized honey mixed with liquid honey. In fact, by appearing as a light object on a dark background, a single crystal is large enough to be visible (Fig. 5).

Fermentation of Honey*

Fermentation of honey is caused by the action of sugar-tolerant yeasts upon levulose and dextrose, resulting in the formation of alcohol and carbon dioxide. The alcohol in the presence of oxygen then may be broken down into acetic acid and water. As a result, honey that has fermented may have a sour taste. Due to the release of the carbon dioxide gas, fermenting granulated honey will show a lightened color, whitish streaks, or mottling, and if liquefied it will exhibit considerable foaming, particularly during heating. Upon standing, such granulated honey will partially liquefy, eventually forming an upper liquid mass capped by a foamy layer.

Fermentation of honey is often called "honey spoilage." Compared with other yeast fermentations it is relatively slow. The degree of

---

*The author has used material here from a corresponding section in the chapter by Dr. V. G. Milum in the 1949 edition of this book.

spoilage or effect upon flavor and quality depends upon the length of time fermentation is allowed to proceed before being stopped by heating or other treatment. Most honey spoilage by fermentation results after granulation. Since the greater proportion of honeys granulate after extraction and thereby become liable to fermentation, all honey producers and bottlers should be thoroughly acquainted with the factors affecting granulation and fermentation. Necessary steps should be taken to prevent spoilage by fermentation of any honey placed in storage.

Ordinary yeasts do not cause fermentation of honey because they cannot grow in the higher sugar concentration. Spoilage by bacteria is not possible because of the high acidity of honey. The primary sources of the sugar-tolerant yeasts are the flowers and the soils (Fabian and Quinet,[21] Lochhead and Heron[43]). Lochhead and Farrell[44] have shown that the soils in established apiaries contain sugar-tolerant yeasts, while the air and the equipment in the honey house are contaminated with them. Similarly, combs in the hive, particularly those containing honey from the previous season, and wet extracting combs in storage, may be abundant sources of yeasts.

It should be assumed that all honeys contain yeasts when planning for their care. The number of yeasts in various honeys will vary between rather wide limits, from one in 10 grams to 100,000 per gram; the greatest number usually being present in honeys with the highest moisture content. Uncapped combs usually have a greater number of yeasts than capped combs from the same super, the former having higher moisture content due to incomplete ripening or to absorption of moisture.

The chief factors in honey fermentation are yeast and moisture content. Interrelated with these are the storage conditions and presence of granulation. Lochhead[42] has pointed out that the honeys with less than 17.1 per cent water will not ferment in a year, no matter what the yeast count may be. If the moisture content lies between 17.1 and 18 per cent, honey with a yeast count of 1000 per gram or less will be safe from fermentation for a year; between 18.1 and 19 per cent moisture, a count must be only 10 per gram to assure a honey keeping for a year. Above this moisture level, more than one yeast spore per gram means an active danger of fermentation. Granulation of honey always increases the liability of fermentation because of the appreciable increase in the moisture content of the remaining liquid portion. Most honey that ferments does so after granulation. According to Wilson and Marvin,[94] honey yeasts will not grow below 52° F., hence storage at 50° F. or below should protect honey from fermentation. Temperatures of 52 to 60° should be avoided because they encourage granulation. Storage at higher temperatures (100° F.) would also prevent fermentation but honey is damaged by storage at such elevated temperatures.

If honey is heated at 145° F. for 30 minutes it will be safe from fermentation if protected from further yeast contamination. Townsend[84] has found that the vegetative forms of five honey yeasts common in Canada are destroyed in honey of 18.6 per cent moisture by the time-temperature conditions shown below.

TABLE 8. Conditions Required to Kill Yeasts in Honey*

Time at Indicated Temperature	Temperature
470 min.	125°F.
170	130
60	135
22	140
7.5	145
2.8**	150
1.0**	155

*Calculated from data of Townsend.[84] "Come-up" time not included.
**Extrapolated from logarithmic curve constructed from Townsend's data.

Where unheated honey is stored in bulk overwinter, it may be relatively safe during cold weather but is most liable to spoil in the spring or if shipped to a warmer storage place during the winter.

To summarize:

1. All honey should be considered to contain yeasts.
2. Honey is more liable to fermentation after granulation.
3. Honey of over 17 per cent moisture may and over 19 per cent will ferment.
4. Storage below 50° F. will prevent fermentation during such storage but not later.
5. Heating to 145° F. for 30 minutes, or equivalent, will destroy honey yeasts and thus prevent fermentation.

Processing and Storage of Honey

The flavor and desirability of well-ripened honey are at their peak in the comb. Man's efforts to convert it to his use must inevitably result in some deterioration, but whether it is significant depends on the treatment received in the hands of the beekeeper and subsequent handlers. The best processing is the least processing that will meet the objectives. While "raw" honey will always have its devotees, today's retail markets require a honey that will not ferment—one that will remain liquid and have an attractive appearance. These objectives are sometimes met at the expense of honey's most valuable asset, flavor, but with proper methods can be attained with preservation of the original full flavor and aroma.

Heat is the only practical agency for preventing granulation and fermentation but it is a cause of deterioration of honey quality. Application of heat by the so-called "flash" method, a continuous process in which a honey is heated very rapidly in small quantity in a closed system, strained or filtered and then rapidly cooled, probably represents the least heat exposure that will accomplish the desired ends. Treatment in a closed system minimizes losses of volatile aroma during the heating period, and cooling minimizes heat-induced flavor and color changes and allows a higher heat to be used for a shorter time. Townsend and Adie[87] have described equipment that will heat and cool 300 or 600 lbs. of honey per hour, either for a liquid or granulated honey pack. Honey must have a preliminary straining before being heated so that off-odors or flavors will not be imparted by the action of hot honey on the extraneous material.

With honey becoming less of a seasonal commodity since modern merchandising requires year-round availability, the proper storage of honey grows more important. Honey for export may be stored before or after shipping, or both, and unfavorable storage conditions can bring about enough lowering of honey quality to cause considerable confusion between buyer and seller. Honey stored under government loan may deteriorate seriously in color. The changes that take place in honey during storage have only recently been examined in detail. It has long been known that honey darkens with age and Milum[58] has shown that heat processing does not increase the later darkening of honey. His data demonstrate the dependence of honey darkening upon temperature of storage.

De Boer[10] noted that the changes which are brought about in honey by heating also occur during long storage of honey. He specifically referred to the production of hydroxymethylfurfural, a degredation product of honey sugars, and a weakening of honey enzymes. He did not agree with earlier investigators that the ratio of fructose to dextrose decreased. It has recently been found (White, Riethof, and Kushnir[107]) that during storage of honey at ordinary temperatures (76° F. $\pm 3°$) about 9 per cent of the simple sugars are converted into more complex forms, with twice as much dextrose disappearing as levulose. Thus the ratio of levulose to dextrose does decline considerably. Acidity of some honey increases in storage, and half of the diastase in a honey will be lost after 17 months of such storage. Thus an unheated honey can be naturally low in diastase if it has been stored for an appreciable time.

All of these deteriorative changes can be avoided by storing honey at low temperatures. For this purpose temperatures should be below 50° F. for unheated honey though great advantage will result from avoiding temperatures over 60° F. In fact, honey kept at very low temperatures for years cannot be distinguished in properties, flavor, color, and aroma from the season's freshest product. It must be remembered, however, that the 50 to 60° interval is particularly dangerous for unheated honey from the fermentation viewpoint. Storage temperatures in the 80's and particularly the 90's, even for relatively short times, must be avoided for a quality product. Deterioration in color, flavor, and enzyme content is particularly rapid in this range.

Preparation of Honey for Market. This is the title of a comprehensive bulletin by Townsend[85] of Ontario Agricultural College. Detailed procedures and diagrams are given describing the removal of moisture from honey before extraction (with details on hot rooms), uncapping, and straining, including details on the O.A.C. and a modified strainer, as well as the O.A.C. pressure strainer. Small-scale extraction and straining also are described.

For melting honey for repacking, Townsend describes a cabinet that will melt ten cans of honey overnight in which the honey does not exceed 135° F. A procedure for packing liquid honey and finely granulated honey is given in detail. Processing equipment such as a continuous-flow mixer for honey spread, a continuous-flow, high-temperature short-time pasturizer, including cooling for 300 or 600 lbs. of honey per hour, is also described. When remelting coarsely granulated honey in inverted 60-lb. cans, difficulty can arise through the flowing away of the more liquid part before the coarse dextrose crystals can redissolve. This can result in a substantial fraction of the contents remaining unmelted, as a crude dextrose hydrate in the can. Several such occurrences have recently been described (White[95]).

EXHIBITION OF HONEY

Honey shows are becoming increasingly popular as a means of reminding the public of the goodness of honey. These exhibitions serve as a potential means of improving honey quality by demonstrating the possibilities of careful handling, and in providing a common ground of competition where the hobbyist can meet the larger producer on even terms.

Showing honey is not difficult but it does require a high level of care and attention to detail. All instructions for entries must be followed to the letter. For liquid honey, careful settling and straining are required, as judges note even the presence of a single bubble on the surface of the honey. Caps must be clean inside and out and jars should be selected for uniformity and uniformly filled. Dust and fine crystals, not easily visible to the unaided eye, may be easily visualized by a judge using the polariscope described in this chapter. Body or moisture content is important; ordinarily there is a maximum moisture value beyond which an entry is disqualified, with additional credit being awarded for lower moisture content to a full count of points for moisture at some lower value. Flavor is an important attribute, with judgment being similar to that of the U.S. Grades.

In judging finely granulated honey, the texture is probably the most important factor. Absence of grittiness, solidified foam and extraneous material on the surface is highly important. The honey must be neither too hard to spread nor so soft that it runs from the knife, and flavor is as important as with liquid honey. Moisture judgment is not made, since texture and firmness fix the limits.

The score sheet shown here is that of The Eastern Apicultural Society and will provide an idea of the weight given to the various factors by the judges.

HONEY JUDGING SCORE SHEET

EXTRACTED HONEY

1. Degree of density -- 20 points
   a. All entries with water content above 18.6 per cent disqualified
2. Freedom from crystals --- 10 ”
3. Degree of cleanliness and freedom from foam (clarity) -------- 30 ”
4. Cleanliness and neatness of containers --------------------- 10 ”
5. Flavor --- 30 ”
   a. Absence of: off-flavor, overheating, and fermentation

                                                  100 points

COMB HONEY AND BULK HONEY FRAME

1. Uniformity of appearance --------------------------------------- 20 points
2. Absence of uncapped cells ----------------------------------- 10 ”
3. Uniformity of color -- 15 ”
4. Absence of watery cappings ------------------------------------ 10 ”
5. Cleanliness of section and frame ----------------------------- 15 ”
6. Freedom from granulation and pollen ----------------------- 5 ”
7. Uniformity of weight -- 15 ”
8. Total weight of entry --- 10 ”

                                                  100 points

FINELY GRANULATED HONEY

1. Fineness of crystals --- 35 points
2. Degree of uniformity and firmness --------------------------- 25 ”
3. Degree of cleanliness and freedom from foam ---------------- 15 ”
4. Flavor --- 25 ”
   a. Absence of: off-flavor, overheating, and fermentation

                                                  100 points

CHUNK HONEY

1. Neatness of cut --- 20 points
   Ragged edges, parallel cuts, four-sided cut, and uniformity of
   size of cut
2. Absence of watery cappings, uncapped cells, and pollen cells -- 20 ”
3. Cleanliness of product -- 20 ”
   a. No travel stain, specks of foreign matter, flakes of wax,
   foam and crystallization
4. Uniformity of appearance -------------------------------------- 30 ”
   a. Uniformity of capping structure, color, and thickness of comb
5. Density and flavor of liquid part ---------------------------- 10 ”

                                                  100 points

The Utilization of Honey

Honey is primarily a high-energy carbohydrate food. The amount of honey used for food far outweighs any of the miscellaneous non-food uses that have been described in the technical and popular literature.

FIGURE 6. Mild-flavored honey drizzled on grapefruit is an ideal sweetener and detracts from the tartness. Honey also is an ideal sweetener for berries and peaches. (*U.S.D.A. photo*)

Probably more honey is used directly at the table, than in any other food use (Fig. 6).

Carbohydrates provide most of the energy we need to live and act, though there is no definite nutritional requirement for them. People and animals can survive without them because the body can use fats and protein for this purpose. In general, carbohydrates in our diets may be complex polysaccharides such as starch, which is said to be nutritionally the most important carbohydrate. Only two disaccharide-type sugars (*see* "The Sugars of Honey") are of nutritional importance, sucrose (cane or beet sugar) and lactose, which makes up about 40 per cent of the solids of milk. The monosaccharides, the building blocks of the more complex carbohydrates, also occur in the free form; dextrose and levulose are found in honey and fruits.

Before they can be used by the body, all carbohydrates except monosaccharides must be hydrolyzed or digested into their simple sugar components. These monosaccharides are absorbed into the bloodstream from the intestine, with dextrose entering the bloodstream directly. Galactose (from milk sugar) and levulose are thought to be at least partly converted to dextrose as they pass through the intestinal wall.

The energy from carbohydrates becomes available to the body when dextrose is broken down in the tissues. It is similar to burning, with the great difference that oxidation in the tissues is slower and stepwise. It has been said to be in many ways like a reversal of photosynthesis, the process by which the carbohydrates are made by plants.

Thus we see that honey in providing dextrose and levulose; the latter in higher amounts, is an energy source *par excellence* in which the sugars are ready for assimilation immediately on reaching the intestine. The substantial proportion of dextrose can enter the bloodstream directly, while the fructose provides a slower acting reserve since it must ultimately be converted to dextrose before use.

HONEY IN COOKING AND BAKING*
"If you a cook of note would be,
Use honey in your recipe."
Harriett M. Grace[27]

This subject is one that includes a world of information and countless recipes which have appeared in the bee journals and in cookbooks. The American Honey Institute, Madison, Wisconsin, serves as a source for dissemination of such materials and the reader is referred to its publications, as well as to the bulletins and circulars issued by the home economics staffs of the various colleges and experimental stations.

Honey not only adds flavor in baking, but it has the distinct advantage that the final product, although seemingly dry upon coming from the oven, soon acquires a moist texture and remains palatable, without drying, over a longer period than similar products in which cane sugar is used as the sweetening agent. This quality is due to the ability of the levulose portion of the honey to absorb and hold moisture.

Every honey producer knows countless ways in which honey may be used in menus. The following are just a few suggestions: honey iced tea, honey fruitcake, honey fudge, honey oatmeal cookies, honey-glazed baked ham, honey French dressing, and hot honey lemonade (Fig. 7).

While tested recipes using honey are to be recommended, honey may be substituted as the sweetening agent where any recipe calls for sugar. In muffins, bread, and rolls, calling for a small amount of sugar, honey can replace the sugar measure for measure without any other adjustment. For cakes and cookies, which require a large amount of sugar, honey can be used measure for measure but the amount of liquid must be reduced one-fourth cup for each cup of honey used,

---

*The author has used material here from a corresponding section in the chapter by Dr. V. G. Milum in the 1949 edition of this book.

FIGURE 7. Beehive cookies attractively decorated with skeps and floral designs make an inviting display along with the skep of honey and beeswax candles. (*Photo courtesy of The American Honey Institute*)

or in the same proportion for fractions of a cup. Moderate oven temperatures, 350° to 375° F., are suggested to prevent the product from becoming too brown.

Commercial bakers have been thought to be the largest users of honey in the food industry. There is a place for honey in the largest bakery as well as the retail bakery on the corner. Though much honey is now used, the industry is so large that even a modest increase would greatly benefit the beekeepers' markets. The larger bakers (as well as other segments of the food industry) may hesitate to use honey because they fear the effects of the natural variability of honey (flavor, color, and moisture content) on their production schedules and product quality. Recent studies on the role of honey in commercial baking (Johnson, et al.[35]) carried out at Kansas State University have shown that definite advantages in flavor, keeping quality, texture, and "eating quality" arise from judicious use of honey in many types of baked goods, including breads, yeast-raised sweet goods, cakes, fruitcakes, cookies, and pies of several types. Of all the variable characteristics in honey, bakers need be careful only of flavor and color, the latter only in light-colored cakes and white bread (Fig. 8).

FIGURE 8. Breads from many lands made with honey. Honey adds flavor, keeping quality, texture, and better "eating quality" to many bakery products. (*Photo courtesy of Dr. John A. Johnson*)

Although candies made with honey are among the most delectable, commercial use of honey in confectionery is limited. Relatively little research is done by the candy industry; rather they depend upon their suppliers for this service. Here, as in pharmacy, the use of honey has declined over the years. The candymaking characteristics of honey (high monosaccharide content, especially levulose) limit the amounts that can be used in many formulas, while high temperatures in candy-making are quite destructive to honey flavor and color. Here a new product, a dried honey (Turkot et al.[88]), may be of value since it is effectively a low moisture (1 per cent) hard candy made without damage to flavor or color. Such a product could be useful in prepared baking mixes also.

Honey is an optional ingredient under the Federal Standards of Identity for fruit jellies, jams, and preserves. A prune juice "mellowed" with honey has a good market; in fact honey is the only sweetening agent that may be added to prune juice under the Standards of Identity. An important use for honey is in cereal coatings; a peanut butter enjoying a wide market has honey on the list of ingredients.

HONEY IN INFANT AND CHILD FEEDING*

Honey has been used widely in infant feeding with success. Many controlled experiments have given conclusive evidence of its value in

---

*The author has used material here from a corresponding section in the chapter by Dr. V. G. Milum in the 1949 edition of this book.

correcting various deficiencies in infants and older children. Dr. Paul Luttinger,[51] a pediatrist and pathologist of the Bronx Hospital, New York, recommended the use of honey in any condition of the intestinal tract where the assimilation of starch or the disaccharides is delayed and where prompt absorption is desired. He preferred honey to alcohol, especially in bronchopneumonia, and used it in cases of summer diarrhea in the proportion of 1 teaspoon of honey to 8 ounces of barley water.

Dr. Luttinger highly recommended the use of honey in infant feeding because it does not produce acidosis, its rapid absorption prevents it from undergoing alcoholic fermentation, its free acids favor the absorption of fats, it complements the iron deficiency in human and cow's milk, it increases appetite and peristalsis, and it has a soothing effect which reduces fretfulness.

Some of these attributes of honey seem to have been verified by subsequent investigators. Dr. Paula Emerich[20] found that anemic children had a greater increase in hemoglobin content of blood when receiving honey and milk than when milk only was added to the normal diet. Weight gains were somewhat lower in the honey group. Haydak and associates[31] concluded that "dark honey can play a role in prevention and cure of nutritional anemia in rats, while light honey is less effective as a source of the blood-forming elements."

Numerous observers, including Rolleder,[72] Muniagurria,[61] Lahdensuu,[41] Stancanelli,[78] and Farioli,[22] in tests using honey in feeding children of various ages, found special values for honey as compared to other sugars. Included in the observed benefits were an increase in the hemoglobin content of the blood, relief from constipation, better weight gains, a decrease of diarrhea and vomiting, more rapid increase in blood sugars than after sucrose administration, better weight gains when honey was substituted for dextromaltose after faulty nutrition, and good honey tolerance with infants suffering from rickets, inflammation of the intestine, malnourishment and prematurity.

Schlutz and his associates of the University of Chicago[75,76] in tests of 11 children found that with the exception of glucose, honey was absorbed most quickly of various sugars in the first 15 minutes following ingestion, yet it did not flood the bloodstream with exogenous sugars until the fasting level was again reached. They concluded that honey should have a wider use in infant feeding.

Dr. Knott and his associates[39] in a study of 14 healthy male infants for the first 6 months of their lives found better calcium retention with honey than with corn sirup. However, as other factors favoring calcium retention were made more favorable, honey had less effect because each infant has an upper level of responses which is optional for the storage of calcium. Their general conclusion was that honey deserves a wider use in infant dietaries.

More recent work in this field is that of Vignec and Julia[90] who compared honey with a dextrin-containing maltose preparation and with corn sirup as a formula supplement, using 387 infants. Honey was found superior to corn sirup with respect to average weekly weight gain, linear growth measure, and hemoglobin values. It was not superior to the other carbohydrate in these respects but less gastro-enteritis and physiological anemia developed in the honey group. They noted that most infants responded avidly to the honey formulas; this was found useful in managing prematures. They concluded that honey has a definite place in infant feeding.

With this amount of definite evidence in the case of infants and children there seem to be plenty of reasons for including honey, not only in the diets of infants and children, but in the diets of adults as well, and particularly those who are undergoing vigorous exercise under exacting conditions. Formulas which give beneficial results in infant feeding may be found in the references cited.

HONEY FOR ATHLETICS AND STRENUOUS OCCUPATIONS

Honey has been used with beneficial results by athletes in football, basketball, track including marathon running, swimming, wrestling, and 6-day bicycle racing. It has been used as a source of energy in climbing Mt. Rainer, in crossing the Grand Canyon, and in the conquest of Mt. Everest by Sir Edmund Hillary. Honey was used before and during the attempts of deep-sea divers to recover the gold of the sunken Lusitania.

Honey, as explained elsewhere, is readily assimilated, giving athletes a quick source of energy and enabling them to recuperate rapidly from severe exertion with less evidence of fatigue. The latter is particularly true when taken soon after an athletic event. Honey may be used either alone or diluted with orange juice.

HONEY AND DIABETES

One may sometimes note in the beekeeping press that honey may be used by diabetics with no ill effects. This is nonsense, since honey does contain a good proportion of dextrose, the sugar that diabetics cannot handle. Certainly, however, the dietary of the stabilized diabetic could include honey on the basis of its composition as compared with cane or beet sugar. Honey averages 31 per cent dextrose, and tupelo honey around 25 per cent. About 38 per cent of the average honey is levulose. Sucrose content averages about 1.3 per cent. Cane sugar yields in effect (after hydrolysis in the intestine) 52.5 per cent of each sugar. On a weight basis, honey is approximately as sweet as granulated sugar; hence more sweetening power might be considered available to the diabetic at a lower dextrose "price" from honey than from granulated sugar. Any substituting of honey into the diet of the diabetic should be under the direction of a physician.

SUGARS IN THE DIET

Older views of the function of carbohydrates in the diet were that they were solely sources of energy at the rate of 4 calories per gram. The only differentiation was in their availability to the organism. A tremendous amount of research has been done on the proteins and amino acids in nutrition, less on the fats, and possibly less on the sugars. The interrelationship among all of these classes is being examined. "Increasing numbers of nutritionists have for some time now discarded the once-current but unfortunate concept of dietary carbohydrates as only supplying caloric needs (so-called empty calories)."* An increasing amount of research is being done on the various aspects of carbohydrate digestion, absorption, and metabolism.

According to a recent statement,** "increasing attention will have to be paid to differences between the sugars by all concerned with food and nutrition." Dr. Anthony A. Albanese,[1] Chief of Nutritional Research at St. Luke's Hospital in New York, pointed out that the utilization of dextrose decreases markedly with age, while that of levulose is only slightly affected. His results suggested that levulose or levulose-containing products are sugars of choice for the aged in that they may provide a ready source of energy and an optimal protein-sparing effect. Thus the preference of many of our senior citizens for honey appears to have a solid foundation in nutritional science. Honey is useful in managing premature infants, a source of strength and energy for athletes and active people, and a most valuable protein-sparing carbohydrate for older people, thereby serving man through his entire lifetime.

ANTISEPTIC PROPERTIES OF HONEY

Because of the high density and acidity of honey the nonspore-forming organisms that cause human diseases cannot live in it. It was shown some years ago (Sackett[74]) that various pathogenic bacteria were killed when introduced into honey.

Another type of antibacterial activity has been demonstrated in honey (Dold et al.[18]). This is apparently due to a substance, "inhibine," which is destroyed by heat; its action against organisms is shown in dilute honey solutions and is different from the osmotic effect described above, in which the bacteria are destroyed by dehydration.

MEDICAL USES OF HONEY

A considerable medical literature (largely European) exists on the use in various disorders of honey, honey derivatives, and combinations of honey with various drugs. A number of instances of successful treatment of severe burns with honey appear in the beekeeping literature.

*Nutrition Reviews. 1960. 18:88.
**Chemistry and Industry. 1960. 49:1487.

Its high sugar content, minerals, and antibacterial action are believed responsible for its value as a surgical dressing by Bulman[11] and Seymour and West,[77] explaining a honey use known to the ancient Egyptians and popular in the Middle Ages.

Honey has been found (Martensen-Larsen[55]) to be valuable in the detoxification of drunkenness, restoring a sober state in a relatively short time.

Although honey was at one time widely used in pharmacy it was displaced long ago. Recently it was shown (Rubin et al.[73]) that honey can be used successfully as a vehicle, sweetening and flavoring a number of medicinal preparations. Stable palatable formulations of ferrous sulfate, triple sulfa, and terpin hydrate were made, as well as several effective cough preparations. Formulations containing the vitamins riboflavin and thiamine as well as riboflavin alone are sufficiently stable for commercial use.

HONEY WINE

Strictly speaking, wines are made from grapes; those made from honey are more properly "meads." They were possibly man's earliest alcoholic drinks, being known in India thousands of years ago, and the history of mead, like that of honey, can be traced through five thousand years. Classic meads may be blended with herbs; many types are recorded, such as sack mead, metheglin, sack metheglin, bochet, cyser, pyment, hippocras, and melomel.

Generally mead is not commercially available, but many beekeepers and others find it of interest to make their own. An extensive annotated bibliography is available (Morse[60]) from Cornell University. Four simple recipes have been published by Morse.[59] More detailed instructions are available (Dennis[16]).

Honeydew

This is a sweet liquid excreted by homopterous insects, principally plant lice (aphids) and scale insects, feeding on plants. It is frequently gathered and stored by bees and is generally considered inferior to honey in flavor and quality. It may often be found on leaves of such trees as oak, beech, poplar, ash, elm, hickory, maple, tulip, willow, linden, and fruit trees as well as fir, cedar, and spruce. The amount of honeydew collected will depend on the availability of nectar, which is generally preferred by the bees.

An average composition of honeydew is given in Table 9 (White[98]). It is based on 14 samples from the 1956 and 1957 crops, including alfalfa, cedar, hickory, oak, and several unidentified types.

Comparison of these values with those given for honey shows honeydew to be lower in levulose and dextrose, darker in color, and higher in pH, higher sugars, acidity, ash, and nitrogen. These differences have been noted by others; in fact Kirkwood et al.[37] have proposed a test in which a calculation is made relating the pH, ash, and reducing sugar content to the presence of honeydew.

TABLE 9. Average Composition of Honeydew and Ranges
of Values for 14 Samples

	Average	Standard Deviation	Range
Color	Amber		Ex. Lt. Amber to Dark
Moisture (%)	16.3	1.74	12.2 — 18.2
Levulose (%)	31.80	4.16	23.91 — 38.12
Dextrose (%)	26.08	3.04	19.23 — 31.86
Sucrose (%)	0.80	0.22	0.44 — 1.14
Maltose (%)	8.80	2.51	5.11 — 12.48
Higher Sugars (%)	4.70	1.01	1.28 — 11.50
Undetermined (%)	10.1	4.91	2.7 — 22.4
pH	4.45		3.90 — 4.88
Free Acid (meq./kg.)	49.07	10.57	30.29 — 66.02
Lactone (meq./kg.)	5.80	3.59	0.36 — 14.09
Total Acid (meq./kg.)	54.88	10.84	34.62 — 76.49
Lactone/Free Acid	0.127	0.092	0.007 — 0.385
Ash (%)	0.736	0.271	0.212 — 1.185
Nitrogen (%)	0.100	0.053	0.047 — 0.223
Diastase	31.9[1]		6.7 — 48.4

[1] Based on four samples only.

The sugars of stored honeydew appear to be even more complex than those of honey, perhaps since two sets of enzymes, those of the hemipterous insect and of the honey bee, are involved in honeydew stores. Several investigators have studied the sugars of honeydew as excreted by the insects, using modern methods of analysis. Levulose, dextrose, and melezitose have long been known. Gray and Fraenkel[28] found erlose (fructomaltose) in several honeydews. Duspiva[19] found, in addition, a series of higher sugars related to erlose by the successive stepwise addition of glucose molecules. This was confirmed by Wolf and Ewart.[109] Bacon and Dickinson[6] presented evidence that the melezitose common to many honeydews does not arise from the plant as previously believed but is produced from plant sap sucrose by an enzyme in the aphid involved. To the best of our knowledge, melezitose has never been isolated directly from a plant source. Thus it appears that there are (at least) two types of honeydew: the melezitose type, which can granulate rapidly, even in the comb; and the erlose type, which does not granulate.

The unsuitability of honeydew as winter stores for bees has generally been ascribed to melezitose and "dextrins." Temnov,[83] however, lays the toxic effects of honeydew principally to the mineral salts it contains, especially potassium. Addition of the salts contained in honeydew to floral honey or sirup was found to make them also unsuitable for wintering.

REFERENCES CITED

1. Albanese, A. A. 1954. Clin. and Exptl. **3**:154.

2. Ammon, R. 1949. Biochem. Z. **319**:295-299.

3. Anon. 1957. Am. Bee J. **97**:281.

4. Austin, G. H. 1953. Can. Bee J. **61**:10-12,20-23.

5. ----------------. 1958. 10th Intern. Congr. Entomol. Proc. (1956) **4**:1001-1006.

6. Bacon, J. S. D., and B. Dickinson. 1955. Biochem. J. **61**:xv-xvi.

7. Bailey, M. E., E. A. Fieger, and E. Oertel. 1954. Gl. Bee Cult. **82**:401-403, 472-474.

8. Bauer, F. W. 1960. Calif. Expt. Sta. Bull. **776**. 71 pp.

9. Boer, H. E. de. 1932. Bee World **13**(2):14-18.

10. ----------------. 1934. Chem. Weekblad **31**:482-487.

11. Bulman, M. W. 1955. Brit. Bee J. **83**:664-665.

12. Chataway, H. D. 1932. Can. J. Res. **6**:532-537.

13. ----------------. 1935. Can. Bee J. **43**:215.

14. Church, J. 1954. Fed. Proc. **13**:26.

15. Cocker, L. C. 1951. J. Sci. Food Agr. **2**:411-414.

16. Dennis, C. B. 1957. A background to mead making. 3d ed. Central Assoc Beekeepers. Ilford, Essex, England. 15 pp.

17. Dingemanse, E. 1938. Acta. Brev. neerl. Phys. Pharm. Microbiol. **8**:55-58.

18. Dold, H., D. H. Du, and S. T. Dziao. 1937. Z. Hyg. Infectionskr. **120**:155-167.

19. Duspiva, F. 1954. Verhand. Deut. Zool. Gesel. 439-447.

20. Emerich, P. 1923. Umden. Schweiz. Bienen Ztg. **46**:136-142.

21. Fabian, F. W., and R. I. Quinet. 1928. Mich. Agr. Expt. Sta. Tech. Bull. **92**. 41 pp.

22. Farioli, A. 1937. Riv. di Clin. Pediat. **34**:337.

23. Feinberg, B. 1951. Am. Bee J. **91**:471.

24. Fellenberg, Th. von, and J. Ruffy. 1933. Mitt. geb. Lebensm. Forsch. **24**:367-392.

25. Furgala, B., T. A. Gochnauer, and F. G. Holdaway. 1958. Bee World **39**:203-205.

26. Goldschmidt, S., and H. Burkert. 1955. Z. Physiol. Chem. **300**:188-200.

27. Grace, Harriett M. 1947. New favorite recipes. Am. Honey Inst., Madison, Wis.

28. Gray, H. E., and G. Fraenkel. 1953. Science **118**:304-305.

29. Hadorn, H., and A. S. Kovacs. 1960. Mitt. Lebesm. Hyg. **51**:373-390.

30. Haydak, M. H., L. S. Palmer, and M. C. Tanquary. 1942. J. Pediatrics **26**(6):763-768.

31. Haydak, M. H., L. S. Palmer, M. C. Tanquary, and A. E. Vivino. 1942. J. Nutrition **23**:581-587.

32. ----------------. 1943. J. Nutrition **26**:319-321.

33. Herrick, A. D. 1948. Food regulations and compliance. Revere Pub. Co., New York. p. 433.

34. Johnson, J. A., R. K. Eskew, and J. B. Claffey. 1960. Food Technol. 14:387-390.
35. Johnson, J. A., P. Nordin, and D. Miller. 1957. Bakers Digest 31:33-34,36,38,40.
36. Killion, C. E. 1950. Am. Bee J. 90:14-16.
37. Kirkwood, K. C., I. J. Mitchell, and I. Smith. 1960. Analyst 85:412-416.
38. Kitzes, G., H. A. Schuette, and C. A. Elvehjem. 1943. J. Nutrition 26:241-249.
39. Knott, M. E., C. F. Shukers, and F. W. Schlutz. 1941. J. Pediatrics 19:485-494.
40. Komamine, A. 1960. Soumen Kemistlehti. B 33:185-187.
41. Lahdensuu, S. 1931. Acta. Soc. Med. Fenn. Duodecim. 15:1.
42. Lochhead, A. G. 1933. Zent. Bakt. Parasitenk. 2 abt. 88:296.
43. Lochhead, A. G., and D. A. Heron. 1929. Can. Dept. Agr. Bull 116 (N.S.)
44. Lochhead, A. G., and Leone Farrell. 1930. Can. J. Res. 3:51-64.
45. _____ 1931. Can. J. Res. 5:54-58.
46. Lothrop, R. E. 1937. Am. Bee J. 77:290-294.
47. Lothrop, R. E., and H. S. Paine. 1931. Am. Bee J. 71:280-281,291.
48. _____ 1932. Am. Bee J. 72:444-450.
49. _____ 1933. Am. Bee J. 73:53,57.
50. Lovell, H. B. 1956. Honey plants manual. A. I. Root Co., Medina, O. 64 pp.
51. Luttinger, P. 1922. N. Y. Med. J. and Med. Rec. 116:153-155.
52. Marquart, P., and G. Vogg. 1952. Arzneim. Forsch. 2:152-155,205-211.
53. Martin, E. C. 1939. J. Econ. Entomol. 32:660-663.
54. _____ 1958. Bee World 39:165-178.
55. Martensen-Larsen, O. 1954. Brit. Med. J. 4885. p. 468.
56. Maurizio, A. 1954. Arch. Verebungsforsch. Sozialanthropol. U. Rassenhyg. 29:340-346.
57. _____ 1959. Ann. Abielle 4:291-341.
58. Milum, V. G. 1948. J. Econ. Entomol. 41:495-505.
59. Morse, R. G. 1954. Gl. Bee Cult. 82:716-717.
60. _____ 1958. Dept. Entomol. Cornell Univ. 13 pp. (processed)
61. Muniagurria, C. 1931. Bull. Soc. de Pediatrics de Paris 29:227.
62. Munro, J. A. 1943. J. Econ. Entomol. 36:769-777.
63. Nelson, E. K., and H. H. Mottern. 1931. Ind. Eng. Chem. 23:335-336.
64. Nichol, H. 1937. Bee World 28:103-105.
65. Oliver, R. W. 1940. Am. Bee J. 80:158.
66. Oppen, F. C., and H. A. Schuette. 1939. Ind. Eng. Chem. 11:130-131.
67. Paine, H. S., S. I. Gertler, and R E. Lothrup. 1934. Ind. Eng. Chem. 26:73-81.
68. Park, O. W. 1932. Iowa Agr. Expt. Sta. Res. Bull. 151. 33 pp
69. Pellett, F. C. 1947. American honey plants. Orange Judd Co., New York. 467 pp.
70. Planta, A. von. 1886. Z. Physiol. Chem. 10:227-247.
71. Pryce-Jones, J. 1953. In Blair, G. W. Scott. Foodstuffs, their plasticity, fluidity, and consistency. Inter-science Pub., Inc., New York. pp. 148-176.
72. Rolleder, A. 1934. Bienen Vater 66:281-284,341-342. Rev. Bee World 15:137.
73. Rubin, N., A. R. Gennaro, C. N. Sideri, and A. Osol. 1959. Am. J. Pharm. 131:246-254.

74. Sackett, W. G. 1919. Col. Agr. Expt. Sta. Bull. **252**. 18 pp.

75. Schlutz, F. W., and E. M. Knott. 1938. J. Pediatrics **13**:465-473.

76. Schlutz, F. W., E. M. Knott, J. L. Gedgoud, and I. Loewenstamm. 1938. J. Pediatrics **12**:716-724.

77. Seymour, F. I., and K. S. West. 1951. Med. Times **79**:104-107.

78. Stancanelli, G. 1933. Pediatria **41**: 524.

79. Stephen, W. A. 1941. Sci. Agr. **22**:157-169.

80. Stinson, E. E., M. H. Subers, J. Petty, and J. W. White, Jr. 1960. Arch. Biochem. Bioph. **89**:6-12.

81. Taufel, K., and R. Reiss. 1952. Z. Lebensm. Untersuch. u. Forsch. **94**:1-10.

82. Taufel, K., and K. Muller. 1953. Z. Lebensm. Untersuch. u. Forsch. **96**:81-83.

83. Temnov, V. A. 1958. Abstr. XVII Intern. Beekeeping Congr. Rome. p. 117.

84. Townsend, G. F. 1939. J. Econ. Entomol. **32**:650-654.

85. ----------------- 1961. Ont. Dept. Agr. Publ. **544**. 24 pp.

86. Townsend, G. F., and P. W. Burke. 1952. Ont. Agr. Coll. Circ. **123**. 4 pp.

87. Townsend, G. F., and A. Adie. 1956. Ont. Agr. Coll. Circ. **216**. (rev.) 10 pp.

88. Turkot, V. A., R. K. Eskew, and J. B. Claffey. 1960. Food Technol. **14**:387-390.

89. Vansell, G. H., and S. B. Freeman. 1929. J. Econ. Entomol. **22**:922-926.

90. Vignec, J., and J. F. Julia. 1954. Am. J. Diseases of Children **88**:443-451.

91. Villumstad, E. 1951. Beekeeping Trial Rept. **12**. (Norwegian) Govt. teachers' school.

92. Watanabe, T., and K. Aso. 1959. Nature **183**:1740.

93. ----------------- 1960. Tohuku J. Agr. Res. **11**:109-115.

94. Wilson, H. F., and G. E. Marvin. 1932. J. Econ. Entomol. **25**:525-528.

95. White, J. W., Jr. 1958. Gl. Bee Culture **86**:730-732.

96. ----------------- 1959a. Am. Com. Bee Res. Assoc. 1st Meeting Abstr. p. 1.

97. ----------------- 1959b. J. Assoc. Offic. Agr. Chem. **42**:341-348.

98. ----------------- 1960. Gl. Bee Cult. **88**:686-689.

99. ----------------- 1961a. Gl. Bee Cult. **89**:292-293.

100. ----------------- 1961b. Gl. Bee Cult. **89**:422.

101. ----------------- 1961c. Gl. Bee Cult. **89**:166-169.

102. ----------------- 1961d. Gl. Bee Cult. **89**:230-233.

103. White, J. W., Jr., and N. Hoban. 1959. Arch. Biochem. Bioph. **80**:386-392.

104. White, J. W., Jr., and J. Maher. 1951. Am. Bee J. **91**(9):376-377.

105. ----------------- 1953a. Arch Biochem. Bioph. **42**:360-367.

106. ----------------- 1953b. J. Am. Chem. Soc. **75**:1259.

107. White, J. W., Jr., M. L. Riethof, and I. Kushnir. 1961. J. Food Sci. **26**:63-71.

108. White, J. W., Jr., M. L. Riethof, M. H. Subers, and I. Kushnir. 1962. U.S. Dept. Agr. Tech. Bull. **1261**. 124 pp.

109. Wolf, J. P., and W. H. Ewart. 1955. Arch. Bioph. **58**:365-372.

110. Wykes, G. R. 1950. Lecture leaflet. Central Assoc. Beekeepers. Ilford, Essex, England.

111. Wykes, G. R. 1952. New Phytol. **51**:210-215.

112. ----------------- 1953. Biochem. J. **53**:294-296.

CHAPTER XV

MARKETING THE HONEY CROP

by ROBERT BANKER*

THE UNITED STATES IS one of the largest honey-producing countries in the world. According to the U.S. Department of Agriculture, annual production has averaged 244,000,000 pounds for the period 1950 through 1960 (see Table 1). It is estimated that 50 to 60 per cent of this production is handled, processed, packed, or exported by commercial packers and dealers. The balance is sold by the producer direct to retail stores or to consumers through mail-order sales, door-to-door selling, roadside stands, or from the producer's home or honey house.

Other than production figures and export and import statistics, little information is available on the actual use of this huge amount of honey. It is difficult, therefore, to ascertain the poundage sold in consumer-size packages for home consumption and the amount used by industries in

TABLE 1. HONEY AND BEESWAX: Number of Colonies, Average Yield, Production and Producers' Stocks, 1949-61

Year	Number of colonies	Yield per colony	Honey production	Producers' stocks		Per capita consump-tion	Beeswax production
				Sept. 15	Dec. 15		
	1,000	POUNDS	1,000 POUNDS	1,000 POUNDS	1,000 POUNDS	POUNDS	1,000 POUNDS
1949	5,591	40.6	226,978	115,342	83,204	1.5	4,151
1950	5,612	41.5	233,013	120,274	83,365	1.6	4,275
1951	5,559	46.4	258,116	114,680	71,416	1.7	4,705
1952	5,493	49.5	272,011	n.a.	77,299	1.6	4,812
1953	5,520	40.5	223,770	n.a.	53,408	1.4	4,081
1954	5,451	39.7	216,419	80,723	41,056	1.3	4,011
1955	5,300	47.7	252,981	92,445	57,944	1.4	4,584
1956	5,315	40.2	213,421	83,460	49,234	1.2	4,095
1957	5,397	45.2	243,902	98,931	64,520	1.2	4,503
1958	5,420	49.0	265,677	107,690	72,635	1.4	4,793
1959	5,438	45.5	247,523	101,275	62,979	1.4	4,417
1960	5,430	47.9	260,128	93,575	56,737	1.5	4,728
1961	5,517	50.0	275,979	104,457			

Source: Crop Reporting Board, U. S. Department of Agriculture.

*Robert Banker. Producer-packer. Formerly secretary of The American Beekeeping Federation. Presently a member of the Executive Committee of The American Beekeeping Federation and president of the Minnesota Beekeepers' Association.

[407]

baked goods, candies, confections, and many other products in which honey is an ingredient.

Available information seems to indicate that, in spite of a large population increase, the per capita consumption of honey in the United States is declining at a rather rapid rate. The per capita consumption of honey is approximately half that of Canada, and even less than half that of many European countries where, in spite of lower earning power, honey commands a much higher price to the consumer.

This low per capita consumption of honey may be attributed, at least in part, to the lack of national promotion. The American Honey Institute has done a remarkable job in promoting honey with the limited funds it has available, but those funds are insufficient for effective national promotion. Some states have promotional programs in varying amounts but this often is not consistent, which impairs its effectiveness. In California, producers and packers participate in a marketing agreement that collects funds from both for honey promotion and research. This is responsible, at least in part, for a 2.3 pounds per capita consumption in the West as compared with as little as 0.7 pound in some other areas.

Nationally something less than $100,000 is expended for honey promotion, or less than $1 for every 2,500 pounds of honey produced. This is, of course, exclusive of brand advertising by individual packers.

The marketing of honey has been a problem practically as long as the industry has been in existence. Minutes of state associations as far back as 1880 to 1890 indicate that marketing even then was a problem. It is a problem that probably will never be solved entirely, but certainly improvement could be made by a concerted and consistent nationwide program of honey promotion.

Marketing Extracted Honey in Bulk Containers

Factors that affect the quality of honey also influence its marketability. Extreme care should be used in all phases of removing and extracting the crop and its preparation for market to ensure that nothing is done to detract from its natural, delectable flavor and appearance. Recommended procedures for extracting the crop can be found in Chapter XI, "Extracting the Honey Crop." Assuming that these procedures have been followed, the producer is ready to pack the crop into bulk containers or to process it further for consumer packaging.

Until the early 1950's, nearly all bulk honey was packed in 60-pound tin containers. A large amount still is packed in this manner, but at present there is a trend to the 55-gallon steel drum with a removable head sealed by a gasket and having a baked-on lacquer lining. The largest cooperative receives 95 per cent of its honey in these drums. Perhaps 50 per cent of honey moving through regular channels of commerce is now packed in drums.

FIGURE 1. Drums of honey in storage at the Sioux Honey Plant in Georgia are stacked four high by means of a special lift truck.

In addition to cans and drums, some bulk honey is packed in pliofilm bags inside sturdy corrugated cartons. A limited amount is pumped into tank trailers and transported direct to the packing plant.

Drums are efficient and economical both for producers and packers. The initial cost is lower than that of cans. They can be easily cleaned and sterilized for reuse and, if necessary, can be completely reconditioned for less than half of their original cost. It is necessary to have a barrel truck (Fig. 1) to handle them and, depending on the honey house, it may be necessary to have a drum hoist or to use a tractor with a loader to lift them onto a truck. Unless facilities are available to double-deck them, drums require more storage space. However, the use of drums requires less labor in filling, handling, and final processing. Packers prefer them over cans both from a labor-saving standpoint and also because there is less shrinkage in processing.

Each producer will have to select the bulk container best suited to his operation, keeping in mind the market to be supplied. In some cases it may be necessary to use a combination of bulk containers to meet the demands of the market.

SAMPLING THE BUYER

Bulk honey is sold generally on the basis of samples. No single factor lends itself to misunderstandings and disagreements as much as a shipment of honey improperly represented by inaccurate samples. To avoid this, each producer should develop a systematic and accurate method of drawing samples which will preclude any chance of misrepresentation when received by the buyer.

Most packers have established standards for the color, flavor, and moisture content which they strive to maintain in their packed honey. In purchasing lots of honey for their requirements these standards become the basis for their purchases. To purchase a car or truckload of honey on the basis of samples and to find on arrival a wide variation in color, flavor, or moisture content, without any means of segregating the lots, can be expensive and nerve wracking, and results in disagreement and ill feelings between producer and packer.

It is difficult to make precise recommendations for an accurate sampling method due to variations in floral sources available, the extracting equipment, size of storage tanks, and the temperature of the honey. All will have a bearing on the number of samples required. Very few producers will have a crop, or even a car or a truckload, that can be represented by just one sample.

Generally a 1- or 2-pound sample should be drawn from each tank, each yard's production, or each day's run. The sample should be drawn from the middle of the lot or run and should be marked with a letter, number, or date, and all the containers represented by the sample should be marked with the same identification. A record should be kept of each lot and the number of containers in it. This may seem time-consuming but after a system has been developed suited to the operation, very little time and effort is consumed.

The 1- or 2-pound sample is sufficient to permit sending 2- or 4-ounce samples to a number of buyers. By using the same style and size of container, the producer can detect, to a certain extent, variations in color and moisture content even without grading equipment.

SELLING AT WHOLESALE

Accurate samples are a big factor in building confidence and understanding between producer and packer and will result in higher prices to the producer. If the packer knows exactly what he is going to receive, he doesn't have to make allowances for discrepancies and variations which sometime occur. Variations in flavor, color, and moisture content will all be identified and the packer can readily process and blend to meet his particular standards. The producer knows exactly what he has for sale and is in position to demand and get a top market price.

Trading in bulk honey usually begins by the producer sending samples to a packer or dealer representing a quantity of honey. The buyer will want to know the number and type of containers represented, whether the containers are new or used, and the asking price. Negotiations will usually be concluded by a contract form or letter of acceptance stating that the producer is to deliver a specified quantity of honey of a given color, flavor, and moisture content for an established price with containers either included or to be exchanged and returned.

Before accepting or signing such agreements, the producer should determine the financial and moral responsibility of the packer. Most packers are reliable but producers have suffered heavy losses at times by shipping to an unscrupulous and financially irresponsible buyer. The packer usually will obtain information on the producer's responsibility and integrity through whatever sources he has available.

The producer also should know what he has to sell and what it is worth. "Honey Market News" is a semi-monthly bulletin available free on request from the Agricultural Marketing Service, Fruit and Vegetable Division, U.S. Department of Agriculture, Washington 25, D. C. This bulletin, plus state publications and information obtained from other producers, will serve as a guide to actual market prices.

Bulk honey moves to market by commercial trucklines, railroads, or even the producer's own truck. Rail rates usually will be lowest but the chances of damage to the shipment perhaps will be the greatest. Trucklines are popular since they will load the shipment at the producer's plant. If railroads are used, damage-free cars should be insisted upon. A damage-free car is a new type which employs a series of removable gates and locks to break up the load into several compartments, thus minimizing possibility of damage and loss.

GRADING EXTRACTED HONEY

The United States standards for grades of extracted honey are established by the U.S. Department of Agriculture. It should be emphasized that they are only standards and not compulsory. Honey can be sold in any state except Minnesota without stating the grade on the label. The use of the U.S. standards or grades is confined to consumer packaged honey and bulk honey going into industrial channels. Virtually none of the crop sold by producers at wholesale carries a grade. Technically, if the grades are stated on the label, the honey must meet those requirements, but food authorities in checking honey are more concerned with possible contamination than factors of grade.

Copies of the U.S. standards for grades are available from the Agricultural Marketing Service, U.S.D.A., Washington 25, D. C., on request. The following description of the grades, taken from a California publication,[1] will acquaint the reader with the principal points in the standards:

"U.S. grades are based on four factors: soluble solids (or moisture content), flavor, absence of defects, and clarity. After determination of soluble solids, the specific grade is determined by means of a scoring system." The characteristics are weighted as follows: flavor is given 50 possible points, absence of defects is allowed a maximum of 40 points, and clarity is permitted a maximum of 10 points. This makes a possible total score of 100 points. Each characteristic is judged as "good," "reasonably good," or "fairly good" in decreasing amounts of points.

U.S. Grade A or *U.S. Fancy* is a honey which contains not less than 81.4 per cent soluble solids; possesses a good flavor for the predominant floral source or, when blended, a good flavor for the blend of floral sources; is free from defects; and is of such quality with respect to clarity as to score not less than 90 points.

U.S. Grade B or *U.S. Choice* is a honey which contains not less than 81.4 per cent soluble solids; possesses a reasonably good flavor for the predominant floral source or, when blended, a reasonably good flavor for the blend of floral sources; is reasonably free from defects; is reasonably clear; and scores not less than 80 points.

U.S. Grade C or *U.S. Standard* is honey for reprocessing which contains not less than 80 per cent soluble solids; possesses a fairly good flavor for the predominant floral source or, when blended, a fairly good flavor for the blend of floral sources; is fairly free from defects; and is of such quality as to score not less than 70 points.

U.S. Grade D or *Substandard* is a honey which fails to meet the requirements of *U.S. Grade C* or *U.S. Standard*.

HONEY GRADING EQUIPMENT

The most frequently used equipment for grading honey is the honey refractometer, the Pfund grader, and the U.S.D.A. color comparator.

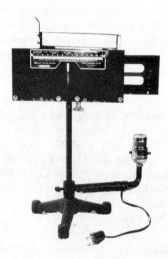

FIGURE 2. The Bausch & Lomb honey refractometer quickly determines the moisture content of honey.

FIGURE 3. The Pfund color grader is used widely throughout the honey industry today.

The refractometer (Fig. 2) is a small instrument easily held in the palm of the hand. A few drops of honey are placed on a hinged portion, then pressed against a glass prism. Calibrated readings are obtained through the eyepiece and converted to actual moisture content by adding or substracting the reading of the temperature correction thermometer. Accurate readings can be obtained in a matter of seconds.

The Pfund grader (Fig. 3) is used most generally for determining the color of honey. A wedge-shaped glass trough is filled with honey and compared to a colored glass wedge, using either artificial or natural light for the comparison. The color of honey is recorded in millimeters as follows:

Water white	0 to 8
Extra white	8 to 16.5
White	16.5 to 34
Extra light amber	34 to 50
Light amber	50 to 85
Amber	85 to 114
Dark	114 and over

The U.S.D.A. color comparator (Fig. 4) employs colored glass slides and also bottles filled with materials which provide different degrees of turbidity. Clear glass bottles contain the honey for color comparison. This instrument provides for six color classifications, as does the Pfund grader, and also allows for turbidity in the samples to be classified. It is not as practical as the Pfund grader in establishing color so blending of different lots cannot be accomplished as readily to obtain a specific color.

FILTERING HONEY

Many commercial packers and some producer-packers filter honey. Filtration of honey gives it an artificial brilliance which doubtless adds to its eye appeal. Some packers have a firm conviction that this process removes at least a portion of its vitamin content and delicate flavor,[2] and therefore do not filter their honey. Nevertheless, most packers filter

FIGURE 4. The U.S.D.A. color comparator enables the producer and the packer to classify honey as to color and turbidity.

honey as a fast and efficient means of removing tiny foreign particles which have been incorporated into honey and not removed during extracting and clarifying processes.

It still is undetermined whether honey that has been filtered with activated carbon, or any substance that removes color and flavor, can be sold as honey, inasmuch as the Food and Drug Administration has thus far not passed on the product.

Marketing Consumer-Packaged Honey

To be marketed successfully, honey must be of high quality, attractively labeled, and neatly packaged. Each jar of honey should be as uniform in color, flavor, and moisture content as is humanly possible. The housewife who buys a certain pack and rebuys because she likes it, has the right to expect the same as her previous purchase. If it is necessary for the packer to deviate, especially in flavor, the label should be changed or the floral source prominently designated.

Honey should be free of any foreign particles or air bubbles, and should be processed carefully to avoid any damage to its delicate flavor and aroma. Containers should be sparkling clean. Labels should be colorful to attract the eye and should be neat and sized for the container.

Consumer-packaged honey should be displayed prominently and in quantity (Fig. 5). Most consumers buy honey only on impulse so the display must catch the eye. Containers showing signs of granulation should be replaced at once. A good product, attractively packaged and presented to the public, will virtually sell itself; a poor product will be a detriment to its packer and the honey industry.

It is natural that honey must be priced competitively in today's market places, but a good product, attractively packaged, need not be underpriced. Price-cutting practices will destroy buyer confidence and may lead to price depression in an area or even in the nation, if carried to the extreme. Know your product and be able to talk intelligently about its food value and uses. Promote and advertise honey at every opportunity. Display your product at local and state fairs and at food shows. Service your market regularly and provide a variety of packs. It is far better to spend money for advertising and promotion than to cut prices.

CO-OPERATIVE MARKETING

There are a number of co-operative marketing organizations in the United States. Most of them can be considered small and some are strictly bulk-honey co-ops with members pooling and selling their production in bulk containers. Only the Sioux Honey Association can be considered as operating on a national basis. Its headquarters is Sioux City, Iowa, and it operates five other plants throughout the country.

FIGURE 5. An excellent exhibit of the many kinds of consumer packages for both extracted and comb honey. *(Photo courtesy of Sioux Honey Association)*

It is estimated that approximately 15 per cent of packaged honey is processed and marketed by the co-operatives. Co-operative marketing is gaining in popularity, particularly among large honey producers. While this offers many advantages to producers, there are some disadvantages just as there are when marketing through independent packers and dealers. Each producer thus must decide which type of marketing is the most advantageous to him and market his crop accordingly.

PRODUCER MARKETING

There are many honey producers, both large and small, who bottle and sell part or all of their production, and even buy additional honey. This group is commonly referred to as producer-packers. Although honey sales of this kind account for upwards to half of the national production, the number of producer-packers seems to be declining. This type of operation usually is most successful when different members of a family assume responsibility for separate phases of the business.

Few individuals have the time and temperament, much less the ability and necessary equipment, to make producing and packing successful and profitable on a large scale. Competition in the food field is becoming increasingly keener. If a brand of honey is to remain on grocers' shelves, it must not only compare favorably with competitive brands but be backed by an aggressive and forceful sales promotion program. A great deal of emphasis must be placed on each phase of the business to make producing-packing a successful, profitable, and well-integrated operation.

Many producer-packers confine their sales to door-to-door selling, to a few local stores, or to roadside stands usually selling honey in combination with vegetables, fruits, and other produce. Others employ brokers or sales agents whose sales cover a large area or even make deliveries direct to retailers in their area on a specific route at regular intervals.

Those who confine their sales to a local area undoubtedly will have less difficulty in establishing and maintaining a satisfactory sales level, if the quality of the pack is good, because of the natural attraction to the consumer that a locally packed product seems to enjoy. Many producers may be overlooking a profitable market for a portion of their crop by not making their honey available to local consumers (Fig. 6). Others will find this market well supplied with other brands to the extent that consumer packaging would not be wise or profitable.

COMMERCIAL PACKING OF HONEY

Packing of honey as a main enterprise or supplemented by the packing of certain other food products is limited to perhaps 30 to 40 concerns in this country. Most have automatic equipment for labeling, filling and capping, and most use filters. Very few, if any, have national

FIGURE 6. This New York State producer's fine honey house and display quarters attract many customers throughout the year.

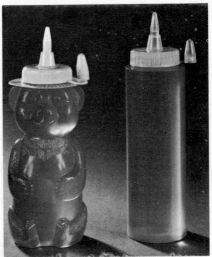

FIGURE 7. An example of an attractive gift package for liquid honey.

FIGURE 8. The plastic "squeeze" bottle dispenses honey without "drip."

distribution of their advertised brand. Some use their own sales personnel in addition to brokers but most employ food brokers or other sales agents to sell their output. Many use warehousing facilities in areas of concentrated distribution to retail outlets. Most do a considerable amount of advertising to keep their brand name in front of the public eye, and to assist them in maintaining shelf space. Several provide display racks on a rotating basis.

Most pack a wide variety of types and sizes of containers. A few pack honeys by floral source, such as orange, sage, buckwheat, and gallberry. Some have attractive gift packages (Fig. 7); others pack for industrial uses.

Consumer-Size Packages. Honey is packaged in glass, tin, plastic, and paper containers. Glass is the most popular and is used in a wide variety of sizes and shapes up to 10 pounds. Tin containers are not used as extensively due to their cost and lack of eye appeal.

Plastic in a variety of shapes, usually 12-oz. containers, is best suited as a table honey dispenser. The plastic honey container first was introduced as a round cylinder with a drip-proof spout and its reception as a honey dispenser has been almost phenomenal. By a silk-screening process, it can be attractively labeled for a particular brand. Plastic containers have been a boon to the honey industry and an answer to the housewife's prayer for a honey container without a drip (Fig. 8).

Various containers are used for packing finely granulated honey, creamed honey, and honey butter, products which will be discussed later in this chapter. The use of such containers is increasing.

Marketing Comb Honey

Comb honey in all forms requires special and careful preparation
for the market. Such honey is marketed in the form of section comb
honey, chunk, and cut-comb honey. U.S. grades for these types of
honey are available from the U.S.D.A., Agricultural Marketing Service,
Washington 25, D. C.

The production of all forms of comb honey is small in relation to
the volume of extracted honey produced. Section comb honey requires
experience to produce and its grading and marketing is expensive.
Its production has declined to the point where it is not available in
some areas, and where available only in limited quantities in a few
retail stores.

The production of chunk honey (Fig. 9) (a jar of liquid honey
containing not less than 50 per cent by volume of comb honey) is
extensive in the gallberry area of the Southeast, with limited output

FIGURE 9. A prize-winning pack of chunk honey. Comb honey surrounded by liquid
honey has consumer eye appeal.

in other scattered areas. Perhaps the biggest deterrent to its expansion in production is the tendency of the liquid honey to granulate.

Comb honey, when properly prepared for market, has an excellent eye appeal to the consumer. If the market for this type of honey were to be expanded, an educational program would be required. Quite often honey producers are asked how to eat comb honey, what to do with the beeswax, and how to keep it in the home.

Marketing Finely Granulated or Creamed Honey

Honey for this purpose should be from a floral source that granulates to a fine, smooth, soft, creamy consistency, or the product should be prepared by the addition of finely ground crystallized honey.

Finely granulated or creamed honey is packed in a variety of paper, plastic, and glass containers. Its consistency should be soft, rather than hard, to allow easy spreading. The quality of the honey should be the best and it should be packaged attractively. Maintaining its creamy condition on grocers' shelves is a problem, particularly in hot, humid areas.

Information obtained from packers indicates that the consumption of creamed honey is increasing in this country. Presently, it is available in most retail stores. Although this type of honey has not gained the popularity it has enjoyed in Canada, or in parts of Europe, its consumption still is a considerable factor in our total honey consumption.

The Export-Import Balance

Honey exports consistently have been a factor in the market price of honey. Exports reached their peak during the past decade in 1953 when, with the assistance of an Expert Subsidy Program by the Government, nearly 33 million pounds were exported and less than 10 million pounds were imported (see Table 2).

The sharp decline in exports from 1958 through 1960, accompanied by the increase in imports during the same period, may not be a continuing trend, although it is generally conceded that with our present prices for honey and the availability of honey from other countries produced at lower costs because of cheap labor, we may face difficulties in obtaining a higher percentage of the export market.

With the developments of super markets in Europe, consumer packages of honey are becoming increasingly popular. Previously, all honey sold in most of Europe and especially in Germany was dispensed by the merchant from the 60-pound can. This is no longer true and within the last 2 years some have started exporting consumer-size packages to Europe. The dark, strong-flavored honeys, formerly exported to this market, are being replaced at lower prices from other sources, thus cutting off our market for types of honeys which have not been popular in this country.

TABLE 2. HONEY: Exports and Imports by Countries, 1950-60

– – – 1,000 pounds – – –

COUNTRY	1950	1951	1952	1953	1954	1955	1956	1957	1958	1959	1960
EXPORTS FROM U.S.											
DESTINATION											
West Germany	2,031	2,459	12,491	20,664	13,694	10,142	7,816	11,019	13,775	5,107	4,752
Canada	19	212	53	359	3,957	5,149	3,456	4,277	4,666	4,130	1,942
Belgium¹	2,929	2,057	939	1,915	1,489	1,627	1,971	1,540	1,161	1,121	849
Netherlands	3,398	4,540	5,077	7,297	3,030	1,937	2,526	1,413	1,304	792	436
United Kingdom								53	555	646	284
Philippines	2	35	106	126	44	49	85	170	51	202	239
Switzerland	576	840	1,285	616	717	820	1,014	774	304	141	243
France		1,146	1,397	937	949	437	739	263	83	100	238
Austria	110	331	154								
Italy	197	98	1,622	696	164	44	281		36		
Other	171	952	233	240	236	280	352	290	474	268	410
Total Exports	9,433	12,670	23,357	32,850	24,280	20,485	18,240	19,799	22,409	12,507	9,394
IMPORTS INTO U.S.											
ORIGIN											
Mexico	5,143	1,638	1,500	4,976	5,570	6,382	3,183	3,666	3,427	2,951	4,491
Argentina	1,035	192	338							1,145	7,043
Guatemala	523	923	1,178	1,537	1,237	1,278	642	722	238	115	118
Canada	252	266	277	540	242	28	128	27	24	98	119
Dominican Republic	16	74	69	83	234	52	79	58	49	28	180
Spain										1	151
West Germany			1	1	2	3	1	2	10	28	51
Cuba	4,316	4,404	4,295	1,953	1,671	1,978	615	159	34	33	26
El Salvador	424	371	169	377	122	88	71	61			
Costa Rica	94	158	430	264		7					
Chile	65	59	2				1	1	16	2	
Brazil	108				2					18	2
Other	42	89	224	54	72	40	61	59	149	90	182
Total Imports	12,018	8,174	8,483	9,785	9,152	9,856	4,781	4,755	3,947	4,509	12,363

¹ Includes Luxembourg.
Source: Bureau of Census, U. S. Department of Commerce.

Through the Foreign Agricultural Service, the U.S. Department of Agriculture has started the promotion of honey at Food Fairs and Expositions in Europe. The exhibiting of honey, along with other of our agricultural products, has indicated a keen interest in our packaged honey. It appears that packaged honey can be sold competitively in some of the major European markets.

Concurrent with the decline in exports, in the latter part of the last decade, has been an increase in imports of honey, principally from Argentina and Mexico. Both countries had large crops in 1960 when our domestic crop was only slightly above average and the demand for honey was excellent. Mexican and Argentine honeys generally are of table grade, having flavors distinctly different from our clover honey, but suitable for blending and for industrial uses. The production of honey in Argentina may be at its peak since the areas in which honey production is profitable are limited, and the increase in Mexican production is limited by the lack of roads.

Thus, the importation of honeys may not increase to any great extent in the immediate future, but we must expect that they may continue at their present level. It has been suggested that a practical way of controlling these imports, which are a factor in our markets, is to increase the duty or tariffs. To do this in view of current trends is a highly complicated and involved procedure, almost impossible to obtain. The best way to counteract the increased imports is to develop an organized promotional program to increase the domestic consumption of honey to the extent that we can absorb these imports.

Through existing legislation, there are controls available to us whereby we could establish the quality of honey coming into this country and require that imported honey be labeled as to source. In order to do this, the honey industry must submit to a marketing agreement and order program which we do not have at present.

Honey Stabilization Programs of the Government

During the past decade, an immeasurable degree of assistance has been given the honey industry by various programs of the U.S. Department of Agriculture in an effort to stabilize the price of honey.

In 1950, the first price support program was made available to the industry at 60 per cent of parity. The program was initiated as a handler-type program with the honey delivered before a loan could be obtained. In 1952, loans were made available to producers at 70 per cent of parity and this type of program has continued on a producer-loan basis from 60 to 75 per cent of parity. Table 3 indicates the influence of this program on the average price received by producers, starting with 10.2 cents a pound and 67 per cent of parity in 1950 to 13.0 cents and 91 per cent of parity in 1960. The acquisition of honey

TABLE 3. HONEY: Production, Price Support Operations, Average Prices Received by Producers, Support Prices, and Levels of Support, 1949-61[1]

Year	Production	Loan and purchase operations	CCC acquisitions	Average price rec'd by producers [2]	Average price as per cent of parity	National average support price [2]	Level of support	Support price as per cent of average price
	mil. lbs.	mil. lbs.	mil. lbs.	cents	per cent	cents	per cent	per cent
1949	227.0	—	—	9.7	64	—	—	—
1950	233.0	—	[3]7.4	10.2	67	9.0	60	88
1951	258.1	—	[3]17.8	10.3	66	10.0	60	97
1952	272.0	14.3	7.0	11.4	73	11.4	70	100
1953	223.8	4.1	0.5	11.5	79	10.5	70	91
1954	216.4	2.2	—	11.8	84	10.2	70	86
1955	253.0	2.0	—	12.9	92	9.9	70	77
1956	213.4	1.8	—	13.6	98	9.7	70	71
1957	243.9	4.1	0.1	13.4	97	9.7	70	72
1958	265.7	17.5	2.0	12.0	88	9.6	70	80
1959	247.5	1.3	—	12.5	91	8.3	60	66
1960	260.1	1.0	—	13.0	91	8.6	60	66
1961	276.0					11.2	75	

[1] Honey price support program became effective with the 1950 crop.
[2] Adjusted to 60-pound container basis.
[3] Acquired through direct packer purchase program.

by the Commodity Credit Corporation since 1952 has been extremely small. It is described by many in the U.S. Department of Agriculture as an "ideal" program, and has been of immeasurable benefit to producers and packers in establishing a floor price for honey.

Depending on the size of the crop and economical conditions, the honey industry has had at times the help of other Governmental programs, such as export subsidies which enabled us to restore our markets in Europe, the diversion payments for the development of new honey products, and the promotional efforts of the Plentiful Foods Division when honey was in surplus.

If it had not been for these price stabilization programs of the U.S. Department of Agriculture, the honey industry could have been in a much worse condition than it is at present. These programs, as they are intended to be, have been of value during years when production was above average and even a relatively small carry-over would create a depression in price.

Industrial Uses of Honey

The Baking Industry. This is by far the largest consumer of industrial honey. Breads, rolls, cookies, pastries, and many other foods are enhanced by the addition of honey. Bakers find that the use of honey in breads results in better flavor, texture, crust, crust color, and better keeping qualities. Honey graham crackers have almost become a staple in many homes and those making them emphasize honey in their promotion.

The work done by Johnson, Nordin, and Miller[3] on the utilization of honey in baked products has been extremely helpful in gaining further acceptance of honey. Two recipe books entitled, "Honey Improves Baked Products" and "Honey in Your Baking"—the first for the baker and the latter for the housewife—give formulas and recipes for making bread, rolls, cakes, cookies, pies, and icing. These beautifully illustrated booklets are available at a nominal cost for the promotion of these uses of honey from the Distribution Center, Umberger Hall, Kansas State University, Manhattan, Kansas.

The type of honeys sold to the bakery trade must be of good quality. Some strong-flavored honeys are not desirable for bakery use, particularly heartsease honey which results in objectionable flavors and odors in the baked product. Color usually is not a major factor except for white baked products where the color should not exceed 70 mm. on the Pfund grader (light amber or better). Floral source, color, and moisture content requirements vary according to the baker's product. Some bakers require a high quality, table-grade honey but bakers generally use honeys that would not find ready acceptance on the table.

The baking industry is a tremendous outlet for a large portion of the honey crop. This use of honey is gradually increasing. With promotion, it could easily become a greater consumer of honey. Bakers have definite standards for honey which must be met. Variations within shipments or from different sources of supply may upset their formulas and the resulting products. Every effort should be made to provide a uniform, top-quality product for the baking industry.

Dried Honey. This is a new product developed at the Eastern Utilization Research and Development Division.[4] Presently, it is not in commercial production but at least one large packer now is planning to install equipment for its production. White[5] stated: "Dried honey to succeed should be used: 1. where liquid honey cannot be used because of process or product requirements, or 2. where substantial advantage exists over liquid honey in handling or adaptability. Reconstitution to liquid honey before use is not the intended use of the product. The material is, of course, far more stable in storage than liquid honey, as far as flavor and color changes are concerned. It does have storage limitations as respects to temperature, however."

Tests show that dried honey enhances the baked product as well as when liquid honey is used. There is no leftover sticky container to be disposed of, and less shrinkage. Information indicates that dried honey has good market possibilities, although its cost may be somewhat higher, and will require the development of new formulas for uses. Its many advantages may overcome these disadvantages and make it a popular additional outlet for honey.

The Restaurant Trade. Perhaps one of the most overlooked outlets for honey, the restaurant trade, presents a terrific potential for honey sales because of the habit to eat out in our present period of high standards of living. The possibilities of restaurant honey consumption can be confirmed by the following report.

A chain of four restaurants in a medium-sized western city, plus a single restaurant in a small city, consumed in 1 year eleven hundred 60-pound cans of honey. These five restaurants featured honey and hot biscuits in their advertising. Honey was available at all times on the tables in plastic containers. A dispensing receptacle with a no-drip gate was provided for the employees to fill the plastic dispensers.

Honey Butter. A mixture of creamery butter and 20 to 30 per cent of table-grade honey provides a fine flavored product with a soft, creamy texture. It is delicious on hot rolls but must be kept refrigerated to prevent it from becoming rancid. A New York firm has a patent on a similar product which does not become rancid. The percentage of honey in this product is not high but this use attributes to our marketing of honey.

Honey Candies. Delicious candies containing honey are prepared by special and usually secret formulas. They are available only in the areas in which they are produced. A few large candymakers manufacture bars and nougats containing honey for national distribution. Usually, the best table-grade honeys are required. Although the quantity of honey used for this purpose is not large, this use of honey could be increased by adequate promotion.

Other Uses for Honey. There are many other food products in which honey is used in variable amounts, such as cake mixes, cereals, ice cream, honey vinegar, mead, and wine. One recently attracting attention is a popcorn coated with a caramel-like preparation of honey and butter. Food processors continually are looking for new products to attract the consumers' dollars. Honey blends well in combination with many other ingredients in today's highly competitive food market and, in most instances, enhances the final product. Undoubtedly, in the future, more food products will include honey as an ingredient.

REFERENCES CITED

1. Bauer, Frederick W. 1960. Calif. Agr. Expt. Sta. Bull. **776**. 71 pp.
2. Haydak, M. H., L. S. Palmer, M. C. Tanquary, and A. E. Vivino. 1942. J. Nutrition **23**(6):581-588.
3. Johnson, J. A., P. Nordin, and D. Miller. 1957. Bakers Digest **31**:33-34, 36.
4. Turkot, V. A., R. K. Eskew, and J. B. Claffey. 1960. Food Technol. **14**:387-390.
5. White, J. W., Jr. Personal communication.

CHAPTER XVI

THE PRODUCTION AND USES
OF BEESWAX

by Roy A. Grout*

IN ANCIENT TIMES beeswax was much more important to man than it is today, simply because there were no other known waxes or waxlike substances. Honey was the only known sweet and beeswax was procured when the comb was crushed to obtain the honey. Beeswax is mentioned in the Scriptures and in ancient Greek mythology. Down through the centuries — the Greek and Roman eras and the Middle Ages — beeswax was used in cosmetics, in pharmaceuticals, as a modeling and sculpturing medium, in candles, and for many other purposes.

It was not until the turn of the present century that other waxes and waxlike substances came into commercial importance, bringing with them a relative decline in the importance of beeswax in commerce. These waxes came from a variety of things.

From the vegetable kingdom we obtain *carnauba wax,* the hardest and most brilliant wax in nature, from a species of palm tree grown principally in Brazil, South America; *candelilla wax* from a Mexican desert plant; *ouricury wax,* also from the leaves of a species of palm tree grown in Brazil; *bayberry wax* from the berries of the myrtle bush in this country; *Japan wax* from a species of sumac in Japan; and others of lesser commercial importance, including *sugar cane wax, palm wax, esparto wax, flax wax, cotton wax* and many others.

From the animal kingdom, in addition to *beeswax,* are obtained *spermaceti* from the head region of certain whales and dolphins; *wool wax* or *lanolin* from the wool of sheep; *Chinese insect wax,* an insect secretion; and *shellac wax* obtained in the refining of shellac, also an insect secretion.

In the mineral kingdom, we find *ozokerite* mined from the earth in Utah in this country and in Austria. When refined and bleached it is known as *ceresin wax. Montan wax* is obtained in the steam distillation of lignite, and is considered by some as being semimineral and semivegetable in origin. The petroleum waxes, while chemically not true waxes, are waxlike and are of great commercial importance. They include *paraffin* and *microcrystalline waxes.*

There are also many synthetic waxes that are being used in increasing amounts. These include the chlorinated, sulfonated and hydro-

---

*Roy A. Grout. Production manager of Dadant & Sons, Inc. Associate editor of the *American Bee Journal*. Specialist in the production and uses of beeswax.

genated oils, fats, and waxes, and the high molecular weight glycols, alcohols, stearates, and other compounds.

In spite of the many waxes or waxlike substances, beeswax, the "old man" of the wax kingdom, has not lost its commercial importance.

AMOUNT OF BEESWAX PRODUCED

It is difficult to estimate the quantity of beeswax produced in this country because a part of the production never reaches the market, being consumed in the form of comb honey, used about the farm and home, or lost in many ways. Statistics issued by the U.S.D.A. Crop Reporting Board for 1961 give the production of beeswax as 5,092,000 pounds and the production of honey as 274,088,000 pounds. This was a record large crop, being 13 to 14 per cent larger than the 1955 to 1959 average production.

Voorhies, Todd, and Galbraith,[4] stated that since 1900 the ratio of beeswax production to the amount of honey produced is probably about one to sixty-eight (1:68), adding that future beeswax production will be influenced, as in the past, by changes in production methods. In recent years, the production of beeswax has approximated 2 pounds to 100 pounds of honey produced, a ratio of 1:50.

AMOUNT OF BEESWAX IMPORTED

It is of interest to point out that this country imports more beeswax than it produces; over half of the beeswax consumed comes from abroad—Brazil, Chile, Cuba, the West Indies, Mexico, Central America, Africa, Madagascar, and Egypt are the principal countries of origin. Many other countries of the world produce beeswax but in most of them, as in our own, it is consumed at home. With but few exceptions, this beeswax is produced by various races and strains of the honey bee, *Apis mellifera* L.

According to Smith,[2] the beeswax of India and the rest of Asia is called Ghedda wax and has physical and chemical properties which differ from beeswax. Ghedda wax is mainly the product of *Apis dorsata* though the wax of *Apis florea* and *A. cerana syn. indica* may be included in varying amounts. Ghedda wax also may contain the wax of the stingless bees of the genus *Trigona*. Likewise this often is true of beeswax of Mexico and South America which may contain the wax of stingless bees of the genus *Melipona*. Since the wax produced by these bees has different chemical and physical properties than that produced by the honey bees of this country, it cannot be considered pure beeswax by U. S. standards.

Sources of Crude Beeswax

The beekeeper's sources of crude beeswax (Fig. 1) are cappings, bits of comb, burr and brace combs, and combs which have become unfit for use for various reasons. Cappings yield from 10 to 12 pounds of

FIGURE 1. Crude beeswax in cake form ready to be trucked to market.

beeswax per 1,000 pounds of extracted honey. When cappings are cut deep, the yield may amount to 15 and even 18 pounds of beeswax. The bits of combs removed during work with the bees, if diligently collected and saved, can amount to approximately a half pound of beeswax per colony each year. It usually is stated that a set of ten combs of Langstroth size will yield about 2½ pounds of beeswax, the amount depending on the age and condition of the combs.

CAPPINGS

Cappings are obtained when the surface of combs of honey are cut away prior to extracting the honey. The honey which is removed with the cappings is separated from the wax by draining, centrifugal force, or pressure, or by melting the cappings in some type of cappings melter. A few operators have devised methods whereby the bees remove the honey from the cappings before they are melted.

When cappings are drained, some honey still remains with them. This honey may be washed out with warm water or the cappings can be melted in a large amount of hot water. If too little water is used, a good proportion of the wax on congealing may be found to be granular in appearance, or if boiled too vigorously or too long may appear spongy. While this material is essentially beeswax, it is difficult to get it to return to solid form by further melting over water. Dry heat seems to be the best way of returning it to a form that will congeal into a solid cake.

When cappings are melted in a cappings melter, a solid cake of beeswax is obtained. These cakes may be sticky with honey and should be washed after scraping the sediment from the bottom, or remelted over an adequate quantity of water to clean them further. The scrapings from the bottom of cakes should be saved as this material is rich in beeswax, and should be rendered with other beeswax refuse. Only new combs should be melted with cappings. Frame and hive scrapings and old combs should be kept separate and melted into cake form in a different manner. The best grades of light yellow colored beeswax are obtained from cappings. For additional information on methods of handling cappings, see Chapter XI, "Extracting the Honey Crop."

BITS OF COMB

Especially during the honeyflow, many bits of comb are scraped from the top bars, or other parts of the hive, and usually placed in front of the entrance for the bees to clean them of nectar and honey. This should not be done if disease is prevalent or when there is likelihood of robbing. Before leaving the apiary these bits of comb should be collected and either placed in a solar wax extractor or in containers for future melting and protected from the ravages of the wax moth. At times, they may be left in parts of the hive for the bees to clean, or they may be collected as they are.

The solar wax extractor (Fig. 2) is useful to many beekeepers and is simple and economical to construct. It should be bee tight and ample in size for the beekeeper's requirements. For best results, it is placed facing the South so that it will receive the maximum hours of sunshine. Needless to say, it functions best in warm, sunny climates. It is useful for melting the accumulation of bits of comb but it also may be used for melting cappings, super combs, or even an occasional comb darkened through long use. The refuse or slumgum which accumulates

FIGURE 2. The solar wax extractor is a useful piece of equipment for melting many bits of combs and cappings. (*Photo by Eaton's*)

should be saved and rendered with old combs or slumgum because it still contains much beeswax.

OLD COMBS

Some beeswax can be recovered from old combs by melting them in hot water or in a steam chest, but the remaining refuse will contain a substantial amount of beeswax.

A common method is to soak the combs in warm water for a day or more, place them in a sack and submerge in boiling water with no further treatment than to squeeze and turn the sack to aid the recovery of the beeswax. This method is likely to be inefficient.

The steam chest, if properly constructed and operated, gives sufficiently good results to warrant consideration. Usually steam is introduced into a closed tank below the combs. A low steam pressure of several pounds is maintained by weighting the lid to keep the steamer closed. Frames containing combs may be placed in racks in the steamer, suspended above the bottom with a series of coarse screens to catch and hold the refuse material. The beeswax drips and runs through the screens and is drawn off at the bottom from time to time with the condensed steam. While not considered as effective as the hot-water press, its efficiency is relatively high and it can be used for cleaning frames and sterilizing equipment.

The common method of recovering wax from old combs is the *hot-water* press which was developed in Germany and is known as the Herschiser wax press. The size of the press should be about 20 by 20 by 20 inches if a capacity of about 75 pounds of beeswax per day (a yield from about 300 combs) is desired. Two openings in the bottom are provided, one for a drain and the other for the introduction of hot water for raising the liquid wax toward the top. Steam is introduced at the bottom of the press.

It is advisable to break up the combs and soak them in warm water for 24 hours prior to pressing. The pollen and other waste materials in the combs will absorb water which results in these materials absorbing less wax when pressed and a greater yield of wax is obtained.

The comb material then is placed in burlap and the sides folded over and fastened to contain the comb material under the pressure of the screw of the press. This is called a "cheese." Usually three cheeses, separated by wood-slatted mats, are pressed at each operation. The water is kept boiling gently and pressure is applied intermittently by means of the screw to press the wax from the interior of the cheeses. At the end of the operation, requiring several hours, the steam is shut off and the water level raised to float the beeswax out the opening at the top of the press.

Instead of the screw, some use hydraulic rams which create greater pressure and speed up the pressing operation. These operators usually melt the combs in an open tank of boiling water, skimming or dipping off the wax which melts and rises to the surface. They then put the remaining refuse while hot into a cheese and press it quickly. While the output of wax is relatively high, the greater pressure can result in wax that is higher in foreign content and moisture.

In Europe are found centrifugal devices for recovering beeswax from melted comb material. These centrifuges are expensive and are used mainly by those who make a business of recovering beeswax for beekeepers in the general area. It is reported that their efficiency is high but results in beeswax having a relatively high moisture content. Their use in this country has not yet been accepted and beekeepers still resort to rendering in some other way.

Beekeepers who do not have means for efficient rendering of combs can melt them in hot water, collecting all the material and allowing it to congeal in containers until they have a sufficient amount for shipment to a rendering center. Melted-down comb material is virtually safe from moth damage, and the bulk of the material is reduced for convenience in shipping.

SLUMGUM

Slumgum is the material remaining after some melting treatment has been performed on cappings or combs. It may be more or less rich in beeswax even though its appearance may lead one to think it is worthless. Unless the beekeeper has a good system of rendering such material and knows how to use it properly, it will pay him to investigate. Certain rendering firms guarantee the freight on a minimum shipment of slumgum, enabling the beekeeper to determine the efficiency of his rendering methods.

Even the best commercial methods of rendering old combs and slumgum result in a refuse which still contains some beeswax. The only known way to recover this last bit of beeswax is by solvents, but results in a gummy, waxy material because the solvents also extract the resins and gums of pollen, propolis, and other materials. The resulting product is not suitable for marketing as pure beeswax.

PROPOLIS

Propolis is a resinous material gathered by bees from the exudations of the buds of certain trees. As seen in the beehive, propolis usually is admixed with beeswax, and is not difficult to recognize because of its brownish-green color, and its sticky, gummy consistency in warm weather. The bees use it to fill cracks, reduce openings, cover objectionable objects, and for a number of other purposes. Often its use is objectionable to the beekeeper because it makes removal of frames difficult in cold weather and sticks to the hands in warm weather. It may be removed from the hands with alcohol or other solvent.

Propolis is mentioned here because it is a natural contaminant of beeswax. Because some of the resins of propolis are soluble in beeswax, whenever possible, frame and hive scrapings containing it should be kept separate from all forms of beeswax. Propolis may lower the melting point of beeswax, make it softer and more sticky, and change other chemical and physical characteristics. For further information on propolis, see Chapter IV, "Activities of Bees."

In rendering comb material which is high in propolis content, a large amount of propolis settles to the bottom of the container while the beeswax rises to the surface. The settled propolis is gummy and sticky, becoming hard and brittle when cold.

The commercial beekeeper does not collect or save propolis. But it is of interest that the old Italian violin makers of Cremona used a propolis varnish to create such masterpieces as the Stradivarius violins.

Preparing Crude Beeswax for Market

According to Bisson and his associates,[1] wax scales are white in color and fairly uniform in their physical and chemical characteristics. From the time the worker bees begin to manipulate the wax scales for comb construction, the beeswax undergoes certain changes. Propolis and pollen are probably the most important contaminants and sources of color in beeswax.

When the cappings and combs are melted, the liquid beeswax comes into intimate contact with the other foreign materials and further changes take place. Crude beeswax often contains parts of bees, dirt, straw, leaves, honey, pollen, propolis, and many other foreign materials.

It is good practice to melt beeswax in an excess of water. It is advisable to acidulate the water with one tablespoonful of vinegar for each gallon of water. Strong acids, like sulfuric acid, should not be used because they are dangerous if not properly handled and can be injurious to the wax. The liquid beeswax should be boiled gently; vigorous and prolonged boiling will result in damage to the beeswax.

When beeswax is melted in the absence of water, discoloration will occur when the temperature exceeds 185° F. for a period of time. Live steam should not be directed against beeswax in a melter because it results in a partial saponification, harmful to beeswax. If beeswax is melted over an open flame, it should be done with extreme care. Beeswax is flammable and fires have resulted when melting beeswax in this manner.

Tanks used for melting beeswax should be made of tinned copper, heavily coated tinned iron known as "dairy tin," stainless steel, or aluminum. Bisson and his associates demonstrated that beeswax is discolored very little by glass, stainless steel, aluminum, nickel, and platinum. Monel metal, iron, and zinc turn beeswax gray or brown, while brass and copper cause it to become green in color. Most rendering equipment used by the beekeeper is made of galvanized iron which serves all practical purposes providing the beeswax is melted in the presence of water. Black iron tanks should not be used because they discolor beeswax rapidly.

Containers for molding beeswax can be of any suitable material because the liquid beeswax soon congeals and is little affected by them. They should be flared to facilitate removal. An inch or two of hot water in the bottom of the molds also will help. The bottom of the cakes of beeswax should be scraped to remove the material which has settled. These scrapings should be saved and rendered with additional lots of comb or slumgum because they contain much beeswax.

REFINING BEESWAX

Beeswax is refined by melting and boiling gently over water in large tanks where it remains in the liquid state for many hours. The lighter impurities rise to the surface and are skimmed off, and the heavier impurities settle to the bottom of the liquid wax or into the lower water layer. Some refiners use chemicals to speed the refining process and improve the color, particularly of darker grades of beeswax. Repeated washing and rinsing with hot water may be used until the liquid beeswax is clear and clean (Fig. 3). Beeswax also has been refined by centrifuging.

Commercially refined beeswax is light yellow to brown in color and of fairly uniform quality. It usually is marketed in the form of 20-pound slabs, 1-pound cakes, and small shapes weighing approximately 1 ounce.

BLEACHING BEESWAX

United States beeswax does not bleach readily, neither by chemical means nor when exposed to the sun's rays. Bleachable grades of beeswax consumed in this country mainly come from Brazil, Chile, Cuba, Africa, and Egypt. Usually the beeswax is given some chemical treatment to refine and bleach it, with the process being completed by exposure to the sun's rays either in the liquid form or in the form of fine shreds. The bleaching chemicals include the bichromates, permanganates, peroxides, and chlorine compounds. Diatomaceous earth and carbon are added to the liquid wax, after refining, then agitated and filtered prior to chemical bleaching, or a cleaning filtration may be used after the beeswax has been chemically bleached. Bleached beeswax is marketed in large slabs, pound cakes, discs weighing from 2 to 3 ounces, and small ounce cakes.

Physical and Chemical Properties of Beeswax

The United States Pharmacopeia,[8] defines bleached beeswax or *Cera Alba* as "White wax is the bleached, purified wax from the honeycomb of the bee, *Apis mellifera* Linné (Family *Apidae*)." It further

FIGURE 3. Fully refined pure beeswax, ready for manufacturing processes.

describes it as a yellowish white solid, somewhat translucent in thin layers, with a faint characteristic odor, free from rancidity, and with a specific gravity of about 0.95. Although not included in the recent edition of the U.S.P., refined yellow beeswax was called *Cera Flava* and was defined as the "Purified honeycomb of the bee." It was described as varying in color from yellow to grayish-brown, having an agreeable honeylike odor, and a faint characteristic taste.

Federal Specification C-B-191a,[7] entitled "Beeswax; Technical Grade," covers the purchase of refined yellow beeswax by all the Federal agencies. It states that the specific gravity shall be not less than 0.950 nor more than 0.970 at 25.0°/25.0° C., the softening point not less than 60.5° nor more than 64.0° C., the acid number not less than 16.5 nor more than 21.0, the saponification number not less than 86 nor more than 96, and the ratio number not less than 3.5 nor more than 4.3. In addition, the beeswax must be free from rosin, conform to the chloroform test and the saponification cloud test, and be certified that it is solely natural beeswax from the honeycomb.

U. S. P. bleached beeswax must have a melting range of 62° to 65° C. (143.6 to 149.0° F.), an acid value of not less than 17 nor more than 24, an ester value of not less than 72 and not more than 79, and successfully pass the tests for absence of carnauba wax, the saponification cloud test, and a test for fats, fatty acids, Japan wax, rosin, and soap.

Beeswax is insoluble in water, sparingly soluble in cold alcohol, completely soluble in chloroform, ether, and in fixed and volatile oils. It is partly soluble in cold benzene and carbon disulfide, and is completely soluble in these solvents at about 30° C. (86° F.).

Because of the possibility of the use of microcrystalline wax as an additive to beeswax in the production of bee comb foundation in this country, something which manufacturers have agreed to not do, Johnathan W. White, Jr. and associates,[5,6] made a long series of experiments establishing new methods for the analyses of beeswax and especially for the determination of the hydrocarbon content of beeswax. For 59 samples of crude yellow beeswax from the United States, they found the melting point to be 63.56° C. (146.4° F.), acid number 18.33, ester number 72.61, ratio number 3.96, the hydrocarbon content 14.59, the hydrocarbon freezing point 54.9° C. (130.8° F.), and the saponification cloud test 62.5° C. (144.5° F.).

This work of White and his associates is of significance because it demonstrates that U. S. beeswax specifications have limits that should be narrowed and tests which should be more precise for establishing purity of beeswax. Their work on hydrocarbon content should be of real interest to countries abroad where it is reported that bee comb foundation is being made from materials other than pure beeswax.

BLOOM ON BEESWAX

On standing for a period of time, particularly in cold weather, a powdery substance forms on the surface of beeswax. It sometimes is referred to by beekeepers as mildew or mould, although it resembles neither one. Little is understood concerning the cause of bloom or its composition. It forms on the surface of beeswax apparently due to molecular rearrangement that occurs under optimum temperature conditions. If rubbed off, it may appear again. According to Vansell and Bisson,[3] it has a melting point of 39° C. (102° F.) which is approximately 43° F. below the melting point of beeswax. This phenomenon is peculiar to only a few substances and can be considered a characteristic of pure beeswax on this account.

Uses of Beeswax

COSMETICS

The largest consumer of beeswax in this country is the cosmetic industry (Fig. 4). Bleached beeswax is the ingredient which results in the white, pearly emulsion of all typical cold creams. Many other types of creams, ointments, lotions, pomades, lipsticks, rouges, and others contain beeswax in their formulas. Undoubtedly, the expansion of this industry in the past several decades has taken up the slack of a decreasing demand for beeswax on the part of industries which turned to materials that were more readily available and usually lower in price.

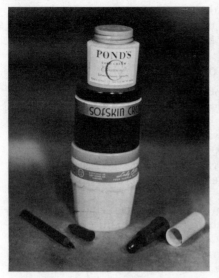 

FIGURE 4. Cosmetics of many kinds contain pure beeswax. Bleached beeswax is responsible for the white pearly emulsion of cold creams.

FIGURE 5. Candles were first made from beeswax — perhaps the reason why the Church selected beeswax candles for religious services of Mass.

CHURCH CANDLES

Probably the next largest use of beeswax is in the production of church candles (Fig. 5). The Jewish, Greek Catholic, Episcopalian, and certain other faiths use beeswax candles to some extent, but the chief user is the Roman Orthodox Catholic Church.

In antiquity, the Church sought the purest sources of light for its religious ceremonies, selecting beeswax and olive oil. Originally, it was required that the candles burned on the altar during the services of Mass and the Benediction of the Blessed Sacrament be of pure beeswax. In the earlier development of the Church in this country, pure beeswax candles could not always be obtained and allowances had to be made, resulting in a ruling that the candles must be of greater part beeswax. Today most manufacturers make 51 per cent, 60 per cent, and pure beeswax candles. The percentages in other countries vary in the amount of beeswax content.

COMB FOUNDATION

For a long time, it has been a recognized good beekeeping practice to use full sheets of foundation made from pure beeswax. This doubtless is the third major use for beeswax in this country. This usage of beeswax is unique because it is the only field of use in which it is not consumed or lost. When the combs become unsuitable for further use in the beehive, they are melted and returned to the market as crude beeswax. In a way this is the most important use of beeswax because pure beeswax foundation used in the beehive becomes the birthplace of more beeswax as the bees add to it in the construction of their combs.

OTHER USES OF BEESWAX

The pharmaceutical industry uses beeswax in the preparation of salves, ointments, cerates, camphor ices, pomades, sticky wax, and other preparations. The dental trade uses beeswax in the form of impression wax, base plate wax, and in other wax compounds. Beeswax is used in foundries in the form of wax fillets for rounding the corners of small patterns; in the form of sheets of varying thickness; as an ingredient of modeling compounds; and in the "lost wax" process for producing precision castings.

Polishes for floors, furniture, stoves, shoes, leather, and other items sometimes contain beeswax in their formulas. In this field of use, beeswax largely has been replaced by carnauba wax, from which polishes are made that dry to a bright luster without buffing or polishing. While there is evidence that polishes made from beeswax give greater service and protection, the convenience of application without the necessity of buffing has met with popularity.

Formerly quantities of beeswax were used in electrical insulation. Beeswax still finds use in electrical embedding compounds, but its use largely has been replaced by resins and waxes, usually lower in cost. In general, beeswax is used in many ways for waterproofing, protection, and beautification.

Interesting minor uses include adhesive compositions, crayons, chewing gum, an ingredient of inks, basketball molding, grafting wax, ski wax, thread wax, ironing wax, polishing telescopic lenses, and waxing archers' bow strings.

REFERENCES CITED

1. Bisson, C. S., G. H. Vansell, and W. B. Dye. 1940. U. S. Dept. Agr. Tech. Bull. **716**. 24 p.

2. Smith, Francis G. 1960. Beekeeping in the tropics. Longmans, London. p. 198.

3. Vansell, G. H., and C. S. Bisson. 1940. Calif. Agr. Expt. Sta. Circ. **E-495.**

4. Voorhies, E. C., F. E. Todd, and J. K. Galbraith. 1933. Calif. Agr. Expt. Sta. Bull. **555**. 84 pp.

5. White, J. W., Jr., M. L. Reithof, and I. Kushnir. 1960. J. Offic. Agr. Chem. 43:781-790.

6. White, J. W., Jr., M. K. Reader, and M. L. Reithof. 1960. J. Offic. Agr. Chem. 43:778-780.

7. Beeswax, technical grade. Federal Specification C-B-191a. 1954.

8. The Pharmacopeia of the United States of America. 1960. 16th Rev. Mack Pub. Co., Easton, Pa.

CHAPTER XVII

THE PRODUCTION OF QUEENS, PACKAGE BEES, AND ROYAL JELLY

by G. H. Cale, Jr.*

THE RELATIONSHIP THAT EXISTS between a queen bee and her colony is so close that success or failure during a production season often depends upon the quality of the queen mother of the colony. If all other colony management practices are of the highest quality, the honey crop produced is entirely a matter of queen quality—since the worker bees that produce this crop are complete daughters of the queen, which heads the colony, and the sperm in her spermatheca.

Farrar[3] has pointed out the influence of colony population on honey production, showing a mathematical relationship between each bee in the population and the total honey production. More recently, Moeller[12] arrived at somewhat similar relationships using varying honey-bee stock lines for his measurements.

The above merely emphasizes some facts that have been pointed out by many workers over a long period of years. The field force of a colony of bees is dependent upon the quality of the queen. To reduce swarming, and to have maximum worker-bee population and maximum honey production, require almost yearly requeening of colonies with properly reared and mated queens of superior stock. Many honey producers who winter their colonies seem to forget that their spring-management problems can be partially solved by requeening with queens of superior stock in the fall of the previous year.

QUEEN BREEDING

Any queen-rearing effort must, of necessity, involve the choice of a queen mother from which young virgin queens will be reared. For thousands of years, bees have maintained themselves by natural swarming and supersedure of failing queens. The advent of queen rearing— both amateur and commercial—meant that some man-made selection process, rather than natural selection, would be applied to honey bees for the first time in their long natural history. Dr. C. C. Miller's advice to "breed from the best" is sufficient for the amateur queen raiser—but is inadequate for commercial queen breeding. Three methods are generally used today, each of which is briefly described in the following paragraphs.

---

*G. H. Cale, Jr. Ph.D. In charge of the hybrid bee-breeding program of Dadant & Sons, Inc. for many years. Developer of Starline and Midnite hybrid queens.

Breeding from the Best. Dr. Miller's advice is still appropriate for those who want to rear only a few queens. Careful selection should be made of a queen mother that has shown her egg-laying potential and her longevity. The worker progeny of this potential queen mother should also be evaluated for wintering ability, vigor in honey production, reasonable temper, and other desirable characteristics. Considerable care should be taken to be sure that characteristics being studied are true measures of the individual under consideration. Frequently, worker bees will drift from one colony to another, thus causing extra population and a honey yield not truly representative of the potential worth of the queen mother of the colony.

Linebreeding. Essentially, this system of breeding refers to the method of selective breeding within a relatively small closed population. Linebreeding is sometimes used by commercial queen breeders, although many tend to select their breeding stock by the previous method. Large numbers of colonies are a necessity for even small success with linebreeding methods. The same desirable characteristics, previously mentioned, need to be considered carefully.

Several lines, representing different "pools of inheritance," need to be maintained. These lines should be obtained from widely separated areas of the country in order to reduce the possibility of common ancestry. In addition to selling queens to his customers, the queen breeder must requeen several hundred colonies of his own for each of the lines involved. This requeening must be done in the summer and fall. The following year all colonies are watched closely for desirable characteristics, and selections for queen mothers for a year later are made on the basis of line averages, rather than individual colony averages.

Unfortunately, because of certain "killer" factors in the honey bee, linebreeding cannot be perpetuated for a great length of time. Mackensen[10] has shown beyond any doubt that these factors of viability do exist. The beekeeper first notices their presence by a scattered sealed-brood pattern. Eggs in such colonies fail to hatch, thus causing the scattered appearance of the sealed brood (Fig. 1). Hatchability of eggs may fall to less than 50 per cent.

Hatchability may be restored by introducing some outside strains of bees, but such introduction automatically changes the values of the previous stock. Some years of work and selection are then necessary to bring the various lines back to previous levels. This process must be repeated time after time to linebreed with bees.

This continued change in linebred bees accounts for the extreme variability to be found in all characteristics used to measure the value of lines. Temper may vary from gentle in one year to very cross in another year. All of these characteristics are controlled by heredity, and

FIGURE 1. The many uncapped brood cells resulting in the scattered appearance of the sealed brood may be due to the eggs failing to hatch. *(Photo courtesy of J. E. Eckert)*

linebreeding in bees does not control heredity—since selections are based only on the queen mother and matings are an unknown random factor.

Hybrid Breeding. This breeding method takes full advantage of Mackensen's discoveries in bees, as well as the best of hereditary (as opposed to racial) hybrid vigor as outlined originally by Shull,[19] in 1910, and well documented by hundreds of research papers since. Members of the Apiculture Research Branch of the U.S. Department of Agriculture (personal communications) have repeatedly pointed out the values of this type of bee breeding since 1946.

Early work, showing the value of hybrid breeding, could not be utilized in the honey bee without mating control. Although earlier attempts had been made at mating control, real effort did not start until Watson[21] devised and demonstrated a microsyringe (Fig. 2) for controlled instrumental insemination in 1926. Even then, complete success was not assured before Laidlaw's[5] morphological studies revealed the proper techniques for use of the instruments and Mackensen[9] demonstrated the use of carbon dioxide to stimulate initial oviposition.

Hybrid breeding is accomplished by controlled instrumental insemination (Fig. 3), rather than depending upon unknown natural matings. Lines of bees are formed by first deliberately inbreeding a number of widely differing strains. Such inbreeding makes the lines uniform in their hereditary characteristics—including the factors of viability studied by Mackensen. After fixation by inbreeding, these inbred strains are then crossed together in various experimental 4-way hybrid combinations. Because factors of viability are controlled, hatchability of eggs approaches 100 per cent (Fig. 4)—instead of the lower hatchability

FIGURE 2. The Roberts and Mackensen insemination apparatus. *(Photo courtesy of U.S.D.A. and the University of Wisconsin)*

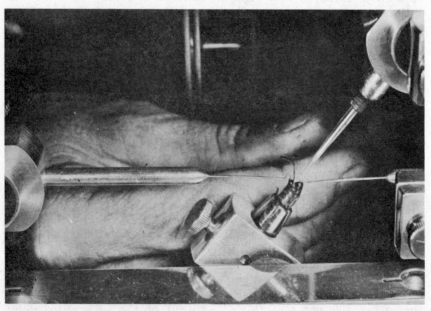

FIGURE 3. A queen being artificially inseminated using the Roberts and Mackensen apparatus. *(Photo courtesy of U.S.D.A. and the University of Wisconsin)*

FIGURE 4. A beautiful comb of sealed brood. A solid brood pattern such as this is the goal of the bee breeder. *(Photo by O. W. Park)*

present in linebred stock. In addition vigor has been demonstrated so that hybrids have shown a 34 per cent increase in honey yield over the average of linebred strains (Cale and Gowen[1]).

Hybrid breeding in bees is in its infancy. However, it is certain that future bee breeding will take advantage of this system to an even greater extent. Honey bees at least 100 per cent more productive than our current stock are not only possible, but are already in the immediate future.

The Production of Queens

Queens are raised by the worker bees of a colony under three conditions: 1. Accidental loss of the queen mother; 2. swarming impulse; and 3. supersedure impulse. In the first case given, queens are usually reared from already developing larvae; in the latter two cases, the queens are usually reared from a prepared cell into which the queen lays an egg. In general, all home and commercial queen-rearing methods—of which there are a multitude—are based around conditions one and two (above).

HOME METHODS OF QUEEN REARING

Only one method of home queen rearing will be given here. For further information the reader is referred to the following authors: Pellett,[15] Snelgrove,[20] and Laidlaw and Eckert.[6]

Dr. C. C. Miller[11] described a home method of raising queens that is probably the most practical one for those who wish to rear relatively few queens for their own use. The first step in the Miller method is to select a colony from the standpoint of good honey production, gentle bees, and other desirable characteristics. This colony is then set aside to be used for queen-rearing and breeding purposes.

An empty brood frame is fitted with triangular pieces of foundation about 2 inches wide at the top and tapering to a point about halfway to the bottom bar of the frame. Four to five such strips of starter foundation are placed along the top bar of the frame (Fig. 5). The breeder colony is then deprived of all but two frames of sealed brood in the center of the hive body. The balance of the frames in the brood chamber should contain honey and pollen in abundance. The prepared frame, with starter foundation, is then placed between the two frames of sealed brood. Within a very few days, the bees will have constructed worker cells on the starter foundation and the queen will quickly use this new area for egg laying. At that time, the special queen-rearing frame should be removed and placed in the center of a strong colony. This cell-finishing colony should have the queen removed and should have an ample supply of pollen and honey, or—in the absence of honey—it should be fed a thick sugar sirup. In addition, combs containing young larvae and eggs should also be removed. All the nurse force of the colony thus concentrates its attention on the hatching

FIGURE 5. Frame containing strips of comb foundation for rearing queens by the Miller method. (*Photo courtesy of J. E. Eckert*)

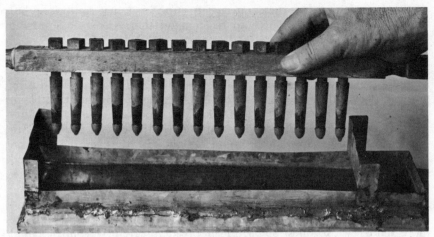

FIGURE 6. A wooden bar containing 15 shaped hardwood sticks which are dipped in beeswax to make the wax-cell cups. *(Photo courtesy of J. E. Eckert)*

larvae that have been added. Because they are queenless, a number of queen cells will be started.

A new frame with starter foundation may be added to the breeder colony at the same time the first queen-rearing frame is removed. In 9 days the first ripe queen cells are ready to be removed from the queenless cell-finishing colony. At this time the individual cells, along with a piece of protecting comb, are cut loose from the comb and inserted into single queenless nuclei or colonies. The cell-finishing colony may be kept in use over a long period of time by adding frames of emerging brood weekly and by paying careful attention to adequate pollen and honey supply within the colony. Close observation should be maintained for presence of laying workers, and the use of the colony for finishing of cells should be discontinued if laying workers develop.

COMMERCIAL QUEEN REARING

The system devised by Doolittle,[2] has come to be used almost universally for the commercial production of queen bees. There have been many changes, modifications, and improvements in the Doolittle method over the years. Hundreds of variations of this system can be found today among the men who commercially rear queens for sale. It would be impossible, here, to give all the possible variations. Instead, the major requirements of good queen rearing will be given with one example of a popular system for each step.

Transferring or Grafting. Prepared queen-cell cups, either manufactured or prepared by dipping shaped hardwood sticks (Fig. 6) into melted beeswax, are fastened to a wooden bar. This cell bar is just long enough to fit between the end bars in a standard frame.

Some prefer to use these queen-cell cups in a dry condition; but the writer would agree with and recommend the system of those who "prime" the cell cups with a small amount of fresh royal jelly (Fig. 7). If it serves no other purpose, the jelly helps to prevent larval tissue from drying out during the grafting process. A small grafting house should be a part of a good queen-rearing outfit. Temperatures during grafting (larval transfer from worker cell to queen cup) should be kept at least in the range of 80° to 90° F., and moderately high humidity should be maintained. Humidity can be controlled sufficiently with damp cloths either around the room or laid directly over the cells on the cell-bar frames. It is not wise to depend upon daylight; a good daylight-type fluorescent light should be available.

Dark, well-polished combs preferably should be used for grafting purposes. It is easier to see the larvae in the bottom of the cells, and easier to remove the larvae from the older, tougher combs than from the more tender white ones. Some queen breeders carefully control larval age by confining the queen to three combs in the center of the brood chamber with excluder division boards. The two outer combs within the excluded area are solid with pollen and honey, while the center comb is a dark, polished comb added daily. After 24 hours the center comb will contain sufficient eggs for a large graft and may be transferred to an incubator colony for care until the larvae are of grafting age. The two sides of the breeder colony can be supplied with frames of emerging brood to maintain colony strength.

The incubator colony is usually a strong 2-story colony with the queen confined to the lower hive body by an excluder. As they are added, frames of eggs are dated and placed in the upper chamber. Not all colonies will serve since some bees do not seem to supply sufficient larval food. Grafting is easier when the larvae are floating in a large bed of royal jelly (Fig. 8). The incubator colony requires ample amounts of pollen and honey—or thick sugar sirup.

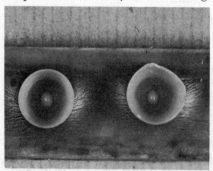

FIGURE 7. Two wax-cell cups "primed" with royal jelly. (*Photo courtesy of J. E. Eckert*)

FIGURE 8. A 36-hour-old larva lying in a bed of royal jelly. (*Photo courtesy of J. E. Eckert*)

A comb containing the young larvae is removed from the breeder or incubator hive and carried to the grafting house for larval transfer. Only very young larvae should be used—preferably larvae between 12 to 18 hours of age. The larvae are then transferred to the prepared queen-cell cups with a grafting needle (Fig. 9). This grafting needle varies with the individual but can be a pointed stick, match, feather, or metal flattened and made slightly spoon-shaped at the tip (Fig. 10). Manufactured grafting needles are available from bee supply houses.

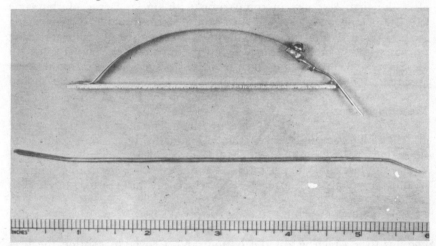

FIGURE 9. Two types of grafting needles: straight needle (bottom)); Pierce or Macy automatic needle (upper). *(Photo courtesy of J. E. Eckert)*

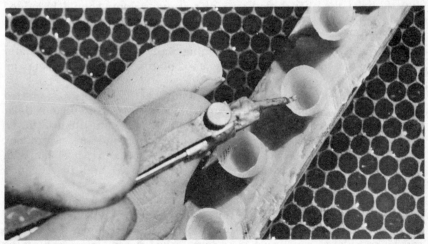

FIGURE 10. A closeup view of transferring or grafting a very young larva into a wax-cell cup which has previously been attached to the cell bar.

Larval transfer, or grafting, represents the first opportunity for careless work to reduce the quality of the finished queen. Haydak[4] and others have shown that there are distinct differences between the food of young queen larvae and young worker larvae. Some of these researchers measured food differences as far back as 1888—indicating that the knowledge of this difference has been available for many years. Perret-Maisonneuve,[16] quoting work of various European investigators, pointed out that ovarian growth of worker larvae was very retarded after the first 24 hours in comparison with queen larvae of the same age. Whitcomb and Oertel,[22] in a study of controllable queen-rearing factors, pointed out that older worker larvae used for queen-rearing purposes led to an increase in the supersedure rate in comparison with queens reared by grafting larvae of a younger age. It would seem apparent, therefore, that for quality queens the grafted larvae should most certainly be under 24 hours of age—preferably as young as 12 to 18 hours of age.

Starting Queen Cells. There are many methods for starting the grafted cells. Essentially, all methods should involve certain prime considerations: 1. An abundance of young nurse bees; 2. ample supplies of natural pollen and honey; and 3. a queenless or swarming impulse within the colony or cluster area in which the just-grafted queen cells are to be placed.

One method to achieve the results given above is with the so-called swarm box. The swarm box is usually about one-half the size of a hive body, with a screen across the bottom and a cover to confine the bees completely. One good comb of honey and two of pollen should be placed in the swarm box. From 4 to 5 pounds of young nurse bees—shaken directly from the open brood area of a strong colony—should be added to the combs of honey and pollen. In addition, in hot, dry weather some water should be furnished the bees. Water can be furnished easily by passing the pollen combs under running water and working the water down into the cells by rubbing the face of the combs with the palm of the hand.

Within 1 hour the swarm box is ready to receive the just-grafted cells. Pollen and honey combs should be spread apart so that cell-bar frames (Fig. 11) may be placed between them. Not more than 60 to 80 cells should be given to the swarm box at a time and the swarm box should not be used for more than one batch of cells. After 24 hours in the swarm box the cells are ready to be removed and placed in a finishing colony.

Whitcomb and Oertel[22] compared queens reared from swarm boxes with 60 cells and queens reared from swarm boxes with 120 cells. During the course of this study more than 3500 cells were used and results can be considered conclusive. The overstocked swarm boxes containing 120 to 160 cells finished only 55.7 per cent of the cells given them,

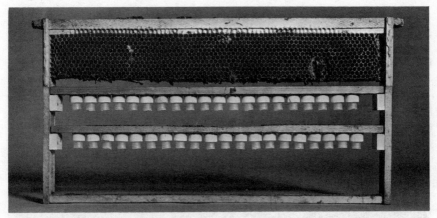

FIGURE 11. A cell-bar frame containing two cell bars each with twenty wax-cell cups is ready to be placed in the swarm box.

while boxes with 60 cells finished 81.98 per cent of their cells. In addition, supersedure was greater among queens reared from overstocked swarm boxes but otherwise treated equally. More than 21 per cent of such queens were superseded by the end of their 8th week of life.

The swarm box, therefore, is the second queen-rearing operation in which poor procedure can produce an inferior queen. All evidence would indicate that—other things being equal—a poor swarm box, overcrowded with cells, can result in poor queens and increased supersedure.

Finishing Queen Cells. Once the grafted cells have been accepted by some form of cell-starting colony or swarm box, they must then be cared for and reared during their larval and pupal development. Many forms of cell-finishing colonies may be used, but only the queenright cell finisher will be described here. Again certain prime conditions must be considered. The colony must be amply provisioned with both pollen and honey. Colony population should be at a maximum, with a good queen and more than ample brood (Fig. 12) thus assuring a constant supply of nursing-age bees in large numbers.

The 2-story queenright cell builder is suitable for a finishing colony in most commercial operations. The queen is kept confined to the lower story by a queen excluder. The cell-bar frame, with not more than 18 cells (preferably less), is placed above the excluder. About 24 hours before the cells are given, the cell-finishing colony should be prepared to receive these cells. Frames of young larvae are raised above the excluder to draw the nurse bees of the colony up into the cell-finishing portion of the colony. It is recommended that four frames of young larvae be moved to the center of the upper story of the colony. In addition, a comb of honey should be placed on each side of the second body, followed by a comb of pollen.

FIGURE 12. A strong queenright colony overflowing with bees ensures a good population of nurse bees to care for and to finish the bars of queen cells. (*Photo courtesy of E. C. Bessonet*)

The cell-bar frame (Fig. 13) is removed from the swarm box and placed in the center of the upper story of the cell-finishing colony—with two frames of young larvae, one comb of pollen and one comb of honey on either side. In addition, the cell-finishing colony should be fed continuously. This feeding should be done even if the colonies are under flow conditions.

Maintenance of the cell-finishing colony is important. In addition to continuous feeding, the colony must be watched closely for presence of swarm cells and for strength. New queens should be given for old ones, and occasionally additional frames of sealed brood must be added to boost the strength to a swarming pitch.

Many queen breeders add a cell-bar frame to the cell-finishing colony each 3d day. **This practice is not recommended.** Instead, cell bars should be given every 5th day. The worker bees will start to seal queen cells toward the end of the 4th day after they are placed within the cell-finishing colony. Placing an additional 18 or more cells in this colony every 3 or 4 days means that the nurse bees of the colony must feed, for at least a portion of the development period, 36 or more queen cells. Lineburg,[8] as well as others, has reported on the activities of nurse bees. These studies involved nursing activities for the developing worker larvae; however it is safe to assume that the developing queen larva (Fig. 14) receives as much attention as, if not more than, the developing worker.

The data involved actual activities of the feeding of larvae during the various stages of development. It is notable that during the last

FIGURE 13. A cell-bar frame containing one cell bar with a dozen finished queen cells. (*Photo courtesy of Carl E. Killion*)

24-hour period prior to sealing the cell, more than 3500 nursing trips are made to the cell. One has to use only a little arithmetic to see what is involved if the colony of bees must feed 36 or more queen cells at the same time. Oertel[14] has shown that the developing queen larva continues to feed and gain in weight for about 12 hours after the cell is sealed by the worker bees (Fig. 15). An abundant supply of fresh royal jelly, therefore, must be present in the cell at the time of sealing.

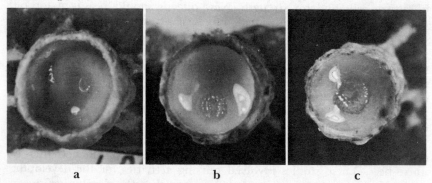

a   b   c

FIGURE 14. Growth of larvae in queen cells; *a,* 1 day after grafting; *b,* 2 days after grafting; *c,* 3 days after grafting. (*Photos courtesy of J. E. Eckert*)

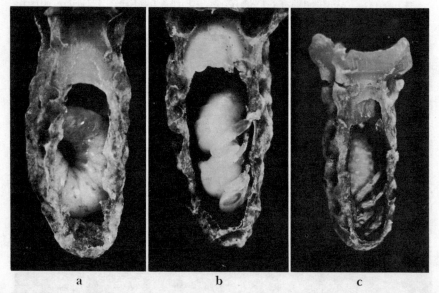

a   b   c

FIGURE 15. Development of the queen: *a,* spinning stage; *b,* pupal stage; *c,* adult shortly before emergence. Note the surplus of royal jelly in the top of each queen cell. (*Photos courtesy of J. E. Eckert*)

Further evidence of the effect of too many cells in the cell-finishing colony is supplied by the work of Whitcomb and Oertel.[22] These authors showed that there was a definite decrease in percentage of finished cells when too many cells were given to the cell finisher. The same data indicate also a reduction in the average weight, in milligrams, of virgins on emergence from the overstocked cell-finishing colony, as well as an increase in the loss by supersedure in comparison with the cell-finishing colony that has not been overstocked.

It is quite evident that malpractice in the cell-finishing colonies is also capable of contributing to poor queens and early supersedure. The case with the swarm box, as well as the age of larvae used for grafting purposes, has been cited. These facts are well understood in a practical way by some queen breeders; however, unfortunately, some queen breeders still exist who have decided that a queen is a bee with six legs and four wings capable of laying eggs—irregardless of whether or not this queen bee is capable of longevity and maximum egg laying.

Nelson,[13] in his *Embryology of the Honey Bee,* points out that, at the time of hatching, the young female larva of the honey bee has already started to differentiate the ovaries of the bee. This would clearly indicate that obtaining a maximum egg-tubule number, should perfect queen rearing be practiced, would necessitate development designed to achieve maximum growth of the ovarioles. This is seldom, if ever, achieved under natural queen-rearing conditions and can be approached only under the best of artificial queen-rearing conditions. Poorly reared queens will have as few as 125 egg tubes in each ovary instead of the maximum potential of 200. On the other hand, queens reared under excellent conditions with due thought and care on the part of the queen rearer, will be queens having as many as 180, or slightly more, ovarioles or egg tubes in each ovary.

QUEEN NUCLEI

On the 10th day after grafting, the finished queen cells are ready to be placed into individual queen-mating nuclei. Considerable care should be used in handling these ripe queen cells, since damage to the still unhatched virgin queen can occur. In particular, the cells should be closely guarded against chilling. Excess chilling during this critical period frequently results in damage, and curled wings that make it impossible for the virgin queen to seek a mate.

Queen-mating nuclei range in size from extreme baby nuclei to large 2- or 3-frame full-depth nuclei. In general, the smaller nuclei are preferred by commercial queen breeders. The smaller nucleus is easier to stock, easier to feed, easier in which to find the mated queen, and easier to break up at the end of the queen-rearing season. The small nucleus is, however, more difficult to maintain during the warmer summer months because it swarms readily. There is no valid reason to suppose that a larger nucleus is preferable to the small nucleus box from the standpoint of queen qualitv.

Frequently as many as 2000 nuclei are to be found in one nucleus yard (Fig. 16). Where these nuclei are placed in long straight rows, close together, and with the entrances all facing the same direction, a certain amount of confusion in flight occurs. This tends to lead to excess robbing and to drifting of the young queens when they make their exploratory or mating flights. A higher percentage of cell acceptance and fully mated queens will occur if the nuclei are spread farther apart, with entrances more in a random manner than all pointing in the same compass direction.

Frequently the nucleus is stocked with package bees, with sugar sirup and a queen cell being given to the nucleus at the same time. Of course, when the first lot of mated queens are removed, the nucleus will have brood in various stages and need not be restocked with package bees. However, additional feed frequently is given at the time of adding the next queen cell. The young virgin queen flies and mates from the 4th to the 7th day of her life. Contrary to opinion held in

FIGURE 16. A queen-mating yard in the South containing hundreds of baby nuclei arranged to prevent loss of queens by drifting during their mating flights. (*Photo courtesy of E. C. Bessonet*)

years past, the virgin queen does mate more than once, and frequently mates in a multiple manner on each separate mating flight. The works of Roberts,[17] and others, have substantiated this fact beyond any doubt. From 7 to 10 days following mating, the young queen starts to lay eggs and is then ready for use or shipment.

TESTED QUEENS

Normally, queens in the small nuclei are removed and sold even before the brood is sealed. Because of its size, the baby nucleus cannot support the large population that would result by prolonged egg laying within the unit. Excess population quickly results in swarming. The larger nucleus, using the standard brood frame or the 6¼-inch shallow frame, can be maintained successfully with a larger population and for more prolonged egg-laying periods.

Some queen breeders advertise "tested" queens and "breeder" queens. These classifications are somewhat deceiving and need clarification. By "tested," one would assume that some qualities had been determined as equal to some specified standards. In fact, the so-called tested queens fall into one or the other of two categories, varying between the individuals who rear queens for sale. Some regard a tested queen as one which has shown evidence of sealed worker brood, while others regard the queen as tested when her brood emerges and is observed to be true to racial color. Actually, no real test is involved.

A "breeder" queen, by its very name, implies that the queen has been kept for a long period of time. During this time, the implication is that daughter queens have been reared, mated, and their worker progeny tested for some economically valuable characteristics. A breeder queen, therefore, is a queen which must be 2 or more years old. Seldom are such queens available for sale.

SHIPPING QUEENS

The standard queen-mailing cage made of wood is now used almost universally for sending queen bees through the mail (Fig. 17). One end of the cage is provisioned with candy. The use of candy for bees was devised by Scholz in Europe and first reported by Langstroth[7] in his 1859 edition of *The Hive and the Honey Bee.* One pint of honey and 4 pounds of confectioners' sugar were used in the mixture. The candy was prepared by warming the honey to 150° F. in a double boiler, and then adding the powdered sugar with continuous stirring. The mass of semiprepared candy was then kneaded on a bread board, adding additional powdered sugar until the right consistency was reached. In later years, after discovery of the bacterial nature of the brood diseases, the use of honey for making candy has been discontinued. Instead, candy today is made by the same process with the substitution of the commercial inverted sugar sirup, Nulomoline, for honey.

The queen, along with eight or ten attendant worker bees, is placed inside the cage. In order to reduce the danger of nosema infection (see Chapter XIX), some queen breeders follow the practice of feeding Fumidil-B to a number of supply colonies. Queens are removed from individual nuclei, placed in mailing cages, and then all the attendant worker bees are secured from colonies which have been under constant feed with Fumidil-B. This assures that the nurse bees which will care for the queen in transit are free of disease, thus helping to ensure a disease-free queen upon receipt by the purchaser.

Larger numbers of queens are frequently shipped in a battery, or package cage. This is a package cage designed to hold special frames containing queen cages, a can of sugar sirup, and about 2 pounds of worker bees. The queens are in individual queen cages that are supplied with candy in the normal manner. However, no worker bees are placed within the queen cage. Instead, the queens are fed by the worker bees of the package. Battery cages are recommended for shipments of 50 or more queens. When received by the buyer, such queens are easier to introduce to individual colonies, and show a decreased supersedure rate.

THE MATING YARD

Too frequently nuclei are established and stocked with worker bees and a queen cell, with no attention given to a proper source of drones within the mating area. Since some nuclei yards are composed of 2000 or more nuclei, with a possibility of up to 1000 virgins seeking a mate

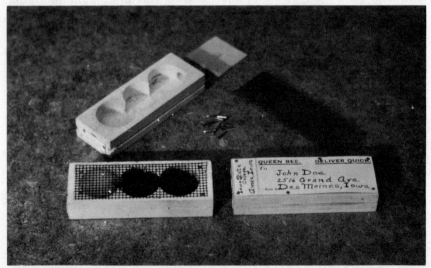

FIGURE 17. The queen-mailing cage showing the three-hole wooden block, the block covered with screen wire with the candy in one end, and lastly covered with the address card. (*Photo by O. W. Park*)

during the mating period, it should be obvious that a bountiful supply of drones is necessary. As pointed out previously, the virgin queen does mate more than once, and the average is a mating between the virgin and some 8, or slightly more, drones. Those engaged in large-scale queen rearing, therefore, must cope with the necessity for large numbers of drones in the air at all times. Very few queen breeders today follow the practice of surrounding their nucleus yard with colonies of bees at varying distances from $1/4$ to 3 miles in all directions. Yet, this practice should be followed for good matings. In addition, all of these colonies in the mating area should be well stocked with mixed worker and drone comb so that at least two combs with good drone areas are available in each body of a 2-story colony.

Still another problem needs consideration for the nucleus yard. Frequently, especially in early spring, virgin queens will be held in by inclement, cool, and wet weather. A sudden rise in the temperature and sunshine will bring large numbers of virgins from the nuclei rapidly. This is especially true when the nucleus is in the sun as the small colony quickly responds to the weather change. Scattered throughout the nucleus yard should be additional drone colonies, again amply provisioned as above with combs containing drone areas available for the use of the queen.

Failure to observe these drone requirements can often lead to queens being mailed that are only partially mated. The spermatheca of the queen bee is capable of containing upwards of 5 million sperm. A few of these are released each time an egg is deposited in a worker cell, and, unless fully mated, a queen will become a drone layer rather quickly.

SPECIAL CONSIDERATIONS FOR HYBRID BREEDING

Crossbreeding (see Chapter II, p. 33) is a system of breeding which achieves a form of hybrid vigor by crossing two geographical races such as Carnica x Mellifera. A more controlled hybrid breeding utilizes the classical methods of corn production by crossing together inbred lines of bees, each of which adds something to the final hybrid or double hybrid cross. The last 10 years has seen an increase, by more than 900 per cent, in the utilization of hybrid bees by commercial operators as well as hobbyist and sideline beekeepers. The commercial queen breeder offering hybrid stock must follow slightly different methods than those breeding a common-stock bee.

In the late summer and fall preceding the package-bee and queen season, the hybrid breeder must rear and requeen his outyard colonies with a special 2-way hybrid drone mother. These colonies are then used for package-bee production, as well as for stocking the mating nuclei, thus assuring the proper type of drones throughout his outfit. In addition, the hybrid breeder must carefully saturate the mating area with the proper drones. This is done by seeking semi-isolation, and then establishing a circular mating area within which hundreds of drone colonies are maintained. At the center of this circle is the nucleus yard. A different type of queen is supplied for a grafting mother, so that the resulting mating will bring about a double hybrid which is a combination of four inbred lines. Recent tests of properly established mating areas have shown that more than 90 per cent of correct mating occurs when the hybrid mating yards are established in the manner above. Both Starline and Midnite hybrid bees are well known to the beekeeping industry and are examples of double hybrid bees formed from inbred lines. The advantage of hybrid breeding is simply that hybrids may be recreated at any moment in the future from the constant inbred lines and that a search may always continue for better inbreds from which still better hybrids may be formed.

In the future, hybrid breeding undoubtedly will also consider the concept of crossbreeding mentioned in Chapter II. There is every reason to believe that hybrid breeding, using inbred lines as well as geographical races, can provide still better bees to the industry. Cale and Gowen[1] have shown production increases of 34 per cent with current hybrids, while Ruttner[18] has shown similar percentage increases by crosses between geographical races. The combination of these two types of crossings will undoubtedly yield bees that are at least 100 per cent better than the standard bees available today.

The Production of Package Bees

The package bee industry is almost completely centered in the southern states and in California, where colonies of bees normally build to strength early, thus achieving sufficient strength to enable the operator to remove the excess bees, placing them in a wire cage for sale by the pound.

The package bee industry as such, started to develop in the early 1900's, coming into its own during the first World War and in the period following this era. Some variation still exists within the industry in the size of cage used; however, the average package-bee cage is about 5½ x 9 x 16 inches with two of the sides screened with a 10- or 12-mesh black screen wire (Fig. 18). A No. 3 can, containing sugar sirup, is inverted and suspended from the top of the cage and furnished with two or three small holes from which the worker bees can secure food in transit. In addition, the majority of packages are shipped with one queen bee suspended in a cage near the center of the top of the package. Some package-bee producers ship the queen with attendants and candy, while others ship the queen alone in the cage, depending upon the worker bees of the package to feed and care for the queen. Sometimes the queen is actually shipped loose with the bees in the cage.

Good package-bee locations would be areas where early and sustained spring bloom supply a continuous honeyflow to the colony. Unfortunately, not too many such areas exist, and many commercial package-bee producers find it necessary to feed their colonies large quantities of sugar sirup—especially during the build-up period and the intensive 8-week shipping season from March 15th to May 15th. Some of the package-bee producers use a single story Langstroth hive for the package-bee producing colonies, while others use a 2-story hive with an excluder confining the queen below. Those who practice this latter method then smoke the bees at the entrance, forcing them up through the excluder, and secure the package bees from above by shaking the combs of bees into a funnel that is inserted inside the package cage (Fig. 19). Still others use a 2-story colony without an excluder, allowing the queen full range of both hive bodies.

Regardless of which system is used, the better package-bee producer will make every effort to reduce the number of drones that are shipped with the package, since these bumbling fellows do nothing to help the buildup of the package-bee colony in the North. In addition, considerable care should be taken to see that reasonably young worker bees are sent with the package. After its receipt in the North, the package must be installed and 3 weeks must elapse after the queen starts to lay before any new workers emerge to supplement the force of bees that was shipped with the original package. If older bees are shipped with the package, the colony in the North will reduce to a very small size prior

FIGURE 18. The screen cage used for shipment of package bees.

to the emergence of young bees. This, of course, will result in a lowered honey production on the part of the package-bee colony in the North. In addition, allowances for shrinkage in weight during shipment should be made so the purchaser will receive full weight. Partly, the amount of this allowance depends on honeyflow and feeding conditions at the time of shaking the package bees. A 2-pound package will shrink from 1 to 7 ounces in shipment. Taking all of this into consideration, the package-bee producer should allow at least 25 per cent of extra weight to offset the loss of weight in shipment.

SHIPPING PACKAGE BEES

When several packages are sent to the same customer, they are generally crated in groups of three with a space of 4 to 5 inches between the packages to provide adequate ventilation and prevent the bees from being overheated in transit (Fig. 20). Packages are usually shipped by express if the number to be sent is large; however, parcel post shipments of 5 or less packages seem to be the accepted practice today for small shipments. Many of the larger buyers of package bees have found it desirable to drive to the South with their trucks to bring their own packages back to their locations in the North. Undoubtedly, this has resulted in a large amount of savings over the cost of express shipments.

FIGURE 19. Shaking bees from combs into a funnel inserted in a package shipping cage at Stover Apiaries. (*Photo by Ross E. Hutchins*)

FIGURE 20. Three or more cages of package bees are "crated" in this manner for shipment by express or parcel post.

In recent years, considerable controversy has arisen regarding the presence of nosema-infected bees in package bees (see Chapter XIX). Certainly nosema is present in the South, just as it is in the northern part of the country. Proper use of the drug, Fumidil-B, can adequately control nosema and lead to the shipment of package bees free from this particular disease. Of course, this does not alter the responsibility of the northern receiver to continue the Fumidil-B treatment, since the nosema spores can live over in his colony from one year to the next—even though the empty combs are stored without bees for the winter period.

The Production of Royal Jelly

Royal jelly, a glandular secretion of the nurse bees, is fed to honey-bee larvae the first few days of their lives, and to the queen bees throughout the developmental period and continuing through their adult lives. The peculiar properties of royal jelly that are capable of turning a sexless, short-lived worker bee into a fully mature female capable of living 10 to 20 times as long have been a matter of interest and controversey for many years. The purpose of this section, however, is the production of royal jelly, and not its possibilities and potentialities for human consumption or treatment. R. B. Willson[23,24] has done an excellent job of reviewing the research work that has been done on royal jelly. The reader is referred to these reviews for further information along this line.

In general, royal-jelly production is closely tied to a knowledge of queen production. The royal jelly is secured from freshly started queen cells, and current recommendations are that such jelly should be harvested as early as 2 or at most 3 days after the grafted larvae are introduced into the cell-building colonies.

SMALL SCALE PRODUCTION

The beekeeper interested in a small amount of royal jelly for his own use, or for that of his family, can supply himself by dequeening one or more of his colonies and then collecting the royal jelly from the cells constructed by the queenless colony. Collection of the jelly is easily accomplished by removing the larva, and then removing the royal jelly with a standard jelly spoon that is sometimes used in normal queen-rearing practices. The stored jelly should be kept under refrigeration. There are some difficulties in the maintenance of colony strength, and the colony used once for royal-jelly production should be given its queen, following removal of the cells, and then allowed to "rest" and build up its strength for about 10 days before it is again dequeened for cell production. Three or four colonies run in this manner during the course of one season will produce a rather large amount of royal jelly. Of course, the beekeeper must be prepared to be content with jelly production at the expense of honey production, and perhaps the loss of a colony or two in the process of repeated dequeening.

LARGE SCALE PRODUCTION

In general, large scale royal-jelly production follows much the same procedure as is used by the commercial queen breeder. Of course, there is no need for queen-rearing nuclei, since the interest is only in the jelly which is obtained within 3 days after grafting.

Cell-building colonies must be available, and as pointed out for queen rearing, these cell builders must be very strong colonies, amply provided with food, pollen, and water. Queenless colonies may be used for this purpose; however, the queenright colony is generally accepted as the better method. As before, the queen is confined to the lower chamber by an excluder, with the second chamber containing ample supplies of pollen, honey, and open brood to lure the nurse bees of the colony into that portion of the hive where the cells are to be placed.

Cells may be started in a swarm box much as was described for queen production. However, if the cell-building colonies are very strong, and fresh larvae are added to the cells immediately after the royal jelly has been removed, these newly grafted cells may frequently be placed back into the cell-building colony without the necessity of using a swarm box. By trial, it may be determined easily that some colonies accept and mature more and better cells than others. Those that do a poor job of cell acceptance or cell feeding should be eliminated and replaced with additional colonies for trial.

The cell-building colony is provided in its upper body with a frame of grafted queen larvae of 20 or 30 cells on a cell bar. For maximum production, on the 2d day another frame of grafted cells is added; on the 3d, still another frame of cells is given; on the 4th day, the first frame of cells which has been in the building colony for 3 days is ready to be removed for extraction of the royal jelly. The empty cells, resupplied with a new larval graft, are then reinserted into the colony for the production of another lot of jelly.

The whole procedure is not as simple as it may sound. The cell-building colonies must be kept well supplied with food, and must have a continual supply of nurse bees to do the cell building and to secrete the royal jelly. Frequently the output of a single queen below is not sufficient to maintain this strength, and the colony must be reinforced with emerging brood from other colonies, or package bees, consisting almost entirely of young nurse bees, must be added to the colony. At least once each week, preferably even more frequently, open larvae from the lower brood chamber must be raised above the excluder and sealed brood from above placed below.

Jelly Removal.   The grafting needle is used to remove the larvae. Following this, the jelly itself may be removed with a standard commercial jelly spoon; however, this method would be very slow for large scale production. Instead, a commercial vacuum pump is used to suck the jelly from the cells. A small amount of jelly should be left in the bottom of the cells to serve as a starter for the next batch of larvae which should be grafted onto this fresh royal jelly as soon as possible and the cell bar returned to the finishing colony.

Jelly Preparation and Sale.   For cleanliness and uniformity, the jelly should be filtered through fine cheesecloth or bolting cloth and stored immediately at refrigerator temperatures until ready for processing or sale. For short-term storage, normal refrigerator temperatures are sufficient; long periods of storage should be accomplished in a deepfreeze. The jelly should be placed in glass or plastic containers with weighed measurements in ounces or pounds, since most sales are made on this basis. Sales channels for the raw royal jelly are the special dietary and vitamin producers, and toiletry manufacturers. Some producers are offering royal jelly with honey, the amount of jelly being added to the honey varying with each producer. Generally, for human consumption, the jelly is packaged in 50 mm. capsules by houses which are especially equipped with the proper capsules to assure against deterioration and to do the work on a commercial scale. For this purpose, the jelly is quite frequently dehydrated to a powder and then added to a bland carrier or mixed with vitamins.

A word of caution is in order here. The producer should bear in mind that no claims can be made for the curative powers of the jelly in connection with the product offered for sale, since there have been no accepted scientific proofs of the value of this product. It is not recognized as a drug by either the American Medical Association or by the U. S. Food & Drug Administration. Labeling should merely state that the material is royal jelly, the amount, and that it is a supplementary food product and not offered as a therapeutic. Further research effort is continuing on a small scale in this hemisphere, and it is hoped that the results of this research work will lead to a greater understanding of the value of royal jelly as a human food or dietary supplement.

REFERENCES CITED

1. Cale, G. H., Jr., and J. W. Gowen. 1956. Genetics **41**(2):292-303.
2. Doolittle, G. M. 1915. Scientific queen rearing. Am. Bee J., Hamilton, Ill. 126 pp.
3. Farrar, C.L. 1937. J. Agr. Research **54**:945-954.
4. Haydak, M. H. 1943. J. Econ. Entomol. **33**(5):778-792.
5. Laidlaw, H. H., Jr. 1944. J. Morphol. **74**(3):426-465.
6. Laidlaw, H. H., Jr., and J. E. Eckert. 1962. Queen rearing. Univ. Calif. Press, Berkeley and Los Angeles, Calif. 165 pp.
7. Langstroth, L. L. 1859. A practical treatise on the hive and the honey bee. A. O. Moore Co., New York. p. 272.
8. Lineburg, Bruce. 1925. Gl. Bee Cult. **15**:42-43.
9. Mackensen, O. W. 1947. J. Econ. Entomol. **40**(3):344-349.
10. ----------------- 1951. Genetics **36**:500-509.
11. Miller, C. C. 1912. Am. Bee J. **52**(8):243.
12. Moeller, F. E. 1961. U.S.D.A. Agr. Research Serv., Prod. Research Rept. **55**. 20 pp.
13. Nelson, James A. 1915. The embryology of the honey bee. Princeton Univ. Press, Princeton, N. J. 282 pp.
14. Oertel, E. 1930. J. Morphol. Physiol. **50**:295-340.
15. Pellett, Frank C. 1945. Practical queen rearing. Am. Bee J., Hamilton, Ill. 102 pp.
16. Perret-Maisonneuve, A. 1926. L'apiculture intensive et l'elevage des reines. 3d ed. 550 pp.
17. Roberts, Wm. G. 1944. Gl. Bee Cult. **72**(6):255-259,303.
18. Ruttner, F. 1957. Deutsche Bienenwirtschaft **8**:81-87.
19. Shull, G. H. 1910. Am. Breeders Mag. **1**:98-107.
20. Snelgrove, L. E. 1946. Queen rearing. I. Snelgrove, Bleadon, Somerset, England. 344 pp.
21. Watson, Lloyd R. 1927. Am. Bee J. **67**:235-236,300-302,364-365.
22. Whitcomb, W., Jr., and E. Oertel. 1938. Personal communication.
23. Willson, R. B. 1955. Am. Bee J. **95**:15-21,55-59.
24. ----------------- 1957. Am. Bee J. **97**:356-359,396-399.

CHAPTER XVIII

THE HONEY BEE AS A POLLINATING AGENT

by H. B. LOVELL[*]

POLLINATION OF FLOWERS IS a rather complicated process. In 1877, Charles Darwin[1] showed that cross-pollination greatly increased the size and vigor of plants raised from seed and that, under natural conditions, such cross-pollinated plants would be certain to crowd out and overwhelm weak and sickly plants produced by self-pollination. He further concluded that nature abhors perpetual inbreeding or self-pollination. This has led to the widely accepted theory of hybrid vigor.

TYPES OF POLLINATION

Self-pollination occurs in perfect or hermaphroditic flowers where pollen from the anthers falls on the stigma of the same flower, or is moved there by the visits of insects.

Close-pollination happens when pollen from the anthers comes into contact with the stigmas of flowers on the same plant, or in the case of cuttings or other vegetative reproduction, when the pollen from the flowers of one cutting falls on the stigma of a flower from a cutting of the same original plant or tree. To all practical purposes this is a special example of self-pollination.

Cross-pollination is the transfer of pollen from the flowers of one plant to another plant of the same species, which was derived from a different seed.

Interpollination is the transfer of pollen from one variety to a different variety of the same species.

Hybrid pollination is the designation formerly reserved for crossing between distinct species, but has recently been applied to crossings between inbred strains of the same species, as in the case of hybrid corn and tomatoes.

NATURAL PLANT ADAPTATION

In nature a number of adaptations have been developed which tend to promote cross-pollination; these include:

Dioecious plants, in which staminate (male) flowers and pistillate (female) flowers are borne on different individuals, as in the case of the maples, willows, hollies, poplars, and tupelos.

---

[*]Harvey B. Lovell, Ph.D. Professor of Zoology, University of Louisville, Louisville, Kentucky. Authority on American honey plants. Author of many articles on honey plants and pollination, co-author of a textbook on zoology.

Monoecious plants, in which the stamens and pistils are in different flowers on the same plant. In such cases self-pollination is possible, but studies have shown that pollen from different plants grows much more rapidly and usually successfully fertilizes the egg cells. Examples are the squash, melon, cucumber, and corn.

Protandrous flowers, in which the anthers mature and shed their pollen before the stigmas mature (Fig. 1). This makes self-pollination almost impossible and occurs in a wide variety of honey plants and fruit trees.

Protogynous flowers, in which the stigmas mature first and usually wither before the anthers mature. This is a rather uncommon adaptation and one that may defeat its own purpose because the first flowers to open, on a plant being in the pistillate stage, have no possible way to obtain pollination.

Dimorphic flowers, which have flowers of two types, as the name dimorphic indicates, occur in the primrose and fireweed. Some have long styles and short anthers, and others have short styles and long anthers. Visiting bees carry the pollen from short-styled flowers to long-styled flowers and *vice versa*. Studies have shown that only such pollen is viable in many of these species.

THE IMPORTANCE OF HONEY-BEE POLLINATION

Honey bees have long been recognized as the most important agent in the pollination of many of our most valuable crops. They are rapidly becoming indispensable because of the decline of our wild bees due to excessive application of poisonous sprays used in the control of pests on such crops as apples, pears, peaches, and cotton.

There are a large number of crops which benefit from insect pollination, particularly by the honey bee (Fig. 2). Even those which are regularly self-pollinated produce more and better fruits when visited by bees. In fact, all crops not wind-pollinated need the agency of insects to set a complete crop.

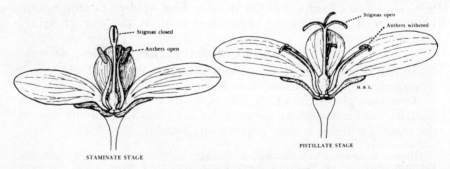

FIGURE 1. Diagram of the flower of spring beauty, an example of a protandrous flower.

It has been claimed that the value of bees in the pollination of crops is 10 to 20 times the value of the honey and wax which they produce. When an apple tree is screened entirely from honey bees and other insects, it sets less than 1 per cent of a normal crop; in fact, if a hive of bees is placed under the screen it may set no crop, since most apples are sterile to their own pollen.

THE POLLINATION OF FRUITS

In early times most people set out mixed orchards, but large fruit growers thought this was wasteful of labor, since it was necessary to harvest the different varieties separately, and assumed it would be more efficient to plant pure stands. Unfortunately for this practice, most varieties of fruit belong to a single clone which has been reproduced by grafting from a single original tree or vine. As a result, all the trees of a particular variety have the same chromosomes and produce the same kind of pollen. Such close-pollination will not bring about a set of fruit in self-sterile varieties.

Years ago it was discovered that Bartlett pears are sterile to the pollen of all other Bartlett pear trees. The Old Dominion Fruit Company, in 1875, planted along the James River, in Virginia, an orchard of 22,000 Bartlett pears, but in spite of good weather and excellent care they failed to yield a crop. In 1892, Waite,[17] was sent to study the orchard. He noticed that in some places where the Bartlett pears had died out, other varieties had been set out, such as Clapp's Favorite or Buffum. Around these trees the Bartletts were heavily laden with fruit. Mixed orchards in the vicinity also bore well.

FIGURE 2. These beehives are placed at the edge of an orchard. The bees have access to the blossoms in near-by fields and pastures as well as to those on the fruit trees. (*U.S.D.A. photo*)

Waite selected a number of unopened buds and removed the stamens and pollinated part of them with pollen from Bartlett pears, and part with pollen from other varieties, and then encased those buds in paper bags to prevent the entrance of other pollen which might be brought by pollinating insects. In the whole orchard a week after the petals had fallen, nearly all the young pears fell off, leaving most of the trees barren. Of the flowers in the bags, none of those pollinated by Bartlett pollen set any fruit, whereas a large proportion of the crosses set fruit.

Waite then experimented with 38 different varieties of pears and found most of them sterile to their own pollen and also to pollen from the same variety. He found that self-sterile varieties were Bartlett, Anjou, Clapp's Favorite, Howell, Lawrence, and Winter Nellis. Self-fertile varieties included Angoulême, Bosc, Buffum, and Flemish Beauty. Even these produced larger and more perfect pears when crossed with other varieties. Waite recommended that every third row of Bartletts be cut out and replaced with another variety which bloomed at the same time. When this was done, they obtained good crops of pears.

It is hard to convince fruit growers that they should study the scientific reports of experiment stations. In 1918, Weldon[19] wrote: "There are thousands of acres of Bartletts being planted in California each season with utter disregard of the benefits that might be derived by planting one or more other varieties for cross-pollination. In certain new pear-growing sections the writer has recently seen thousands of acres of Bartletts, in blocks of 5 acres to more than 100 acres, each with no other varieties near, except possibly an occasional tree of some favorite pear planted for home use."

The California Agricultural Experiment Station found it necessary to repeat Waite's now classical experiment in the West. They directed Tufts[15] to check up on the effect of the famous California climate on the fruitfulness of the Bartletts. In the highly favorable conditions of the Vaca Valley, the Bartletts were able to set a fair percentage of fruit when self-pollinated. The set was greater when they were interpollinated with such varieties as Easter, Howell, and Comice; also, less fruit dropped off before ripening. In the foothill orchards of Nevada County, Tufts found the Bartlett pear to be nearly as self-barren as Waite had found it in Virginia.

Tufts carefully compared the set of fruit in two orchards of Bartletts in Nevada County. In the first orchard the Bartletts had been top-grafted to other varieties; the second orchard was a pure stand of Bartletts. The mixed orchard produced a crop almost three times as great in spite of the fact that it lost a lot of fruit as a result of pear blight.

In Oregon, Brown and Childs,[3] of the Oregon Experimental Station, had been studying the pollination of the pear, this time the variety known as Anjou which is famous for its flavor and keeping qualities.

They first showed by careful experiments that wind plays no part in its pollination. They also reported the following significant incident. In 1927 the set of fruit on Anjou trees in two valleys in Oregon varied greatly. In one the conditions for the flight of bees was excellent, bringing about an average set of 20.2 per cent. In the other valley, also under scientific observation, where cloudy weather with showers prevailed for 6 days during the height of the blooming period, only 1.5 per cent set of pears were obtained. The authors rightly concluded that bad weather caused a failure of the set of fruit only because it prevented the flight of pollinizing insects to the flowers. Could better evidence be found for the need of bees during fruit bloom?

In northern states and Canada, the plum is consistently one of the three most important fruit trees. Pioneer studies in this group of fruits have been made by Waugh[18] at the Vermont Agricultural Experiment Station. After years of hand crossings and bagging experiments between various varieties, Waugh wrote, "Plums should always be planted on the assumption that they will require interpollination."

In California there are 21 kinds of Japanese plums that are commercially profitable. Philp and Vansell[14] found that only four were self-fertile, and even those "set much better" if insects had other varieties to furnish pollen for crossing.

Similar studies, begun by Waite, also have shown that most varieties of apple are self-sterile. Gowen,[10] while at the University of Maine, summarized many studies and added some of his own. He found that such well-known favorites as Stark, McIntosh, Red Astrachan, Wealthy, and several others are barren when pollinated by pollen from flowers of the same variety.

At Belding, Michigan, 11 acres of Northern Spy apples had never yielded more than 1500 bushels over a period of 8 years and these came largely from the north side of the orchard close to which was located a small home orchard of mixed varieties. In 1925, 40 colonies of bees were moved in, increasing the crop materially. But in 1927 bouquets of Ben Davis were placed in tubs near the apiary and 40 tubs with blooming branches of Ben Davis were scattered through the orchard; in some cases tubs with flowers were actually hung in the trees. That year they harvested 5200 bushels of apples, an increase of over 300 per cent. The use of bouquets (Fig. 3) of a variety suitable for pollination has been widely used in various parts of the country as an emergency measure, as it takes several years to get a new variety to grow large enough to produce enough blooms for cross-pollination. For greater speed it is often desirable to graft branches of a pollinating variety directly in the tree to be pollinated, as this gives the maximum ease of pollination.

A most discouraging thing about apple raising is the "June drop." Apples as well as many other fruits may begin their development, and then for no apparent reason cease to grow, soon turn yellow, and drop off. Section such an apple and you will find that it lacks normal seeds. The reason: self-pollination or at least close-pollination—the pollen tubes failed to reach the egg within the ovary; good interpollination would have prevented this. Some varieties of apple are self-fertile, such as the Baldwin, Oldenburg, Shiawasee, Washington, and Yellow Newtown found in Oregon. But they produce bigger and better fruit when interpollinated. Several other varieties are partly self-sterile.

Many orchardists have been hard to convince. They raise the question: "Will not such apples (or pears, etc.) be mongrels with a reduction in commercial value?" Botanists place the apple and pear in the category of false fruits (or accessory fruits) because most of the edible portion is really derived from the enlarged tip of the stem of the mother tree. Only the seeds and possibly the core contain the hereditary characteristics of the father tree and we don't eat those. The chief difference is that due to hybrid vigor such apples are larger and better shaped.

This is quite different from the case of corn, which changes color if the plant is pollinated by another variety. In corn the starch is derived from fusion of nuclei from both sexes and shows the dominant characters of either.

Since so many people are allergic to windblown pollen, it is not surprising that fruit growers often insist that their trees are pollinated by the wind. To test this hypothesis scientifically, Lewis and Vincent[13] of the Oregon Agricultural Experiment Station selected a 7-year-old apple tree and removed the stamens and petals from every one of its 1500 buds before they opened. They then left these emasculated flowers

FIGURE 3. A large boquet of apple blossoms of a variety suitable for cross-pollination is suspended beneath a limb of the tree.

exposed to both wind and insects and took turns watching the tree continually while it was in bloom. The experimental tree was only 20 feet from another apple tree which bloomed profusely. During all the days that the pistils of these flowers remained receptive, only 8 bees were seen to visit the petalless tree. More than twice this number were counted on the normal tree. Only 5 of the 1500 blossoms set fruit. This is most convincing proof that apple trees are not wind-pollinated.

Cherries are equally dependent upon bees for cross-pollination. Buckholder[4] reported that a 200-colony apiary was situated not far from the end of an 80-acre cherry orchard. The trees near the apiary bore a heavy crop, but there was a rapid decrease of cherries as the distance from the apiary increased. The owner of the orchard became so convinced of the importance of bees that he paid the beekeeper to scatter some of his colonies through the orchard during the blooming period.

Sweet cherries have presented a slightly different problem since several of the most popular varieties not only are self-sterile but sterile to the pollen of some other varieties. A high percentage of commercial varieties of sweet cherries belong to the varieties—Lambert, Napoleon, and Bing, which are self-sterile and intersterile. It is no wonder that large plantings set little or no fruit until Gardner carefully performed pollination experiments. He found that, by self-pollinating and cross-pollinating, these 3 varieties could be interpollinated by Black Republican, Tartarian, and Waterhouse.

Peaches are usually capable of self-pollination although bees are useful to bring this about. There are, however, two varieties of peaches, the Hale and the Mikado, which are self-sterile.

The picture of the great citrus industry in the Deep South is not entirely clear. Some oranges, grapefruits, and lemons require pollination, whereas others do not. Seedless oranges such as the Washington Navel and Satsuma do not. In fact, pollination tends to increase the number of seeds in seedless varieties, but many varieties produce more and better fruit if cross-pollinated by bees.

Twenty-eight varieties of grapes were so nearly self-sterile that they were unmarketable; 104 varieties were self-fertile but of these 66 had loose clusters and only 38 produced compact clusters when self-pollinated. Nearly all the self-sterile varieties are hybrids which cannot pollinate each other, presumably because they produce defective pollen. A vineyard of self-sterile varieties will produce no fruit unless there are sufficient self-fertile vines mixed in to provide proper pollination.

Cranberries are grown in vast bogs covering acres on Cape Cod and in New Jersey. The flowers produce very little nectar and attract but few bees or other insects, therefore the amount of cranberries produced is much below expectations. Some years ago at Halifax, on one side of a bog of 126 acres, 3 colonies of bees were placed. It was very noticeable that there was a much larger crop of cranberries near the hives than in other parts of the bog. The late E. R. Root reported, "In my travels over the United States I never saw a situation that better proved the value of bees."

In 1925, Hutson[12] enclosed two patches of cranberries in 12-mesh wire netting. One cage was given bees, the other was not; at the end of the blooming period the unfertilized cranberry flowers persisted and were counted directly and the number of fruits was also determined. In the cage with bees, out of 2385 blossoms, 1335 berries developed— a set of 56 per cent. In the cage without bees, out of 2185 blossoms only 185 set berries—a set of 8.4 per cent. However, a careful study of the bog showed that the average native insect population was 3 leaf-cutting bees, 5 syrphids, and 448 bumble bees (mostly *Bombus impatiens*) to the acre. As the cranberries bloomed from July 4 to 11 when the weather is usually favorable to insect flights, it appeared to Hutson that there were enough insect pollinators to produce a good crop without honey bees. Unfortunately he did not carry out a control experiment to prove this. Experiments by Franklin[8] in Massachusetts indicated twice as large a crop on vines exposed to pollinating insects as on those enclosed in a cage.

The strawberry represents a very special case. Some plants are pistillate, some staminate, and some hermaphroditic, that is, possess both stamens and pistils. It is the practice in cultivation to plant 3 rows of pistillate plants to one row of staminate. Of course the staminate plants, since they lack ovaries and ovules, cannot possibly produce any fruit. Untrained horticulturists sometimes notice this and dig up the staminate plants and so have almost no crop at all. In addition to this, some of the perfect varieties are sterile to their own pollen. As it is customary to expand the strawberry patch by transplanting the runners, there is danger of many plants belonging to the same clone. To avoid disappointment and loss it is better to plant several varieties.

Blueberry culture has become the leading occupation of many farmers in the Northeast. In southern New Jersey, there are thousands of acres of peaty barrens devoted to the culture of highbush blueberries, which produce very large berries of the size and color of Concord grapes. These plants will not produce fruit if self-pollinated, nor will plants that come from cuttings from the same bush pollinate each other.

In southeastern Maine, in Washington County, there are thousands of acres of sterile, rocky, acid soil comprising an area known as the blueberry barrens. Here wild blueberries *(Vaccinium angustifolium)* grow in profusion (Fig. 4). The operators remove other bushes and every 3 or 4 years they burn the area to give the blueberry bushes a new start; they also spray them to kill the blueberry maggot. The big problem is to bring in enough colonies of bees to pollinate properly the tens of thousands of flowers per acre. As there are not enough colonies in the vicinity, beekeepers bring in bees from as far away as Massachusetts; but blueberries do not yield much nectar and the beekeeper loses most of his early summer crop of honey. Prices charged for pollination are from $8 to $10 per colony. Some beekeepers also use the same colonies to pollinate fruit orchards early in the spring and so make a good living just from their profits from pollination.

It has recently been discovered that the blueberry crop can be greatly increased by using more colonies for pollination and, instead of increasing the acreage, blueberry farmers are starting to increase the number of colonies of bees used for pollination. At least 2 hives per acre scattered over the barrens are essential, and more will do a better job.

The gourd family, which includes many of our best known vegetables, such as the cucumber, gourd, melon, pumpkin, watermelon, and squash, has a unique problem of pollination. The vines are monoecious; that is, the stamens and pistils are in different flowers on the same plant. As the pollen is too sticky to be windblown, it is absolutely necessary for pollination to be accomplished by bees or other insects, and when bees are absent the blossoms have to be hand-pollinated.

In Massachusetts many acres of cucumbers are raised under glass in greenhouses. At first the operators tried to pollinate their crop with brushes but soon found that they missed too many blooms. Some two thousand colonies of bees are now used in these greenhouses to pollinate the crop. One grower alone uses 80 colonies of bees. Even in

FIGURE 4. Wild blueberry. The branch from the control plant (above) open to insect pollination shows a normal crop. The branch from a plant grown under a screen cage (below) is barren of fruit. (*Photo by J. H. Lovell*)

the open, large plantings of the gourd family will not set an adequate crop without the presence of an apiary nearby.

Most of the almonds in the United States are grown in California. Sixteen varieties of these have been shown to require interpollination and must be planted in mixed orchards. One year there was a very rainy season in the almond belt and most of the orchards failed to yield 300 pounds of almonds to the acre—some much less. One grower, Otto Riemer, was fortunate enough to have an apiary of 8 colonies in his orchard; between showers his bees were able to make the short flights necessary to bring about pollination. As a result, he harvested a ton of fine almonds per acre, which was about 600 per cent more than his less fortunate neighbors gathered. Since then, according to Mr. Riemer, the orchardmen in his vicinity, now thoroughly convinced of the value of bees, have been hiring some of his colonies to pollinate their orchards.

THE POLLINATION OF LEGUMES

Almost every large farmer uses legumes to restore nitrates to his soil at regular intervals; as a result there is a good demand for legume seeds. Nearly all the well-known legumes require pollination by insects, especially bees. Most of the small clovers such as white, alsike, crimson, ball, and the sweet clovers are easily pollinated by the honey bee (Fig. 5). These plants yield so much high quality nectar that beekeepers are happy to place their apiaries in or near fields of these species free.

FIGURE 5. At left, a honey bee gathering nectar from white clover; at right, a honey bee collecting pollen from an alfalfa blossom. (*Photo at left by W. Wittekindt, at right by J. E. Eckert*)

In fact, they will sometimes give a 60-pound can of honey to the owner for the privilege of using such a location.

In the case of red clover *(Trifolium pratense)* the floral tubes are longer than the tongue of the honey bee, with the result that the honey bee has great difficulty reaching the nectar and will desert the flowers for an easier-to-reach species blooming in the vicinity. The natural pollinators of red clover are bumble bees which have tongues two to three times as long as honey bees.

When the farmers in New Zealand attempted to grow red clover, it set no seed so it was necessary and costly to import their seed from Europe. There were no bumble bees or other long-tongued bees in these islands capable of reaching the nectar, so several European species of bumble bees were imported. The introduction was successful and New Zealand farmers soon found that they could raise their own seed.

CROPS REGULARLY POLLINATED BY BEES

Fruit Crops

almond	cranberry	mango	plum
apple	cucumber	muskmelon	pumpkin
apricot	dewberry	nectarine	prune
avocado	gooseberry	orange	raspberry
blackberry	grape	peach	strawberry
blueberry	grapefruit	pear	tung
cherry	huckleberry	persimmon	watermelon

Seed Crops

alfalfa	clover, ball	cotton	radish
asparagus	clover, crimson	flax	rape
broccoli	clover, ladino	kale	rutabaga
brussels sprouts	clover, red	kohlrabi	sunflower
buckwheat	clover, strawberry	lespedeza	tomato
cabbage	clover, sweet	onion	trefoil
carrot	clover, white	parsnip	turnip
clover, alsike	collards	pepper	vetches

To the above list, many of which are technically fruits, could be added many wild plants, including trees, which are valuable in conserving soil and moisture.

THE USE OF HONEY BEES IN POLLINATION

Inasmuch as the honey bee is the only species of bees which can be kept in hives and moved from one location to another, it is the one best adapted to use in pollination of crops. At least one colony of bees to the acre would seem to be the minimum although in many cases two colonies per acre are desirable. In the case of legumes, the rule appears to be the more the better; an acre of legumes contains several thousand more blossoms than an acre of apple or peach trees (Fig. 6). The size and strength of the colony is also an important factor in pollination; weak colonies do very little pollinating.

Farrar[7] presents a useful formula for renting of bees for pollination. He suggests $5.00 for a colony with a cluster spread of 5 to 6 frames (this can be determined by lifting the cover when the temperature is about 60° F.). He recommended deducting $1.25 for each frame less than 5 and adding $1.00 for each frame more than 6. Economical conditions and other circumstances will, of course, vary this amount.

Vansell[16] and others have found that honey bees concentrate their attention on plants with the highest concentration of sugar in their nectar. In areas of diversified agriculture, bees often have access to a wide variety of nectar sources; they will leave plants with a low concentration of sugar for those with a high concentration. Where alfalfa and sweet clover are grown in close proximity, they will concentrate on the sweet clover and neglect the alfalfa.

Frisch[9] in Germany found that he could encourage bees to visit a certain species of plant by steeping blossoms of the desirable plant in sugar sirup in order to instill the fragrance of this plant throughout the hive. This seems to encourage the bees to search for flowers with that fragrance. While a few have reported successfully using this method for sending bees to pollinate certain crops, it has not been adopted to any extent so far.

FIGURE 6. A group of colonies in an alfalfa field in California where pollination is big business. (*Photo courtesy of Charles Reed*)

Since honey bees are not native to North America and were introduced by the early settlers, what then are the natural pollinators? Waite, after studies in Washington, D. C. and New York State, concluded that the natural pollinators are small black burrowing bees belonging to the genera *Halictus* and *Andrena*. Brittain[2] reported that the scarcity of the honey bee in the Annapolis Valley accentuated the importance of the native solitary bees in apple pollination. He found that *Halictus* is by far the most important genus followed by *Andrena carlini* and *A. Wilkella*.

On the other hand, in highly cultivated areas such as New Jersey, where the nesting sites of most wild bees have been destroyed, Brittain found that they are now too scarce to be effective. Most writers give honey bees preference as pollinators because of their industrious habits and the ease with which colonies can be placed in proper locations.

Hendrickson[11] found that wild bees were not numerous enough in California to pollinate French prunes. In the Sorosis orchard at Saratoga, when there were only 6 colonies of honey bees to pollinate 180 acres, the set of fruit was only 3.6 per cent. The next year the number of colonies of bees was increased to 115 with the result that the set of fruit jumped to 13.2 per cent and 200,000 more bushels of prunes were harvested.

Several observers have found that a single honey bee may confine her activities to a few branches of a single tree for a long time and so not bring about cross-pollination. If several hives are placed close together,

FIGURE 7. Grouping the colonies in an orchard at blooming time ensures cross-pollination of the blossoms and results in a good set of fruit of superior quality.

the bees are concentrated to a point that there is not enough territory for all of them to have separate areas in which to work. Many bees are forced to roam from one tree to another in search of nectar or pollen and so bring about cross-pollination. Therefore, Butler, Jeffree, and Kalmus[6] recommended that colonies not be scattered singly throughout an orchard (Fig. 7). Butler[5] found that this increased the number of "wandering" bees so necessary for the proper set of fruits which need interpollination.

In recent years, orchardists have purchased pollen of appropriate varieties and have placed it in special cages at the front of their hives so that honey bees had to crawl over the pollen when leaving the hive. Thus they would arrive at the trees already dusted with a pollen suitable for interpollination. Such pollen is collected in the South and shipped to later-blooming northern orchards. This requires careful timing to get the pollen to the orchard at the right time. A Louisville orchardist who tried this successfully for several years discontinued the service because the pollen arrived too late to do his trees any good in 2 consecutive seasons.

REFERENCES CITED

1. Darwin, Charles. 1877. The effects of cross and self-fertilization in the vegetable kingdom. D. Appleton & Co., New York. 482 pp.

2. Brittain, W. H. 1933. Canada Dept. Agr. Bull. **162**. New Ser. 178 pp.

3. Brown, G. G., and L. Childs. 1929. Ore. Agr. Expt. Sta. Bull. **239**. 15 pp.

4. Buckholder, G. L. Purdue Agr. Expt. Sta. Bull.

5. Butler, C. G. 1945. J. Expt. Biol. **1-2**:5-12.

6. Butler, C. G., E. P. Jeffrey, and H. Kalmus. 1943. J. Expt. Biol. **20**(1):65-73.

7. Farrar, C. L. 1929. Mass. Agr. Coll. Ext. Serv. Circ. **7**. 10 pp.

8. Franklin, H. J. 1912. Mass. Agr. Expt. Sta. 25th Ann. Rpt. 28 pp.

9. Frisch, K. v. 1943. Naturwissenschaft **31**:445-460.

10. Gowen, John W. 1920. Me. Agr. Expt. Sta. Bull. **287**. pp.61-88

11. Hendrickson, A. H. 1917. Calif. Agr. Expt. Sta. Bull. **274**. pp.127-132.

12. Hutson, Ray. 1925. J. Econ. Entomol. **18**:387-391.

13. Lewis, C. I., and C. C. Vincent. 1909. Ore. Agr. Expt. Sta. Bull. **104**. 40 pp.

14. Philp, G. L., and G. H. Vansell. 1932. Calif Agr. Coll. Circ. **62**. 27 pp.

15. Tufts, Warren P. 1919. Calif. Agr. Expt. Sta. Bull. **307**. pp.369-390.

16. Vansell, George H. 1942. U.S.D.A. Circ. **650**. 31 pp.

17. Waite, Merton B. 1894. U.S.D.A. Div. Veg. Pathol. Bull. **5**. 110 pp.

18. Waugh, F. A. 1896, 1897, 1898, 1899. Rpt. Vt. Agr. Expt. Sta. **10,11,12,13**.

19. Weldon, G. P. 1918. Calif. Comm. Hort. Mo. Bull. **7**(5):219-410.

CHAPTER XIX

DISEASES AND ENEMIES OF THE HONEY BEE

by T. A. GOCHNAUER[*]

A KNOWLEDGE OF BEE DISEASES and their control is a sometimes disagreeable but always a necessary requirement for either the hobbyist or the commercial beekeeper. This has been true since the time of Aristotle, whose description of a disorder of bees in his *Historium Animalium* has been cited by White,[176] Steinhaus,[159] and Foote[50] as one of the first written records of bee diseases. The actual causes of diseases did not begin to be understood until the latter part of the 19th century when the developing fields of microscopy and bacteriology made possible the observation of bacteria in diseased larvae, and the growth and study of such bacteria in the laboratory.[35,128,177]

One of the pioneers in this field was G. F. White who isolated and studied *Bacillus larvae* from foulbrood outbreaks and confirmed through his studies the presence of two foulbrood diseases, giving them their names, American foulbrood and European foulbrood. He was among the first to demonstrate that the latter disease was **not** caused by *Bacillus alvei* but by a streptococcus which was successfully cultured and studied some 30 years later by Bailey in England. White's work, and that of his fellow scientists in Europe and America, made possible the eventual development of antibiotic treatment for bee diseases, a reasoned basis for breeding disease-resistant strains of bees, and modern-day experimental attempts to sterilize infected hive materials effectively and safely.

Sulfathiazole was introduced by Haseman and Childers[77] for control of American foulbrood disease in 1944; had they not done so, others would have, for in quick succession came observations on the effectiveness of streptomycin for European foulbrood;[22,126] Terramycin[**] for American foulbrood[61] and for European foulbrood;[101] and erythromycin for European foulbrood.[136,184]

Vast numbers of antiprotozoan compounds were tested for possible control of nosema disease of adult bees[135] before one, fumagillin,[103] was finally found effective. It is perhaps curious that fumagillin is produced by a mold, *Aspergillus fumigatus,* which is itself a disease organism and a cause of stonebrood of bees.

---

[*]Gochnauer, T. A., Ph.D. Chairman of the Apiculture Section, Department of Agriculture, Research Branch, Ottawa, Canada. Formerly project leader, honey-bee diseases and their control, University of Minnesota, St. Paul.
[**]Terramycin is the trade name applied by Pfizer & Co., Inc. for oxytetracycline.

Bee research has not relied exclusively on drugs to control bee diseases. Breeding of strains of bees resistant to infection by *Bacillus larvae* has been carried on from both practical and theoretical approaches[42,106,137,138,149] and certain strains of bees resistant to this disease have been developed.

Disinfection of diseased combs by means other than boiling or burning has been an aim long sought by beekeepers. Previous studies on chemical disinfectants such as chlorine and formalin have largely been abandoned, and workers have turned to various forms of penetrating rays. Experimental sterilization of diseased combs has been obtained by the use of high energy beta rays[104] and by gamma radiation produced by cobalt 60.[105,163] Practical use of the latter method requires irradiators with large chambers, but these may become available as reactor technology improves.

However, treatment methods are of no use to the beekeeper who fails, either through ignorance or inadequate inspection, to find disease in his apiary soon enough to start prompt treatment. Although in many areas modern inspection services are available, backed by diagnostic laboratories, the main responsibility for the health of his bees must lie with the beekeeper himself. If the beekeeper cannot diagnose the exact cause of trouble in his hive (sometimes the symptoms of some of the diseases, poisoning, and other hazards are quite confusing) he should call quickly on his inspection service or laboratory for aid. If such help is not available, some sort of organization may be needed to obtain it. More than one local association was originally formed for the purpose of getting legislation to help control outbreaks of American foulbrood disease in its area. In more recent times, beekeepers have become more concerned with problems of European foulbrood disease, nosema, prevention of spread of acarine disease to the United States, and the growing problems of insecticide damage; these problems have often required the writing of regulations with broader scope.

American Foulbrood

American foulbrood disease is the most widespread and persistent of the brood diseases. Other brood diseases may be more damaging in some areas and at some times of the year, but none has the reputation of long term, year in and year out damage produced by American foulbrood. The disease can be recognized by a number of symptoms:

1. The disease usually attacks only worker brood (Figs. 1, 2), although queen and drone larvae are as susceptible as worker brood on direct inoculation.[100,102,186]

2. The larvae die with few exceptions after they have been capped and are lying straight in the cell (Fig. 3). The nurse bees usually note the death of the larvae, possibly by their lack of movement[153] and partially uncap the cells leaving a ragged looking hole in the capping

(Fig. 4); in some strains of bees, no attempt is made to uncap larvae, and the capping is drawn into the cell as the larvae dry and shrink. The usual overall appearance is one of partially uncapped cells scattered through the brood area. Any cell that remains capped after the surrounding brood has emerged must be a suspect.

3. If the capping is removed from diseased cells, the larvae are visible as formless masses of tan to brown gelatinous matter. A toothpick inserted into such cells will cause the sticky gelatinous residue to string out in a thread when the toothpick is removed (rope test) (Fig. 5). If the larvae pupate before death, the pupal tongue is visible as a fine thread from the bottom to the top of the cell (Figs. 6, 7).

4. The strong odor from which the term foulbrood has come is characteristic of the disease. It has been described as that of a gluepot, but in this day of plastic and resin glues, another term must be sought. The ability to detect the odor varies from person to person.

5. As the disease increases, the adult bees become sluggish and less inclined to clean out dead brood. It may be that the toxic substances produced in infected larvae affect the adult bees as they clean the combs.[140,141,143,144]

6. If the dead larvae are not removed, the larval remains dry into scales (Fig. 8). In dark brood combs, the scales are difficult to see, unless viewed under an ultraviolet light[124] of 360 millimicron wavelength (black light). Under this light, the scales stand out as brilliant fluorescing white-yellow scales against a dark background. Healthy larvae have a faint purplish hue. The scales appear in normal light as flat, roughened, coffee-colored flakes which closely fit the lower side of the cell. They are brittle and easily broken in dry winter weather, but become softened and more pliable in moist summer weather. They are normally removed from the cell with difficulty.

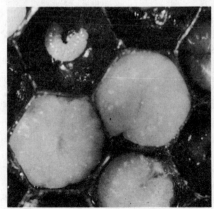
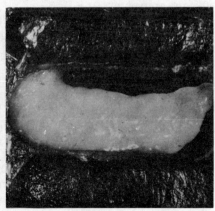

FIGURE 1. Normal brood—larvae in coiled stages. (*Photo by M. V. Smih*)

FIGURE 2. Normal brood—prepupal stage. (*Photo by M. V. Smith*)

LABORATORY EXAMINATION

Mixed infections of American and European foulbrood, larvae dead with peculiar symptoms, or destruction of colonies deemed infected by inspection services often require that laboratory examination be made. Such examinations may be made on toothpick smears wrapped in paper, but are best done on pieces of brood comb containing the affected larvae. These should be cut from the brood nest, placed in a box or other bee-tight container and shipped to a diagnostic laboratory. The container should not be airtight or mold will grow in the samples. Some states and provinces provide their own service for beekeepers. Other beekeepers may mail samples to the nearest federal laboratories for examination. It is best to supply information on the history of the colonies so that disease, if found, may be traced, and information on the effects of drug treatment and other practices can be evaluated.

The Holst Milk Test. American foulbrood may be detected in scale samples by the Holst milk test. If scales are placed in skim milk at body temperature,[91] the milk is curdled and then digested. Holst modified this procedure by placing scales in dilute skim milk (1:5) at body temperature.[90] Under these conditions, if the scales or ropy larvae contained *B. larvae* spores, the milk became clear in 15 minutes. Scales from formalin treated hives, healthy larvae, or larvae dead of other diseases did not clear the milk. Thus the test was positive identification of *B. larvae* infected brood. Bee bread was later reported as being capable of clearing milk and giving a false test.[88] It was shown this was the result of settling of dilute skim milk by acid in the bee bread, and not of true digestion.[142] If scales are swirled too vigorously in the skim milk, they give off large numbers of *B. larvae* spores and produce cloudiness which masks the clearing of the milk. The milk test was originally designed for field use by inspectors, but is now seldom used for this purpose.

Microscopic Examination. Infection of honey-bee larvae by *Bacillus larvae* results in formation of large numbers of spores in the larvae after about 10 days' time. The presence of such spores in larvae that show the typical ropy reaction or in scales is nearly always positive proof of American foulbrood disease. The larva, scale, or toothpick smear is mixed with a little water on a microscope slide, and spread to produce a thin film. The film is dried, and the slide then heated briefly in a gas flame. A few drops of carbol fuchsin stain (e.g., 0.3 gram basic fuchsin and 5 grams phenol in 10 ml. alcohol and 100 ml. water) are placed on the slide, for about 15 seconds, and excess stain washed off with water. A cover slip is placed on the wet slide, and the slide examined under the oil immersion lens. The red-stained spores break loose from the larval residues and float free in the water. There they may be seen easily by focusing the microscope up away from the slide.

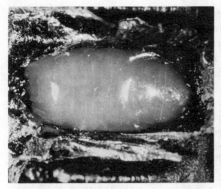

FIGURE 3. American foulbrood—larva in early stage.

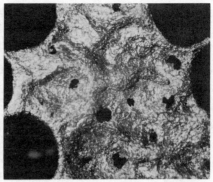

FIGURE 4. American foulbrood—appearance of brood cappings.

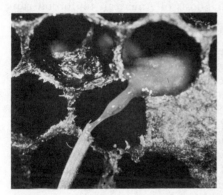

FIGURE 5. American foulbrood—ropiness test being demonstrated.

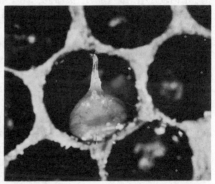

FIGURE 6. American foulbrood—front view of pupa in early stage.

FIGURE 7. American foulbrood—side view of pupa in early stage.

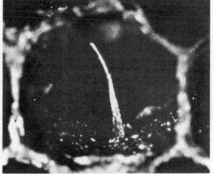

FIGURE 8. American foulbrood—front view of dried scale showing tongue attachment.

(This series of photos by M. V. Smith, Ontario Agricultural College)

Cultural Examination. The growth of *B. larvae* in laboratory media has been confined in the past to preparations made laboriously from such things as egg yolk, carrot extracts, and so on. In recent years a commercially prepared laboratory medium, brain-liver-heart medium (Difco), has been reported to give excellent growth.[99] If a single crystal of potassium nitrate is added per liter of medium during its preparation, enough nitrite is produced by growth of *B. larvae* to be detectable and give a positive confirmation of the presence of *B. larvae*. Cultures of *B. larvae* can be positively identified also by serological techniques. Rabbits, when immunized by inoculation with cultures of *B. larvae,* develop protective antibodies in their blood; these antibodies react specifically with cultures or extracts from *B. larvae* cells.[107] Bacterial cells taken from infected larvae are mixed with such antibodies; clumping of the cells by the antibodies is proof that the cells are indeed those of *B. larvae,* and diagnosis of American foulbrood can be made. Such tests can be made in a few hours, without need to make cultures from diseased brood.[145]

Cultures of *B. larvae* can also be positively identified by the attack of certain specific bacterial viruses, which can be obtained from "carrier strains" of virus-infected cultures.[63,64,67,156] A bit of such a *B. larvae* culture is passed through bacteria-retaining filters. The filtrate is tested for its ability to destroy specifically cultures of *B. larvae*. Smirnova[156] has suggested that pooled virus with activity for large numbers of strains of *B. larvae* could be used as a treatment for American foulbrood disease. Afrikian[1] suggested the same possibility for control of a bacterial disease of silkworms. However, treatment of infected silkworms with an antibacterial virus gave no protection against disease. It is likely that bacteriophages of *B. larvae* will best be used for diagnosis of the type of *B. larvae* cell with respect to source, exposure to antibiotics, and such, much as has been the case for use of bacteriophages in human medicine.[133]

European Foulbrood

European foulbrood disease is a disease of the brood that confuses beekeeper and research worker alike. The symptoms vary with the stage of infection, and the search for the cause of the disease has produced such bacterial species as *Bacillus alvei, Streptococcus pluton (Bacillus pluton* White), *Bacterium eurydice, Bacillus laterosporus (Bacillus orpheus* White), and *Streptococcus apis.*

The effect of the disease on the colony varies, too, from nil to severe attacks on brood, associated with crawling bees and severe dwindling of colony strength.[35] Outbreaks of disease showing such symptoms have occurred in Minnesota and Colorado. Other areas having severe infections have included Saskatchewan and northern Alberta. Unfortunately, a complete picture of the distribution and severity of

European foulbrood disease is often hard to obtain, since mild outbreaks of a temporary nature often go unreported. If inspection of colonies is made before or after the peak of infection, negative reports are apt to be made.

White[178] showed very early in his investigation that *B. alvei* and *Streptococcus apis* did not cause infection when fed to colonies; *Bacterium eurydice* and *Bacillus laterosporus* were likewise not primary pathogens. He named *Bacillus pluton* as the primary cause, with the statement that the name "probably will be changed later." It is interesting that in his description of *Bacillus larvae,* from American foulbrood,[176] he made the comment that European foulbrood "seems to cause the most rapid loss to the apiarist."

His results were confirmed to a large extent by the isolation and culture of *Streptococcus pluton* some 30 years later by Bailey at Rothamsted.[7] Bailey explained the seasonal rise and fall of infection so frequently observed with this disease on several grounds: 1. The larvae, infected by *S. pluton,* are partially starved because of food consumption by the bacterium; in times of brood rearing, the bee to brood ratio decreases and starvation is greater; 2. larvae that die from infection are rapidly removed by house bees if excess brood is present, and do not serve as sources of infection; and 3. the introduction of *Bacterium eurydice* by foraging bees seems to spark a virulent outbreak not caused by *S. pluton* alone. The infectivity of diseased combs is not maintained, perhaps, as long as that for American foulbrood[76] but *S. pluton* can be preserved for at least 3 years in the dried state.[11]

Late treatment of disease with antibiotics may help infected larvae survive, and contaminate the comb with more streptococci, thus prolonging infection. Bailey's explanation of results of infection of worker brood may not extend completely to cover the cases of infected queen larvae. These larvae are supplied with, presumably, an excess of food; yet, they succumb to infection as rapidly, apparently, as does worker brood. Loss of the queen thus leads to death of the colony as it is unable to requeen itself. The appearance of crawling worker bees, characteristic of heavy infection[35] could result from partial starvation of the brood; yet it appears at the height of an attack when larval mortality is at its greatest level.

Symptoms. European foulbrood should be suspected whenever brood dies in the coiled, uncapped stage (Figs. 9, 10, 11). Dead larvae are frequently found, in early stages, in the second or third cycle of brood following installation of package bees in the North. Queen and drone larvae are attacked as readily as worker brood, and this fact creates havoc in queen rearing or royal jelly producing yards. As infection persists in the hive, the larvae may survive for longer periods, and symptoms quite like American foulbrood are produced (capped cells with punctures, slight ropiness of older larvae). However, the pupal tongue

FIGURE 9. European foulbrood. Note the unsealed larvae in various stages of collapse. From Bulletin 100, British Ministry of Agriculture, Fisheries, and Food. *(Reproduced by permission of the Controller of H. M. Stationery Office)*

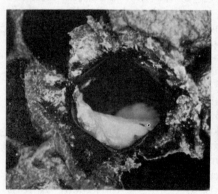

FIGURE 10. European foulbrood—advanced larva twisted in cell. *(Photo by M. V. Smith)*

FIGURE 11. European foulbrood—prepupa with head raised. *(Photo by M. V. Smith)*

is not seen, and the odor of dead capped brood is very sour or putrid. It has been colorfully described as being like that of rotten herring. The scales, when formed, are irregular in shape, ranging from coiled small larvae with the tracheae visible as white cross streaks to dark brown scales very similar in appearance to those formed by American foulbrood. In all cases, however, the scales do not adhere to the comb, but are easily removed.

Microscopic Examination. The smear or larval sample may be spread on a slide and heat treated as has been described for examination of American foulbrood larvae. It is helpful, if the larvae have not decayed, to dissect out the midgut and smear this on a slide. After fixing, usually by heating in a flame, the smear may be stained with Gram's stain. This stain is helpful in showing the streptococci characteristic of early infection, and helps differentiate short cells of *Bacterium eurydice* (which stain red) from the oval-shaped *Streptococcus pluton* cells (which are normally blue staining). The latter usually occur in the form of clusters. If older larvae are examined, it is common to find the spindle-shaped spores of *Bacillus alvei*. During early stages of spore formation, these may appear as blue staining prespores with red stained spindles at the ends. Later, the mature spore may stain a faint pink, with the characteristic spindle which remains intact.

On some outbreaks of European foulbrood other bacteria may be seen. *Bacillus laterosporus* is easily identified by its commalike shape, caused by a blue-stained parasporal body on one side of the unstained spore.

Because of the wide variation that sometimes occurs in the organisms associated with European foulbrood and with larvae dead of unknown causes, caution must be used in interpreting each variation seen as a separate disease. It may be that "parafoulbrood" is an example of too great a reliance on symptoms and microscopic examination. The symptoms are listed as intermediate between American and European foulbrood diseases,[51] and an organism called *Bacillus para-alvei* was obtained[31] from infected brood. However, since *B. alvei* does not cause European foulbrood, one might well question whether *B. para-alvei* causes parafoulbrood. Tarr[169] considered that *B. para-alvei* was the same as *B. alvei* except that the former had a round, rather than oval, spore. Parafoulbrood does not respond to sulfathiazole,[43] a characteristic of European foulbrood. Unfortunately, no information seems available on whether larvae suffering from parafoulbrood contain streptococci similar to *S. pluton*.

The symptoms of European foulbrood itself vary with the presence or absence of *B. alvei*. Infection seems to develop faster in its absence,[165] and it may be that alvein,[72] the antibiotic produced by *B. alvei*, actually slows the growth of *S. pluton*. Until further evidence is gained to the contrary, it might be best to consider parafoulbrood as another manifestation of European foulbrood.

Other sporeforming bacteria have been isolated from dead larvae. *Bacillus pulvifaciens*[97] and *Bacillus apiarius*[98] are examples of such organisms which were thought to be disease organisms, but which apparently were unable to infect and grow in healthy larvae. The presence or absence of bacteria in dead larvae is, of itself, no proof of the presence or absence of disease.

Still other sporeforming bacteria may come into contact with bees and brood in the future. Of interest to beekeepers is the insect pathogen, *Bacillus thuringiensis*,[160] which has been used as an insecticide for the control of certain lepidopterous larvae such as the corn borer, alfalfa caterpillar, and other crop pests. The potential of these biological insecticides is twofold: their successful development could lead to a reduction of chemical insecticides on certain crops on which bees forage; the strains of *B. thuringiensis* so far tested have had no effect on honey-bee brood or adults,[119,182] Azuma has found that any organisms found in the gut of test larvae were eliminated on pupation.[4]

Virus Diseases of Bees

Bees are attacked by a wide range of parasites, and virus or viruslike infections are among them. Some insect viruses produce granules or crystals in the host that are visible under ordinary microscopes, making diagnosis and detection reasonably easy. Unfortunately, the virus bodies attacking bees do not do so, and the major description of some of these unknown agents has been based on their ability to pass through bacteria-retaining filters and to cause infection in healthy bees. Thus, diagnosis has been restricted to the symptoms of infection.

Sacbrood disease is the best known viruslike infection of bees.[179] It kills larvae for the most part in the capped stage (although coiled larvae can be killed in severe infections)[130] and the raised head visible through openings in the cappings is characteristic (Figs. 12, 13). Infected larvae removed from the cells by a toothpick usually come out easily, and appear saclike, hence the name. The skin remains intact, but the internal tissues are watery, perhaps due to failure of moulting to occur[58] and microscopic examination shows no bacteria. Most infections appear during the build-up period, and disappear during the flow. Severity of infection varies from a few cells per frame to almost 50 per cent infection.

Electron microscope studies of infected larvae have shown[161] the presence of round or oval particles about 60 millimicrons in diameter

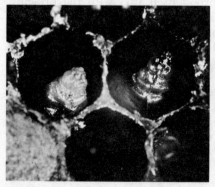

FIGURE 12. Sacbrood—prepupae, front view, cappings removed. *(Photo by M. V. Smith)*

FIGURE 13. Sacbrood—side view of prepupa stage. *(Photo by M. V. Smith)*

(a micron is a millionth of a meter, which is about 39 inches. A millimicron is one thousandth of a micron). These particles may be the viruses that cause disease. The incubation period between infection and appearance of symptoms is about 7 days.[179] The larvae dry down to scales after death, but the scales are not a good source of infection as the virus soon loses activity on storage. Apparently it continues as a latent, or hidden infection in the bees themselves, only becoming evident when conditions are favorable for its growth.

Paralysis or infectious virus disease of adult bees is even less well understood. The adults become shiny through loss of hair and are afflicted with a trembling motion. The wings are unhooked, and one may see healthy bees trying to remove diseased bees from the entrance. Burnside[27,30] showed that filtrates from sick bees could sometimes infect caged healthy bees, but the results of his experiments were not conclusive. Steinhaus[161] was unable to find evidence of virus particles in infected bees by the electron microscope. Burnside felt that requeening was helpful in controlling this disease, but unless one were sure of the stock used to requeen the colonies, it is uncertain what benefits might be gained. In case of serious attacks of paralysis, perhaps, any change in stock might be for the better.

Fyg[56,57] has suggested that a large percentage of queens which become drone layers prematurely, and have a good supply of sperms in the spermatheca, may be infected with a virus, which can be recognized by formation of microscopically visible bodies in the tissues of the queen.

Other European workers have reported that bees showing symptoms of paralysis (black, shiny, unable to fly) contain typical black particles in the gut. Such bees were ground and filtrates made from them, and the filtrates fed to healthy bees, reproducing the infection. Heated filtrates did not infect.[175] These results suggest either the presence of a viruslike disease agent or some toxic effect. Virus paralysis has been reported as being common in Bulgaria, where it is combated by requeening affected colonies and by feeding an antibiotic, biomycin.[152]

Fungous Diseases of Bees

Fungous infections of brood and of adult bees appear in colonies with excessive hive moisture. While stored combs kept in damp places frequently develop heavy mold growth, most of the molds are not pathogens, and may be removed by strong colonies of bees without too much difficulty. Infections of larvae and adults by pathogenic molds have been briefly described by Burnside.[26,33] The terms "stonebrood" and "chalkbrood" are used to describe larvae attacked by such molds, as the larvae become mummified or chalky in appearance with infection (Figs. 14, 15). If necessary, such diseases might be controlled with some of the new antifungal agents being developed, such as actidione, but

FIGURE 14. Chalk brood—white "mummies" in cells uncapped by bees. (*Reproduced by permission of the Controller of H. M. Stationery Office*)

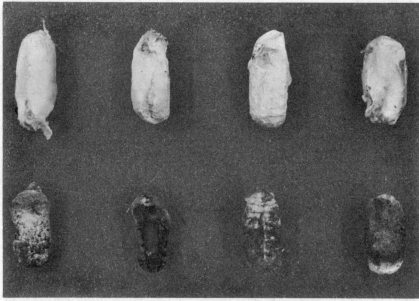

FIGURE 15. Chalk brood—"mummies" removed from their cells. (*Reproduced by permission of the Controller of H. M. Stationery Office*)

no need has arisen, and to the author's knowledge no attempts made in this direction.

Unknown Brood Diseases

From time to time, losses of larvae occur which cannot be explained. Midsummer mortality of pupae nearly ready to emerge or losses of brood that may result from poisoning, chilling, or starvation sometimes cause confusion, and difficulty in diagnosis. In most cases, the disorders are temporary and do not persist long enough for studies to be made on them. Occasional outbreaks of brood disease have been associated with applications of insecticides[132] or with presumed plant poisons.[164] It could be that colonies weakened by some sort of poisoning could be affected by European foulbrood disease in areas where the disease is not a normal problem.

One must be very careful, however, not to confuse insecticide poisonings with naturally occurring brood or adult diseases. Sudden losses of brood or of bees may occur in infected colonies in such a severe form that poisoning is suspected. This was the case in some of the first virulent outbreaks of European foulbrood in Minnesota; it was not until negative reports were made on the presence of insecticides in the dead bees, and diagnosis of European foulbrood was made on the brood, that the true cause of the losses became clear.[62] The beekeeper who suspects insecticide poisoning of his bees would be well advised to rule out, by proper laboratory examination, the possibility that his losses resulted from infectious and highly virulent bee diseases.

Diseases of Adult Bees

The diseases of adult bees pose some difficult problems in their control. Some, such as "virus paralysis" previously discussed, are known only by their symptoms, and cannot be diagnosed in any other way. Nosema disease, while characterized in heavily infected bees by some symptoms useful for the beekeeper, cannot be recognized in early stages without laboratory examination. Acarine disease, caused by infestation of the tracheae of the adult bee by a microscopic mite, *Acarapis woodi,* requires fine dissection of the large tracheae of the adult bee, coupled with microscopic examination, to confirm the diagnosis. The adult diseases can exist in a "quiet" form, without obvious loss of adult bees, only to become virulent and damaging under conditions not yet fully understood.

NOSEMA DISEASE

One of the most widespread of the adult bee diseases is that of nosema. Morgenthaler,[131] in his historical account of nosema disease since its discovery by Zander, notes how fearful U.S.D.A. authorities were that the disease might be brought to this continent, only to find ("what a surprise") that it was already here. A historical review is also given by White.[180]

The symptoms, **when observed,** have included the following: the wings of infected bees are disjointed, the abdomens distended, and the stinging reflex absent;[46] if the bee is grasped by head and sting region and pulled apart, the honey stomach, ventriculus, and small intestine usually string out in that order, and the condition of the ventriculus can be observed. If it is brownish in color, and not enlarged over normal size (the normal condition must first be learned by the examiner), nosema infection is probably mild or absent (Fig. 16). If the ventriculus is swollen, soft in consistency, and white in color, nosema can definitely be suspected.[180]

Nosema can be diagnosed with certainty only by microscopic examination (Fig. 17), as the behavior of infected bees is unchanged until they are near death. They then crawl about in the hive and in the grass in front of the hive, unable to fly. Bees affected by other disorders, however, may behave in much the same way.[35,81]

The highest level of infection is normally found in spring,[39,60,74,185] but peaks of infection have been reported in both spring and fall.[116]

The life cycle of *Nosema apis* is vaguely similar to that of *Bacillus larvae*. The spore must be swallowed by the bee to begin infection. Vegetative cells are not infectious.[6,69] The spore germinates within about 2 hours after feeding.[6] Only the epithelial cells lining the ventriculus seem to be attacked, but the method of attack is not clear. Possibly the vegetative stage is placed in or near the cell through the polar filament which is present within the ungerminated spore.[6,108,111] Once in the cells, the vegetative cell multiplies and eventually the cell is filled with new spores. This process requires about 7 to 10 days,[32,180,185] although some workers have reported spores formed in shorter times.[69]

The bee does not secrete digestive enzymes directly into the gut; normally, the epithelial cells are shed into the gut, where they burst, and release their contents, including the digestive fluids.[131] The infected cells are likewise cast off, but on bursting, release spores. The epithelial cells are constantly being renewed, and if infection of new cells is blocked, a cure can be obtained.

The effects of nosema infection on the individual bee are numerous. The ability of nurse bees to feed brood is reduced by infection.[78,79] The length of life of the bee is reduced, particularly when under the stress of rearing brood;[147] active brood rearing, under unfavorable weather conditions, may increase the disease in the nurse bees.[41,158] Infected queens tend to lay infertile eggs and are soon superseded or die as a result of infection.[18,47]

The susceptibility of the queen to infection has been measured by feeding individual queens known levels of nosema spores and the subsequent development of infection has been determined by a microscope

FIGURE 16. The effect of nosema on the midgut of the bee. Note the swollen, whitish appearance of the infected gut (bottom). The crossbands are almost gone. *(Photo courtesy Canada Department of Agriculture)*

counting chamber.[55] By this means, it has been shown that queens given doses as low as 1,000 spores each can be infected, resulting in their supersedure.[53] Considerable variation exists in the ability of the queen to continue egg laying after infection; some are superseded early at low levels of infection, while others persist for some time. The cause of losses of queens installed in package colonies is sometimes hard to determine, because daily observation is required in order to recover all queens superseded because of nosema infection.[52] In two recent surveys of nosema infection in queens dead or superseded in package colonies, 4 to 12 per cent were found infected with nosema[40,52] but because of the above factors these losses were probably underestimates of the true losses sustained.

The effects of infection on the colony have been measured in a number of ways. Nectar collection may be depressed, even in the absence of visible symptoms.[73] Brood production is also reduced by infection[74] without necessarily visible symptoms.

The nosema organism develops most rapidly in bees kept at temperatures less than best for brood rearing.[32] Above 99°F, almost no development occurs.[121] Infected bees in the winter cluster apparently seek the warmer regions of the hive, for they are found in greatest numbers just above the brood area.[125] Yet, Bailey[10] found bees artificially inoculated and introduced into colonies in summer have developed as high spore counts as those treated similarly during the spring. Perhaps these results testify to the relative coolness of the British summers.

Bailey thinks the usual peak of infection which occurs in spring results from contamination of the hive by infected bees confined to the combs through the winter period. In the summer, infected bees are free to fly and shed their contaminated feces outside the hive, and the normal turnover reduces the level of spores contaminating the combs. Doull has suggested that bees affected by queenlessness, hive manipulation, and other "stresses" are more readily infected, and may produce more spores per bee, thus creating a severe outbreak of nosema.[38]

The percentage of infected hive bees rises in most cases when brood rearing is reduced, and when bees are confined to the hive. Hence, the level rises during the winter, and may result in winter mortality, spring dwindling in the presence of adequate stores, abnormal supersedure, or, the most dramatic, a sudden outbreak of crawling bees at the beginning of a major flow. The cause of these losses may not be recognized unless laboratory examination is made.

Some authorities think[131] that nosema disease is seldom damaging unless accompanied by amoeba disease (Fig. 18). This disease is caused by another protozoan, *Malpighamoeba mellificae,* which inhabits the malpighian tubules of the bee. Its life cycle is longer than that of *Nosema apis,* and the cyst form is less frequently seen. The disease is seldom seen and recorded in North America, possibly because the vegetative form is not recognized. The author has seen but one case, which appeared in some test cages. According to Morgenthaler, the best place to search for cysts is in the droppings on hives following winter and the spring cleansing flights. Growth of the amoeba organism in culture, recently reported,[155] would make it possible to study the vegetative form so that it could be more easily recognized in the infected bee.

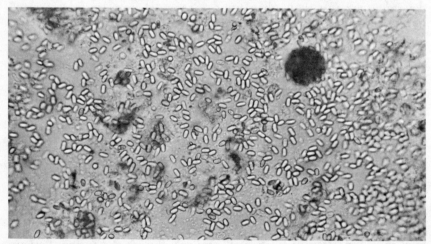

FIGURE 17. Spores of *Nosema apis* (x750). (*Reproduced by permission of the Controller of H. M. Stationery Office*)

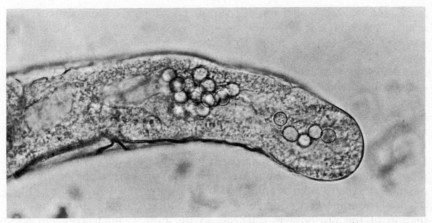

FIGURE 18. Amoeba disease. Cysts of *Malpighamoeba mellificae* in distal end of Malpighian tubule of worker honey bee (x 1000). *(Reproduced by permission of the Controller of H. M. Stationery Office)*

ACARINE

Acarine disease is the name given to an infestation of adult bees by a microscopic mite, *Acarapis woodi* (Rennie).[87,148] The mite (Fig. 19) was obtained from bees showing symptoms of a severe disease that had attacked bees on the Isle of Wight, in the English Channel, in 1904.[93] The mite has not been found in the United States or Canada, and a ban exists on the importation of adult bees into the two countries from any outside source in order to prevent entry of the mite. A brief description of the history of acarine disease, and of some of the steps that might be taken, should it be found in the United States or Canada, has been given by Jaycox.[93]

Quite recently, a shipment of bees from California to Australia was found to have mites which were first declared to be *Acarapis woodi;*[20] this description was vigorously disputed by Eckert,[45] who reported that none of the mites found was internal, and that they differed in morphology from the dreaded acarine mite. Later[44] he made a study of external mites in the U.S. and Canada, and found them widely distributed, but also clearly distinguishable from the internal mite. Nonetheless, there was an anxious period until the identification was established. The finding that the external mites were so widely distributed, however, emphasizes that many potential causes of disease are often passed by because they are not looked for, or because they seem harmless at the time. A close watch should be kept for all potential disease-causing organisms because one never knows when changes in conditions may make a potential hazard a real and present danger.

The internal mite spends most of its life cycle in the first thoracic trachea of the adult bee (Figs. 20, 21). When the host bee dies, the mite leaves the trachea, and from a position on the body hairs searches for a new host, which it does by "ambushing" a passing bee, attaching to its body hairs. It then enters the thoracic spiracle, guided by the airstream. The mite survives only a few hours on the dead host if it cannot find a new one; it has difficulty in attaching itself to a new host from comb foundation.[83,86] However, the mite is capable of surviving for longer periods outside its host. It can feed through the exterior surface,[151] and can, under experimental conditions, be maintained and even cultured in the hemolymph or blood of bees in the laboratory.

The symptoms of infestation are much like those recorded for the other adult bee diseases and intoxication: the bees crawl about unable to fly, and with wings disjointed; dwindling and mortality of colonies have been said to occur rapidly with colonies dying within a month.[37] The only sure method of diagnosis of infestation is by microscopic examination of the prothoracic tracheae, as the mite is microscopic in size. Bees suffering from these symptoms should be examined for presence of the mite, as well as for nosema disease, and other possible causes.

The effects of infestation on the length of life of the bee and on the colony as a whole have been recently reinvestigated by Bailey.[9,13] His results cast doubt on previously reported effects of infestation, as longevity of the bees was only slightly reduced by the parasite; high levels of parasitism in the colony were associated with poor seasons and weakened colonies. He did not feel that his results followed selection of resistant strains of bees since the initial outbreak of the Isle of Wight disease. From the standpoint of American beekeeping, his results should

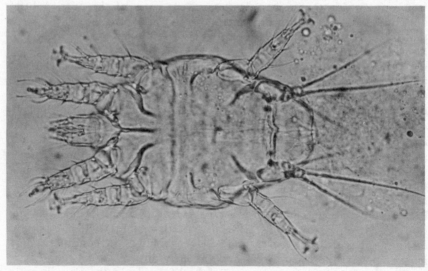

FIGURE 19. *Acarapis woodi* female (x approx. 500) that causes acarine disease. (*Reproduced by permission of the Controller of H. M. Stationery Office*)

be repeated on American stocks before the assumption can be made that the American beekeeper need not fear this disease.

Long-term exposure to infestation could develop resistance in widespread populations of bees, and a claim has been made for the Carniolan bee as an example.[162] No beekeeper would want to go through this

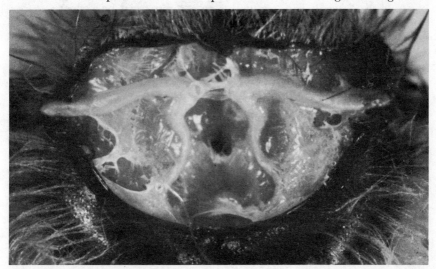

FIGURE 20. Examination of bees for acarine disease—healthy tracheae. (*Reproduced by permission of the Controller of H. M. Stationery Office*)

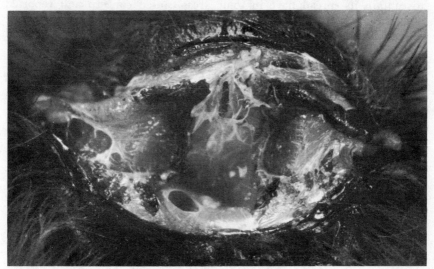

FIGURE 21. Examination of bees for acarine disease—bilateral infestation. (*Reproduced by permission of the Controller of H. M. Stationery Office*)

process, however, if it could be avoided. Control of the infestations involves laborious methods of treating the hives with miticides such as chlorobenzilate or ovotran,[12] or of manipulating colonies. Colonies apparently may be freed of infestation if all the old bees are removed and destroyed, and new colonies prepared from the emerging brood.[129] Such methods are hardly acceptable to a commercial beekeeper.

A study of climatic conditions relative to the known incidence of acarine disease has led one worker to the prediction that the mite could not survive in most regions of the U.S.A., with the exception of the Pacific Northwest, the Great Lakes regions, and the maritimes.[95]

A great deal of effort has been expended in developing means to import new stocks of honey bees for research or commercial development without risking the importation of acarine disease at the same time. The preservation and shipment of honey-bee semen,[167] the shipment of isolated larvae and pupae,[157] and shipment of queen cells free of adult bees[173] are attempts to eliminate presence of mites on imported stock. Why are such elaborate precautions taken in the face of some of the reports on lack of damage by mites cited above? Simply because one can never be sure that mites will not survive in the United States and cause severe damage to U.S. beekeeping unless actual tests are made under U.S. conditions. Responsible persons are reluctant to sponsor such tests because of the possibility of escape of the parasite. Beekeepers in the northeastern states have been affected by the accidental release (by scientists involved in laboratory experiments) of the gypsy moth; spray programs which have been developed to try to contain its spread have in some areas caused concern and reported damage to honey-bee colonies. Let the beekeeper who wishes to import foreign stock without proper authority keep in mind the potential damage he may cause by accidental release of pests of the bee world.

Other Mites. Pollen mites sometimes cause loss of pollen in stored combs or in combs of colonies weakened by disease. These small mites may be controlled by naphthalene or by acetic acid fumigation[85] when necessary. They are not harmful to the colonies.

SEPTICEMIA

Septicemia is a bacterial disease of the adult bee which is apparently spread by contact rather than by feeding. Infection spreads to the blood via the tracheae, or breathing tubes, and results in disintegration of the affected bee, with loss of legs, wings, and other appendages. The bees literally fall apart. An odor, reminiscent of "dirty socks" is characteristically present. Septicemia can be diagnosed, in the crawling bee, by cutting a leg and examining (under the microscope) the hemolymph expressed from the stump. If the smear is treated with Gram's stain, the short red staining rods are an indication of the presence of the causative agent. This disease was first studied by Burnside[24] and the name *Bacillus apisepticus*[25] given to the organism. Modern studies at Ottawa led to the reclassification of the organism as *Pseudomonas apiseptica* Burnside.[115] Other organisms were reported to cause an outbreak of crawling disease in Switzerland.[181] The organisms were classed as *Serratia* sp. The bees did not break apart as did those affected with classic septicemia, but septicemia was produced and the route of infection was similar to that of *Ps. apiseptica*.

Septicemia seems to be associated with high moisture and close confinement. It is not normally a serious disease of hive bees and no treatment is presently recommended.

Treatment and Control of Bee Diseases

The control of an infectious disease, whether of livestock, plants, bees, or man, begins with prevention of disease which is usually simpler and less expensive than is treatment. Furthermore, the effects of treatment of a disease condition, while they may restore colony development or production to near normal, seldom result in a colony fully equal to an uninfected one. Prevention of bee disease is more likely if the beekeeper buys only fully inspected or new equipment, and if he lives in an area reasonably removed from his beekeeping neighbors. When, however, the beekeeper moves from place to place in search of ever better nectar flows, when he acquires large numbers of colonies and must hire help to run them, when he buys used equipment from a wide variety of sources to fill his needs for brood chambers and supers, he runs the risk—some would say certainty—that he will encounter disease and will need to take measures to save his equipment, produce a crop, and prevent spread of infection to his neighbor.

Most emphasis has been placed on the detection and control of American foulbrood disease. As more knowledge accumulates about the other diseases, the need for their control has become plain and the overall task more complicated. The increasing price squeeze operating against the beekeeper means that he must pay more attention to losses caused by the "minor" diseases if he is to get the maximum production from his colonies.

AMERICAN FOULBROOD CONTROL

The basis of most control systems has been the local and regional inspection systems provided in areas where bees are of importance. Their main aim has been to prevent the spread of American foulbrood to new areas, and their principal methods are inspection and destruction of colonies found diseased. The addition of drug control has, where misused, hindered this aim; where used to best advantage, it has vastly increased protection for the individual beekeeper against spread of this disease. The use of drugs in such areas may be permitted or tolerated; the finding of disease in apiaries being treated is a mark of failure of the drug to work, and is considered added cause for destruction of the diseased colonies. The infected colony is gassed, usually with calcium cyanide, which forms hydrogen cyanide gas in the presence of water vapor. This gas is very poisonous, and some areas prohibit its use except by licensed exterminators. The frames are burned in pits, with care taken to avoid dripping of honey where bees can get at it, and the hive bodies are scorched or scrubbed out.

If facilities exist, the frames from diseased hives may be saved for reuse, and the wax recovered. Although *B. larvae* spores resist heat, and may grow in the laboratory after several minute's exposure to pressure sterilizer temperatures, they rapidly lose their ability to **infect** larvae. A half-hour treatment in boiling water renders frames and wax safe to use.[28,29]

Where sulfa feeding is practiced, the methods used make a great difference in the results to be expected. Anderson has shown that bees from diseased hives, when united and hived on clean comb, were protected by a single feeding of sulfa. However, diseased colonies simply fed 1 gram of sulfa without any further manipulation were all found diseased in the year following treatment.[2] He also did some work in a commercial apiary, in which disease was spreading despite burning of infected colonies. The spread was reduced, but not eliminated, when he fed medicated sirup and reduced winter stores to a minimum to prevent carry-over of contaminated honey. Anderson found that sulfa applied as dusts failed to control infection, and resulted in loss of brood when dusting was heavy.

Eckert[43] described a more intensive method of treatment in which each hive body, during treatment, was given a queen, and the combs moved through each brood nest to stimulate egg laying and cell cleaning during the time the sulfa was in the hive. At the end of the treatment, the bodies were united. Haseman[75] modified his original procedure of sulfa feeding by suggesting removal of the worst combs so that the task of the bees could be reduced. Clearly the task of hive bees in removing scale is formidable. A single comb may contain several hundred dead larvae, each with 1 to 2 billion *B. larvae* spores. The author has occasionally been embarrassed by failure to produce disease in colonies given a billion spores in sirup, but such a dose in itself is much less persistent and less concentrated than is the same dose present in one tightly adhering scale.

While it is possible for the well-trained and equipped beekeeper to recover diseased comb by use of specialized management methods plus sulfathiazole, the difficulties involved make it plain that not every beekeeper can be successful in such attempts.

The use of sulfathiazole as an effective preventive, in cases of healthy colonies exposed to infection, has been very well demonstrated. Katznelson[96] found that swarms, shaken from infected colonies fed sulfa treated sirup and hived on fresh comb, did not produce infection, while those held for as long as 48 hours on plain food could develop foulbrood when hived. The results suggest that sulfa as a preventive offers good protection to colonies exposed to infection by means of swarming, robbing, or drifting activities. Sulfa is very stable in sirup or honey, retaining its activity for at least 3 years.[99] Sulfathiazole is relatively nontoxic to bees, and does not interfere with package colony growth.[65]

Precautions to Observe During Drug Treatment. It has been shown clearly that antibiotics do not sterilize the diseased hive and that recurrence of disease may follow the end of treatment.[96] Other possible hazards of drug treatment include the following:

1. The drug fed may be toxic for bees or brood. Proper choice of drug and timing of treatment can lessen this effect. The dosage used should be adjusted to colony size. A rough figure can be suggested: a dosage of $1/4$ to $1/2$ gram active drug per brood body, so that a double brood chamber might receive from half to a full gram of drug per treatment. A package colony would be given not more than $1/2$ gram at a feeding. Moffett and Wilson[127] found that dusts containing Terramycin injured weak colonies. Larvae and eggs were removed from cells which the dusts entered; no damage was done to strong colonies. However, they applied the dusts in the form of a hollow square over the brood chamber so that uncapped larvae would receive the least amount of dust possible (Fig. 22).

2. Drug-resistant strains of disease organisms may arise during treatment. Strains of *B. larvae* have been recovered with high resistance to penicillin and to various other drugs.[146,174] A clear relationship between failure of drug treatment and development of drug-resistant strains has not been firmly established, however. The author has found no evidence of Terramycin resistance in *B. larvae* strains taken from colonies after treatment with Terramycin.[68] The development of resistant strains may be lessened by emphasis on preventative rather than curative treatment, or by choice of drugs used.

3. Honey from colonies receiving treatment may be contaminated by the drug applied. This can be prevented by avoiding treatment during the flow. Use of Terramycin prior to the flow, in place of the more stable drugs such as streptomycin and sulfathiazole, may reduce the chance of contamination of surplus honey with active antibiotics.*

4. The colony of bees being treated may not take up the dusts or sirup offered, or may not remove diseased brood during treatment. In

---

*Recognition has been given by the Food and Drug Administration for the use of Terramycin, sulfathiazole, and Fumidil B for the control of bee diseases. However, none of these materials can be permitted in market honey; detection of residues of these (or other agents) in honey may result in seizure of the contaminated product. Therefore, treatment of diseases during the time surplus is being stored is *not* advised.

some colonies, the queen may avoid the diseased area, and the house bees thus may not be stimulated to remove the dead brood. Thorough inspections during the course of treatment are needed to make sure that such behaviors do not happen, and thus make the treatment ineffective.

Farrar has advocated[49] the use of a mixture of streptomycin and sulfa in sirup which is sprayed or sprinkled over the bees in the cluster in the brood chambers. He uses a sirup containing 1 gram sulfathiazole and 0.6 gram streptomycin per gallon, sprinkled over colonies at intervals and at such a rate that no sirup runs out on the bottom board. He suggests that such a treatment effectively controls both foulbroods by forcing the bees to take up the treatment. Contamination of surplus honey is said to be avoided.

Colonies which have young and active queens, and in which the brood nest is rapidly expanding and in need of stores, are most likely to benefit from attempts at drug feeding. Colonies in the North, which have short buildup periods, followed by short, heavy flows are most apt to be helped by curative treatment. Package bees are, indeed, the most likely candidates for this sort of treatment, provided that care is taken to avoid the toxic effects mentioned. The size and number of doses given naturally have an effect on the level of antibiotic remaining in the hive at a given time. In general, the larger the dose, the longer it remains at an effective level; however, a treatment split into small

FIGURE 22. Wilson suggests placing the dust on the outside frames and on the edges of the other frames, as a help in preventing the sifting of the material into cells containing brood. *(Photo courtesy of J. O. Moffett and W. T. Wilson)*

doses fed at intervals will reach a greater number of larvae.[21] In order to keep dose levels below a toxic value, and to protect as many larvae as possible, repeated treatments are better than a single large one. Wilson[183] has found that European foulbrood is effectively controlled by repeated treatments of small doses of erythromycin in powder form. His results further indicated that the colonies were cured, as no recurrence of disease was found up to 10 months after treatment was stopped. He also found that a single large dose could be used with success if mixed in a cake of queen-cage candy, so that the antibiotic was available for a long period of time.

Because there are so many variables and uncertainties affecting the response of infected or exposed colonies to antibiotic treatment, many authorities prefer to restrict control measures to inspection and destruction of diseased colonies. However, this procedure gives no guarantee of freedom from disease: American foulbrood may persist at low levels for some time, and its long incubation time in the infected larvae[139] makes it possible for the inspector to miss fresh outbreaks; further, seasonally affected diseases, such as European foulbrood or nosema, cannot be adequately controlled by an annual inspection. It is likely that a well-planned treatment program combined with personal inspection by the beekeeper and periodic inspection by responsible authorities can do most to reduce the disease level in a given apiary to the lowest possible level.

On the other hand, there can be no purpose in treating an apiary in which no disease has ever been found. The expense of the drugs and the reduction in brood rearing produced by some dosages of drugs dictate against routine preventive feeding in the absence of a known problem.

Biological Control of American Foulbrood. One of the earliest steps taken to control foulbrood by means other than manipulation or by drugs has been the selection and breeding of disease-resistant strains of bees. This work, reported by Park,[137,138] was continued by Rothenbuhler and his associates at Iowa State University.* His resistant lines of bees possess the spore filtration activity[172] outlined by Sturtevant and Revell,[166] and the housecleaning activity[171] described by Woodrow and Holst.[187] In addition, the larvae themselves possess ability to survive inoculation with direct application of *B. larvae* spores. Woodrow[186] had not observed this trait in his stocks, nor did Hitchcock in subsequent studies.[89] This trait was not absolute, as larvae of all lines were susceptible until about the 13th hour in the resistant line and about 24 hours in the susceptible one.[15]

The mechanism of larval resistance is not clear. Gary[59] found that the blood of larvae contained an agent which clumped *B. larvae* cells;

---

*Dr. W. C. Rothenbuhler at the time of publication of this book has gone to Ohio State University where he plans to continue his research on the genetics of the honey bee.

this agent increased with the age of the larvae. This agent might prevent the invasion of the blood of the larvae by vegetative rods growing in the gut of infected larvae. Different rates of growth of rods in the gut of inoculated larvae have been observed by Bamrick;[14] his studies indicate that the spores germinate in 24 hours after feeding, in excellent agreement with those of Woodrow and Holst,[187] and Schulz-Langner.[154] He found a wide variation in growth rate of rods in different larvae. In some, the rods grew heavily, and penetrated into the blood very quickly; in others, little growth occurred and the larvae pupated without blood infection. In general, it seems that resistance to American foulbrood disease is recessive in a given line of honey bees; that is, on crossbreeding, the trait tends to disappear.[125] Previously, too, many strains of resistant bees had a bad reputation for temper, although this trait was not always present. Eventually, a number of strains of resistant bees may be developed and crossbred to give disease resistance with fewer undesirable traits. Age of the adult bees affects expression of a resistant trait, as house bees of a resistant strain lost their tendency to remove diseased brood after reaching about 4 weeks of age.[171]

Lavie[117] has reported an antibiotic substance in extracts from bees, and found higher levels of the substance in bees from infected hives. Antibiotic activity has been reported in extracts from royal jelly,[17] from pollen,[150] from propolis,[36] and from the attractive substance produced by queens.[118] With all these antibiotic substances present in the hive, it is perhaps surprising that diseases develop at all. On the other hand, a great many antibiotics active by laboratory tests are not effective in the animal. The antibiotic activity of royal jelly, for example, is greatly reduced at the free acid level in the honey-bee adult or larva, which is near neutrality.[16,71,92] Fortunately for the beekeeper, sulfathiazole, which is almost inactive against *B. larvae* on most laboratory media, is quite active in the bee larva.[154]

EUROPEAN FOULBROOD CONTROL

European foulbrood, the so-called "good" foulbrood, actually presents a greater challenge to the researcher and to the beekeeper alike than does American foulbrood. Indeed, according to the foulbrood orders currently in force in Great Britain, European foulbrood is treated exactly the same way as American foulbrood.[3] Colonies found infected are burned, and if this does not stop the recurrence of infection in an apiary, the entire apiary may be destroyed.

Since the severity of European foulbrood fluctuates widely within a single season as well as from season to season, its course is not always easy to predict. As a result, its control is sometimes more difficult than that of American foulbrood disease.

European foulbrood is not controlled by requeening with Italian queens of stocks currently available. Various attempts have been made

to control the infection with various sterilizing agents, with few reports of complete success. The best and most certain control, in areas
where virulent outbreaks frequently occur, is pretreatment with one
of the antibiotic agents found effective. Pankiw[136] found that package
colonies hived at Beaverlodge, Alberta, responded best to treatment
with the equivalent of a quarter gram of erythromycin, Terramycin,
or streptomycin applied within 4 weeks after hiving, and at 4-week
intervals thereafter until the flow. The increases of honey yields which
follow proper timing of treatment have been reported by Burke.[23]

Overwintered colonies may benefit from a similar plan of treatment,
except that the outbreaks cannot be timed with the hiving of packages,
but must be based on previous records of initial outbreaks in the area.
The wintered colony, as previously described, may need a larger dose
than the package colony. In very strong wintered colonies, dead larvae
may not be seen, as brood is ejected very rapidly by the house bees. The
brood pattern may simply become somewhat scattered, as in the case of
a failing queen, but may be quickly righted by the application of
antibiotics.

The same problems that apply to antibiotic treatment of American
foulbrood, of course, may apply to treatment of European foulbrood.
Wilson and Moffett[184] noted that some colonies that had not responded
to streptomycin or Terramycin did respond to treatment with erythromycin. Because of the complexity of the bacteriology of this infection,
the emergence of drug resistance is difficult to measure. The beekeeper
does have alternatives to chemical control of this infection. A lack of
stores, poor winter and spring conditions, and other factors have been
blamed,[134] and some suggest that, if colonies are kept strong, European
foulbrood can make little headway. Hard and fast rules about the
behavior of this disease are, however, difficult to establish. It may be
that some areas with short periods between the establishment of the
colonies and the beginning of the major flow are more prone to this
disease because of the need to build colonies so rapidly. On the other
hand, Moffett (personal communication) has stated that apparently
healthy colonies brought into the San Luis Valley in Colorado have
developed the disease, and have recovered on being removed from
the area. Such local variation in expression of this disease is quite
commonly reported.

Strains of bees resistant to infection with this complex of diseases
have received little study. Perhaps this results from the lack of knowledge
of the cause of infection, as well as the variable nature of outbreaks of
the disease. Resistance to American foulbrood disease unfortunately
does not confer resistance to European foulbrood infection.

The method of application of antibiotics for this disease depends
somewhat on local conditions. If it normally appears during light flows,
when sirups are not accepted in feeder pails or frames, dusting or

spraying are the methods of choice. Strong colonies are not seriously affected by loss of brood from dusts. Spraying has certain disadvantages in that robbing can occur if sirup drips through to the bottom board, and some colonies cannot hold much sirup. Moffett[126] found that colonies treated with a sprayer needed a streptomycin mixture prepared at 0.5 gram per **pint** of spray, at the rate of 0.1 to 0.2 pint per colony.

Treatment of mixed infections, on either preventive or therapeutic basis, can be carried out either with the streptomycin-sulfa mixture mentioned by Farrar, or by Terramycin which controls both infections. Erythromycin does not control American foulbrood. If one is hiving package colonies in an area likely to produce infection, it is well to begin the packages on a gallon of thick sirup treated with a half gram of sulfa, and then, prior to the normal time of appearance of European foulbrood, change to Terramycin. Terramycin fed to newly hived packages tends to reduce brood production and may bring about an increase in the nosema level. This reaction is not likely to happen in established colonies.

TREATMENT OF NOSEMA DISEASE

Treatment of European foulbrood may pose its problems, but those of nosema disease are even more formidable. One can see very quickly the damage wrought by the foulbroods, but unless the beekeeper is very alert he may never know that he is suffering losses from nosema. Therefore, it is often difficult to demonstrate losses from the disease and equally so to show the benefits from treatment. Progress in its control, therefore, has sometimes been tantalizingly slow.

Again, a knowledge of the normal course of infection is needed, and treatment, when applied, must be given before the peak of infection is reached and thus before the symptoms of dwindling, supersedure, and such appear. All too frequently the beekeeper waits to apply treatment until after severe damage has been done.

Two methods have been developed to combat nosema. Bailey[8] prefers the treatment of combs from infected colonies with glacial acetic acid. The supers to be treated are stacked and rags soaked in the acid placed between each super. Each stack is treated for 7 days and aired for another 7 before re-use. Brood combs are withdrawn from the colony for treatment by raising the queen and a marked frame of brood above an excluder. The rest of the combs are supplied from treated supers. The old brood chamber and the marked frame is then removed and fumigated after the brood has emerged. This is done at a time when the level of infected bees is at a low ebb. This method was adopted at Rothamsted, since he found that, under his conditions, fumagillin did not produce a permanent cure of the disease. Furthermore, fumigation was found to control amoeba infection which did not respond to fumagillin. His experiments indicated that wax moths were also controlled by such treatment. In North America, fumigation of stored supers could be routinely carried out in storage rooms; possibly, package-bee operations would benefit by extraction and fumigation of the brood boxes at the end of the season. However, fumigation of combs will not prevent the constant introduction of new infection by the use of package bees for honey production or for replacement and increase.

Farrar[47] has shown that such packages are frequently a source of infection, and that such infection can be controlled by the feeding of the antibiotic, fumagillin, on hiving the packages.[48] Fumagillin is a sensitive, water-insoluble compound, and is available in the form of a complex salt, protected with buffers and other additives against the harmful effects of alkali and of oxygen, and sold under the trade name Fumidil B.* Each gram of Fumidil B contains the equivalent of 20 milligrams fumagillin activity, and it is generally recommended that each overwintered colony be given 100 to 200 milligrams of fumagillin on being prepared for winter and that packages on being hived be fed 50 to 100 milligrams. Translated into spoonfuls of powder, the figures become 1 to 2 teaspoons for the wintered colony and ½ to 1 teaspoonful for the package on hiving. For best results, the mixture should be prepared according to the manufacturer's recommendations, in a gallon of 2:1 sugar sirup, so that the period of treatment extends as long as possible. Good results have also been reported for the use of fumagillin prepared in dusts.[116] Wintering nuclei have been reported to be completely protected against nosema by the use of Fumidil B prepared in a candy.[19,84] Much of the success of the above two methods depends on the length of time the colony takes to consume the dusts or the candy supplied.

Stability of Fumagillin. It has generally been assumed that fumagillin breaks down rapidly in sugar sirup, and thus that it has activity only for a matter of weeks after being prepared. Standard laboratory assays for fumagillin activity have been difficult to carry out on the drug in honey or sirup.[114] However, Furgala[54] has shown that Fumidil B fed to wintering colonies in sufficient volume of sirup suppresses infection through the winter, and that sirup taken from the treated colonies in spring still has antinosema activity. Successful application of this observation requires that a good part of surplus honey normally left on the hive for winter be replaced by medicated sirup. Fumidil B given a wintered colony in a small volume of sirup may be rapidly consumed, leaving the colony without protection for the greater part of winter.

Compatibility of Fumagillin with Other Drugs. Early preparations of fumagillin were quite sensitive to alkaline conditions, and it was

---

*Fumidil B is the trade name applied by Abbott Laboratories for their fumagillin preparation.

feared that exposure of the drug to sodium sulfathiazole, or to sirup made up from highly alkaline waters would reduce its activity. However, the author has previously shown that as little as 40 milligrams fumagillin activity fed with sodium sulfathiazole could still suppress the development of nosema in package colonies.[66] Studies are in progress to see whether commercial fumagillin has any harmful effect on the activity of sulfa, Terramycin, or other antifoulbrood agents.

Workers in the Soviet Union have been reporting excellent control of nosema, with increased honey yields, by use of fumagillin. New strains of the antibiotic producing mold have been developed, and various preparations have been made for testing, including a water-soluble compound.[112,113,123,188]

The chemical nature of fumagillin has recently been determined and this knowledge will help in the search for more active compounds.[168] Previously the search for other active compounds has always been based on the known activities, that is, compounds which, like fumagillin, controlled amoebic dysentery, or had certain antivirus properties, with a long list of failures resulting.

Management Methods for Control of Nosema. European workers have suggested that factors which improve brood rearing also stimulate the growth of the nosema organism,[69] or that losses due to nosema are increased by active brood rearing.[147,158] Colony manipulation and stimulative spring feeding have been cited as stress factors that increase the susceptibility of the bees to infection.[38] As yet, no one seems to have suggested ways to avoid these stresses. Colony manipulation is essential if brood diseases are to be detected and held in check. Brood rearing, particularly in the North, must be carried on with vigor if the colonies are to be ready for the flow.

Some management practices can be used to lessen effects of nosema:

1. Excessive winter moisture should be avoided by proper packing of colonies, adequate ventilation, and the use of well-ripened stores.

2. Young bees should be used for wintering. A good queen is essential, and, if necessary, the colony can be moved before wintering to lose the older field bees.

3. In some areas, location affects the nosema level. Colonies in Australian conditions developed less nosema if kept in the sun.[116] A survey conducted in California indicated that in that area apiary environment had little effect.[94]

4. Bee flight, by removing heavily infected bees and by preventing soiling of the combs, lessens the nosema level and should be encouraged.

5. Adequate pollen supplies, needed for brood rearing, may spare the drain on nurse bee protein and render them less susceptible to damage from infection.

6. Provision of running water may reduce contamination of water supplies by feces shed by foraging bees as they leave the hive.[180]

7. Combs badly spotted by feces should not be given to colonies, especially in the spring. White did not observe an increase in nosema in colonies given such combs, but the work of Bailey certainly suggests that this is a dangerous practice unless the combs are fumigated.[5]

8. Care should be used in feeding or dusting of colonies for foulbrood control. Excessive amounts of antibiotic can increase the nosema level in the treated colony.[65]

Treatment of other conditions, such as sacbrood, paralysis, amoeba disease, and temporary undiagnosed conditions cannot be made with certainty. What the medical profession would call "supportive" measures can be taken. In the beekeeping profession, these are called "good beekeeping" but such methods vary from beekeeper to beekeeper. Requeening is frequently advised for control of sacbrood, paralysis, and other disorders. Diseases such as septicemia appear to result from close confinement in high moisture, and proper hive ventilation may serve to reduce the likelihood of this infection from developing.

THE STRATEGY OF BEE DISEASE CONTROL

The beekeeper is often puzzled by the various recommendations made for disease control, and by differences of opinion among the various scientists who have made studies in this field. However, if he keeps a few main points in mind, some of the differences in recommendations may be explained, and the beekeeper is then left with a good idea of how to proceed in his own individual case. In the first place, his problem may vary from no disease at all to disease widespread throughout his operation. He may suffer from only American foulbrood disease, or he may have a mixture of American foulbrood, European foulbrood, some sacbrood, and quite possibly a bad outbreak of nosema all in one season. Obviously, different methods of control are required for each case.

If the beekeeper has been operating a self-contained unit in a reasonably small area, and encounters only an occasional case of American foulbrood, there is little point in beginning drug treatment to control the disease. If the infected colonies are found and removed promptly, there will be little opportunity for infection to spread. On the other hand, if removal of infected colonies does not prevent the spread of infection, the next step is to treat all normal colonies with sulfathiazole in recommended amounts to lessen the spread of infection. At the same time, a search for the source of infection should be continued. Terramycin dusts can be substituted for sulfathiazole where minor flows, or the presence of European foulbrood, make sulfa sirup ineffective.

An operator who uses large numbers of hives purchased from other beekeepers, who moves from place to place, or who has had a history of infection, should use some form of preventive feeding during intervals when colonies need feed; in addition, regular inspection must be practiced, and such procedures as regular replacement of defective combs and complete extraction of supers must be maintained. These practices will help keep potential residues of infectious material at a low level. The point to keep in mind is basically simple; if fresh outbreaks of infection are prevented, the residues of infected material will be reduced to a level which is no longer infective. If, during a treatment program, freshly infected larvae are found in any numbers, the program will undoubtedly fail.

Recent research has been aimed at developing methods to control the major infectious diseases in one formulation to be given bees. The addition of fumagillin-containing compounds to sulfathiazole or to Terramycin preparations cannot yet be recommended, on the basis of current knowledge. Therefore, the beekeeper who has a problem with these diseases is wise to avoid a multiple drug treatment; this can be done, for example, by feeding the fumagillin compound in sirup as recommended, and by giving the sulfathiazole or Terramycin treatment in a separate feeding or by a dust as experience has shown to be effective.

The beekeeper must always be on the alert for the appearance of any new disease, or for changes in the characteristics of old diseases. If infection should appear in cases where treatment is being given, one or more of the events discussed previously under "Precautions to Observe During Drug Treatment" may have happened.

The beekeeper cannot assume that new drugs will constantly be found to replace any that may become ineffective. The beekeeper has one advantage denied to many another program of control of unwanted parasites. His problems with disease are very largely confined to a relatively small area: that of the colony itself. He does not have to contend with pests scattered around through vast areas, such as those engaged in mosquito control. Thus he can concentrate his treatments in the small area of the hive, and not suffer from some of the unwanted side effects. Therefore, if drug-resistant strains of disease organisms do appear in large numbers, he still has the option of destroying them by the orthodox methods of burning or boiling the diseased material.

Pests and Enemies of the Apiary

Infectious diseases are not the only problem facing the beekeeper who wishes to keep his colonies in good condition and at top production. External enemies of a number of kinds may attack the bees or destroy the hive. An impressive list of enemies of adult bees has been compiled by Ma.[122] Fortunately the colony seldom is exposed to very many at once. One of the most persistent problems is produced by the wax moth.

WAX MOTH DAMAGE AND ITS CONTROL

The wax moth (*Galleria mellonella* L.) is a cause of substantial losses of combs left untended by bees either in storage or in colonies weakened by some condition. The female moth lays eggs in small cracks in the hive bodies; in split comb sections, they may be laid in the split part. The larvae, or wax worms, hatch after a period of 5 days to over a month, dependent on temperature, and begin to burrow into the combs. The larvae do not need wax for their development,[80] but depend on growth factors present in brood comb or in comb containing large amounts of pollen. Therefore, the greatest damage is normally seen in brood combs left unprotected. However, the slight damage produced by small larvae in section comb honey produced for the market is enough to spoil the product for sale. Cobana sections or split-comb sections may sometimes be found with small amounts of frass or larval excreta in the crevices, such that the sections are unsalable.

In strong colonies, damage from wax moths is minimal, but large numbers may build up in honey houses or storage buildings if exposed combs are available. In the North, hives stored in unheated storage buildings are usually kept free of moths by freezing temperatures in winter, and by constant use in the summer. Catastrophic losses can occur in migratory operations in which combs left unprotected in the South are stored for any period of time before use on the colonies.

Combs in storage can be protected by fumigation against moths. Previous fumigants used have included carbon disulfide, which is inflammable, and calcium cyanide, which is highly poisonous. Methyl bromide, another fumigant, is also highly poisonous. Ethylene dibromide was reported by Krebs to be highly effective for wax moth control.[109] It is nonexplosive, is less volatile than methyl bromide, and is said to be safe for the operator, if direct contact on the skin and exposure to fumes in a closed room are avoided. The material forms fumes that are heavier than air, and so should be applied as directed on the top of a stack of supers. Honey supers may conveniently be stacked on a platform outside, covered with a polyethylene sheet and fumigated if needed.

All stages of larvae, adults, and eggs are killed. The author has used it to control moths in contaminated combs being kept as a source of experimental material, and moths of all sorts were eliminated by treatment. Cale has reported favorable results from treatment of stored supers with this agent.[34] The treatment of cut comb or sections with this fumigant should be done with utmost caution. All comb exposed should be completely aired for at least 24 hours, preferably with forced ventilation.[82]

As mentioned previously, acetic acid used to control nosema infection has been claimed to control the wax moth. Paradichlorobenzene may also be used to kill adults and larvae. The material must be renewed when it has volatized.

Preparations of *Bacillus thuringiensis* or closely related strains of bacterial insecticides have been used for control of the wax moth and the Mediterranean flour moth, *Ephestia kühniella* Zeller.[70,110] These bacteria are not harmful to bees or to man; confirmation of their effect on moths affecting combs would make them a useful supplement for control of these pests.

ANTS AND TERMITES

Ants and termites sometimes cause problems in the apiary. Ants may invade the hive and cause damage to the honey stored in the combs, and interrupt the general work of the colony. Termites, of course, can tunnel into the bottom boards and other exposed wood parts of the beehive and destroy them. The latter damage may be lessened by placing the hives on concrete or metal stands; the termites must then build tubes in order to pass from the ground to the wooden hive material, and their presence may be more easily detected. Ant and termite nests may be destroyed by treating them with chlordane insecticide, using care, or course, to avoid exposure of the colonies to the agents used. Some rot-proofing compounds are used to lessen mold growth in the wood and discourage invasion by termites.

BEARS, SKUNKS AND OTHER ENEMIES

Damage to an apiary by bears occurs in many areas in the country, from Florida north as far as bees and bears may occur together. The bear may destroy one or two hives in its first visit to an apiary, and then return at intervals to sample more of the colonies. In remote areas with little wildlife protection, such marauders are simply shot on their return to the yard. The growing concern of conservation and naturalist interests in preservation of wildlife has caused bounty payments on bear to be removed in many areas; this causes beekeepers concern. Electric fences, supplemented with matting to prevent the bear from digging underneath, may discourage such raids. Electric fences are not inexpensive, and necessitate regular maintenance to provide against short circuits or power failure; therefore, they are probably limited to areas where shooting or trapping is completely forbidden and in which the nectar flow justifies the expense.

Skunks are insect eaters as well as are bears, and their presence in an apiary can be bad news. Depressions in front of the hive, and scratches around the entrance, are indications that a skunk has made a visit. Skunks may be controlled by trapping or by poisoning; both methods have their drawbacks. A skunk that is trapped creates quite an odor in the apiary; some beekeepers tie the trap to a small log so that the skunk will try to drag himself away from the site, but be restrained somewhat by the log so that the trap can be recovered. Skunks may also be poisoned by strychnine baits, but these must be avoided wherever pets or children might find the bait. The skunk population is often a reservoir for the rabies virus, and it may be that better control methods will be found to limit it in areas where rabies is a problem.

Mice may be a problem in wintering hives if the entrance is not protected by a mouse guard or some other barrier. Once the cluster has moved out of the lower portion of the brood body, the mouse may enter and build nests at the sacrifice of a number of good brood combs. The bees seem not to regard the mouse as an intruder; yet, when a hive is opened by the beekeeper and the mouse evicted, the bees may sting it unmercifully.

Other predators can sometimes be observed preying on bees. Birds, wasps, robber flies, toads, and frogs—all can take their toll. Under some specific conditions, any minor pest is capable of becoming a major problem.

Summary

Fortunately for the beekeeper, these problems do not all descend at once, and often tend to change from year to year. Hopefully, we can look forward to the time when a better understanding of the life cycles of the diseases and pests of the apiary can give us the means to combat each one by some slight change in methods, or type of feeding, or the strain of bees used. Just as the wheat grower or the corn producer has made available to him new varieties with improved capacity for resistance to adverse factors, the beekeeper may some day have strains of bees tailored to his needs.

Tarr[170] has made a very interesting observation concerning *B. larvae*, the cause of American foulbrood. When he noted that the vegetative form was not pathogenic for larvae, he suggested that if a method were produced to keep *B. larvae* from forming spores, control might be simplified. Most antibiotics now used act in some way to prevent germination or growth of the spore. However, some completely different type of chemical might be found that would hinder the spore-forming process, and break the link of infection at an entirely different spot.

The prospect of developing vaccines for control of bee diseases is one which requires an entirely novel approach for its completion. Insects have an entirely different system of defense from that of mammals, and have relatively short lives.

No system of control exists or will be found with completely satisfactory results or without some drawbacks. The threefold combination of development of experimental procedures, practical applications by the beekeepers, and legal supervision by apiary inspectors sometimes creates a machine that thrashes, flails, and appears to go nowhere. But perhaps we get a better perspective of our problems when we ask this question: would beekeepers be willing to return to the skep hive and the black bee, and to keeping bees without the assistance of an apiary law, or occasionally useful advice from an inspector or even a university professor?

REFERENCES CITED

1. Afrikian, E. G. 1960. J. Insect Pathol. 2:299-304.

2. Anderson, E. J. 1954. Sci. for the Farmer, N.S. 1:3-4. Penn. St. Univ. St. Coll.

3. Anonymous. 1959. Ministry of Agr., Fisheries and Food, London. Bull. 100.

4. Azuma, R. 1960. Personal communication.

5. Bailey, L. 1954. Bee World 35:111-113.

6. ----------------- 1955. Parasitol. 45:86-94.

7. ----------------- 1956. Nature 178:1130.

8. ----------------- 1957. Am. Bee J. 97:24-26.

9. ----------------- 1958. Parasitol. 48:493-506.

10. ----------------- 1959. J. Insect Pathol. 1:347-350.

11. ----------------- 1961. Am. Bee J. 101:89-92.

12. Bailey, L., and E. Carlisle. 1956. Bee World 37:85-94.

13. Bailey, L., and D. C. Lee. 1959. J. Insect Pathol. 1:15-24.

14. Bamrick, J. F. 1960. Thesis, Iowa State Univ., Ames.

15. Bamrick, J. F., and W. C. Rothenbuhler. 1961. J. Insect Pathol. 3:381-390.

16. Bishop, G. H. 1923. J. Biol. Chem. 58:543-582.

17. Blum, M. S., A. F. Novak, and S. Taber, III. 1959. Sci. 130:452-453.

18. Bogdan, T., A. Popa, and N. Foti. 1959. Apicultura 32:6-11.

19. Böttcher, F. K., H. Hirschfelder, and K. Weiss. 1961. Der Imkerfreund 16:77-84.

20. Brimblecombe, A. R., and C. Roff. 1961. Nature 190:561.

21. Brizard, A. 1961. Bull. Apicole 4:131-137.

22. Brizard, A., and R. Matrille. 1952. Rev. Francaise d'Apicult. 3:85-87.

23. Burke, P. W. 1955. Can. Bee J. 63(4):16-18.

24. Burnside, C. E. 1928. J. Econ. Entomol. 21:379-386.

25. ----------------- 1929. IV Intern. Congr. Entomol. 2:757-767.

26. ----------------- 1930. U.S.D.A. Tech. Bull. 149. 43 pp.

27. ----------------- 1933. J. Econ. Entomol. 26:162-168.

28. ----------------- 1940. J. Econ. Entomol. 33:399-405.

29. ----------------- 1945. J. Econ. Entomol. 38:365-368.

30. ----------------- 1945. Am. Bee J. 85:354-355,363.

31. Burnside, C. E., and R. E. Foster. 1935. J. Econ. Entomol. 28:578-584.

32. Burnside, C. E., and I. L. Revell. 1948. J. Econ. Entomol. 41:603-607.

33. Burnside, C. E., A. P. Sturtevant, and E. C. Holst. 1949. U.S.D.A. Cir. 392.

34. Cale, G. H., Sr. 1958. Am. Bee J. 98:271-272.

35. Cheshire, F. R., and W. W. Cheyne. 1885. J. Roy. Microscop. Soc. Ser. II, 5:581-601.

36. Chvidchenko, A. 1950. Apiculteur 94:213-214.

37. Digges, J. G. 1932. The practical bee guide. 7th edn. Talbot Press Ltd., Dublin. 306 pp.

38. Doull, K. M. 1961. J. Insect Pathol. 3:297-309.

39. Doull, K. M., and K. M. Cellier. 1961. J. Insect Pathol. 3:280-288.

40. Doull, K. M., and J. E. Eckert. 1962. J. Econ. Entomol. 55:313-317.

41. Dreher, K. 1956. Die Biene 92:11-14.

42. Eckert, J. E. 1951. Am. Bee J. 91:200-201.

43. _____ 1953. J. Econ. Entomol. 46:382-383.

44. _____ 1961. J. Insect Pathol. 3:409-425.

45. _____ 1961. Nature 191:933.

46. Fantham, H. B., and A. Porter. 1912. Ann. Trop. Med. Parasitol. 6:145-162.

47. Farrar, C. L. 1947. J. Econ. Entomol. 40:333-338.

48. _____ 1954. Am. Bee J. 94:52-53,60.

49. _____ 1960. Am. Bee J. 100:192-193.

50. Foote, H. L. 1959. Calif. State Dept. Agr. Mimeo., Sacramento. 9 pp.

51. Foster, R. E., and C. E. Burnside. 1933. Gl. Bee Cult. 61:86-89.

52. Furgala, B. 1962. Gl. Bee Cult. 90:294-295.

53. _____ 1962. Accepted for publ. J. Insect Pathol.

54. _____ 1962. J. Apicult. Res. (in press).

55. Furgala, B., and M. J. Maunder. 1961. Bee World 42:249-252.

56. Fyg, W. 1951. XIV Intern. Congr. Beekeeping (Leamington) Mimeo. 6 pp.

57. _____ 1957. Schweiz. Bienen-Ztg. 80:154-157,187-192.

58. _____ 1959. Bee World 40:57-66,85-96.

59. Gary, N. D., C. I. Nelson, and J. A. Munro. 1948. J. Econ. Entomol. 41:661-663.

60. Girardeau, J. H., Jr. 1961. Bull. Entomol. Soc. Am. 7:170. Abstr. 128a.

61. Gochnauer, T. A. 1951. Proc. N. Cen. St. Br., Am. Assoc. Econ. Entomol. p. 42.

62. _____ 1953. Am. Bee J. 93:326-327.

63. _____ 1954. Rpt. Ia. St. Apiarist 1954:34-36.

64. _____ 1955. Bee World 36:101-103.

65. _____ 1957. Am. Bee J. 97:104-106.

66. _____ 1957. Gl. Bee Cult. 85:528-529.

67. _____ 1958. Proc. X Intern. Congr. Entomol. (1956)4:1091-1096.

68. Gochnauer, T. A., and O. Feet. 1961. Bacteriol. Proc. Soc. Am. Bacteriol. p. 81.

69. Goetze, G., F. Eberhardt, and B. Zeutzschel. 1959. Inst. f. Bienenkunde, Friedrich-Wilhelms Univ., Bonn. 51 pp.

70. Golebiowska, Z. 1960. Biuletyn Instytuta Ochrony Roslin VIII:55-65.

71. Gontarski, H. 1951. XIV Intern. Beekeeping Congr. 22E. 3 pp.

72. Gulliver, K., A. M. Holmes, and E. P. Abraham. 1949. Brit. J. Exptl. Pathol. 30:209-213.

73. Hammer, O., and E. Karmo. 1947. Schweiz. Bienen-Ztg. 4:190-194.

74. Harder, A., and J. Kundert. 1951. Schweiz. Bienen-Ztg. 74(N.F.):531-544.

75. Haseman, L. 1946. Am. Bee J. 86:276-277.

76. _____ 1961. Am. Bee J. 101:298-299.

77. Haseman, L., and L. F. Childers. 1944. Univ. Mo. Agr. Exptl. Sta. Bull. **482**. 6 pp.

78. Hassanein, M. H. 1951. Ann. Appl. Biol. **38**:844-846.

79. ----------------. 1952. Proc. Roy. Entomol. Soc. London Ser. A. **27**:22-27.

80. Haydak, M. H. 1936. Ann. Entomol. Soc. Am. **29**:581-588.

81. Hertig, M. 1923. J. Parasitol. **9**:109-140.

82. Heuser, S. G. 1961. J. Sci. Food Agr. **12**:103-115.

83. Hirschfelder, H. 1952. Zeitschr. Bienenforsch. **1**:141-147.

84. ----------------. 1961. Der Imkerfreund **16**:185-188.

85. ----------------. 1961. Bayerisches Landwirtschaftliches Jahrbuch **38**:368-372.

86. Hirschfelder, H., and H. Sachs. 1952. Bee World **33**:201-209.

87. Hirst, S. 1921. Ann. Mag. Nat. Hist. **7**(9):509-519.

88. Hitchcock, J. D. 1956. Am. Bee J. **96**:487-489.

89. ----------------. 1958. Proc. X Intern. Congr. Entomol. **4**:1097-1103 (1956).

90. Holst, E. C. 1946. Am. Bee J. **86**:14, 34.

91. Holst, E. C., and A. P. Sturtevant. 1940. J. Bacteriol. **40**:723-731.

92. Hoskins, W. M., and A. S. Harrison. 1934. J. Econ. Entomol. **27**:924-942.

93. Jaycox, E. R. 1958. Calif. Dept. Agr. Bull. **47**:215-221.

94. ----------------. 1960. J. Econ. Entomol. **53**:95-98.

95. Jeffree, E. P. 1959. Bee World **40**:4-15.

96. Katznelson, H. 1950. Can. Bee J. **58**(2):4-8.

97. ----------------. 1950. J. Bacteriol. **59**:153-155.

98. ----------------. 1956. J. Bacteriol. **70**:635-636.

99. ----------------. 1958. Proc. X Intern. Congr. Entomol. **4**:1105-1108.

100. ----------------. 1961. Proc. Entomol. Soc. Ont. 1960. **91**:22-26.

101. Katznelson, H., J. H. Arnott, and S. E. Bland. 1952. Sci. Agr. **32**:180-184.

102. Katznelson, H., and C. A. Jamieson. 1950. Sci. Agr. **30**:90-92.

103. ----------------. 1952. Sci. **115**:70-71.

104. Katznelson, H., C. A. Jamieson, E. J. Lawton, and W. D. Bellamy. 1952. Can. J. Technol. **30**:95-103.

105. Katznelson, H., and J. Robb. 1962. Can. J. Microbiol. **8**:175-179.

106. Keck, C. B. 1949. Am. Bee J. **89**:514-515,542.

107. Klockow, G. 1925. Dissert., Tierärz. Hochsch., Berlin.

108. Kramer, J. P. 1960. J. Insect Pathol. **2**:433-439.

109. Krebs, H. M. 1957. Am. Bee J. **97**:132-133.

110. Krieg, A., and J. Franz. 1959. Naturwissensch. **46**:22-23.

111. Kudo, R. 1920. J. Parasitol. **7**:85-90.

112. Kulikov, N. S. 1960. Pchelovodstvo **37**:43-46.

113. ----------------. 1961. Pchelovodstvo **38**:43-44.

114. Landerkin, G. B., and H. Katznelson. 1957. Appl. Microbiol. **5**:152-154.

115. ----------------. 1959. Can. J. Microbiol. **5**:169-172.

116. Langridge, D. F. 1961. Bee World 42:36-40.

117. Lavie, P. 1959. Compt. Rend. Acad. Sci. 248:455-457.

118. Lavie, P., and J. Pain. 1959. Compt. Rend. Acad. Sci. 248:3753-3755.

119. Lecompte, J., and D. Martouret. 1959. Ann. Abeilles 2:171-175.

120. Lewis, L. F., and W. C. Rothenbuhler. 1961. J. Insect Pathol. 3:197-215.

121. Lotmar, R. 1943. Beihefte z. Schweiz. Bienen-Ztg. 1:261-284.

122. Ma, S. C. 1949. Utah State Agr. Expt. Sta. Mimeo Ser. 356. 4 pp.

123. Maksimova, R. A., Z. E. Bekker, and A. D. Smirnova. 1959. Antibiotiki 4:525-529. (Russian p. 14. Transl. Cons. Bur., New York)

124. Michael, A. S. 1951. Gl. Bee Cult. 79:654-655.

125. Moeller, F. E. 1956. J. Econ. Entomol. 49:743-745.

126. Moffett, J. O. 1952. Colo. Farm and Home Res. 3:3,11.

127. Moffett, J. O., and W. T. Wilson. 1957. Am. Bee J. 97:22-23.

128. Moore, V. A., and G. F. White. 1903. N. Y. St. Dept. Agr. Rpt. 10 pp.

129. Morgenthaler, O. 1932. Ztschr. f. Angew. Ent. Beihefte 19:449-489.

130. ---------------- 1947. Schweiz. Bienen-Ztg. 70:148-151.

131. ---------------- 1959. Südwestdeutscher Imker 11:166-172.

132. Morse, R. A. 1961. Gl. Bee Cult. 88:489-491.

133. Mudd, S. 1959. Sci. Am. 200:41-45.

134. Müller, F. 1951. Schweiz. Bienen-Ztg. 74:318-322.

135. Palmer-Jones, T., and D. S. Robinson. 1951. New Zealand J. Sci. Technol. A. 32:28-38.

136. Pankiw, P., and C. A. Jamieson. 1958. Proc. X Intern. Congr. Entomol. (1956) 4:1109-1112.

137. Park, O. W. 1937. J. Econ. Entomol. 30:504-512.

138. ---------------- 1937. Gl. Bee Cult. 65:82-84,117,148-150,176,232-233,300,321.

139. ---------------- 1953. Iowa Acad. Sci. 60:707-715.

140. Patel, N. G. 1959. Thesis. Univ. Minn., St. Paul.

141. Patel, N. G., and L. K. Cutkomp. 1961. J. Econ. Entomol. 54:773-777.

142. Patel, N. G., and T. A. Gochnauer. 1958. Bee World 39:36-38.

143. ---------------- 1959. J. Insect Pathol. 1:190-192.

144. ---------------- 1959. Bacteriol. Proc. (Soc. Am. Bacteriol.) p. 21.

145. Poltev, V. J. 1960. Offic. Rpt. XVII Intern. Beekeeping Congr. 2:59-63.

146. Popi, V. B., and A. Popa. 1958. Apicultura 31:54-58.

147. Poteikina, E. A. 1960. Pchelovodstvo 37:18-19.

148. Rennie, J. 1921. Roy. Soc. Edinburgh 52(4):768-779.

149. Rothenbuhler, W. C., and V. C. Thompson. 1956. J. Econ. Entomol. 49:470-475.

150. Rousseau, M., E. Barbier, and J. Valin. 1957. L'Abeille de France. 388:397-399.

151. Sachs, H. G. 1958. Zeitschr. f. Bienenforsch. 4:107-113.

152. Savoy, D. 1959. Pchelarstvo 5:13-14. **Abstr. in** Bee World 42:25.

153. Schulz-Langner, E. 1960. Zeitschr. f. Bienenforsch. 5:1-7.

154. _____. 1960. Zool. Beitr., Berl. 5:393-418.

155. _____. 1961. Naturwissensch. 48:137.

156. Smirnova, N. I. 1954. Combined Plenum of Sections of Sericulture, Beekeeping, Plant Protection and Veterinary. Lenin All Union Agr. Acad. Sci., Leningrad. Abstr. p. 62.

157. Smith, M. V. 1962. Bee World 43:42-44.

158. Steche, W. 1960. Zeitschr. f. Bienenforsch. 5:49-92.

159. Steinhaus, E. A. 1949. Principles of insect pathology. McGraw-Hill, N. Y. p. 230.

160. _____. 1951. Hilgardia 20:359-381.

161. _____. 1951. Hilgardia 20:629-678.

162. Stejskal, M. 1959. Bienenmütterchen 11:7-10.

163. Studier, H. 1958. Am. Bee J. 98:192.

164. _____. 1962. Am. Bee J. 102:128-129.

165. Sturtevant, A. P. 1925. J. Econ. Entomol. 18:400-405.

166. Sturtevant, A. P., and I. L. Revell. 1953. J. Econ. Entomol. 46:855-860.

167. Taber, S., and M. S. Blum. 1960. Sci. 131:1734-1735.

168. Tarbell, D. S. et al. 1961. J. Am. Chem. Soc. 83:3096-3113.

169. Tarr, H. L. A. 1936. Zentr. f. Bakteriol., Parasitenk., Infektionskrankheiten II Abt. Bd. 94:509-511.

170. _____. 1937. Ann. Appl. Biol. 24:377-384.

171. Thompson, V. C. 1961. Am. Comm. Bee Res. Assoc. Abstr. p. 7.

172. Thompson, V. C., and W. C. Rothenbuhler. 1957. J. Econ. Entomol. 50:731-737.

173. Todd, F. E. 1962. Personal communication.

174. Toumanoff, C. 1960. XVII Intern. Congr. Beekeeping 1:64-66.

175. Vecchi, M. A., and C. Zambonelli. 1961. Bull. Apicole 4:181-195.

176. White, G. F. 1906. U.S.D.A. Bur. Entomol. Tech. Ser. 14. 50 pp.

177. _____. 1907. U.S.D.A. Bur. Entomol. Circ. 94. 4 pp.

178. _____. 1912. U.S.D.A. Bur. Entomol. Circ. 157. 15 pp.

179. _____. 1917. U.S.D.A. Bull. 431. 55 pp.

180. _____. 1919. U.S.D.A. Bull. 780. 59 pp.

181. Wille, H., and L. Pinter. 1961. Bull. Apicole 4:141-180.

182. Wilson, W. T. 1962. J. Insect Pathol. 4:269-270.

183. _____. 1962. Am. Bee J. 102:351-354.

184. Wilson, W. T., and J. O. Moffett. 1957. J. Econ. Entomol. 50:194-196.

185. Winkel, A. J. 1939. Mededeelingen van den Veeartsenijkundigen Dienst. 89 pp.

186. Woodrow, A. W. 1942. J. Econ. Entomol. 35:892-895.

187. Woodrow, A. W., and C. E. Holst. 1942. J. Econ. Entomol. 35:327-330.

188. Zubchenkov, V. I. 1958. Pchelovodstvo 35:46-50.

CHAPTER XX

INJURY TO BEES BY POISONING

by J. E. ECKERT[*]

THE CONTROL OF agricultural pests is an important factor in the economic production of an adequate food supply for the teeming millions of people throughout the world. Practically every species of plant has insect enemies and diseases which influence its growth. The mechanization of agriculture and the resultant enlargement of farming units has required the application of increasingly larger amounts of pesticides, weedicides, fungicides, soil fumigants, defoliators, blossom thinners and other chemicals. The increased acreage favors the survival of the plant pests and very few pests have ever been eradicated by chemical means. Unfortunately, the honey bee is susceptible to many of the chemicals used in this chemical warfare against insects and plant diseases. As a result, the beekeeping industry is confronted with a continuous hazard of chemical poisoning that overshadows all others, including the bee diseases.

The increased acreages of various crops has required the development of agricultural aviation and the improvement in land machines for the application of the pesticides. Vast quantities of poisons can now be spread over a large acreage in a relatively short time. These practices have enabled the farmer to increase production of high-quality food products to meet the demands of an ever increasing population that over the years has moved from the farm to city or manufacturing areas. In 1960 the agricultural aviation industry is said to have applied approximately 700 million pounds of dry chemicals and 100 million gallons of liquids on an equivalent of about one-fifth of the tilled land of the United States. Since the other four-fifths of the tilled land has to receive similar treatment by land machines the total amount of chemicals applied to our farm crops runs into astronomical figures. In California alone, in 1958, aircraft sprayed or dusted 5,308,542 acres using 1,389 planes belonging to 221 firms.

The honey bee has been recognized for years as one of the important corner stones of our agricultural economy because of the services it renders through pollination in the production of a majority of our fruits, vegetables, seed and pasture crops. The practice of chemical weed control, the elimination of fences and open ditches has eliminated many of the solitary bees that once nested in such sites and served to pollinate the family orchard or smaller farms. The solitary bees also are

---

[*] John E. Eckert, Ph. D. Professor of Entomology and Apiculturist, Emeritus, University of California, Davis. Coauthor of the recent book entitled "Beekeeping."

susceptible to poisoning. Consequently, the honey bee has become more important as a pollinator and is the only insect that can be moved quickly and in the desired numbers to effect the pollination of cultivated crops and orchards. Nevertheless, the beekeeping industry is having an increasingly difficult time in maintaining itself in the highly cultivated areas because of the losses from chemical poisoning, and the need of making expensive moves to avoid such losses.

LITTLE DANGER OF HONEY BEING POISONED

With such large quantities of poisons being applied to cultivated land, to pastures, and to forage crops, one might suppose that honey would contain some of the poisons. But this is **not** the case. In order to protect human health and welfare, Federal and State Regulations have been enacted which tend to regulate the sale and application of a majority of the materials that are highly toxic to man or to domestic animals. Agricultural chemicals have to be registered on a federal basis before they can be offered for sale, and before they can be registered, statistics have to be presented by the manufacturers to show that the chemicals are not injurious to plants or animals when applied as directed. Defoliants, plant regulators, and weedicides, of course, fall into another field of production but they, too, have to be cleared of any injury to other plants, man or domestic animals under specified conditions of control. State and county regulations also are enacted in many instances to regulate the method and timing of the application of the materials in order to minimize possible injury caused by drift and poisonous residues. All of these regulations tend to offer some protection to the beekeeping industry and to reduce the hazards of poisonous contamination of marketable food products.

The anatomy, physiology, and behavior of the honey bee is such that when bees become affected by poisons they do not behave in a normal manner. If injured physically, they soon lose their sense of orientation, or ability to fly, and die away from the hive. This happens in most cases where bees are affected by contact insecticides, fumigants or stomach poisons at some distance from their hives.

Should the bees return to the hive with a load of poisoned nectar, there are further natural provisions against a general contamination of the honey. The hive bees process every drop of nectar brought in by the field bees and so may be exposed to any toxic substance it may contain for a longer period than the field bees. Hive bees have the tendency to leave the hive when they feel the effects of poisons and generally die with the nectar in their honey stomachs. Hive bees also fight, and drive out of the hive, members of their own colony that are abnormal or return with chemical odors that are offensive to the guard bees. When poisons are applied near the hive, some bees may get back to their hives with the poisons on their bodies and contaminate some of the house bees. This may result in many dead collecting before the entrance, again removing the poisons from the hive.

Unfortunately, bees can collect pollens contaminated with various poisons and store them in their combs for brood food. When the nurse bees elaborate such pollens into brood food, they become poisoned frequently before they can feed many larvae. Such bees generally die on the bottom board or in front of the hive, sometimes causing piles of dead bees in front of the entrance or at some distance from the hive. Some or all of the larvae are also killed. Populations of hives become so reduced that the colonies either die or are too small to pollinate blossoms properly or to gather surplus honey. **Beekeeping and agriculture are indeed fortunate that poisons are not introduced into honey.**

THE DETECTION OF POISONING IN APIARIES

The field force of an apiary may be killed within a few hours if the bees are struck by toxic sprays or dusts while in flight, or if the bees are working the blossoms of the plants at the time of treatment. The populations in the hives and the flight from the apiary will be noticeably reduced. Some or all of the brood may be killed and the nurse bees will continue to die as long as any of the poisoned pollen remains in the combs. Drinking water and even the dew collected from poisoned plants may serve further to reduce the field and hive force over a period of days. The wholesale applications of highly toxic substances to forests, or sometimes in mosquito abatement districts, also have had adverse effects on colony populations. The more poisons that are applied in a given area, or the extent of drift over fields adjacent to those being treated, the greater will be the effect of chemical poisoning on colonies within flying range of the areas treated.

If the field force only is killed and the colonies have a strong force of hive bees and brood, the colony populations may be renewed within a period of 10 days to 2 weeks. This may happen between visits of the beekeeper who sometimes blames the shortage of honey on adverse seasonal conditions. Beekeepers have visited their apiaries with the intention of putting on or taking off supers, only to find their colonies greatly weakened or destroyed. In such instances, it is extremely difficult to secure complete evidence as to the source of the poison or the cause of the loss, by a chemical diagnosis of the dead bees in front of the hives. Sometimes this can be done, but it usually takes about a pint of dead bees for each chemical examination and any one of a dozen or more poisons might have been used.

Under a migratory system of beekeeping, apiaries may not be visited more frequently than once a month. In such cases, where colonies have been killed outright by chemical poisons, the greater wax moth may cause considerable damage to the combs before the loss of the bees has been discovered. This also happens when poisoned pollen is stored in the combs to such an extent as to kill colonies in early spring.

In the alfalfa seed areas, in orchards or under various crop conditions where hives of bees are concentrated for pollination purposes, pesticides applied to adjacent crops have decimated the field forces of the colonies to such an extent that the bees are of little economic value, either as pollinators or in the production of honey. Bees cannot be confined to the seed fields or orchards and will at times fly a considerable distance for a better supply of nectar or pollen. Under adverse conditions, the flight from the hives is greatly reduced for a considerable period and the set of seed or fruit is severely affected. It may be necessary to exchange the weakened colonies for stronger ones, at considerable expense to the beekeeper and the farmers renting them for pollination purposes.

The appearance of an apiary after a severe case of chemical poisoning will vary with the type of poison, distance of application from the apiary, the presence of grass or weeds in the apiary, wind, and other factors. In some cases the ground is densely covered with dead or dying bees, with piles of bees in front of the hives (Fig. 1). In the

FIGURE 1. Evidence of destruction of colonies by sevin applied to sweet corn while in bloom. (*Photo by James E. Bunch*)

case of poisoning from sevin, the remaining bees are extremely irritable, will attack their own bees as they return from the field, and frequently will remove the dead for some distance from in front of their hives. Where very young bees are found on the ground, poisoned pollen in the combs is indicated.

Insecticides Toxic to Bees

Although most chemicals used as insecticides are harmful to bees, some are more toxic than others. In recent years, many new chlorinated hydrocarbons, organic phosphates, and other chemicals have replaced the older arsenicals, pyrethrum, derris, and nicotine compounds that used to be the standard pesticides used. Anderson and Atkins,[2] Johansson,[7] Eckert,[5] members of the U.S. Bee Culture Research Investigations, and many others have checked the toxicity of many pesticides to bees under laboratory and field conditions and the work remains a continuing project (see Table 1).

The pesticides are generally divided into three groups: those that are highly toxic, the moderately toxic, and the relatively nontoxic compounds. Since bees are seriously affected by the contact poisons, even some that are included in Group 3, an effort should be made to minimize losses by the application of the poisons at such times and under conditions suitable to keep the sprays or dusts from directly striking the bees. For example, toxaphene and DDT can cause serious reduction in the strength of colonies if the dusts or sprays are applied over the hives when the bees are clustering on the outside, or are actively working the fields when the sprays or dusts are applied.

Dusts are more destructive to bees than the sprays, particularly when applied over the hives. The dusts can drift into the entrances of the hives or can be carried in on the body hairs to contaminate other bees inside. Dusts also can fall on the bees from portions of the plants while the bees are working the blossoms. Dusts will drift for greater distances beyond the area of application than sprays, and because of this a greater concentration of the dusts has to be applied in the attempted economic control of insects.

Fine particles of sprays will drift in destructive quantities for several hundred feet, the density of the drift being correlated closely with particle size, height of application, wind velocity, convection currents and other physical factors (Brooks,[4] Akesson and Bates,[1] and Eckert[6]).

The arsenicals are very injurious because they can be carried into the hive with pollen and cause a loss of brood and hive bees. Fortunately, the arsenicals have been replaced largely by newer compounds, some of which are less toxic. Among the other highly toxic pesticides that are commonly reported by beekeepers as causing serious losses are chlordane, dieldrin, malathion, parathion, methyl parathion, phosdrin, and sevin. Of these, dieldrin, malathion, parathion, and sevin cause the

TABLE 1. TOXICITY OF PESTICIDES TO HONEY BEES

University of California Agricultural Extension Service, OSA 115, 1961

L. D. ANDERSON and E. L. ATKINS, JR.

GROUP 1 — HIGHLY TOXIC PESTICIDES

Severe losses may be expected if the following materials are used when bees are present, at treatment time or within a few days thereafter, except as indicated by footnotes.

Aldrin[2]	Dibrom[2,3]	Heptachlor[2]	Parathion[1,2]
Arsenicals[1,2]	Dicapthon	Lindane[2]	Phosdrin[1,2,3]
BHC[2]	Dieldrin[2]	Malathion[2,4]	Phosphamidon[2]
Chlordane[2]	Dimethoate[2]	Metacide[1]	Sabadilla[5]
Chlorthion	DNOSBP (DN-211)	Methyl Iso-Systox	Sevin[2]
DDVP	EPN[1]	Methyl Parathion[1]	TEPP[1,2,3]
Diazinon[2]	Guthion	Methyl Trithion	Zectran[2]

GROUP 2 — MODERATELY TOXIC PESTICIDES

These can be used around bees if dosage, timing, and method of application are correct, but should not be applied directly on bees in the field or at the colonies.

Chlorobenzilate	DDT[2,7]	Eradex	Korlan	Thimet[1,6]
Co-Ral	Di-Syston[1,6]	Fenson	Perthane	Thiodan[2]
DDD (TDE)	Endrin[2]	Isodrin	Tartar Emetic	Trithion[2]

GROUP 3 — RELATIVELY NONTOXIC PESTICIDES

These can be used around bees with minimum of injury (*Herbicides; **Fungicides).

Allethrin	Dilan[2]	*Monuron	Ryania
*Amitrol	DMC	**Mylone	*Sesone
Aramite	DNOCHP (DN-111)	**Nabam	*Sesin
Bacillus	Dylox (Dipterex)[2]	Neotran	Silica Gel (SG-78)[2]
thuringiensis	Ethion[2]	Nemagon[2]	*Simazine
**Bordeaux mixture[2]	**Ferbam	Nicotine	**Sulfur[2]
**Captan	Genite 923	*NPA	Sulphenone
**Copper oxychloride	Glyoxide	Olancha clay	Systox (Demeton)[1,2]
sulfate	*IPC	OMPA[1]	Tedion
**Copper sulfate	**Karathane	Ovex (Ovotran)	Tetram
(monohydrated)	Kelthane[2]	**Phaltan	**Thiram
Cryolite	Kepone	Phostex	Toxaphene[2]
**Cuprous oxide	**Maneb	**Phygon (Dichlone)	**Zineb
**Cunilate	*MCPA	Pyrethrin	**Ziram
**Cyprex	Menazon	Pyrolite	*2,4-D[1]
*Dalapon	Methoxychlor[2]	Rotenone	*2,4,5-T[1]
Delnav[2]	Mitox		

[1.] Permit required by California state regulation for most uses of these materials. Permit required for 2,4-D and 2,4,5-T as weed treatments but not as hormone sprays on citrus.

[2.] These materials have been laboratory tested, and field tested mainly on seed alfalfa and cotton; all others laboratory tested only. Further field testing may change the group location of some of these materials.

[3.] Dibrom, Phosdrin, and TEPP have such short residual activity that they kill only bees contacted at treatment time or shortly thereafter. These materials are usually safe to use when bees are not in flight; they are not safe to use around colonies.

[4.] Malathion has been used on many thousands of acres of blooming alfalfa without serious loss to bees. However, occasional heavy losses have occurred, particularly under extremely high temperature conditions. If applied to alfalfa in bloom it should be only as a spray, and the application should be made early in the morning when bees are not foraging in the field. Covering of colonies is preferred for airplane applications.

[5.] Usually Sabadilla dosages are low enough so that they present no problem.

[6.] No problem exists when Thimet and Di-Syston are used as seed treatments.

[7.] DDT may be less toxic to bees at high temperatures.

greatest damage, probably because of their greater use. Sevin, dieldrin, and parathion are the archkillers of all times, and beekeeping cannot exist in areas where these are applied frequently on blooming plants, or where they drift over plants on which bees are working. Chlordane and parathion, in particular, are highly toxic as fumigants, as well as on contact and when taken internally with pollen, nectar, or water. Dieldrin, chlordane, and sevin have a rather long residual action, while malathion and parathion deteriorate faster. Water solutions of the phosphates are reduced in toxicity within 24 to 48 hours. This indicates that it would be comparatively safe to move colonies into an area in which the phosphates had been applied if the move is made 48 hours after application. In the case of dieldrin, chlordane, or sevin, colonies should not be returned to treated fields for a week to 10 days after treatment.

TEPP (tetraethyl pyrophosphate) is a highly toxic compound but has a short residual action, even shorter than parathion. Consequently the hive bees are seldom injured seriously and bees may safely work the treated plants within 24 hours. Trithion, dibrom, and phosdrin are in the same category but should not be applied to crops in bloom when bees are working in the field. The systemic insecticides, such as Thimet, Systox, and Schradan, are rapidly absorbed by the plants and, if they are not applied while the plants are in bloom, will not prove very hazardous to bees. The fungicides, blossom thinners, and defoliants are generally not toxic to bees if they are not applied when bees are working the blossoms.

None of the highly toxic materials should ever be used inside of a comb room or immediately in front of colonies. In one experiment, the walls of a comb room, 10 by 12 by 8 feet, were sprayed with a 5-per cent suspension of chlordane in water as a means of controlling ants. Bees in cages were killed when placed in this room 1 year after the walls had been sprayed. Two combs left in the room for 2 weeks and then placed in 3-frame nuclei killed the bees in 48 hours. In another test, the ground in front of a number of colonies was sprayed with an oil solution of chlordane to kill ants and grass, the application being applied in the afternoon of a hot day. By the following morning, a majority of the colonies were completely demoralized, some 3-story colonies being killed outright. The bees had pulled the fumes into their hives while attempting to cool them by ventilation. Colonies on stands 8 inches above the grass were injured less seriously and survived.

EVIDENCE OF INJURY IN THE FIELD
AND ORCHARD

When any of the highly toxic pesticides are applied to fruit trees or to cultivated crops in bloom, even though the applications are made early in the morning, by midmorning the trees or fields will be quiet, generally without the sound of any honey bees or other pollinating insects working the blossoms. The bees that were accustomed to visit the treated areas will have been killed. Some may be found hanging to the blossoms or lying on the ground beneath the trees or plants. Occasionally, a few of the bees may be driven away by the change of odor in the field but the pesticides seldom have sufficient repellency to prevent injury to nectar or pollen gatherers. When the field force is killed in this manner, it may be a matter of 24 hours, or even days. before other bees will be attracted to the field, the time interval frequently depending on the residual quality of the pesticides and the severity of the kill.

New scout bees will have to locate the blossoms and convey the information back to their hives. If the scout bees are killed, as well as those already oriented to the treated fields, the time interval for the field or orchard to be repopulated with bees will be longer. When the hive bees as well as the field bees are decimated, normal colonies may have to be moved in before a sufficient force of pollinators can become established.

The set of seed or fruit can be correlated directly with the work of the pollinators when the plants are in the proper physiological condition to set fruit and weather conditions are favorable. A period of

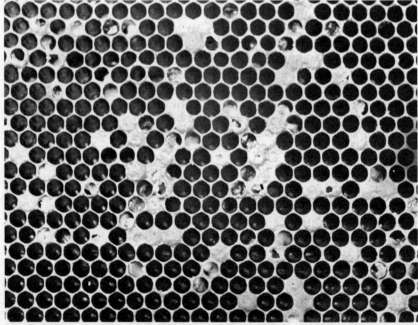

FIGURE 2. Portion of a comb showing brood poisoned by calcium arsenate. Most of the young larvae already have been removed from the cells. *(Photo by J. E. Eckert)*

10 days or 2 weeks without adequate pollination may cause an economic loss in production or in the time of harvest, depending on the nature or blooming period of the plants. The crown set on melons, for example, may be lost if the first blossoms are not properly pollinated, and not only the amount and quality of the yield will be affected but the time of harvesting will be delayed.

Under special conditions, when the field force is only partly killed by a poison that is soon dissipated, such as TEPP, the number of bees visiting the blossoms may even be increased after 24 to 48 hours. This increase apparently is due to the greater attractiveness of the blossoms because of an accumulation of nectar or available pollen, causing scout bees to recruit more bees to the area from near-by hives. This shift in population was evident in one test when approximately 200 colonies in alfalfa seed fields were anaesthetized with nitrous oxide late one afternoon. The weather was hot and dry. The colonies became so disorganized that they did not work the following day, and most of their brood was lost from heat and lack of moisture as well as proper care. However, the population of bees in the fields in which the hives were located, was reduced by only 75 per cent. Twenty-five per cent of the population of the field came from hives located in fields adjacent to those in which the anaesthetized colonies were located, and increased rapidly during the following 48 hours.

EVIDENCE OF POISONING WITHIN THE HIVE

The gross appearance of injury to a colony will vary with the manner and degree of injury caused by a specific poison. A 3-story colony that loses its field force may have a super partially or entirely filled with honey, but with the bees covering only part of the combs in the two lower chambers. An examination of the combs will indicate brood in all stages. The queen may reduce egg laying slightly over the following week, but within 2 weeks the colony population will have been built back to normal by the emerging bees. Flight activity will gradually increase but the colony will have lost most of its productivity in the meantime.

If a colony not only loses its field force but many of the hive bees from poisoned pollen, within a day or 2 the population will be drastically reduced to the queen, a few nurse bees, and recently emerged bees. An examination of the brood combs will reveal many empty cells, from which larvae have been removed, and many sick or dead larvae not yet pulled from their cells (Fig. 2). After a few days, many pupae may also be found dead in their cells, the cappings of some cells having been partially removed. Some of the larvae may die of starvation or neglect. In very servere cases, only a handful of young bees will remain with the queen and sealed brood. Since the queen gets most of her food from nurse bees which feed on uncontaminated pollen, she often survives.

Occasionally, in a severely poisoned apiary, small emergency swarms will issue from the hives, frequently less than a quart of bees in size.

While numerous accounts of losses of bees have been reported from different states and, for that matter, from various parts of the world, two recent reports will suffice to show the extent of losses from pesticides. Schwan[11] reported that 6,714 colonies were killed in Sweden in 1952 or 4.5 per cent of all reported in a survey. A survey of the pesticide situation in California indicated that 37,000 colonies were killed in 1959 or 6.6 per cent of the entire bee population of the state. When this number of colonies is killed outright, two to three times the number were seriously reduced in strength and economic importance for either pollination or for honey production. The monetary loss to beekeepers was large but the value of the seed and fruit lost through lack of pollination was far greater.

TREATMENT OF POISONED COLONIES

If a colony loses only its field force, does not carry in any poisoned pollen, and has plenty of good pollen and honey, nothing need be done except to move it to a safer place if the poison applied has a long residual action. It will not get back into production until its population has been restored by the emerging bees. If the loss occurs at the beginning of the nectarflow, there will be little if any surplus by the end of the season, and the bees may have to be fed their winter stores.

If further applications of pesticides are not to be applied, and there is no evidence of poisoned pollen, colonies need not be moved if conditions are favorable for their development.

If the brood and nurse bees also are affected, poisoned pollen evidently has been gathered and, not only should the apiary be moved to a safe location, but the combs containing the contaminated pollen should be removed. Experience has shown that as long as brood combs contain poisoned pollen, whether from insecticides or from a plant source, normal development of the colony will be retarded if the colony survives at all. In many instances, package bees and swarms have died when placed on combs from colonies which previously had been poisoned. Even when such colonies survive, their development frequently is so retarded that they may be of little or no economic value for several weeks or months (Fig. 3).

Combs containing brood as well as pollen can be concentrated in a limited number of hives until the bees emerge, and then the combs treated to remove the pollen. The combs can be soaked in water for 24 hours and then the pollen washed from the cells and the combs dried. Any pollen that may remain in the cells will become hard and will be removed by the bees without further injury.

The addition of 1 or 2 pounds of bees to a colony that has been weakened by the loss of its field force, but which has no poisoned

FIGURE 3. Bees killed by parathion applied to crops in the vicinity of the apiary. The entire field force was killed as well as many of the hive bees. *(Photo by J. E. Eckert)*

pollen, will cause a quicker recovery to producing strength. Occasionally, weakened colonies can be united, and will produce more than if an effort is made to bring them all back to producing strength. In all cases, surplus combs should be taken from badly weakened colonies and protected from robbing bees and the wax moth until they are needed, and the size of the entrance should be regulated to the strength of the colony and weather conditions.

PESTICIDE CONTROL MEASURES

The federal and state regulations governing the sale and use of pesticides are designed to protect the producer as well as the consumer from the misuse of poisonous materials. Generally, these are governed by health considerations for man, domestic animals, and wild life. In many instances the regulations are for the benefit of the majority of interests in any community in which food products are produced or sold. Beekeeping is given a considerable measure of protection by these regulations, but the use of pesticides still remains an ever-present hazard to the beekeeping industry.

The numerous research agencies at the state, federal, and commercial levels generally take into consideration the need for conserving the beneficial insects when they make recommendations for the application of chemicals in the control of injurious pests. However, this is not always the case and the fact that hives of bees are transportable is given too much weight in determining the type of poison and the method and timing of its application. If bees are of little or no benefit to the crops to be treated, little or no consideration may be given to the need of using materials or methods which will cause the least injury to the bees. However, if crops that require bees for full production are grown in the near vicinity, and the chemicals cannot be confined to the fields treated, then the chemicals that are least toxic to the bees are frequently required, and the timing and method of application are also recommended.

The formation of regional, county, and state committees, composed of the representatives of all parties interested in the end results of pest control, would be helpful in formulating policies governing the sale and use of toxic compounds.

Beekeepers can reduce their losses by becoming familiar with the chemical control programs of the regions in which they operate their colonies. It is also helpful when beekeepers register the number of hives and their locations with the county regulatory officials who have authority over the use of pesticides, and request notification 48 hours in advance of the use of chemical compounds that are likely to be highly injurious to their bees.

The California State Bee Law, Sec. 279.25 reads: "Any person owning or in possession of an apiary who fails to register it, or changes the location of an apiary in violation of Section 275 (a 5-day notice of relocation to the county commissioner), or who fails to provide a sign as required by Section 279.2 (a sign prominently displayed on the entrance side of the apiary, stating in black letters not less than 1 inch in height on a background of contrasting color the owner's name, address, phone number, and brand number) shall NOT be entitled to recover damage for any injury to such apiary by reason of any pest control program."

Whether these regulations are desirable or not, it is helpful for each beekeeper to identify his apiary and to register it with the local regulatory authorities, so he can be notified 48 hours in advance of any actual need or intention of applying pesticides that would be highly toxic to his bees.

The users and applicators of the highly toxic pesticides are generally held liable for any damages caused to the property or interests of others from the misuse or careless application of the compounds. Drifting poisons constitute a major hazard of all dust applications and, to a lesser extent, when sprays are used (Fig. 4). In case of losses to

FIGURE 4. The application of sprays by airplane results in less drift than air application of dusts. However, both may kill bees working the blossoms if the poisons are highly toxic. *(Photo by J. E. Eckert)*

crops or to bees from chemicals applied for pest control, the injured parties should immediately notify the county and state regulatory authorities. The purpose of this notification is to establish the type of poison used and the method, as well as the conditions of application, so that preventive measures can be taken to forestall similar losses in the future.

If pesticides are confined to the fields treated and are used only in minimum quantity when necessary under suitable atmospheric and plant conditions, with due notice issued to all interested parties who might be adversely affected, the loss of bees will be kept at a minimum. Compounds that are least toxic to beneficial insects should be used if they give control of the injurious pests. Applications made in early morning, or in late afternoon, when the pollinators are not active, result in less damage than if made during the hours of major flight of bees. Above all, certain highly toxic pesticides should not be applied to fruit trees, legumes, or other crops while they are in bloom.

Many farmers use land rigs to apply pesticides at night when the air is cool and calm and pollinators are not working. Some night applications even are made by airplanes to fields that are free of surrounding hazards to such flights. Lesser amounts of the pesticides can be used, and with greater efficiency, when drift is cut to a minimum.

Certain hydrocarbons, such as DDT and toxaphene, have largely replaced the arsenicals, and McGregor and Vorhies[9] demonstrated that beekeeping is feasible in the vicinity of cotton fields when the hydro-carbons were used in place of the arsenicals or the more highly toxic compounds. However, the limitation of the amount of residue of hydro-carbons on hay and forage crops, as well as on vegetables and fruit, has forced the substitution of sevin or of certain organic phosphates on such crops, and even on other crops grown adjacent to them. This change has resulted in a marked increase in the loss of bees.

USE OF REPELLENTS

To be effective a bee repellent must be strong enough to prevent the honey bees from collecting poisoned nectar or pollen from sprayed or dusted plants, yet it must not injure any part of the plant or harm the operator applying the poison. Nicotine sulphate, creosote, carbolic acid, lime sulfur, naphthalene, and similar substances commonly men-tioned as bee repellents, have only limited use because the efficiency of each depends upon its volatility. Many poisons are practically in-destructible, their effect continuing at least as long as the flowers are attractive to bees. Some flowers remain open 10 to 12 days and repellents are seldom effective for that long. Other blossoms remain open for only a day and repellents would be more effective.

Bourne,[3] Southwick,[13] Shaw,[12] and other investigators have experi-mented with several materials containing nicotine sulfate, creosote, tar soil, phenol compounds, naphthalene, and other chemicals in search of a suitable repellent to bees. None of the compounds tried were found very effective although some did decrease the number of visits of bees.

METHODS OF REDUCING THE POISONING HAZARDS

Beekeepers who have experienced heavy losses from chemical poison-ing are wary about moving their colonies into seed or fruit areas where little consideration is given to the protection of the pollinators in the pesticide control programs. The rentals of hives in such areas are generally higher, reflecting the hazard each beekeeper takes in accepting pollination contracts. When the grower fully understands the relation-ship of an adequate number of bees to an economic production, he is willing to pay a sufficient rental to get the necessary number of hives of bees. He then will take an interest in his investment to the extent, of not only properly timing the applications of his pesticides and in using the least toxic substances that will control the pests, but also will interest his neighhbor growers in adopting similar programs.

Growers as well as beekeepers are interested in suitable legislation that will protect their crops and bees from the misuse of toxic substances by other growers or commercial agencies. It is desirable, therefore, for grower committees at local, county, and state levels to meet with the legislative and regulatory officials and secure suitable legislation and regulation for the use of toxic substances for the mutual benefit of all interested parties. This frequently involves research and extension agencies to gather evidence and to disseminate and evaluate information about pesticides and their use. The Pure Food and Drug regulations have set tolerances that generally form a basis for the recommended uses of a majority of the toxic pesticides.

Highly toxic materials when applied in commercial quantities should be sold and used under a permit system that would give the regulatory agencies a definite record of their intended use, as well as the power to regulate such uses for the benefit of all of the interests in the areas in which they are used. The 48-hour notice to the bee-keeper or seed grower of the intended use of a highly toxic pesticide to corn, cotton, or sugar beets in the vicinity of fruit or seed acreage, is helpful but is not the answer to the poisoning problem. Frequently the hives cannot be moved because of the condition of the soil, the number of hives involved, or for other reasons. Only under definitely established emergency conditions and supervision should the highly toxic pesticides and weedicides be applied to plants in bloom, and never under conditions where the drift will prove injurious to other interests. The least toxic chemicals should be used when needed, and then in minimum quantities and by such means that will confine the materials to the fields treated without leaving injurious residues.

Beekeepers should become familiar with the pest control programs that might be used seasonally on the crops within a 2-mile radius of their apiaries. They should register and identify their apiary locations and become acquainted with the neighboring farmers, farm advisers, and regulatory officials in all diversified agricultural areas, as well as in the fruit and seed areas. They should know the condition of their colonies and notify the regulatory authorities as soon as any chemical injury of the colonies is apparent.

The temporary covering or closing of hives during the application of pesticides is costly and not always practical, especially in warm weather. Bees require water and adequate ventilation at all times and excessive heat and dryness are definite hazards to the welfare of the colony (Fig. 5).

Poisoning of Bees by Plants

The poisoning of bees from plant products is generally confined to limited areas and, therefore, is much less a problem than chemical poisoning. Nevertheless, poisonous plants do cause serious losses under certain conditions in limited areas. Fortunately, the honey produced from such plants is seldom injurious to man. There are two possible exceptions: the honey from mountain laurel, which has sometimes caused acute illness soon after being eaten, and a honeydew in New Zealand. The mountain laurel is found in restricted areas of the mountains of New Jersey, Virginia, and North Carolina in quantities suffi-

FIGURE 5. Hives adjacent to a seed alfalfa field covered with plastic material prior to the application of poisonous pesticides. Three hives at left are left as a check. *(Photo by Valley Pollination Service, California)*

cient to produce a small amount of honey which has to be discarded by the beekeepers. In New Zealand is an area where bees collect honeydew from a leafhopper, *Scolypopa australis,* feeding on Tutu *(Coriaria arborea)*. The area is closed to beekeeping.[10]

Of the innumerable plants visited by honey bees, comparatively few produce nectar or pollen poisonous to bees or to their brood. The effect of the injurious plants varies with environmental conditions, and the severity of injury is affected by the amount of nectar and pollen gathered from other plants in the same area. The following are the most important plants poisonous to bees or suspected as such in this country: California buckeye *(Aesculus californica)*, black nightshade *(Solanum nigrum)*, death camas *(Zygadenus venenosus)*, dodder (genus *Cuscuta)*, leatherwood *(Cyrilla racemiflora)*, locoweeds (genus *Astragalus)*, mountain laurel *(Kalmia latifolia)*, seaside arrowgrass *(Triglochin maritima)*, whorled milkweed *(Asdepias subverticillata)*, and western false hellebore *(Veratrum californicum)*.

INJURY CAUSED BY POISONOUS PLANTS

The toxic substances in poisonous plants are specific in action and may be confined to the nectar or simply to the pollen. Symptoms of plant poisoning are sometimes difficult to recognize or to be substantiated by chemical or microscopical diagnosis. The presence of symptoms usually is limited to the blooming period of the plant if the nectar is poisonous and, if the colony survives, the symptoms may disappear with the bloom. However, if the toxic substance is in the pollen, the symptoms may linger as long as the supply of pollen remains in the combs.

When only the adult bees are affected, piles of them may be found dead in front of the hive entrance, and there may not be enough adults to take care of the brood or combs. The field bees may die away from the hive and newly emerged bees may leave the hive and crawl upon the ground, or lie there stupefied or dead. Newly emerged bees may have crumpled wings, or fail to shed the last pupal case from the abdomen. When poisoned by California buckeye, some of the field bees become black and shiny from loss of hair and may tremble as in an advanced stage of paralysis. For additional information concerning paralysis, see Chapter XIX, "Diseases and Enemies of the Honey Bee."

Brood affected by plant poisons may die any time between the hatching of the egg and the emergence of the adult. The dead brood generally lacks the brown or black colors associated with American and European foulbrood. In buckeye poisoning, larvae die soon after hatching and are removed quickly. In cases of plant poisoning reported from Florida and Georgia, larvae die in all stages, accumulate in the cells, and appear blue. In one instance, attributed to locoweed poisoning, many individuals died in the late pupal stage, and bees about to emerge dried or mummified in their cells (Fig. 6).

Queens are affected by buckeye poisoning and much of the injury to the colony seems to stem from their behavior. Affected queens produce eggs that do not hatch or the larvae die soon after hatching. The queens also may become incapable of laying or may lay only drone eggs. They frequently recover their egg-laying ability, partially or completely, after the colonies are removed from the buckeye territory or when other plants furnish a pollen source. Affected colonies often try to supersede their queens, but usually fail and colony mortality may

FIGURE 6. Portion of brood comb showing pupae and adults at the stage of emergence killed by locoweed poisoning. Young pupae were partially removed and the heads of adults were worn shiny by the efforts of workers to remove them. *(Photo by J. E. Eckert)*

be high. Some hybrid strains are more resistant to certain plant poisoning than purer strains.

DETECTION OF PLANT POISONING

There is no specific rule for differentiating between plant and insecticide poisoning. Whenever symptoms of poisoning occur, a careful examination should be made of the brood, the amount of pollen present, the colony strength, and the accumulation of dead and deformed bees. In plant poisoning, other than buckeye, investigation may reveal large numbers of dead bees beneath or around the plants, in front of the hives, and all over the ground for some distance away from the hives. The effects usually are more gradual than in chemical poisoning and generally recur in the same area at similar periods each year, but not necessarily with equal severity.

TREATMENT

Familiarity with the nectar and pollen plants within flight range of each apiary is a definite aid in formulating practices to prevent plant poisoning. The seasonal succession of natural plants frequently is changed by extensive grass or brush fires. Wherever the injury causes colony death or reduces colony strength below a producing level, bees should be kept away from the suspected territory during the blooming period of the plant in question. With the California buckeye, about 15 million acres seem to be involved, and thus an important area of land is rendered unavailable for beekeeping for about 6 weeks in early summer. In seasons when other plants within this area provide a substantial source of pollen and nectar, the damage is less severe.

When toxic substances occur in the pollen, the removal of pollen-clogged combs from affected colonies is definitely helpful. Requeening and strengthening by the addition of brood and bees from normal colonies will enable those injured to make a more rapid recovery. Stimulative feeding is helpful also. Invariably, however, prevention is more effective than cure.

Chemical Control of Weeds

The chemical control of weeds by the use of various sprays and dusts, while seldom physically injurious to bees, has become so general as to cause a definite reduction in the pollen and nectar plants in many farming areas. The use of the chemical, 2,4-dichlorophenoxyacetic acid, more commonly known as 2,4-D, has resulted in the elimination of many pollen and nectar plants along highways, ditchbanks, pastures, grain fields, and waste places. Such plants as the mustards, chickweed, dandelion, thistles, sweet clover, willows, and many others of importance as food sources to pollinating insects are susceptible to one or more applications of 2,4-D. Other chemicals are available for killing weeds which are not susceptible to 2,4-D. Because this practice is generally less expensive than cultivation or hand labor, one can expect the use of weed control by chemical means to become much more prevalent than at present. It may change the value of beekeeping locations and cause beekeepers to engage in migratory beekeeping practices in order to build numerically strong colonies for pollination or for honey production. The use of pollen supplements also may assume a more important role in colony management.

Beekeepers can reduce some of these adverse effects by encouraging the planting of pollen- and nectar-producing plants and trees along streets, highways, watersheds, irrigation canals, and streams.

Death of Bees from Smelter Fumes

Before the use of filters, the fumes of smelters caused a heavy deposit of arsenic on the plants and in the soil for many miles around their location. In recent years, however, the installation of filters and precipitation processes have taken most of the previously injurious chemicals out of the fumes coming from the smelters. Destructive amounts of fluorine were traced to Swiss aluminum factories in 1956. Certain plants take up these destructive chemicals from the soil and poison bees that collect their pollen and nectar. The high content of arsenicals in some soils contribute to the deposit of arsenicals on the surfaces of plants by wind action and may prove injurious to bees.[8]

Abnormal Conditions

Abnormal environmental conditions during the blooming period of certain plants may produce effects that often are confused with plant or chemical poisoning. For example, many varieties of eucalyptus in California bloom during the winter, and at times thousands of dead bees are found on the ground under the trees. Many beekeepers attribute these deaths to injurious effects of the nectar, but it seems more probable that the bees are paralyzed by cold. On two separate occasions, hundreds of dead bees were found under black locust trees in bloom. Portions of the intestinal tracts of the bees had been forced between the segments of their abdominal walls as if by some internal explosion. In warm weather, favorable to flight, bees produce a white honey of excellent quality from the bloom of the black locust with no injury to the bees. Frequently, cold, windy weather occurs during the blooming period, and the injury undoubtedly is associated with some abnormal condition of this sort.

Not infrequently colonies expand their brood during warm periods in early spring beyond their ability to keep the brood warm when the advent of cold weather forces the cluster to contract. The exposed brood is frequently killed by exposure. Careful observation will reveal the cause as exposure rather than from chemical or plant poisoning.

REFERENCES CITED

1. Akesson, N. B., and W. E. Bates. 1961. Calif. Agr. 15(12):4-7.
2. Anderson, L. D., and E. L. Atkins. 1958. J. Econ. Entomol. 51(1):103-108.
3. Bourne, A. S. 1927. Mass. Agr. Expt. Sta. Bull. 243. pp. 74-84.
4. Brooks, F. A. 1947. Agr. Eng. 28(6):233-239,244.
5. Eckert, J. E. 1949. J. Econ. Entomol. 42(2):261-265.
6. Eckert, J. E., and H. W. Allinger. 1935. J. Econ. Entomol. 28(3):590-597.
7. Johansen, C. A., M. D. Coffey, and J. A. Quist. 1957. J. Econ. Entomol. 50(6):721-723.
8. Knowlton, G. F., and T. C. Yao. 1947. Utah Agr. Expt. Sta. Mimeo 340.
9. McGregor, S. E., and C. T. Vorhies. 1947. Ariz. Agr. Expt. Sta. Bull. 207.
10. Palmer-Jones, T. 1949. N. Z. J. Sci. Technol. Sec. A 31(2):46-56.
11. Schawn, Bertil. 1961. Kungl. Lantbrukshogskolan och Statens Lantbruksforsok, Statens Husdjursforksok, Sarteyck och Forhandsmeddelande Nr. 144.
12. Shaw, F. R. 1941. J. Econ. Entomol. 34(1):16-21.
13. Southwick, A. M. 1938. Gl. Bee Cult. 66(4):239-240.

ADDITIONAL REFERENCES ON POISONING

Atkins, E. L. Jr., L. D. Anderson, and T. O. Tuft. 1954. J. Econ. Entomol. 47(6):965-969.
Blake, Geo. H. Jr. 1958. J. Econ. Entomol. 51(4):523-527.
Burnside, C. E., and G. H. Vansell. 1936. U.S.D.A. Circ. E-398.
Clarkson, M. R. 1960. N.A.C. News and Pest Rev. 18(4):3-4,14.
Eckert, J. E. 1933. J. Econ. Entomol. 26(1):181-187.
_____ 1944. Gl. Bee Cult. 72(1):1-4.
_____ 1948. Am. Bee J. 88(3):129-131,143-144.
_____ 1961. Gl. Bee Cult. 88(2):73-77.
Eckert, J. E., and K. W. Tucker. 1954. Gl. Bee Cult. 82(9):529-531.
Gable, G. J., and R. L. Patton. 1946. J. Econ. Entomol. 39(2):177-180.
Johansen, C. A. 1956. J. Econ. Entomol. 49(6):825-828.
_____ 1959. Wash. Agr. Expt. Sta. Circ. 356.
Knowlton, G. F., L. W. Jones, and W. P. Nye. 1947. Utah Agr. Coll. Mimeo 338.
Levin, M. D. 1955. J. Econ. Entomol. 48(4):484-485.
Lieberman, F. V., G. E. Bohart, G. F. Knowlton, and W. P. Nye. 1954. J. Econ. Entomol. 47(2):316-320.
Linsley, E. G., and J. W. MacSwain. 1947. J. Econ. Entomol. 40(3):358-363.
Maurizio, A., and M. Straub. 1956. Schweiz. Bienenzig. 79(11):476-486.
Morse, Roger A. 1961. J. Econ. Entomol. 54(3):566-568.
Musgrave, A. J. 1950. 81st Ann. Rep. Entomol. Soc. Ontario. 89-91.
Nye, Wm. P. 1959. J. Econ. Entomol. 52(5):1024-1025.
Potts, S. F. 1946. J. Econ. Entomol. 39(6):716-720.
Rashad, Salah El-Din. 1957. J. Econ. Entomol. 50(5):655-658.
Robbins, W. W., A. F. Crafts, and R. N. Rainer. 1952. McGraw Hill, New York. 503 pp.
Shaw, F. R. 1960. J. Econ. Entomol. 51(4):549-550.
Stephen, W. P. 1961. J. Econ. Entomol. 54(5):989-993.
Sturtevant, A. P., *et al.* 1941. U.S.D.A. Mimeo Ser. E-545. 18 pp.
Wolfenbarger, D. O., and F. A. Robinson. 1957. J. Econ. Entomol. 50(5):694.

INDEX

Abdomen of the bee, 147, **170**
Abnormal conditions, 535
Abushady, A. Z., Italian bees, 29
  races of bees, 26
Acarapis woodi (Rennie), 182, 489, **493**
Acarine disease, 489, **493**
Accommodation cells, 232
Acetic acid, fumigant for wax moth, 509
  treatment for nosema, 504
Acids of honey, 377
Activities connected with swarming, 57,
  119, **121**, 273
  in gathering and storing pollen, 41,
    101, 103
  in gathering and storing water, **115**,
    116, 118
  in gathering nectar, **106**, 109, 111
  in gathering propolis, 119
  of bees in winter, 127
  of drones, 64, 67, 69, **133**, 135
  of hive bees, 50, **71**, 88, 107
  of queenless bees, 125
  of queens, 49, 59, 121, **129**, 268, 273,
    342, 345
Adam, Brother, Anatolian bees, 32
  A. m. mellifera L., 26
  bee breeding, 25, 33
  Carniolan bees, 30
  Cyprian bees, 24
  Italian bees, 28
Adie, A., heating honey, 317
  O.A.C. honey pasteurizer, 392
Adrenalin for bee stings, 213
Africa, bee races of, 13, 24
  beekeeping in, 16
Age, basis for division of labor, **71**, 125
  of larvae in queen rearing, 52, 445
  of queens when mating, 54
  of worker bees, 345
  resistance to disease, 502
Air sacs, 182
Akesson, N. B., drifting of insecticides, 520
Alarm dance, 85
Albanese, A. A., sugars in the diet, 401
Alber, M., races of bees, 20, 132
Alfalfa *(Medicago sativa)*, 196
Alfonsus, E. C., propolis gathering, 119
Alimentary canal, 143, 148, **177**
Alkali bees, pollination by, 13
Allen, M. D., queen activities, 130

swarming activities, 122
Alley, H., Cyprian bees, 24
Almonds, pollination of, 472
Alpatov, W. W., races of bees, 19, 29, 31
Alsike clover, *see* clover
America, beekeeping in, 17
American foulbrood, 293, **478**
  control of, **497**, 501, 507
  cultural examination of, 480, **482**
  strains of bees resistant to, 502
American Honey Institute, 396, 408
Ammon, R., enzymes in honey, 380
Amoeba disease, **492**, 507
Anatolian bees, 23, 32
Anatomy of the honey bee, 141
Ancestry of bees, 35
Anderson, E. J., disease treatment, 498
Anderson, J., life span of workers, 68
Anderson, L. D., toxicity of insecticides, 520
Anderson, R. H., *(A. m. capensis)*, 25
Antennae, 143, 148
  cleaner, 162
Antibiotic activity, 401, 502
Antibiotics in disease control, 483, 503
Ants, enemies of bees, 243, **510**
Anus of bee, 145, 177
Aorta, 179
Apiary, 241
  equipment, 237
  laws relating to, 218
  pests and enemies of, 508
  registration in California, 528
  winter protection for, 242, 362
Apis cerana syn. *indica*, 12, 20, 37, **44**,
  235, 426
Apis dorsata, 13, 20, 37, **43**, 235, 426
Apis florea, 13, 20, 37, **43**, 119, 426
Apis indica, *see* *Apis cerana*
Apis mellifera L., 12, **20**, 36, 44, 426
Apis mellifera acervorum Alp., 30
Apis mellifera adansonii, 12, 16, **24**, 235
Apis mellifera capensis, 17, 24, 64
Apis mellifera carnica Pollman, 30
Apis mellifera caucasica Gorb., 31
Apis mellifera cecropia Kiesw., 32
Apis mellifera cypria, 24
Apis mellifera ligustica Spin., 28
Apis mellifera mellifera L., 26
Apis mellifera syriaca, 24
Apple, pollination of, 467

Martensen-Larsen, O., honey for drunkenness, 402

Martin, E. C., hygroscopic properties, 372
  specific gravity of honey, 375

Masarinae, solitary wasps, 35

Massage dance, 87

Mass dance, 85

Mating, age of queen for, 54
  by instrumental insemination, 189, 439
  flights of queen, 48, **60**, 131, 190, 455
  multiple, **132**, 453
  of queens, 48, **60**, 131, 190, 455
  queen nuclei for, 451, **454**
  sign, 131
  yard, 452, 454

Maurizio, A., honey invertase, 386
  life span of bees, 68
  mixed pollen loads, 98
  nutrition of bees, 101
  pollen collection of, 106
  sugar content of nectar, 383

Maxillae, 143, 148

Mc Gregor, S. E., cotton pollination, 529

Mead, honey wine, 402

Median lobe, 144

Median ventral plate, 143

Mediterranean flour moth, 510

Mehring, Johannes, 12, 220

Melezitose, honeydew, 403

Mellifera, Dark bees, 26

Meliponidae, stingless bees, 13, 39

Merry-go-round, comb tray, 315

Mescal *(Agave americana),* 195

Mesquite *(Prosopis juliflora),* 200

Mesothorax, 147, 158

Metabolism, 183

Metamorphosis of bees, 66

Metathorax of the bee, 147, 158

Methyl bromide, fumigant for wax moth, 509

Mexico, beekeeping in, 17

Meyer, W., comb building, 89
  propolis gathering, 119
  swarm cluster, 124

Mice, enemy of bees, 511
  entrance guard for, 363

Michailov, A. S., cell size, 236
  flight of drones, 134

Micropyle, 142

Midnite hybrid, 456

Miel Carlota, 17

Migratory beekeeping, 191

Milkweed *(Asclepias subverticillata),* 532

Miller, C. C., comb honey, 324, 326
  queen rearing, 437, 442

Milojevic, B. D., division of labor, 73, 125
  laying workers, 126

Milum, V. G., dances of bees, 86
  factors affecting color of honey, 392

Mindt, B., drone activities, 134

Minerals in honey, 378

Mitchener, A. S., 222

Mites *(Acarapis woodi* Renny), 182, 489, **493**
  pollen, 496

Mobilizing dance, 84

Modified Dadant hive, 208, 220

Moeller, F. E., colony populations, 437

Moffett, J. O., disease control, 499, 503

Moisture balance, 359
  content of honey, 372, **377**, 390
  removal from comb honey, 334

Morgenthaler, O., nosema disease, 489

Morse, R. G., honey wine, 402

Motor nerves, 184

Moults of the honey bee, 146

Mountain laurel *(Kalmia* spp.), 195, 531

Mouth, 152, 177

Moving bees, 281
  equipment, 239
  laws relating to, 218
  screens, 282

Mucous glands, 187

Multiple-block board, 328
  matings of queens, **132**, 453

Muniagurria, C., honey in infant feeding, 399

Munroe, J. A., viscosity of honey, 375

Muscles, compressor, 172
  depressor, 168
  dilator, 172
  elevator, 168
  protractor, 172
  retractor, 172

Nassanoff glands, scent-producing, 40

Neck foramen, 149
  organs, 84

Nectar, composition of, 111
  conversion to honey, 40, **383**, 386
  gathering of, **106**, 109, 111
  loads, 114
  poisonous to bees, 531
  secretion of, 192
  sources of, 191
  storing and ripening of, 109

Nectarflow, 293, 342

Nedel, J. O., sense of gravity, 84, 90

Needle, grafting, 445

Nelson, E. K., acids of honey, 377